SCIENCE

· A U T H O R S ·

Dr. Timothy M. Cooney
Chairperson K-12 Science Program
Malcolm Price Laboratory School
University of Northern Iowa
Cedar Falls, Iowa

Dr. Jay M. Pasachoff
Director, Hopkins Observatory
Williams College
Williamstown, Massachusetts

Dr. Naomi Pasachoff
Research Associate
Williams College
Williamstown, Massachusetts

Scott, Foresman and Company
·Editorial Offices: Glenview, Illinois

Regional Offices: Sunnyvale, California • Tucker, Georgia • Glenview, Illinois •
Oakland, New Jersey • Dallas, Texas

Contributors

Consultants

Special Content Consultant
Dr. Abraham Flexer
Associate Director
Museum of Natural History
University of Colorado
Boulder, Colorado

Safety Consultant
Dr. Jack A. Gerlovich
Science Education Safety Specialist
Des Moines, Iowa

Special Education Consultant
Dr. Shirley T. King
Learning Disability Resource
Teacher
Helfrich Park Middle School
Evansville, Indiana

Special Features Consultant
George S. Fichter
Writer in Residence
Stetson University
DeLand, Florida

Reading Consultants
Dr. Robert A. Pavlik
Professor and Chairperson
Reading/Language Arts
Department
Cardinal Stritch College
Milwaukee, Wisconsin

Patricia Torphy Hinske
Reading Specialist
Cardinal Stritch College
Milwaukee, Wisconsin

Reviewers and Content Specialists

Dr. Sue T. Bowden
Regional Science Coordinator
South Central Regional Education
Center
Carthage, North Carolina

John Bowmar
Science Writer
North Attleboro, Massachusetts

Dr. Donna D. Burch
Science Department Chairperson
Chatham Hall
Chatham, Virginia

Dr. Dale Cruikshank
Institute for Astronomy
Honolulu, Hawaii

José B. Cruz, Jr.
Professor and Chairperson
Department of Electrical
Engineering
University of California
Irvine, California

Elston Lee Dame
Chemistry Teacher
Sacred Heart Academy
Louisville, Kentucky

Dr. David G. Haase
Professor of Physics
North Carolina State University
Raleigh, North Carolina

Thomas Kardos
Science Teacher-Coordinator
Suzanne Middle School
Walnut, California

Susanne P. Kemlitz
Physical Science Teacher
Belleville Senior High School
Belleville, New Jersey

Lee Marek
Chemistry Teacher
Naperville North High School
Naperville, Illinois

Jan Migaki
Physics Teacher
North Shore Country Day School
Winnetka, Illinois

Michael J. Padilla
Professor of Science Education
University of Georgia
Athens, Georgia

John Prusko
Classroom Teacher/Science
Specialist
Grove Junior High School
Elk Grove Village, Illinois

William M. Rodgers
Science Teacher
Woodland Hills School District
Pittsburgh, Pennsylvania

Dr. Jody M. Stone
Classroom Teacher/Science
Educator
Price Laboratory School
Cedar Falls, Iowa

Joann S. Stuever
Science Department Chairperson
Hefner Junior High School
Oklahoma City, Oklahoma

Les Wallinga
Science Teacher
Calvin Christian Junior High
School
Wyoming, Michigan

ISBN: 0-673-42184-8
Copyright © 1990
Scott, Foresman and Company, Glenview, Illinois
All rights reserved. Printed in the United States of Ameica.

10-RRW-99989796

CONTENTS

UNIT 1
2

Chapter 1 Studying Physical Science   4
1-1 Investigations in Physical Science   6
Careers in Physical Science Surveyor   8
1-2 Safety in the Physical Science Laboratory   9
1-3 Solving Problems Scientifically   11
Activity 1-1 Testing a Hypothesis   16
1-4 Scientific Measurements   17
Activity 1-2 Graphing in SI Units   23
Science Skills Developing Study Skills   24
Review   25

Chapter 2 Moving Objects   28
2-1 Describing Motion   30
2-2 Contrasting Distance and Displacement   33
2-3 Comparing Speed and Velocity   35
Activity 2-1 Measuring Average Speed   38
2-4 Describing Acceleration   39
Careers in Physical Science Pilot   42
2-5 Understanding Friction   42
Activity 2-2 Exploring Friction   45
Science Skills Interpreting and Making Line Graphs 46
Review   47

Chapter 3 The Laws of Motion   50
3-1 Newton's First Law of Motion   52
3-2 Newton's Second Law of Motion   54
Careers in Physical Science Aerospace Engineer   57
Activity 3-1 Newton's First and Second Laws   58
3-3 Newton's Third Law of Motion   60
Activity 3-2 Newton's Third Law   62
3-4 Balanced and Unbalanced Forces   63
3-5 Circular Motion   66
Science Skills Solving Word Problems and Using
                Equations   70
Review   71

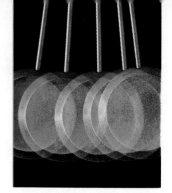

Chapter 4 Gravitation   **74**
4-1 The Motion of Falling Objects   76
Activity 4-1 The Effects of Gravitational Force and
         Air Resistance   79
4-2 Gravity, Mass, and Weight   80
Activity 4-2 Studying Microgravity and Center of
         Gravity   84
4-3 Gravity and the Planets   86
4-4 The Law of Gravity   88
People and Science Albert Einstein   91
Science Skills Drawing Ellipses   92
Review   93
Breakthroughs Around the World Without
         Refueling   96
How It Works Fire Sprinkler Systems   97

UNIT 2   98

Chapter 5 Matter and Its Phases   **100**
5-1 The Phases of Matter   102
5-2 Characteristics of Solids   104
Activty 5-1 Crystalline Solids   107
5-3 Characteristics of Liquids   108
5-4 Characteristics of Gases   113
People and Science Shirley Ann Jackson   117
5-5 Changes in Phase of Matter   118
Activity 5-2 Changing Phases   121
Science Skills Interpreting a Graph that Shows
         Temperature-Time Relationships   122
Review   123

Chapter 6 Properties of Matter   **126**
6-1 The Elements   128
Careers in Physical Science Assayer   133
6-2 Physical Properties and Changes   134
Activity 6-1 Physical Properties   138
6-3 Chemical Properties and Changes   139
Activity 6-2 A Chemical Change   141
Science Skills Using a Bar Graph to Compare
         Densities   142
Review   143

Chapter 7 The Atom   146
7-1 Theories About the Atom   148
Activty 7-1 Inside an Atom   152
7-2 How Atoms Differ   153
Activity 7-2 Isotopes   156
7-3 Classifying Elements   157
People and Science Rosalyn Yalow   165
Science Skills Interpreting the Periodic Table   166
Review   167

Chapter 8 The Atomic Nucleus   170
8-1 The Structure of the Nucleus   172
People and Science Luiz Alvarez   174
8-2 Radioactivity   175
Activity 8-1 Radioactive Decay   180
8-3 Mass, Energy, and the Speed of Light   181
8-4 Nuclear Fission   183
Activity 8-2 Chain Reactions   187
8-5 Nuclear Fusion   188
Science Skills Interpreting and Making Pie Graphs   190
Review   191

Issues Irradiated Foods—Will They Sell?   194
How It Works Neon Signs   195

UNIT 3   196

Chapter 9 Compounds and Mixtures   198
9-1 Identifying Compounds   200
Activity 9-1 Forming a Compound   203
9-2 Identifying Mixtures   204
People and Science Marjorie Smigel   206
9-3 Solutions—One Kind of Mixture   207
9-4 Suspensions—Another Kind of Mixture   210
Activity 9-2 Investigating Suspensions, Solutions,
            and Emulsions   213
Science Skills Graphing and Interpreting Data   214
Review   215

Chapter 10 Holding Atoms Together   218
10-1 Bonding Atoms   220
Activity 10-1 Comparing Bonds   224
10-2 Ionic Bonding   225
People and Science Gilbert Newton Lewis   228
10-3 Covalent Bonding   229
10-4 Chemical Equations and Dot Diagrams   233
Activity 10-2 A Chemical Reaction and Its Equation   237
Science Skills Dot Diagrams and Ionic Compounds   238
Review   239

Chapter 11 Chemical Reactions   **242**
11-1 Recognizing Chemical Reactions   244
Activity 11-1 Controlling the Speed of Chemical
           Reactions   248
11-2 Synthesis and Decomposition Reactions   249
People and Science Jacqueline K. Barton   251
11-3 Single-Replacement and Double-Replacement
     Reactions   252
Activity 11-2 Single-Replacement Reactions with
           Metals   255
11-4 Oxidation-Reduction Reactions   256
11-5 Chemistry of Carbon Compounds   260
Science Skills Classifying and Analyzing Chemical
           Reactions   264
Review   265

Chapter 12 Acids and Bases   **268**
12-1 Properties of Acids and Bases   270
12-2 Acids and Bases in Solution   273
Activity 12-1 Recognizing Acids and Bases   277
12-3 Indicators and the pH Scale   278
Careers in Physical Science Pharmacist   282
12-4 Neutralization Reactions   282
Activity 12-2 A Neutralization Reaction   285
Science Skills Selecting Suitable Indicators   286
Review   287
Issues What is the Best Way to Reduce Acid Rain?   290
How It Works Swimming Pool Chemistry   291

UNIT 4   292

Chapter 13 Work and Machines   **294**
13-1 Machines Make Work Easier   296
13-2 Forms of Levers   300
Activity 13-1 Examining Simple Machines   305
13-3 Forms of Inclined Planes   306
Activity 13-2 Experimenting with Inclined Planes   309
13-4 Compound Machines and Efficiency   310
Careers in Physical Science Automobile Mechanic   313
Science Skills Solving Word Problems   314
Review   315

Chapter 14 Energy and Power   **318**
14-1 Defining Energy   320
14-2 Kinetic Energy   322
14-3 Energy is Conserved   324

Activity 14-1 Investigating Kinetic and Potential
       Energy   327
14-4 Forms of Energy   328
Careers in Physical Science Mechanical Engineer   330
14-5 Measuring Power   331
Activity 14-2 Measuring Human Power   333
Science Skills Calculating Energy Use   334
Review   335

Chapter 15 Heat and Temperature   **338**
15-1 Defining Heat and Temperature   340
15-2 Detecting Heat and Temperature Changes   342
Activity 15-1 Investigating Temperature Changes   345
15-3 Producing Heat   346
15-4 Energy Transfer   348
Activity 15-2 A Material's Effect on Radiant Energy   352
15-5 Expansion and Contraction   353
Careers in Physical Science Heating and Air
                Conditioning System
                Installer   355
Science Skills Graphs of Temperature Changes   356
Review   357

Chapter 16 Energy Resources   **360**
16-1 Energy in Your Life   362
16-2 Fossil Fuels   364
Careers in Physical Science Petroleum Engineer   368
16-3 More Energy Sources   368
Activity 16-1 Light Energy Collector   374
16-4 Making Decisions About Energy Sources   375
Activity 16-2 Insulation   379
Science Skills Distinguishing Fact from Opinion   380
Review   381
Issues How Will the Greenhouse Effect Change
      World Climates?   384
How It Works Five-Speed Bicycle   385

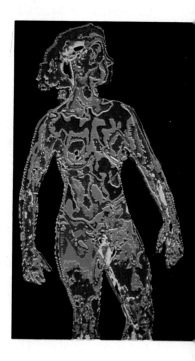

UNIT 5

Chapter 17 Waves — 388

17-1 Properties of Waves — 390
Activity 17-1 Properties of Waves — 393
17-2 Wave Motions — 394
17-3 The Behavior of Waves — 396
Activity 17-2 Reflection — 401
17-4 Electromagnetic Waves — 402
Careers in Physical Science X-ray Technician — 405
Science Skills Graphing Waves — 406
Review — 407

Chapter 18 Light — 410

18-1 The Nature of Light — 412
Activity 18-1 The Path of Light Rays — 415
18-2 The Visible Spectrum — 416
People and Science Max Planck — 419
18-3 How Objects Appear Colored — 420
Activity 18-2 Colors in White Light — 425
Science Skills Reading a Graph of Illumination vs. Distance — 426
Review — 427

Chapter 19 Optics — 430

19-1 Plane Mirrors — 432
19-2 Curved Mirrors — 434
People and Science Roger Angel — 438
19-3 Lenses — 438
Activity 19-1 Lenses — 442
19-4 Eyes, Lenses, and Optical Illusions — 443
19-5 Using Lenses and Mirrors — 447
Activity 19-2 Making a Pinhole Camera — 451
Science Skills Analyzing Images — 452
Review — 453

Chapter 20 Lasers — 456

20-1 Laser Light — 458
Careers in Physical Science Laser Technician — 459
20-2 Different Types of Lasers — 460
Activity 20-1 Laser Model — 464
20-3 Using Lasers — 465
Activity 20-2 Optical Fibers — 473
20-4 Holograms — 474
Science Skills Drawing Graphs and Measuring Angles — 476
Review — 477

Chapter 21 Sound   **480**
21-1 Sound as a Wave   482
Activity 21-1 Properties of Sound   486
21-2 Characteristics of Sound   487
Careers in Physical Science Studio Engineer   491
21-3 Musical Sounds   491
Activity 21-2 Making Music   495
Science Skills Solving Word Problems About Sound   496
Review   497
Breakthroughs Microwaves to Guide Planes to a
                Safe Landing   500
How It Works Lasers as Sighting Devices   501

UNIT 6   502

Chapter 22 Electricity   **504**
22-1 Electric Charge   506
Activity 22-1 Electric Charge   509
22-2 Electric Current   510
22-3 Circuits   515
Activity 22-2 Switches and Fuses   518
22-4 Using Electricity   519
Careers in Physical Science Electrical Engineer   521
Science Skills Interpreting Circuit Diagrams   522
Review   523

Chapter 23 Magnetism   **526**
23-1 Magnetic Properties   528
Activity 23-1 Magnetic Poles   532
23-2 Magnets from Magnetic Substances   533
23-3 Changing Electricity into Magnetism   536
Activity 23-2 Electromagnets   539
23-4 Changing Magnetism into Electricity   540
Careers in Physical Science Service Technician   543
Science Skills Constructing Models   544
Review   545

Chapter 24 Electronic Revolution   **548**
24-1 Electronics   550
Activity 24-1 Breaking Up a Picture   553
24-2 Making Electronic Devices Smaller   554
24-3 Computers   557
Activity 24-2 The Computing Process   561
24-4 Personal Computers and Microprocessors   562
24-5 Using Computers   564
People and Science Noel Runyan   569
Science Skills Looking at Computer Programs   570
Review   571
Breakthroughs Advances in Artificial Pacemakers   574
How It Works Magnetic Levitation Trains   575

UNIT 7 576

Chapter 25 Exploring the Universe   **578**
25-1 The Development of Stars   580
Activity 25-1 Using a Spectroscope   585
25-2 Aging Stars   586
25-3 The Milky Way Galaxy   591
Activity 25-2 Infrared Observations of the Milky
     Way Galaxy   593
25-4 A Universe of Galaxies   594
People and Science Cecilia Payne-Gaposchkin   597
Science Skills Plotting Points to Make a Model of
     the Milky Way   598
Review   599

Chapter 26 The Large and the Small   **602**
26-1 Galaxies and Our Understanding of the
     Universe   604
Activity 26-1 The Expanding Universe   608
26-2 Quasars and Other Active Galaxies   609
26-3 Theories About the Universe   614
Activity 26-2 Curving Space   618
26-4 Whisper from Space   619
People and Science Jocelyn Bell Burnell   621
Science Skills Using Flow Charts to Understand
     Processes in Astronomy   622
Review   623
Issues Are We Alone in the Universe?   626
How It Works Space Telescope   625
Appendices   628
Glossary   638
Index   648
Acknowledgments   659

Introduction to Your Textbook

In studying physical science, you will learn about a fascinating world of matter and energy. Your textbook will help you become acquainted with this world.

Familiarize yourself with the following textbook features to increase your understanding and enjoyment of physical science.

Unit Organization

Physical Science is divided into seven units. Each unit begins with a two-page introduction that gives historical background on some of the scientific discoveries or technological achievements related to the unit topic. Turn to the beginning of Unit 1 on page 2. What important discoveries did Isaac Newton make?

Each unit ends with two features of special interest. The *Breakthroughs* and *Issues* features alternate throughout the book. *Breakthroughs* give background on an important discovery in physical science. *Issues* present information on topics in physical science that affect our lives. *How It Works* describes a common invention or process that works on principles you will have studied in the unit. This feature appears in every unit.

Chapter Organization

Physical Science has 26 chapters. Each chapter begins with an introduction, including an outline to give you an overview of the chapter. The outline will help you prepare to study the chapter.

Every chapter is divided into sections. Each section begins with a section number, a title, and objectives and ends with section review questions. Many special features appear throughout each chapter. Some chapters contain a feature on a career of interest; other chapters contain a biography of a physical scientist. Turn to Chapter 4. What is the name of the scientist whose biography appears in this chapter? All chapters contain margin features that give interesting tidbits of information or ideas for projects you can pursue on your own.

Each chapter ends with a three-page chapter review. Turn to the Chapter 3 review beginning on page 71. Look at the summary, vocabulary list, and review questions. Find the names of books or articles you could read if you wanted to learn more about forces and motion.

Activities and Skills Features

Each chapter contains two laboratory activities that will give you concrete experiences to help you learn science. For each activity the main purpose is stated. What is the purpose of Activity 9–1 on page 203? With all activities, safety comes first. Turn to pages 9–10 and read the safety tips for working in a science laboratory.

A science skills feature appears near the end of each chapter. These one-page features will help you sharpen the skills you need to make learning about science more enjoyable. What science skill is covered in the skills feature on page 598? How can improving this skill help you study physical science?

Resource Section

At the end of the book is a resource section that includes appendices, a glossary, and an index. You can use the appendices as references if you want to find more information about topics covered in *Physical Science*. What page would you turn to if you wanted to find out about Marie Curie? The glossary lists the definitions of vocabulary words that appear in the chapters. The index refers you to the pages where specific topics are covered.

Activities and Science Skills

Activity 1-1	Testing a Hypothesis	16
Activity 1-2	Graphing in SI Units	23
Science Skills	Developing Study Skills	24
Activity 2-1	Measuring Average Speed	38
Activity 2-2	Exploring Friction	45
Science Skills	Interpreting and Making Line Graphs	46
Activity 3-1	Newton's First and Second Laws	58
Activity 3-2	Newton's Third Law	62
Science Skills	Solving Word Problems and Using Equations	70
Activity 4-1	The Effects of Gravitational Force and Air Resistance	79
Activity 4-2	Studying Microgravity and Center of Gravity	84
Science Skills	Drawing Ellipses	92
Activity 5-1	Crystalline Solids	107
Activity 5-2	Changing Phases	121
Science Skills	Interpreting a Graph that Shows Temperature-Time Relationships	122
Activity 6-1	Physical Properties	138
Activity 6-2	A Chemical Change	141
Science Skills	Using a Bar Graph to Compare Densities	142
Activity 7-1	Inside an Atom	152
Activity 7-2	Isotopes	156
Science Skills	Interpreting the Periodic Table	166
Activity 8-1	Radioactive Decay	180
Activity 8-2	Chain Reactions	187
Science Skills	Interpreting and Making Pie Graphs	190
Activity 9-1	Forming a Compound	203
Activity 9-2	Investigating Suspensions, Solutions, and Emulsions	213
Science Skills	Graphing and Interpreting Data	214
Activity 10-1	Comparing Bonds	224
Activity 10-2	A Chemical Reaction and Its Equation	237
Science Skills	Dot Diagrams and Ionicv Compounds	238
Activity 11-1	Controlling the Speed of Chemical Reactions	248
Activity 11-2	Single-Replacement Reactions with Metals	255
Science Skills	Classifying and Analyzing Chemical Reactions	264
Activity 12-1	Recognizing Acids and Bases	277
Activity 12-2	A Neutralization Reaction	285
Science Skills	Selecting Suitable Indicators	286
Activity 13-1	Examining Simple Machines	305
Activity 13-2	Experimenting with Inclined Planes	309

Science Skills	Solving Word Problems	314
Activity 14-1	Investigating Kinetic and Potential Energy	327
Activity 14-2	Measuring Human Power	333
Science Skills	Calculating Energy Use	334
Activity 15-1	Investigating Temperature Change	345
Activity 15-2	A Material's Effect on Radiant Energy	352
Science Skills	Graphing and Interpreting Graphs of Temperature Changes	356
Activity 16-1	Light Energy Collector	373
Activity 16-2	Insulation	379
Science Skills	Distinguishing Fact from Opinion	380
Activity 17-1	Properties of Waves	393
Activity 17-2	Reflection	401
Science Skills	Graphing Waves	406
Activity 18-1	The Path of Light Rays	415
Activity 18-2	Colors in White Light	425
Science Skills	Reading a Graph of Inllumination vs Distance	426
Activity 19-1	Lenses	442
Activity 19-2	Making a Pinhole Camera	451
Science Skills	Analyzing Images	452
Activity 20-1	Laser Model	464
Activity 20-2	Optical Fibers	473
Science Skills	Drawing Graphs and Measuring Angles	476
Activity 21-1	Properties of Sound	486
Activity 21-2	Making Music	495
Science Skills	Solving word Problems About Sound	496
Activity 22-1	Electric Charge	509
Activity 22-2	Switches and Fuses	518
Science Skills	Interpreting Circuit Diagrams	522
Activity 23-1	Magnetic Poles	532
Activity 23-2	Electromagnets	539
Science Skills	Constructing Models	544
Activity 24-1	Breaking Up a Picture	553
Activity 24-2	The Computing Process	561
Science Skills	Looking At Computer Programs	570
Activity 25-1	Using a Spectroscope	585
Activity 25-2	Infrared Observations of the Milky Way Galaxy	593
Science Skills	Plotting Points to Make a Model of the Milky Way	598
Activity 26-1	The Expanding Universe	608
Activity 26-2	Curving Space	618
Science Skills	Using Flow Charts to Understand Processes in Astronomy	622

Measurement and Motion

Replacing myths and mysteries with usable and provable facts constituted a significant step forward in human history. This was the birthday of science, a system of learning how to know about ourselves and the world around us. Science continues to shape our way of life.

3rd Century B.C.

Putting science to work for people began with the ancient Greeks. Among the most famous of the early technologists was Archimedes, who solved problems by using the scientific method. On the use of levers he once said, "Give me a fixed point outside the earth to stand on, and I will move it."

17th Century

Major scientific breakthroughs continue to guide thought and technology ever after. Few have lit the way more prominently than Isaac Newton, who discovered the laws of universal gravitation and of motion. They provided an explanation for happenings on earth and throughout the universe and thus ushered in an era known as the Scientific Revolution.

Chapter 1 Studying Physical Science
Chapter 2 Moving Objects
Chapter 3 The Laws of Motion
Chapter 4 Gravitation

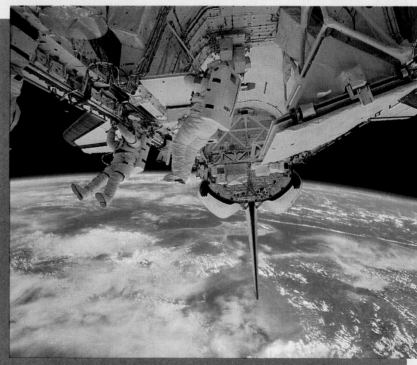

19th Century

Once the forces holding people on earth and keeping the earth and other planets in orbit around the sun were understood, technologists began seriously thinking about how to escape this powerful bondage. Then indeed all of space—the entire universe—would be open to exploration. But the scientists and writers who first dreamed of such a time were years ahead of the technology needed to accomplish these feats.

20th Century

Science fiction became reality when the actual invasion of space was begun. First were the experimental rockets of the 1920s. These were followed during World War II with rockets that sped explosives toward distant targets. In the more peaceful years that followed, the Newtonian principle that for every action there is an equally powerful reaction was employed again and again, boosting tons of equipment and astronauts beyond the effectiveness of Earth's gravity. Next will be colonies in space. Gravity? It will be there, too, but it will be "manufactured" to provide the need for the earth environment to which humans are adapted.

CHAPTER 1
Studying Physical Science

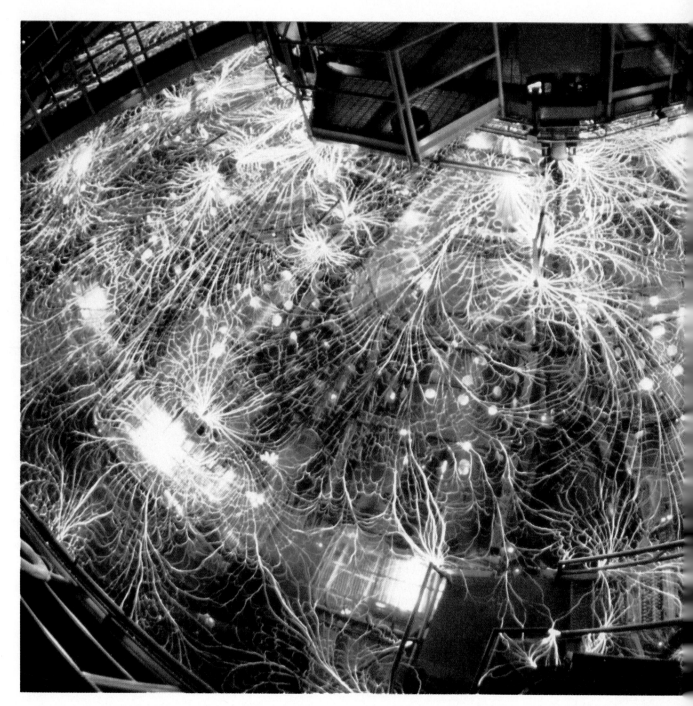

Sparks crackle as physical scientists investigate how to provide power from hydrogen using an intense beam of charged particles. When the beam strikes pellets of a form of hydrogen gas, a miniature atomic explosion takes place. Eventually, a better understanding of this process may lead to a new way of generating electricity for your homes.

Organizing Your Study Skills The outline below will help you see how the chapter is organized and what you should learn as you read.

I. Section 1-1: Investigations in Physical Science
   A. What is physical science?
   B. Why should you study physical science?
   C. How can you benefit from physical science?

II. Section 1-2: Safety in the Physical Science Laboratory
   A. What safety rules should you follow in the laboratory?
   B. What should you do in case of an accident in the laboratory?

III. Section 1-3: Solving Problems Scientifically
   A. How are problems solved scientifically?
   B. How is scientific knowledge revised?

IV. Section 1-4: Scientific Measurements
   A. How is the metric system used?
   B. How are mass and volume measured?
   C. How is density measured?
   D. What are the limits of measurement?
   E. How do scientists keep track of very large or very small numbers?

Objectives

After completing this section you will be able to

A. Define physical science.
B. State reasons why studying physical science is important.
C. List how you can benefit from physical science.

Figure 1-1 Workers use physical science processes to change black and white movies to colored movies.

1-1 Investigations in Physical Science

The Study of Matter and Energy

Science begins with simple curiosity and observations of objects and events in the world around us. From this simple beginning, science becomes the study of the universe and its natural laws.

Different arrangements of matter and energy make up the entire universe. Physical science is the study of the properties and relationships of this matter and energy. Since everything is made of matter and energy, physical science can answer questions about almost any topic you can think of. For example, physical science answers questions such as "Why is the sky blue?" or "How does salt form?" or "What makes stars shine?" Physics, chemistry, and astronomy are examples of physical sciences.

People who do research in the physical sciences study mainly nonliving things. They also study the basic laws that control living things. Applications of physical science can make our lives more enjoyable. Discoveries of physical science enable technicians to add color to old black-and-white movies, such as the picture shown here.

Why Studying Physical Science Is Important

Long ago, striking stones together to make a fire was a daily chore. Over the centuries, people improved the way they lit a fire. But they did not always make such improvements by doing experiments in physical science. The results of physical science research are all around you. Technology is the application of physical science to today's world.

Understanding the movements of objects and the stresses on materials makes it possible to build a bridge. This understanding also helps engineers design an efficient car.

Research in physical science led to technologies that have provided people with many new products and materials. Chemical researchers developed artificial turf for football and baseball fields, nylon and polyester for clothes, and freeze-dried foods.

The curiosity of today's physical science students will lead to new areas of study and more exciting discoveries. Perhaps you might become a scientist who explains what comets are made of, a technologist who invents a new kind of plastic, or an engineer who designs a skyscraper.

However, you do not have to become a scientist or engineer to make your study of physical science worthwhile. As a citizen, you should be able to make informed decisions about how science and technology might affect the society in which you will live. Your knowledge of physical science can help you understand and control the effects of science and technology on your future.

Benefits of Physical Science Research

In the 1940s, a computer was so large that it would have filled your entire classroom. Through research and development, scientists and engineers found new ways of controlling electricity that led to smaller and more capable computers. Physical science research has made possible the desk-top computers used in many schools, as well as the pocket calculators that you or your friends might use.

Every day you benefit from applications of physical science research in many ways. Advances in physical science have produced fireproof fabrics, shatterproof glass, and ways of performing surgery using intense beams of light.

Figure 1-2 Firefighters can now use small computers to help them fight fires. These computers enable firefighters to predict where and how quickly the fire will spread.

Explore!

Use encyclopedias or other reference books to find out how Wallace Carothers discovered a way to make nylon from "coal, air, and water."

Applying Science

Some musicians use computers when they compose music. The computers can be used to make a single musician sound like an entire band. One keyboard can be attached to a number of synthesizers that can make tones that sound like drums, guitars, horns, and pianos.

Also, physical science has improved ways of detecting diseases in people and in treating some diseases. New discoveries about the flow of electricity are already being developed for application.

Physical science research for the United States space program has also helped people in many ways. Some side benefits of space technology include longer-lasting light bulbs, smoke detectors and fire alarms, better fans, and improved pavement materials.

When scientists do basic research in physical science, they often cannot predict what the practical benefits of their work might be. Sometimes practical uses of new discoveries take many more years of research to be developed. Today's research is the bridge between past ideas and future possibilities and might open up brand new fields of study.

Section Review

1. What are three areas of study in physical science?
2. What are two reasons for studying physical science?
3. Describe three ways in which you benefit from physical science.

Challenge: Why should physical scientists be encouraged to do basic research even if they cannot predict the practical uses of their discoveries?

Careers in Physical Science

Surveyor

The next time you cross a city limit, picture the land around you before people built on it. Surveyors were probably there then, doing their job. Surveyors measure and map an area before construction begins.

Surveyors work outdoors with teams of people who help take measurements of the land. From the data they collect, the surveyor draws a map and writes a report about the area. Highway builders, city planners, and boundary makers all use the surveyor's information to better understand the usefulness and safety of building sites.

After high school, surveyors spend two years in technical or junior college. They also get on-the-job training and take a surveyor's license examination.

1-2 Safety in the Physical Science Laboratory

Practicing Laboratory Safety

In 1986, an accident occurred in the nuclear power plant in Chernobyl, U.S.S.R. This accident took place because workers had shut off the safety systems to do experiments. Safety and caution are necessary for successful experiments. In physical science, laboratory accidents can result from carelessness and impatience. You must be responsible for your own safety, even though your teacher will help you stay safe. You must act in a careful and responsible way. To assist you in your laboratory work, study the the following list of laboratory procedures.

Before Beginning a Laboratory Activity

● Read and understand all directions before you begin an activity. If you have any questions, ask your teacher for help.
● Look for and follow all *CAUTIONS* in the activity.
● Know the location of all the safety and first aid equipment in the laboratory. Know how to use the safety equipment and learn your classroom's emergency procedures.

Storing and Handling Chemicals

● Laboratory chemicals can be dangerous. Read all labels. Never use a chemical that is not labeled.
● Wear cover goggles and a safety apron when heating, pouring, or mixing chemicals and water.
● Never taste or smell any chemicals unless the activity procedure instructs you to do so. To smell a chemical, use your hand to fan the vapor toward your nose, as the picture shows. If the odor is irritating, turn your head away quickly.
● Do not mix chemicals unless the activity procedure instructs you to do so.
● Never store an acid, such as vinegar, near a base, such as ammonia.
● Always add acid or base to water to avoid splattering. NEVER add water to an acid or base.
● If an acid or a base spills on your clothes, on your skin, or anywhere in the laboratory, wash the area immediately with water. Inform your teacher.

Figure 1-3 If an experiment directs you to smell a chemical, use your hand to fan the vapor toward your nose.

Figure 1-4 The girl demonstrates how to use a test tube holder.

Using a Bunsen Burner

- Handle Bunsen burners with care. Do not move a burner while it is in use. If your hair is long, tie it back.
- When you are heating a test tube, always point it away from yourself and others. Use a test tube holder, as shown in the picture.
- If a fire starts, DO NOT RUN and DO NOT PANIC. Cover the fire with a safety blanket. Consult with your teacher about how best to clean up.

Handling Glassware

- Never pick up hot glassware with your bare hands. Glass that has been heated does not appear to be hot and can burn your fingers.
- Handle glassware with care. Broken glass has sharp edges.

Handling Electrical Equipment

- Do not touch electrical equipment in use with metal objects.
- Do not use bare wire.
- Never touch electrical equipment with wet hands.
- Wear safety goggles when using lasers.

After Finishing a Laboratory Activity

- Never return unused chemicals to their original bottles. Dispose of them according to your teacher's instructions.
- Return all other materials to their proper places. Clean your laboratory area.

In Case of an Accident

Physical science activities can be fun as well as educational. But the activities must be done with care and caution. Always tell your teacher about any accident. Above all, remain calm. Becoming panicked can make an accident even worse. With some thought and care, your physical science laboratory can be a safe and interesting place to learn.

Section Review

1. What are six main safety rules you should observe in the physical science laboratory?
2. What are important points you should remember in case of an accident in your science laboratory?

Challenge: How does cleaning up after a laboratory activity help prevent accidents?

1-3 Solving Problems Scientifically

Objectives

After completing this section you will be able to

A. Describe how problems are solved scientifically.
B. Explain how scientific knowledge is revised.

The Scientific Method

No perfect rules guide scientists in their research. Many important scientific discoveries have resulted from trial and error, accidental discovery, or experimentation on a different problem. The **scientific method** is a way of gaining new knowledge by using a particular approach to solving problems. The scientific method helps scientists know that their discoveries are valid.

With the scientific method, scientists first must identify a problem. Next they try to think of an explanation for the problem. The explanation they make to answer or solve the problem is their **hypothesis.** For example, suppose you want to test the fastest way to make ice cubes in your freezer. Should you put hot water or cold water in the ice trays? Your hypothesis is that cold water has less energy to give up, so it should freeze sooner.

The next step in the scientific method is to perform experiments or make observations that test your hypothesis. For example, you could fill one tray with hot water and another with cold water. Then you could place them both in the freezer, as the girl in the picture is doing. You could open the freezer every half hour to see if one has frozen.

Figure 1-5 Using the scientific method to test a hypothesis.

What if you found that the hot water froze first? Then your hypothesis was wrong, and you must reject it. You must form a new hypothesis. Perhaps vapor the hot water gives off makes the freezer run more. Perhaps the hot water moves around more in the ice tray as it cools. This could bring the water that needs the most cooling to the top. You must think of further experiments to test these hypotheses. You might experiment to see if the depth of the water matters. You might see if it matters whether your ice tray is metal or plastic. Noting what happens in each case is collecting **data,** the results of observations. In science, you often use equipment to make measurements. The measurements are your data. Sometimes you use your senses to collect data.

Your hypothesis often helps you decide what measurements to make next. Often you have several choices. When you do scientific research, you might get interesting results or you might not. Science combines imagination, creativity, logic, and luck.

If your hypothesis survives many tests, you may call it a **theory.** A theory usually explains many observations. In science, a theory often builds on several hypotheses.

To test a hypothesis, scientists sometimes perform a controlled experiment. In a **controlled experiment,** scientists use two setups. They arrange everything in exactly the same way for both setups except for the variable they are interested in. The **variable** is the quantity that is changed or varied. For example, in the ice-cube experiment, the water temperature was the variable. You could repeat the ice-cube experiment with water of the same temperature in both trays, but use one metal and one plastic tray. In this case, the type of tray is the variable.

Physical scientists cannot always perform controlled experiments. For example, even if scientists are interested in the effects of gravity, they can never prepare a setup in a place completely without gravity. If astronomers want to study how Jupiter's spin affects weather on Jupiter, they cannot stop Jupiter from spinning.

Often physical scientists use models to describe their ideas about the universe. A **model** is often an idea or a set of equations rather than an actual object like a model car. It brings together bits and pieces of different information about a single concept.

Figure 1-6 The lighthouse model explains pulsars. Pulsars give off strong flashes of radio waves as they rotate, just as lighthouses give off strong flashes of light as they rotate.

Astronomers, for example, use the lighthouse model to explain the behavior of a dying or dead star called a pulsar. A pulsar seems to send out regular pulses of radio waves. As the drawing shows, astronomers think that a pulsar actually sends a steady beam of radio waves. Their model says that we detect pulses because we detect the beam only when it points at us, as the pulsar rotates. In the same way, a lighthouse seems to flash light every time its beam points toward you, even though it sends out a steady beam of light. The lighthouse model helps scientists get a better idea of how a pulsar might work.

Revising Scientific Information

Even theories that have been accepted for many years might later prove to be incorrect. So researchers experiment continually to collect more data to improve or reject a theory. As scientists discover new information, they change their ideas to explain the data.

The history of science records several theories that had to be rejected because experiments did not support them. The ancient Greeks thought matter was made up of four basic elements combined in various proportions. These elements were earth, air, fire, and water. This theory of matter was held until the 1700s when several experiments disproved it. In 1783, Henry Cavendish found that water is produced when hydrogen is burned in oxygen. In 1800, William Nicholson and Anthony Carlisle passed an electric current through water and broke it down into hydrogen and oxygen. Thus, experiments had proven that water is not a basic element.

Explore!

Do research on Johannes Kepler and the three laws he worked out to explain how the planets moved in the sky. What theories had to be rejected as a result of his work?

Figure 1-7 Johannes Kepler
(1571-1630)

Figure 1-8 The white region shows the outer layer of the sun. You see it here as the moon blocks the inner part of the sun.

The outer layer of the sun, shown in the picture, has temperatures in the millions of degrees. In the 1960s and 1970s, astronomers thought they knew why this part of the sun was so hot. They thought that sound waves came out from inner levels of the sun and heated the outer layers. Not until the late 1970s was a spacecraft able to measure the sound waves coming out. Scientists discovered that the sound waves were much too weak to heat the outer layers enough. The old theory had to be rejected. Astronomers began their search for a new theory of how the outer part of the sun is heated.

For centuries, most people accepted the idea of the Greek thinker Aristotle that a heavy object falls faster than a light object. In the 1600s, however, the Italian scientist Galileo observed that shape and surface area affect how fast an object falls. He began to wonder if Aristotle was correct.

Galileo, shown in *Figure 1-9*, was one of the first scientists to actually make experiments to test his ideas. He rolled balls of different weights down a ramp. This experiment led him to the hypothesis that objects would fall at the same rate, regardless of their weights, if the air did not slow them down. His experiments had disproved Aristotle's statement. Galileo's own hypothesis became a theory.

One of the more unusual tests of Galileo's theory occurred on the earth's moon. The picture shows how one of the *Apollo 15* astronauts dropped a hammer from one hand and a feather from his other hand. On earth, a feather floats in air and drops much more slowly than a hammer. But when the astronaut dropped them, both objects fell at the same rate and hit the ground at the same time. Galileo was right.

Over the centuries, Galileo's theory has not been proven false. Therefore, it has become a **scientific law**—an accepted explanation that should apply over and over again throughout the universe.

Section Review

1. What must you do with a hypothesis if data show it is false?
2. What hypothesis did Galileo test using balls of different weights?

Challenge: Describe a controlled experiment to test whether salt water boils at the same temperature as tap water. Write a hypothesis and describe how you could test it. Identify your control for the experiment.

Figure 1-10 Astronaut David Scott dropped a hammer and feather on the moon. They hit the moon's surface at the same time, proving that Galileo was right.

Figure 1-9 Galileo testing his theory

Activity 1-1

Testing a Hypothesis

Purpose

To test the hypothesis that salt water will boil faster than distilled water

Materials

- two 100-mL beakers
- Bunsen burner, matches, ring stand, ring, and wire gauze
- distilled water
- salt
- spoon
- clock or watch
- cover goggles
- tongs or hot pad

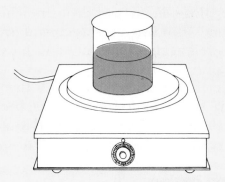

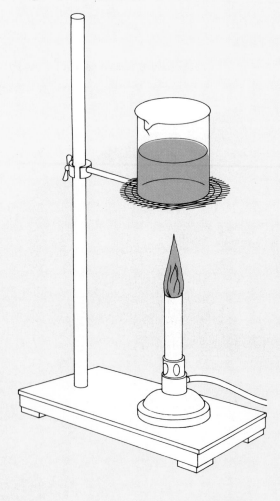

Procedure and Observations

1. Put on your cover goggles.
2. Set up your experiment to boil water as shown in the pictures.
3. Fill both beakers about half full of distilled water. Be sure the beakers contain equal amounts of water.
4. Heat the water in one beaker until it is at a full, bubbling boil. Time how long it takes for the water to boil. Record this observation.
5. Remove the beaker with the tongs or hot pad. *CAUTION: The beaker is very hot. Handle it with care.* Set the beaker aside to cool.
6. Add a spoonful of salt to the water in the second beaker and stir for two minutes. Repeat steps 4 and 5.

Analysis and Conclusions

1. Which factors did you control in both trials?
2. Which variable did you change?
3. What conclusion can you make from this experiment? Explain why you think this is correct.
4. Explain how you could make the experiment more accurate.

1-4 Scientific Measurements

The Metric System

Measuring is important for observing and doing research. Measurements tell how far, how large, and how much. When you measure, you compare a known amount, called a standard, to an unknown amount. In the past, people used familiar objects as standards. The width of a thumb was an inch. The length of the king's foot was called a foot. Since these amounts varied from person to person, or king to king, measurements changed too.

If everyone uses the same standard, people everywhere will get the same answer when they measure the same object. All scientists and most people in the world have agreed to use one system of measurement—the **metric system.** The metric system consists of seven standard units. It also uses prefixes that represent a factor that is a power of ten. The version of the metric system now used is the International System of Units. It is usually referred to as **SI** from its French initials (Le Système International d'Unitès).

The SI unit of length is the **meter** (symbol: m). A football field is just over 90 meters long, and an Olympic swimming pool is 50 meters long. In your classroom, you probably have a meter stick for measuring lengths.

Prefixes are used with meter and other SI units to indicate 1/10, 1/100, 1/1000, or 10, 100, 1000, and so on, times the unit. The table lists some prefixes that can be attached to a unit of measurement. Note that metric symbols do not end with a period. The school notebook shown measures about 25 centimeters (25 cm) high.

Objectives

After completing this section you will be able to

A. Describe how scientists and other people use the metric system.

B. Explain how mass and volume are measured.

C. Describe how density is measured.

D. Explain the limits of measurement.

E. Explain how scientists keep track of very large or very small numbers.

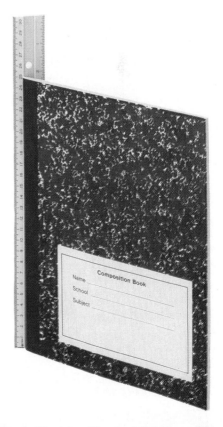

Figure 1-12 The notebook is about 25 cm high.

Figure 1-11 Some metric prefixes

Prefix	Symbol	Amount	Example and Symbol
milli-	m	0.001 ×	millimeter (mm)
centi-	c	0.01 ×	centimeter (cm)
deci-	d	0.1 ×	decimeter (dm)
kilo-	k	1000 ×	kilometer (km)
mega-	M	1 000 000 ×	megameter (Mm)

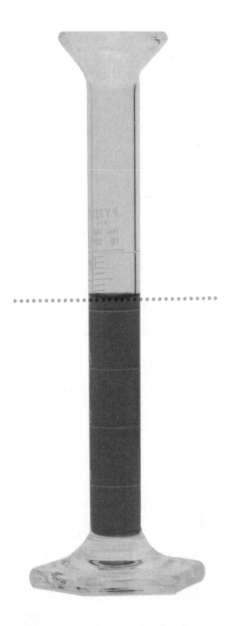

Figure 1-13 The line shows where to read the height of the liquid.

Time and temperature are two other quantities that are standard—or basic—units in SI. Time is measured in seconds (symbol: s). Temperature is often measured in **degrees Celsius** (symbol: °C). The Celsius scale is closely related to the SI temperature scale.

Often SI units are combined to label quantities. Your family car might have the unit "km/hr" on the speedometer. This unit measures how fast the car travels. It is derived from the units kilometer (km) and hour (hr).

Measuring Mass and Volume

Mass is the amount of matter an object has. The **gram** (symbol: g) is a unit that measures mass. A large paper clip has a mass of about one gram. The kilogram (symbol: kg)—1000 grams—is the SI unit for mass.

A **balance** is used to measure the mass of an object in some multiple of the gram, often the kilogram. Centuries ago, people determined the mass of an amount of grain using a stone and a balance. One pan of the balance held the stone. A buyer poured an unknown mass of grain into the second pan. When the two pans of the balance were level, the mass of the grain equaled the mass of the stone. People bought a "stone of grain."

Volume is the amount of space an object takes up. The SI unit of volume is the cubic meter (symbol: m³). Another unit for volume, the **liter** (American symbol: L), is the volume occupied by one kilogram of water. One liter also equals 1000 cubic centimeters (cm³). Some beakers and soft drink bottles hold volumes of one liter.

To measure the volume of liquids, scientists use a cylinder with one open end and markings along its height. This instrument is the **graduated cylinder.** The graduated cylinder shown has equal spaces marked in milliliters (symbol: mL). Notice that the surface of the liquid in the cylinder curves. The curve is the meniscus. Always read the height of the liquid at the horizontal part of the meniscus, as marked in the picture.

Scientists measure the volumes of boxlike objects in another way. Multiplying a box's length by its width by its height tells you its volume. Notice that the box of cereal in *Figure 1-14* measures thirty centimeters long, twenty three centimeters wide, and fifteen centimeters high.

Its volume is:

$$
\begin{aligned}
\text{volume} &= \text{length} \times \text{width} \times \text{height} \\
&= 30 \text{ cm} \times 23 \text{ cm} \times 15 \text{ cm} \\
&= 10\,350 \text{ cm}^3.
\end{aligned}
$$

Notice that multiplying the units with the numbers gives the cubic centimeter (cm^3), another SI unit for volume.

Measuring Density

Measuring how closely mass is packed gives another important quantity. **Density** is the amount of mass in one unit of volume.

The pillows and the iron block in the picture have equal masses. The density of the iron block is greater because its mass takes up less volume. Each liter of the block contains more mass. You calculate density using this equation:

$$\text{density} = \text{mass/volume}.$$

Note that 1 milliliter of water has a mass of 1 gram. Therefore,

$$\text{density of water} = 1 \text{ gram/milliliter}.$$

One milliliter equals one cubic centimeter. Thus, the unit for density is either the gram per milliliter (g/mL) or the gram per cubic centimeter (g/cm^3). The SI unit for density is the kilogram per cubic meter (kg/m^3).

For Practice

Use the proper equation to calculate the following:
1. the volume of a box that measures 20 cm in length, 15 cm in width, and 10 cm in height.
2. the density of 270 g of aluminum in a cylinder that takes up 100 cm^3 of space.

Figure 1-14 The volume of the box is found by multiplying its length × its width × its height.

Figure 1-15 The feathers and the block have the same mass. The density of the block is greater because its mass is packed into a smaller volume.

The Limits of Measurement

Suppose you want to get wall-to-wall carpeting for your bedroom. The carpet store tells you to find the length and width of your room to the nearest millimeter (thousandth of a meter). So you take a meter stick and measure. You measure the room as 3.823 meters long and 3.254 meters wide. You record your measurements on a piece of paper. When you arrive at the store, you realize that you have left the paper at home. So you call home and ask your brother to measure the room for you. He tells you the room is 3.824 meters long and 3.256 meters wide. When you get home, you decide to check the measurements once again. This time you measure the room's length at 3.829 meters and its width at 3.255 meters. Why are the measurements different each time?

At least two possible reasons exist for the different measurements. One reason for the different measurements is that one of you might have made a mistake. Perhaps you measured one meter and then slid the meter stick down to its end, as shown in the picture. You might not have placed it in exactly the right place when you moved it.

Figure 1-16 Measuring the room

A second reason is that measuring instruments can only be used to a certain level of accuracy. Even the same person will get slightly different measurements for the same object if the object is measured too precisely for the measuring instrument. If you measured to the nearest meter, instead of to the nearest millimeter, the answers would probably have been the same each time.

Still another reason could be that no perfect measuring instrument exists. You might have noticed that wooden doors sometimes swell and stick in hot or damp weather. In the same way, measuring instruments can change their original sizes.

To get the most accurate measurements you can for the carpet in your room, you should measure the room several times. Suppose you measure the room four times and include your brother's figures as a fifth measurement. The table lists the five measurements for the room's length and width.

You can now average the five measurements by adding them together and dividing the total by 5. As the table shows, the measurements in the length column add up to 19.131. Dividing by 5 gives 3.826 meters, with a remainder of 1. Should you add another 0 to make the number 19.1310 so that you could get rid of the remainder? The answer is no. You have been using only four significant digits in your original measurements—the one digit before the decimal point and the three digits following the decimal point. If you added the 0 to the total so that your average for the length came out 3.8262, the second 2 would not be a significant digit. Therefore, the average length of the room turns out to be 3.826 meters. The average width of the room is 3.255 meters. These figures might not be perfectly accurate, but they are probably very close.

You could also let the carpet store know that you are not completely certain about your measurements. For example, your measurements of lengths varied from 3.823 to 3.830 meters. The difference between the highest number and the lowest number is called the range of your measurements. So you could tell the carpet store that the range of your measurements is 0.007 meters.

Scientists have known about the uncertainty of measurements for a long time. Uncertainties hold true for all measurements, not just for length and width.

Length	Width
3.823 m	3.254 m
3.829 m	3.255 m
3.830 m	3.251 m
3.825 m	3.259 m
3.824 m	3.256 m
19.131 m	16.275 m
÷ 5	÷ 5
3.826 m	3.255 m

Figure 1-17 Finding the average measurements of the room

Figure 1-18 Scientific notation makes it easier to do calculations involving very large numbers and very small numbers.

For Practice

Write the following numbers in scientific notation.
1. 2462
2. 60 000
3. 73.4
4. 0.274
5. 0.0006543

Keeping Track of Long Numbers

Physical scientists often work with very large or very small numbers. For example, light travels through space at approximately 30 000 000 000 centimeters per second. Instead of keeping track of such long strings of zeros, scientists prefer to use scientific notation. **Scientific notation** is a simple way of keeping track of the number of zeros, as the picture shows.

In scientific notation, a number is written as a product so that the first factor is between 1 and 10; the second factor is a power of ten in exponential form. The number 100 000—a 1 followed by 5 zeros—is written 1×10^5. The exponent 5 tells how many zeros follow the number 1.

In the case of the speed of light, the first factor is 3, and the second factor is 10^{10}. In scientific notation the speed of light is written 3×10^{10} centimeters per second. The number 1989 is written 1.989×10^3. The exponent tells how many places the decimal point moved to the left.

You can also use scientific notation to write very small numbers. For example, the length of light waves that produce violet light is about 0.0000004 meters. Count the number of places the decimal point would have to be moved to the right to make the first factor 4. The decimal point would move 7 places to the right. When the decimal point moves to the right, the exponent is written as a negative number. Therefore, the wavelength of violet light is 4×10^{-7} meters.

Section Review

1. What measurement system do most people in the world use?
2. What is a balance used to measure?
3. What are two units for expressing density?
4. What are two reasons measurements cannot be completely accurate?
5. Why do scientists find it convenient to use scientific notation?

Challenge: The speed of light is almost exactly 3×10^{10} centimeters per second. Using scientific notation, figure out the speed of light in meters per second and in kilometers per second.

Graphing in SI Units

Purpose

To measure and graph quantities

Materials

- 2 meter sticks
- masking tape
- graph paper
- metric ruler
- balance
- small stone
- graduated cylinder
- 3 blocks of different sizes and materials, marked 1, 2, and 3
- water

Procedure and Observations

b

Graph with y-axis labeled "Number of Students" (values 1-13) and x-axis labeled "Height in cm" (values 130, 150, 170, 190, 210, 230, 250)

Part A

1. Tape the meter sticks on the wall with masking tape, as shown in **a.**
2. Stand with your back against the wall and ask your partner to read your height. Record your height to the nearest centimeter. Round off your height to the nearest 10 cm.
3. Write your rounded height on the chalkboard with those of your classmates. Record the data.
4. Copy and label the grid, as shown in **b.**
5. Plot your data as follows. Put your pencil on the bottom horizontal line at the value for the first height. Color in one block above the line.
6. Repeat step 5 for each student's height. If more than one student is the same height, a block should be colored above that height for each student.

a

100 cm

Part B

1. Measure the mass of each block on the balance. Record your data.
2. Measure the length, width, and height of each block with the ruler. Record the data.
3. Calculate each block's volume, using volume = length × width × height. Record each volume.
4. Calculate and record each block's density.
5. Measure the mass of the stone on your balance. Record the mass.
6. Measure the stone's volume using water displacement. First, half fill a graduated cylinder with water. Record the volume of the water. Carefully drop the stone into the water, and record the level of the water in the graduated cylinder. Subtract the first reading from the second. The difference is the stone's volume.
7. Calculate and record the stone's density.

Analysis and Conclusions

1. How accurately can you measure distances and mass with your equipment?
2. Explain how looking at a graph can be more helpful than looking at data.
3. When is measuring volume by water displacement necessary?

Developing Study Skills

In studying physical science, you will learn about properties of matter and energy that affect you every day. Your textbook, *Scott, Foresman Physical Science,* is a tool that has many features to help you study effectively. For example, the second page of each chapter contains an outline that gives an overview of that chapter. Refer to the outline on page 5. How many sections does Chapter 1 have? Read the lettered items under each section. Note each item is a question that will be answered in that section. You can use these questions to prepare for studying.

After you look over a chapter outline, you are ready to study the chapter—section by section. A good way to begin studying a section is by previewing it. To do this, glance at the features, such as the objectives, all headings, and the review questions. Find these features in the picture below. Note what each feature tells you. Previewing a section can help you see how information is organized, what content is covered, and where main points are made.

Next, read a section carefully. Use the outline questions for that section. They correspond to the objectives and will help you focus on the main points. Identify the vocabulary words and note their definitions as you read. Study the figures and tables to reinforce your understanding. Then review your knowledge by answering the questions at the end of the section. They, too, correspond to the objectives.

Practice using your textbook by answering the questions below.

1. What questions could help you review Section 2-4?
2. What are the objectives for Section 11-2?
3. To which section objective does the information on page 400 under the subhead *Interference of Waves* apply?
4. Read the third objective of Section 21-2. On which page can you find information to fulfill that objective?
5. What vocabulary word appears on page 551? How could *Figure 24-3* aid your understanding of this term?

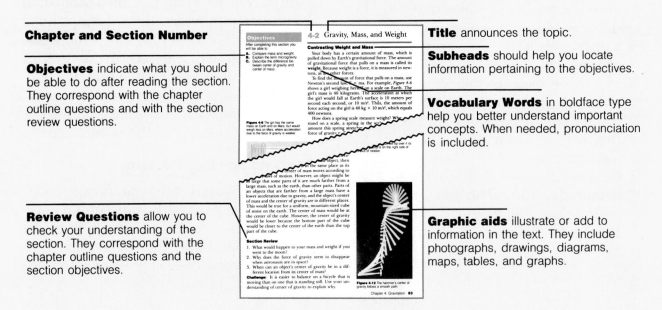

Chapter and Section Number

Objectives indicate what you should be able to do after reading the section. They correspond with the chapter outline questions and with the section review questions.

Review Questions allow you to check your understanding of the section. They correspond with the chapter outline questions and the section objectives.

Title announces the topic.

Subheads should help you locate information pertaining to the objectives.

Vocabulary Words in boldface type help you better understand important concepts. When needed, pronounciation is included.

Graphic aids illustrate or add to information in the text. They include photographs, drawings, diagrams, maps, tables, and graphs.

✔ Summary

1-1 Investigations in Physical Science

A. Physical science is the study of the changes in matter and energy.

B. Knowledge of physical science is helpful in making informed decisions about your future.

C. Benefits from physical science research and technology include computers, synthetic fabrics, and lasers.

1-2 Safety in the Physical Science Laboratory

A. You should know and follow all the safety rules for your laboratory.

B. In case of an accident in the laboratory, remain calm and tell your teacher immediately.

1-3 Solving Problems Scientifically

A. Scientists use the scientific method to solve problems. This method includes making a hypothesis, making observations to test the hypothesis, and drawing conclusions about the hypothesis.

B. Scientific knowledge is revised as scientists discover new information. Sometimes theories and laws must be rejected or changed because new information no longer supports them.

1-4 Scientific Measurements

A. The SI system is used by all scientists and most people in the world. The unit of length is the meter. The unit of time is the second. Temperature can be measured in degrees Celsius.

B. Mass is measured in grams or kilograms. Volume is the amount of space an object takes up and is measured in liters, milliliters, cubic centimeters, or cubic meters.

C. Density is calculated by dividing mass by volume.

D. Measuring instruments can be used only to a certain level of accuracy.

E. Scientists use scientific notation to write very large or very small numbers conveniently.

Vocabulary

For each of the following terms, write a sentence that uses the term correctly.

balance	**hypothesis**	**scientific method**
controlled experiment	**liter**	**scientific notation**
data	**mass**	**SI**
degree Celsius	**meter**	**theory**
density	**metric system**	**variable**
graduated cylinder	**model**	**volume**
gram	**scientific law**	

Check Your Knowledge

Part I: Matching   Match the definition in Column I with the term it defines in Column II.

Column I
1. amount of mass packed into a certain volume
2. amount of matter an object has
3. way of gaining new knowledge using a particular approach to problems
4. quantity that changes in an experiment
5. SI unit of length
6. results of observations and measurements
7. metric unit of volume
8. amount of space an object takes up
9. accepted explanation that has survived many tests over time
10. reasonable guess made to explain a problem

Column II
a. data
b. density
c. gram
d. hypothesis
e. liter
f. mass
g. meter
h. scientific law
i. scientific method
j. variable
k. volume

Part II: Multiple Choice   Choose the letter of the best answer.
11. A kilogram is (a) 100 grams. (b) 10 grams. (c) 1000 grams. (d) 10 000 grams.
12. The order of steps usually followed to solve a scientific problem is (a) test, theory, hypothesis. (b) theory, test, hypothesis. (c) hypothesis, test, theory. (d) theory, hypothesis, test.
13. A set of ideas or equations that physical scientists use to describe their ideas is a (a) variable. (b) model. (c) balance. (d) law.
14. Scientists measure temperature in (a) grams. (b) degrees Celsius. (c) milliliters. (d) centimeters.
15. A hypothesis that has survived many tests and seems to explain many observations is (a) a theory. (b) the scientific method. (c) data. (d) a variable.
16. The version of the metric system now used is (a) mL. (b) SI. (c) MS. (d) km.

17. You would most likely measure the length of a football field in (a) meters. (b) grams. (c) liters. (d) centimeters.
18. A unit you might find on the speedometer of a car is (a) g/mL. (b) m/g. (c) km/hr. (d) mL/s.

Part III: Completion   Write the word or words that correctly complete the sentence.
19. The volume of a liquid can be measured with a(n) _____ .
20. Scientists usually measure mass with a _____.
21. In a _____ _____ scientists use two setups that are exactly the same except for one variable.
22. The system of measurement that consists of standard units and prefixes that are multiples of ten is the _____ system.
23. Scientists use _____ _____ to represent very large or very small numbers.

Check Your Understanding

1. What topics are physical scientists interested in? Why do they investigate them?
2. List four ways to prevent accidents in the physical science laboratory.
3. Give an example of how scientists use models.
4. Which SI unit would you use to measure the distance between cities?
5. Calculate the volume of a shoe box that measures 19 cm in length, 16 cm in width, and 9 cm in height.
6. Calculate the density of 540 g of aluminum that take up 200 cm³ of space.
7. How many cubic centimeters of water could you pour into a container whose capacity is 0.5 L?
8. The density of iron is 7.9 g/cm³. What is the mass of a cube of iron that is 2.0 cm on each edge?
9. Write the following numbers using scientific notation.
   8370   0.0006   45 000   6 000 000

 Apply Your Knowledge

1. When you buy food items at the grocery store, are they more often measured by volume or by mass? Give some examples.
2. How might space exploration affect current theories?
3. Suppose you wanted to know if salt is really necessary in one of your favorite recipes or if it is merely a flavoring. Describe a controlled experiment you could do to find an answer.
4. Why can scientists not always perform controlled experiments?
5. Which has a greater density—a 144 g block of steel that takes up 20 cm³ or 136 grams of mercury that take up 10 mL?

Extend Your Knowledge

Research/Projects

1. Use the *Readers' Guide* in your library to learn about some topics of research that are of current interest to physical scientists. Look under the headings of Chemistry, Physics, and Astronomy. Read one article about each of the three fields and write one or two paragraphs about each topic.
2. Use metric measurements to find the length and width of your bedroom. Measure each dimension five times and calculate the average.

Readings

Baggett, James A. "Science in the Service of Art," *Scholastic Science World*, Dec. 1, 1986, pages 7–10. Describes how physical science technology is used to restore art works and to verify the value.

Wilson, David Gordon. "A Short History of Human-Powered Vehicles," *American Scientist*, July-August 1986, pages 350–357. A brief history of land, water, and air vehicles, including some spectacular successes and failures.

CHAPTER 2
Moving Objects

This chapter presents ideas about motion, such as types of motion and the speed, distance, and direction that an object moves. Anyone who can walk is familiar with one type of motion—movement in a straight line. Many people enjoy another type of motion, which is shown in the photograph. In several of the rides, people are spinning in circles.

Organizing Your Study Skills The outline below will help you see how the chapter is organized and what you should learn as you read.

I. Section 2-1: Describing Motion
   A. What is motion?
   B. How does motion depend on a frame of reference?
   C. What are the three basic kinds of motion?

II. Section 2-2: Contrasting Distance and Displacement
   A. How do distance and displacement differ?
   B. How can displacement be represented?
   C. How are vector and scalar quantities different?

III. Section 2-3: Comparing Speed and Velocity
   A. How is speed determined?
   B. How do speed and velocity differ?
   C. How are arrows used to represent velocity?

IV. Section 2-4: Describing Acceleration
   A. What is acceleration?
   B. In what ways can an object accelerate?

V. Section 2-5: Understanding Friction
   A. What is friction?
   B. What are the types of friction?
   C. How can friction be controlled?

2-1 Describing Motion

After completing this section you
will be able to

A. Define motion.
B. Explain how motion depends
on frames of reference.
C. Describe the three basic kinds
of motion.

How Motion Is Defined

When you ride a bicycle, you know you are moving because you pass trees, houses, and other fixed objects. But suppose you were in a well-cushioned car with no windows. How could you know if you and the car were moving? You would have a hard time deciding if you were moving because you could neither see objects outside your car nor could you feel the car's motion.

Relative motion, which is simply called motion, is defined as a change in the position of one object in relation to the position of some fixed object. You can determine whether an object is moving by comparing its position to that of a fixed object. For example, in the two pictures, the railroad crossing signal is a fixed object. You know the train in the pictures has moved because its position has changed in relation to the crossing signal. In everyday life, you use fixed objects, such as trees, fence posts, and buildings, to recognize motion.

Motion Depends on Frames of Reference

How you see an object's motion depends on which other objects you use to detect its motion. The objects an observer uses to detect motion are called the observer's **frame of reference.**

Figure 2-1 Fixed objects, such as the railroad sign, can be used to detect an object's motion.

Study the motion of the girl and the bus driver in the pictures. If you use the road as a frame of reference, the girl is moving in the second and third pictures, but the driver moves only in the third picture. If you use the bus as a frame of reference, the girl is moving in the second picture only, and the driver never moves.

Whether or not you say you are moving depends on your frame of reference. If you choose the earth as your frame of reference, you say you are not moving as you sit at your desk. But the earth carries you along with it as it revolves around the sun. If you choose the sun as your frame of reference, you say you are revolving around the sun.

Kinds of Motion

You are surrounded by objects that seem to move in many different ways. Yet this great variety of motion is made up of just three basic types. The first type is motion in a straight line—or **translational motion.** The movement of a bus along a straight highway is an example of translational motion.

Another type of motion is **circular motion**—or movement around a central position. A spinning top and a bicycle wheel rotating around its axle are examples of circular motion. The amusement park rides in the picture also exhibit circular motion.

Figure 2-2a No movement of girl or driver relative to the bus or road

b Movement of girl relative to the bus and road

c Movement of girl and driver relative to road only

The third kind of motion is **vibrational motion.** A guitar string moves back-and-forth when it vibrates. Any object that moves back-and-forth from a central position has vibrational motion. *Figure 2-3* shows an example of translational motion, circular motion, and vibrational motion.

Section Review

1. How do you determine whether an object is moving?
2. What affects how you view an object's motion?
3. Describe the three basic kinds of motion.

Challenge: Why does the sun appear to move across the sky, when it is the earth that moves around the sun?

Figure 2-3 Find an example of translational motion, vibrational motion, and circular motion in the picture.

2-2 Contrasting Distance and Displacement

How Distance and Displacement Differ

Imagine that you are taking your dog for a walk. As you stroll slowly down the sidewalk, your dog runs back and forth and from side to side. Sometimes the dog even stands still. By the time you and your dog reach the corner, who has traveled farther, you or your dog?

Figure 2-4 shows the imaginary paths traveled by a boy and his dog. Even though they started and ended at the same place, the dog had much more exercise than the boy did. The dog traveled in many directions, while the boy traveled in a straight line. The dog traveled a greater **distance,** which is the total length along a path between two points.

In studies of motion, a measure slightly different from distance—called displacement—is sometimes used. **Displacement** gives both the length and the direction of an object's path from its starting point straight to its ending point. The boy and the dog ended up at the same place. Even though the dog traveled a greater distance than the boy did, the dog's displacement was the same as the boy's. The solid red lines show that the displacements of the boy and the dog are equal.

Representing Displacement

Displacement measures the distance along a straight line between the start and end of an object's motion. Displacement also states the overall direction of motion.

After completing this section you will be able to

A. Explain how distance and displacement differ.

B. Describe how displacement can be represented.

C. Contrast vector and scalar quantities.

Have You Heard?

The United States has about 6.5 million kilometers of roads—more than any other country in the world.

Figure 2-4 The displacements of the boy and the dog are equal.

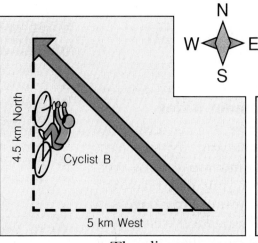
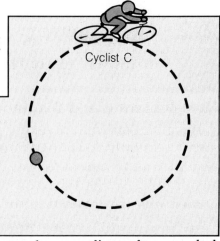
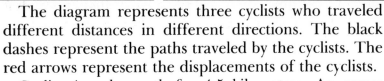

Figure 2-5 Distances and displacements for the cyclists

The diagram represents three cyclists who traveled different distances in different directions. The black dashes represent the paths traveled by the cyclists. The red arrows represent the displacements of the cyclists.

Cyclist A rode north for 4.5 kilometers. An arrow pointing north shows his displacement. Cyclist B rode 5 kilometers west and then 4.5 kilometers north. An arrow pointing approximately northwest shows her displacement. Cyclist C rode in a circle, ending up at the starting point. The diagram shows a red point for Cyclist C because his displacement is zero.

Displacement Is a Vector Quantity

A quantity that represents both size and direction is a **vector quantity.** Displacement is a vector quantity because it describes the length and direction of a moving object's path, as shown in *Figure 2-6*. Displacement can be represented by arrows that are drawn to scale and point in a given direction.

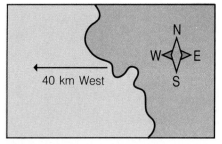

Figure 2-6 A vector quantity represents both size and direction.

A **scalar quantity** is a quantity that represents size only, as shown. Distance is a scalar quantity because it describes the length of an object's path but not its direction. Scalar quantities can be drawn to scale but cannot be represented by arrows. You would know how long to draw the arrow but not the direction to point it.

Section Review

1. How can displacement be less than distance traveled?
2. How can you represent an object's displacement?
3. How do vector and scalar quantities differ?

Challenge: A girl walks two blocks north, then two blocks east, then two blocks south. What distance does she travel? What is her displacement?

142 grams

Figure 2-7 A scalar quantity, such as mass, volume, or time, represents size only.

2-3 Comparing Speed and Velocity

Objectives

After completing this section you will be able to

A. Explain how speed is determined.

B. Contrast speed and velocity.

C. Describe how arrows are used to represent velocity.

Speed Depends on Distance and Time

In most races the first person to cross the finish line wins the race. Officials time the racers to determine their speed—or how fast they moved. **Speed** is the rate at which an object's position changes. Rate tells how quickly something is happening. The greater an object's speed, the greater the distance it travels during each second. Objects moving at high speeds change position more quickly than objects moving at low speeds.

To determine speed, you divide the distance traveled by the time spent traveling that distance.

$$\text{speed} = \text{distance/time}$$

If the girl in the picture swims 50 meters in 25 seconds, her speed is:

$$\text{speed} = 50 \text{ meters/25 seconds}$$
$$= 2 \text{ meters/second.}$$

Does this mean that the girl swam 2 meters during each second of the race? She might have traveled faster at the beginning or end of the race than she did in the middle. The total distance divided by the total time is the average speed. In this case, the swimmer's average speed was 2 meters per second. However, she might never have traveled exactly 2 meters in any one second.

For Practice

Use the speed equation to solve these problems:

1. What is the average speed of a car that travels 420 km in 6 hours?

2. How fast do you walk if you take 2.5 hours to cover 12.5 km?

Figure 2-8 The girl's speed is the rate her body changes position in the water.

Explore!

Use an encyclopedia or books about cars and airplanes to find out how speedometers and air speed indicators work.

You can use a graph to describe an object's motion. At the left is a graph of the distance a car traveled during a trip. After three hours, the car had covered a distance of 90 kilometers. Using the equation, the car's speed was:

$$\text{speed} = \text{distance/time}$$
$$= 90 \text{ kilometers/3 hours}$$
$$= 30 \text{ kilometers/hour.}$$

If you use the graph to calculate the car's speed during each of the three hours, you will find that its speed did not change. The speed was constant. Notice that the graph is a straight line. A plot of distance versus time will always give a straight line when an object moves at a constant speed.

Figure 2-9 Graphing speed

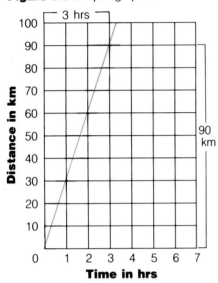

Speed and Velocity Differ

Speed describes how fast an object moves. Speed is a scalar quantity. **Velocity** describes both how fast and in what direction an object moves. Therefore, velocity is a vector quantity. For example, the speed of an eastbound car might be 45 kilometers per hour. Its velocity, however, would be 45 kilometers per hour due east. Another car with the same speed traveling due west would have a different velocity. What is the second car's velocity?

The picture shows two devices you would need in an automobile to determine its velocity. The speedometer indicates the speed of the car, while the compass on the dashboard indicates the car's direction.

Figure 2-10 The speedometer and the compass are needed to determine a car's velocity.

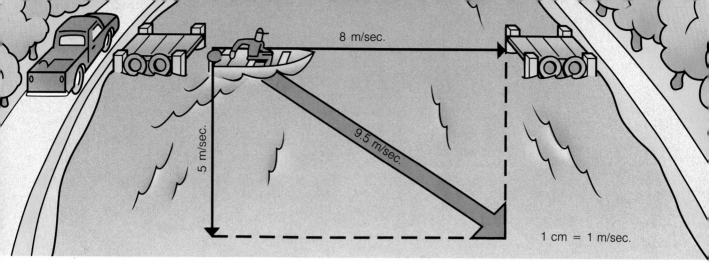

8 m/sec.

5 m/sec.

9.5 m/sec.

1 cm = 1 m/sec.

Representing Velocity

Velocity describes both the speed and the direction of a moving object. The diagram represents a boat about to travel across a river. The boat's motor moves the boat at eight meters per second to the east. However, as the boat moves across, it also drifts downstream because of the river's current. The velocity of the current is five meters per second to the south. The black arrows in the picture represent the velocities of the boat and the current. The arrows point in the direction of the moving objects. The length of each arrow corresponds to the speed. The arrows are drawn using a scale of one centimeter to represent one meter per second.

You can use the arrows to determine the combined effect of the two velocities on the boat. Notice that a rectangle is drawn with the two velocity arrows forming two sides of the rectangle. The red diagonal arrow in the rectangle shows the resulting velocity of the boat. The red arrow is 9.5 centimeters long, representing 9.5 meters per second. Therefore, because of the combined effect of the boat's motor and the river's current, the boat actually travels at 9.5 meters per second. The boat travels approximately to the southeast as it moves from one river bank to the other. If you were in this boat, which way would you steer in order to end up directly across the river from your starting point?

Figure 2-11 The velocity of the boat depends on the velocity of the current.

Section Review

1. How can you determine the speed of an object?
2. How is velocity different from speed?
3. How are arrows used to represent velocity?

Challenge: What is the greatest velocity that a boat on a river can attain if the boat's motor moves it at 10 km/hr and the river's current is 8 km/hr?

Measuring Average Speed

Purpose

To measure the average speed of a moving object

Materials

- small ball
- 2 meter sticks
- 4 thick, hardcover books
- watch or clock with a second hand
- masking tape
- clay
- metric ruler

Procedure and Observations

1. Tape the meter sticks together at a right angle, as in **a**.

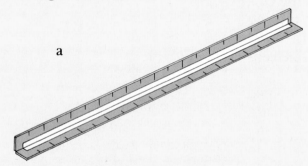

a

2. Place a book under one end of the sticks, and secure the sticks with clay and tape, as in **b**.

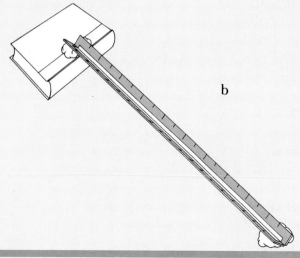

b

Data Table

Height	Trial	Time	Speed	Averaged Speed
1 Book	1			
	2			
	3			
4 Books	1			
	2			
	3			

Distance _____

4. Record the distance in centimeters from the top of the sticks to the bottom.
5. Hold the ball at the top of the elevated end of the sticks.
6. Release the ball while your partner determines the time it takes for the ball to reach the bottom of the sticks.
7. Record the time in the table.
8. Repeat steps 5–7 two more times.
9. Calculate the average speed of the ball for each trial by dividing the distance traveled by the time. Record the three speeds in the table.
10. Average the three speeds by adding them and dividing by three. Record the average in the table.
11. Repeat steps 5–10 using four books to elevate the meter sticks.

Analysis and Conclusions

1. What was the reason for doing three trials at each elevation rather than just one?
2. Compare the ball's averaged speed at the two elevations. Explain your observations.

2-4 Describing Acceleration

Changing Velocity

If you have ever ridden a roller coaster, you might remember the anticipation you felt when being pulled up the first hill. Suddenly, you plunged downward, moving faster and faster. The changing speed and direction of the roller coaster involves changes in its velocity.

Acceleration is the rate of change in velocity. Acceleration tells how fast a moving object's velocity is changing. Because velocity consists of speed and direction, acceleration can involve a change in speed, a change in direction, or both. Acceleration, like velocity and displacement, is a vector quantity.

Examine the pictures of the moving balls. In the first picture, the ball rolls at a constant velocity. It moves the same distance during each second that it rolls. In the second picture, the ball rolls down a slope, gaining speed as it rolls. As the ball accelerates, it travels farther during each second. The ball moves with an ever-changing velocity.

Acceleration can also mean a change in direction. A car traveling around a curve in the road is accelerating because it is changing direction, which is the other part of its velocity. Even though the car moves at a constant speed around the curve, it is accelerating because it is turning.

Objectives

After completing this section you will be able to

A. Define acceleration.
B. Describe ways that an object can accelerate.

Figure 2-12 Time lapse photographs showing the positions of a rolling ball

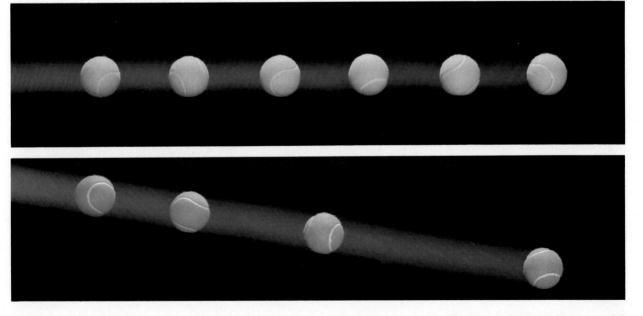

Calculate the acceleration in each problem below:

1. A car accelerates from 44 km/hr to 66 km/hr in 11 seconds. What is the acceleration?
2. What is the acceleration of a car that changes speed from 20 km/hr to 60 km/hr in 5 seconds?

Figure 2-13 The acceleration of the roller coaster is constant as it goes downhill.

An object with a changing velocity can have a constant acceleration. Such an object can change its speed, or its direction, or both, but it does so by the same amount each second. The roller coaster in *Figure 2-13* and the rolling ball have constant accelerations going downhill. Their velocities increase at a constant rate.

You can calculate the size of the acceleration resulting from a change in speed. First, subtract the object's original speed from its final speed. Then divide this difference by the time for the change in speed.

$$\text{size of acceleration} = \frac{\text{final speed} - \text{original speed}}{\text{time for the change of speed}}$$

Suppose two cyclists are traveling in the same direction at 10 kilometers per hour. Then they increase their velocity to 20 kilometers per hour. Cyclist A reaches the higher speed in 10 seconds (10 s). His acceleration is:

$$\text{size of acceleration} = \frac{20 \text{ km/hr} - 10 \text{ km/hr}}{10 \text{ s}}$$

$$= 1 \text{ km/hr/s.}$$

Cyclist A increases his velocity by 1 kilometer per hour each second.

Cyclist B reaches 20 kilometers per hour in 5 seconds. Her acceleration is:

$$\text{size of acceleration} = \frac{20 \text{ km/hr} - 10 \text{ km/hr}}{5 \text{ s}}$$

$$= 2 \text{ km/hr/s.}$$

Cyclist B has twice the acceleration of Cyclist A. She increases her velocity at the rate of 2 kilometers per hour each second.

The Meaning of Acceleration

As with speed, an acceleration of 2 kilometers per hour per second does not always mean that the object accelerated 2 kilometers per hour during each second. The acceleration might have been more or less during some seconds. The equation for determining acceleration gives you the size of the average acceleration. Average acceleration is the total change in the object's speed during the time in which that change took place.

Acceleration does not have to mean an increase in velocity. Slowing down is also acceleration. This kind of acceleration is called *deceleration*.

You can calculate an object's deceleration in the same way that you determine its acceleration. For example, a cyclist slows from 10 kilometers per hour, to a stop in 5 seconds. The graph represents the cyclist's motion. The point at the top of the sloping graph line shows the cyclist's original speed—10 kilometers per hour. The point at the bottom of the graph line shows the cyclist's final speed—0 kilometers per hour. The acceleration is:

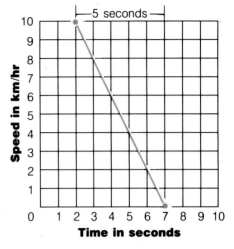

Figure 2-14 Graphing acceleration

$$\text{size of acceleration} = \frac{\text{final speed} - \text{original speed}}{\text{time for change of speed}}$$

$$= \frac{0 \text{ km/hr} - 10 \text{ km/hr}}{5 \text{ s}}$$

$$= -2 \text{ km/hr/s.}$$

The negative number indicates deceleration. The cyclist decelerates 2 kilometers per hour each second. In other words, the cyclist's speed decreased an average of 2 kilometers per hour during each of the 5 seconds that it took her to come to a stop.

Section Review

1. How are constant speed and constant acceleration different?
2. How can an object accelerate without changing speed?

Challenge: How can the brakes and the steering wheel accelerate an automobile?

Pilot

The take-off and landing are the most difficult parts of flying a plane. Slippery runways and bad weather can make the job even more difficult. A pilot must be able to operate a plane under any condition.

Airplane pilots prepare for each trip by making a flight plan. They use weather information to choose the best flight route. A pilot's cockpit controls report on safety conditions, plane position, and control tower data. A plane needs speed to take off against gravity and stay in the air, so pilots watch their velocity closely.

All pilots are licensed. Commercial pilots must have flown for at least 250 hours, pass a written exam, and be in top physical condition to do their job.

2-5 Understanding Friction

Friction Resists Motion

When two surfaces, such as your feet and the sidewalk, are in contact with one another, a resistance to motion is produced. This resistance to motion is **friction.**

Different pairs of surfaces have different amounts of friction. For example, a block of wood slides more easily across an ice skating rink than it does along a sidewalk. A wet sidewalk causes less friction than a dry sidewalk does.

Every surface has tiny high and low spots. You can see or feel these uneven places on a rough surface. On a smooth surface, these high and low spots might be so tiny that you could see them only with a microscope. The high spots on the surfaces overlap each other and catch. The sides of the high spots pressing against each other cause the resistance to motion known as friction.

Kinds of Friction

Friction exists in three forms. **Static friction** occurs between two surfaces that touch but do not move in relation to each other. When two surfaces remain in contact, their high spots are forced together. Static friction holds a filing cabinet in place against a floor. To move the cabinet, you must push or pull hard enough to overcome static friction.

Sliding friction occurs when one object slides over another. If you push the cabinet across a floor, you encounter sliding friction. This type of friction is weaker than static friction. Sliding friction causes surfaces in contact to heat up. When you rub your hands together, friction produces heat that warms your skin. Striking a match against sandpaper produces heat that ignites the match.

Rolling friction occurs between the surface of a wheel or other round object and another surface. When one surface rolls across another, the high spots are lifted away from each other and over the other piece's high spots. This process resists motion less than when the high spots must slide against each other. The man in the picture has used wheels to reduce friction. His job moving the garbage can is easier because he is not trying to slide it. Rolling friction is less than sliding friction and also produces less heat. But when a car travels at high speeds, rolling friction on the tires can cause overheating.

Both rolling and sliding friction cause the surfaces in contact to wear down. However, static friction produces neither heat nor wear.

Figure 2-15 The wheels replace sliding friction with rolling friction.

Figure 2-16 Balls in the roller skate wheel reduce friction.

Reducing Friction

In many cases, people want to reduce friction to allow objects to move more easily and to reduce heating and wearing of the surfaces in contact. One way to reduce friction is with lubricants. A **lubricant** is a slippery material, such as oil, grease, or graphite, placed between surfaces that move over each other. A lubricant forms a smooth, thin layer between the surfaces and keeps their high spots from touching. The lubricant fills in the low spots in the surfaces, and keeps the high spots from rubbing against each other. Oil and grease are lubricants used in automobiles. Bicycle chains and door locks are often lubricated with graphite, a slippery form of carbon, like the "lead" in a pencil.

Another way to reduce friction is to make surfaces that rub against each other very smooth. Less friction occurs between smooth surfaces because their high and low spots are smaller than those of rough surfaces.

A third way to reduce friction is to use wheels, rollers, or balls to substitute rolling friction for sliding friction. The small balls in the wheel of the roller skate, shown here, reduce friction between the wheel and the axle. Using a lubricant would reduce friction even further and allow the skate to move quite easily.

Just because friction resists motion does not mean it is always a problem. You would not want to get rid of friction entirely, even if you could. Friction is helpful because it keeps things from sliding or slipping. Friction is needed to start things moving and then to slow them down or stop them. You need friction in order to walk. Sometimes, instead of reducing friction, you need to increase it. To make an automobile stop quickly, a great deal of friction between the brakes and the wheels and between the tires and the road is needed.

Section Review

1. Explain the cause of friction between two surfaces that are touching.
2. Give an example of each of the three kinds of friction.
3. State three ways of reducing friction and give an example of each.

Challenge: Explain why it could be dangerous to drive an automobile with tires that had badly worn treads.

Exploring Friction

Purpose

To observe the differences between the kinds of friction

Materials

- cover goggles
- short, thick rubber band
- small paper clip
- large index card
- scissors
- glue bottle or similar mass
- tape dispenser that is heavier than the glue bottle
- 2 round pencils
- sheet of thick plastic
- light vegetable oil

Procedure and Observations

PART A

1. Put on your cover goggles. Fold the card in half along its length and slit the fold about 1 cm, as shown in **a**.

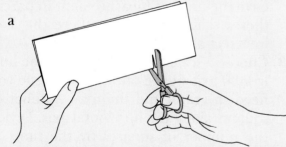

a

2. Slip the rubber band on the paper clip and place the paper clip in the slit, as shown in **b**.
3. Place the glue bottle on the end of the card opposite the rubber band.
4. Gently pull the band to move the card and bottle about 10 cm. Observe how much the rubber band stretches just before the card and bottle start moving. You are measuring static friction.

b

c

5. Note by how much the stretching changes, as the card and bottle move. You are measuring sliding friction.
6. The greater the force needed to overcome friction, the more the rubber band will be stretched. When you stop pulling, mark the point reached by the stretched end of the rubber band on the card. Record your observations.

PART B

1. Replace glue bottle with tape dispenser.
2. Try to move the tape dispenser by pulling the rubber band.
3. Place the pencils under the index card so that the dispenser can roll, as shown in **c**.
4. Try to move the dispenser by pulling on the rubber band. Record what happens. Mark the point reached by the stretched end of the rubber band on the card.

PART C

1. Place the plastic sheet on your table. Coat sheet lightly with oil.
2. Repeat Part A, steps 3–6.
3. Compare the pencil mark you made in Part A with the mark from Part B.

Analysis and Conclusions

1. Compare the strengths of static, sliding, and rolling friction.
2. What effect does a lubricant have on static and sliding friction?

Science Skills

Interpreting and Making Line Graphs

In science, essential information is often presented in line graphs. Line graphs show how one quantity depends on or changes with another.

Part A

The line graph below shows the distance a train traveled in a ten-hour trip. Time is shown on the horizontal axis and distance is shown on the vertical axis. Use the graph to answer these questions.

1. What unit of measurement is used in the scale on the horizontal axis?
2. What unit of measurement is used in the scale on the vertical axis?
3. How far did the train travel between the third and tenth hour? during the entire trip?
4. Determine the train's average speed during the first four hours of its trip.
5. When did the train stop? How can you tell from the graph?
6. Was the train moving at a constant speed during the last five hours of its trip? Explain your answer.

Train Trip: Time vs. Speed

Time (in seconds)	Speed (in meters/second)	Time (in seconds)	Speed (in meters/second)
0	0	25	20
5	5	30	20
10	10	35	10
15	10	40	0
20	15		

Part B

Follow the steps below to make a line graph of the data in the table.

1. On a piece of graph paper draw horizontal and vertical axes that meet at a point near the lower left corner of the paper. Leave enough room below the horizontal axis and next to the vertical axis for labels.
2. Label the axes, using the horizontal axis for time and the vertical axis for speed. Give the units of measurement in parentheses. Label the point where the axes intersect as "0."
3. Choose a scale for each axis. For the horizontal axis figure out the total time you need to graph and the total number of squares along the horizontal axis. Divide the number of squares by the time. If necessary, round this number to a whole number. This will give you the number of squares per unit of time. Then mark off the scale with equal intervals. Repeat this procedure for the vertical axis, substituting the maximum speed for the total time to determine your scale.
4. Plot the data in the table, one point at a time. Connect the points and give your graph a title.

Train Trip: Time vs. Distance

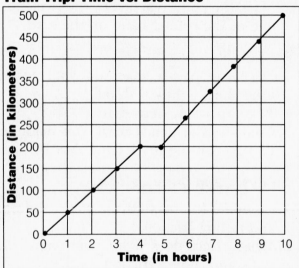

 Summary

2-1 Describing Motion

A. The relative motion of an object is determined by the change in position of that object in relation to other objects that make a frame of reference.

B. All statements about motion depend on the observer's frame of reference.

C. Translational motion, rotational motion, and vibrational motion are the three basic kinds of motion.

2-2 Contrasting Distance and Displacement

A. The distance and direction of an object's motion from the starting point straight to the ending point is the object's displacement.

B. Displacement is shown by arrows drawn to scale and pointing in the direction of displacement.

C. Displacement is a vector quantity because it describes both distance and direction of that motion.

2-3 Comparing Speed and Velocity

A. The speed of an object tells how quickly the object changes position.

B. Velocity describes how fast and in what direction an object moves.

C. Velocity is a vector quantity and can be represented by arrows drawn to scale and pointing in the direction of the velocity.

2-4 Describing Acceleration

A. Any change in speed or direction is acceleration. Acceleration is calculated by subtracting the original speed from the final speed, then dividing by the time for the change.

B. Slowing down is known as deceleration, and it is calculated in the same way as acceleration.

2-5 Understanding Friction

A. The three types of friction are static, sliding, and rolling friction. Static friction is the strongest.

B. Friction between surfaces can be reduced by smoothing the surfaces or by using a lubricant.

Vocabulary

For each of the following terms, write a sentence that uses the term correctly.

acceleration	lubricant	static friction
circular motion	relative motion	translational motion
displacement	rolling friction	vector quantity
distance	scalar quantity	velocity
frame of reference	sliding friction	vibrational motion
friction	speed	

Check Your Knowledge

Part I: Matching   Match the definition in Column I with the correct term in Column II.

Column I
1. the rate of change in velocity
2. caused by the rubbing together of two surfaces
3. a change in position of an object
4. affects how an observer views motion
5. distance divided by time
6. a quantity that has both size and direction
7. the rate of decrease in velocity
8. slippery material that reduces friction
9. speed in a certain direction
10. distance and direction from one point to another

Column II
a. acceleration
b. deceleration
c. displacement
d. distance
e. frame of reference
f. friction
g. lubricant
h. motion
i. speed
j. vector
k. velocity

Part II: Multiple Choice   Choose the letter of the best answer.
11. What is the distance traveled by a jogger who runs once around a 400-m track? (a) 100 m in all directions (b) 0 m (c) 400 m (d) 400 m to the north
12. A truck that travels 180 km in 2 hrs has an average speed of (a) 360 km/hr. (b) 180 km/hr. (c) 90 km/hr. (d) 182 km/hr.
13. An object traveling at a constant velocity (a) changes speed. (b) changes direction. (c) covers equal distances in equal times. (d) covers unequal distances in equal times.
14. A graph can be used to describe an object's (a) motion. (b) speed. (c) acceleration. (d) a, b, and c.
15. An object traveling along a rough surface slows down because of (a) friction. (b) reference points. (c) displacement. (d) constant motion.
16. In 10 hrs, a car traveling at 70 km/hr can cover (a) 7 km. (b) 700 km. (c) 350 km. (d) 710 km.

17. To accelerate, an object must change (a) speed. (b) direction. (c) both speed and direction. (d) either speed or direction.
18. The acceleration of a car that increases speed from 0 km/hr to 50 km/hr in 10 s is (a) 25 km/hr/s. (b) 10 km/hr/s. (c) 500 km/hr/s. (d) 5 km/hr/s.
19. In addition to size, a vector quantity has (a) displacement. (b) direction. (c) speed. (d) friction.

Part III: Completion   Write the word or words that complete the sentence correctly.
20. Total distance divided by total time equals _____ speed.
21. Displacement has both size and _____.
22. The length along a path between two points is _____.
23. Speed describes how quickly a person or object changes _____.
24. The basic types of motion are translational, circular, and _____.

Check Your Understanding

1. Draw a diagram showing some of the possible paths of a cyclist who has a displacement of 10 km to the northeast. Be sure to mark the distance of each path.
2. If the speedometer on a car indicates a constant speed, can you be certain the car is not accelerating? Explain your answer.
3. Calculate the accelerations of the following: (a) a car increasing speed from 0 km/hr to 100 km/hr in 20 s. (b) a bicycle going from 50 km/hr to 0 km/hr in 25 s. (c) a runner going from 0 m/s to 10 m/s in 2 s.
4. A runner travels 2 km due east, then 2 km due south, then 2 km due west. What is the runner's displacement?
5. Describe two ways that friction can be reduced between two surfaces rubbing against each other.
6. An airplane travels from San Diego to San Francisco, a distance of about 740 km, in 2 hours. Calculate the plane's average speed.

 Apply Your Knowledge

1. Explain how an accelerating object can have a constant speed but not a constant velocity?
2. A girl leaves school at 3:00 and starts walking home. Her house is 2 km from school. She walks at the same rate without stopping. She gets home at 3:30. What was her average speed? How fast was she walking at 3:15?
3. Describe at least two situations in which you would want to have a great amount of friction between two surfaces.
4. How is circular motion accelerated motion?

 Extend Your Knowledge

Research/Projects
1. Mark off 100 meters. Find your running speed by timing how long it takes you to run the 100 meters. Check a book of records to compare your speed with the world record.
2. On a map of your state, pick a city and find the shortest highway route from your town to the one you selected. Find the distance of that route by laying a string along the roads on the map and then measuring the string's length. Compare this length to the map's scale.

Readings
Watson, Philip. *Super Motion.* Lothrop, 1982. Colorfully illustrated experiments to explore aspects of force and motion.
Zubrowski, Bernard. *Raceways: Having Fun with Balls and Tracks.* Morrow, 1985. Activities that demonstrate velocity and acceleration will provide fun while designing and building raceways.

CHAPTER 3
The Laws of Motion

Sharply curving bobsled tracks must be steeply banked, or tilted inward, to keep the sleds on the track. If the track is banked at the proper angle for the speed of the sled, the inward force of the walls keeps the sled from sliding outward, without the need for friction. The banked walls of the track also exert a force on the sled.

Organizing Your Study Skills The outline below will help you see how the chapter is organized and what you should learn as you read

I. **Section 3-1: Newton's First Law of Motion**
   A. How does friction affect a moving object?
   B. What is inertia?

II. **Section 3-2: Newton's Second Law of Motion**
   A. How does Newton's second law link force, acceleration, and mass?
   B. How is force measured?
   C. What is momentum?

III. **Section 3-3: Newton's Third Law of Motion**
   A. How does Newton's third law relate action and reaction?
   B. What is the law of conservation of momentum?

IV. **Section 3-4: Balanced and Unbalanced Forces**
   A. How does a net force act on a stationary object?
   B. How does a net force act on a moving object?

V. **Section 3-5: Circular Motion**
   A. How do Newton's laws explain circular motion?
   B. What is centripetal force?
   C. What determines how fast an object rotates?

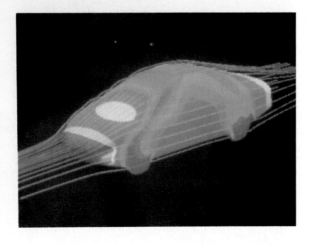

Objectives

After completing this section you will be able to

A. Describe how friction affects a moving object.
B. Explain how Newton's first law relates motion and inertia.

Explore!

Roll a toy car along the floor. Test different ways that you could increase or decrease the friction between the car and the floor.

3-1 Newton's First Law of Motion

Friction Slows Down Moving Objects

The sliding hockey puck in the picture will keep moving straight ahead at the same speed unless something slows it down or stops it. For instance, the puck will stop or change direction if it hits a player's stick or crashes into the side of the rink. Or the puck might slow down because of friction, which occurs when one object rubs against another. Less friction occurs on smooth ice than on rough pavement. This is why a puck glides farther on ice than it would on a sidewalk.

In the 1600s, the physicists Galileo Galilei and Isaac Newton observed moving objects and thought about the nature of motion. At that time, people thought moving objects tend to slow down and stop by themselves. They had not realized that objects slow down and stop because of friction.

Galileo and Newton realized that a moving object keeps moving as long as friction does not slow it enough to stop it. They also observed that a stationary object—one at rest—remains still unless something makes it move. The tendency for an object to resist changes in motion is called **inertia** (in er′shə). A hockey puck resting on ice stays in place because of inertia. Because of its inertia, a sliding puck will move at a constant velocity until something slows, stops, or deflects it.

Figure 3-1 A puck slides farther on ice than on pavement.

The Law of Inertia

Any push or pull that alters the velocity of an object is a **force.** The side of an ice rink exerts a force on a puck that crashes into it. Friction is a force between two surfaces that acts in a direction opposite to an object's motion. Other forces also can act opposite to an object's motion. For example, when you are in a moving car, air particles bouncing off the car apply a force that slows you down. This force is called **air resistance.**

Newton's first law of motion states that if no force acts on a moving object, the object will continue moving at the same speed in the same direction. If the object is stopped, it will remain still. This law is sometimes called the law of inertia.

Newton's first law explains much about the motion of spacecraft. The *Voyager* spacecraft shown in the picture was launched from earth in 1977. Once *Voyager* traveled fast enough, no more power was needed to keep the craft moving. Unlike the earth's atmosphere, outer space has little matter. Therefore, almost no friction occurs in space that would slow a moving spacecraft. The spacecraft keeps moving on its own. Only a force, such as gravity or the firing of rocket engines, would change the spacecraft's motion.

Section Review

1. What effect does friction have on a moving object?
2. What does Newton's first law of motion state?

Challenge: Use Newton's first law to explain why people riding in cars should wear safety belts.

Objectives

After completing this section you will be able to

A. Describe how Newton's second law relates force, acceleration, and mass.

B. Describe how force is measured.

C. Explain what factors affect an object's momentum.

3-2 Newton's Second Law of Motion

Mass, Force, and Acceleration

In his first law, Newton described inertia. He went on to observe that different objects have different amounts of inertia. Newton realized that the amount of inertia an object has is related to its mass. The more mass an object has, the more force is required to change the object's motion. Newton also determined that, for a given amount of time, the greater the force exerted on an object, the greater the acceleration. The resulting acceleration or change in the object's motion is always in the same direction as the force applied.

Newton combined these ideas in his **second law of motion,** which states that an object accelerates because a force acts on it. The stronger the force, the greater the acceleration. Further, Newton defined the mass of an object as the link between the force on the object and the object's acceleration. Newton's relation is shown by the equation $F = ma$. F stands for force, m stands for mass, and a stands for acceleration.

According to Newton's second law, the stronger the force on the model airplanes in the picture, the more they will accelerate. You can get a stronger force by winding the rubber band more. The rubber band will unwind faster, spin the propeller faster, and apply more force to the plane. Newton's second law also says that if you add mass to the plane and apply the same force, the plane will accelerate less. For this reason, airline pilots check that their planes are not carrying too much mass before they take off.

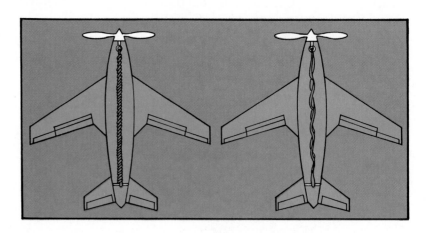

Figure 3-3 How rapidly the model airplanes accelerate depends on how much force acts on them.

Measuring Force

Study the drawing of the horse pulling a 100-kilogram sleigh. The horse pulls the sleigh with a constant force. Newton's second law predicts that the sleigh will accelerate as long as the horse keeps pulling with a force greater than friction. The force needed to accelerate the sleigh is 100 newtons.

$$F = \text{mass} \times \text{acceleration}$$
$$= 100 \text{ kilograms} \times 1 \text{ meter/second/second}$$
$$= 100 \text{ kilogram} \cdot \text{meters/second/second}$$
$$= 100 \text{ newtons}$$

The SI unit to measure force is the **newton** (N). One newton is the force required to accelerate 1 kilogram at the rate of 1 meter per second every second. ($1 \text{ N} = 1 \text{ kg} \cdot \text{m/s/s}$)

If the horse exerts the same force (100 N) on a sleigh that has twice as much mass, it will accelerate at:

$$100 \text{ newtons} = 200 \text{ kilograms} \times a$$
$$a = 100 \text{ newtons}/200 \text{ kilograms}$$
$$= 0.5 \text{ meters/second/second}$$

Notice that doubling the mass when the force is the same cuts the acceleration in half.

For the 100-kilogram sleigh to accelerate at 2 meters per second each second, the horse must pull with a force of 200 newtons.

$$F = 100 \text{ kilograms} \times 2 \text{ meters/second/second}$$
$$= 200 \text{ newtons}$$

For Practice

Use the equation $F = ma$ to solve these problems.
1. How much force is needed to accelerate a 20-kg crate by 3 m/s/s?
2. How many times more force is needed to accelerate the crate twice as much?

Figure 3-4 The force needed to accelerate the sleigh depends on the mass of the sleigh.

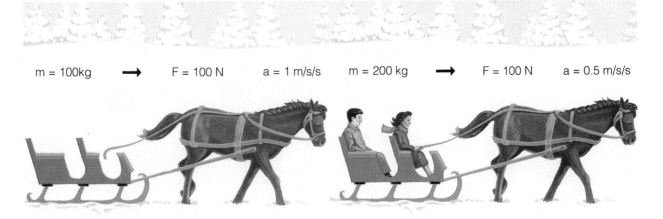

m = 100kg → F = 100 N a = 1 m/s/s   m = 200 kg → F = 100 N a = 0.5 m/s/s

Once the sleigh reaches a certain speed, Newton's first law says that it would continue to move forward at the same rate if it were not slowed by the force of friction acting backward on it. To keep the sleigh moving, the horse has to exert only the small amount of force needed to balance friction between the runners and the snow. If the horse were to continue pulling with the original amount of force, the sleigh would keep accelerating.

Moving Objects Have Momentum

An object's **momentum** is the strength of its motion. The momentum of an object depends on both its mass and its velocity. The faster you throw a ball, the more momentum it has, so the more impact it has when it hits something. In each picture, the momentum of the ball is determined by multiplying its mass times its velocity. A ball with twice the mass will do just as much damage if it moves at half the velocity. A bullet has a small mass, but it has a great momentum because of its high velocity. A train, even a slowly moving one, has a great momentum because of its large mass.

Figure 3-5 The baseball was hit at a slower speed in the lower picture and so had less momentum than it had in the upper picture.

Newton showed that to change an object's momentum, you must apply a force. You must apply more force if you want to change the momentum more quickly. You experience this effect when you ride a bicycle. You must brake harder to stop quickly than to slow down gradually. You stop in both cases because a small force acting over a long time can have the same effect as a large force acting quickly.

The red car and the white car in *Figure 3-6* crashed head on. Both cars had too much momentum to stop instantaneously. Each car provided the force needed to stop the other car. Because of the mass and velocity of both cars, the impact was great enough to destroy them.

Section Review

1. Describe Newton's second law of motion.
2. If you double the force on an object, what happens to its acceleration?
3. What are two ways to increase an object's momentum?

Challenge: Two grocery carts, one empty and the other full of groceries, are accidentally released at the top of a sloping parking lot. Which cart would be easier to catch and then stop? Explain your answer to the second part in terms of Newton's second law.

Explore!

Drop a marble from different heights onto a large mound of clay. Observe how the original height of a falling object affects its momentum.

Figure 3-6 The greater the momentum an object has, the harder it is to stop it.

Careers in Physical Science

Aerospace Engineer

The Wright brothers never guessed that their flight would start a new industry. But after Kitty Hawk, the aerospace business began. Aerospace engineers bring new ideas into this business.

Aerospace engineers invent new types of aircraft and equipment for earth and outer space. They design wings, bodies, and engines for flying machines. They must fully understand the laws of motion in order to do their work. Their models are tested in wind tunnels, temperature cubicles, and flight simulation chambers. Engineers' models that withstand these tests may someday get off the ground.

An aerospace engineer studies flight mechanics, physics, design, math, and other subjects during at least four years of college or university.

Newton's First and Second Laws

Purpose

To observe inertia and to demonstrate the relationship among force, acceleration, and mass

Materials

- index card
- plastic cup
- sandpaper
- nickel
- 3 cylinders of the same size—one metal, one wood, and one polystyrene
- clay
- 3 rulers or books
- string, about 110 cm long
- flat table top
- large paper clip
- 10 large metal washers
- 2 small wooden blocks
- watch or clock with a second hand

a

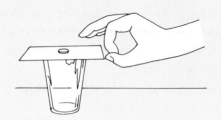

b

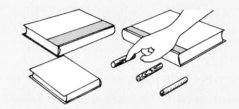

Procedure and Observations

PART A

1. Rest the index card on top of the cup. Place the nickel on the card so it is centered over the cup, as in **a.**
2. Hold the card and slowly slide it to one side until it no longer is resting on the top of the cup. Record what happens to the nickel.
3. Repeat step 1.
4. Flick the card off the top of the cup with a quick motion of your fingers, as in *a*.
5. Record what happened to the nickel.
6. Repeat steps 3–5 with a piece of sandpaper, rough side up, replacing the index card.

PART B

1. Use the rulers or books to make an alley, as in **b.**
2. Roll each cylinder at about the same slow speed toward the closed end of the alley. To attain the same speed, you will have to apply more force to the cylinders that have more mass.
3. Record the time each cylinder takes to reach the end of the alley. The three times should be similar.
4. Using clay, build a very low ridge 4 cm from the closed end of the alley. This ridge will exert a small force on the cylinders.
5. Repeat steps 2–3.
6. Make a slightly larger ridge and repeat steps 2–3.
7. Repeat step 6 until two cylinders are stopped, but the third goes over the ridge.
8. Record the order in which the cylinders stop going over the ridge.

PART C

1. Tie the two ends of the string together to make a loop.
2. Place the loop of string inside the front cover of a book, as in **c.**
3. Unbend the paper clip to form an "S" and hook one end of it to the loop of string.
4. Place the book on a table top about 15 cm from the edge, as in **d.** Allow the paper clip and some of the string to hang over the edge of the table. The bottom of the paper clip should hang down about 30 cm from the table top.
5. Begin hanging washers, one at a time, from the paper clip. Add enough washers so that the book barely moves toward the edge of the table.
6. Return the book to its original position. Add one more washer to the paper clip and release the book. Observe how fast it moves.
7. Repeat step 6.

PART D

1. Keep the same number of washers on the paper clip as you had in Part C, step 6.
2. Place one block of wood on the book, and repeat Part C, step 4.
3. Release the book and observe how fast it moves.
4. Return the book to its original position on the table. Place a second block on the book. Release the book and observe how fast it moves.

Analysis and Conclusions

1. What made the nickel drop into the glass?

c

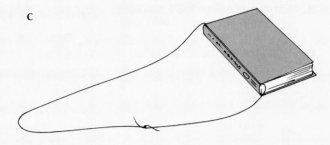

d

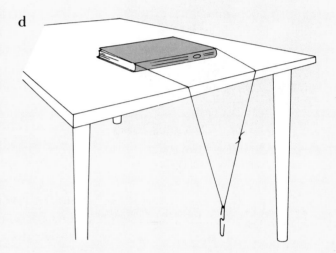

2. What had to be overcome before the card moved?
3. What effect did the sandpaper have in Part A?
4. Which cylinder needed the largest force to stop it? Which cylinder had the largest inertia? Why?
5. Explain how hanging more washers from the paper clip affected the movement of the book.
6. Explain how placing the blocks on the book affected the movement of the book.

After completing this section you will be able to -

A. Explain how Newton's third law of motion links action and reaction.

B. State the law of conservation of momentum.

3-3 Newton's Third Law of Motion

Action and Reaction Are Equal

Suppose you are in a raft on a lake, as shown in the drawing. What happens if you dive into the water from one end? You exert a force on the raft. This force causes the raft to move away from you. At the same time, the raft exerts a force on you, which propels you off the raft. The force of your body against the raft can be referred to as the action force. The force of the raft on your body would be the reaction force.

In his **third law of motion,** Newton concluded that for every action there is an equal and opposite reaction. Whenever one object applies a force on another object, the second object applies a force of equal strength on the first object. The reaction force acts in a direction opposite to the action force. It does not matter which force you call the action and which force you call the reaction. The two forces are always equal and opposite, no matter what you call them.

Study *Figure 3-7.* Notice how both the ball and the racquet are affected. The ball's force on the racquet is equal in strength but opposite in direction to the racquet's force on the ball.

Newton's third law also explains how rockets work. The rocket exerts an action force on gases, which rush out of the rocket's tail when fuel is burned. As a reaction, the gases exert an equal and opposite force on the rocket. This reaction pushes the rocket forward. Newton's third law tells you that this reaction force always exists. The rocket does not need air to push on.

Figure 3-7 Newton's third law of motion explains why objects move as they do.

Figure 3-8 For every action there is an equal but opposite reaction.

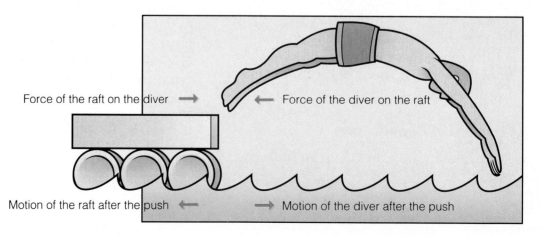

Force of the raft on the diver →   ← Force of the diver on the raft

Motion of the raft after the push ←   → Motion of the diver after the push

Figure 3-9 The law of conservation of momentum in action

Momentum Is Conserved

The billiard balls in the picture illustrate another law of motion that is closely related to Newton's third law. In this game, the balls have equal masses. A player hits the yellow ball, which moves to the right from the left edge of the picture. The yellow ball strikes the red ball and gives the red ball some of its momentum. The red ball moves upward in the picture, and the yellow ball moves downward. Next, the red ball hits the blue ball and gives some of its momentum to the blue ball. Before the collisions, the yellow ball was the only ball in motion. Therefore, it had all the momentum of the group of balls. After the collisions, each ball had some of this momentum. The total amount of momentum was the same before and after the collisions. In this example, the action of one ball made another move. The reaction of the second ball made the first ball move at a different velocity.

The total momentum of the three balls remained the same—it was "conserved." If outside forces do not act on a group of objects, the total amount of momentum the objects have does not change. This statement is the **law of conservation of momentum.** The momentum of any one object in a group can change. But whatever momentum is lost by one object must be gained by another. The total momentum remains the same, as long as no forces from the outside act on the group.

Section Review

1. What is Newton's third law of motion?
2. Explain the law of conservation of momentum.
Challenge: Describe what happens if you throw a baseball to a friend while you are standing on a skateboard. Explain in terms of Newton's third law.

Have You Heard?

An astronaut uses Newton's third law of motion to move in space. Pushing off the spacecraft or throwing an object in one direction causes the astronaut to move in the opposite direction. Similarly, you use Newton's third law when you walk on earth. You push off against the ground in one direction and move in the opposite direction.

Activity 3-2

Newton's Third Law

Purpose

To make models to demonstrate action and reaction

Materials

- cover goggles
- 2 long balloons
- string, 3 m long
- 5 strips of paper, each 1 cm × 3 cm
- tape
- 2 chairs
- table tennis ball

Procedure and Observations

PART A

1. Stretch the string across the room. Tie the ends to the backs of two chairs.
2. Put on your cover goggles. Blow up one balloon and hold the end closed.
3. Ask your partner to attach the balloon to the string as in **a,** using two paper strips and tape.
4. Release the balloon and observe what happens. Record your observations.
5. Repeat step 2 and replace the balloon on the string near the center of the string.
6. Ask your partner to attach the table ten-nis ball to the string with a paper strip and tape. Place the ball behind the open end of the balloon.
7. Repeat step 4.

PART B

1. Blow up the balloon once again and hold the end closed.
2. Ask your partner to blow up a second balloon and hold its end closed. Help your partner attach both balloons to the string near the center. Place the open end of the first balloon next to the closed end of the second balloon, as in **b.**
3. Release both balloons at the same time and observe what happens.

Analysis and Conclusions

1. In Part A, compare the directions of the escaping air and the moving balloon.
2. In Part A, did the escaping air have to hit anything to make the balloon move?
3. Identify the forces affecting the table tennis ball. Use Newton's law to explain why the ball moves as it does.
4. Explain the movement of the second balloon in Part B.

a

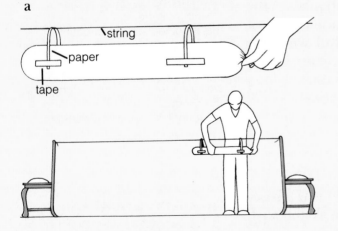

b

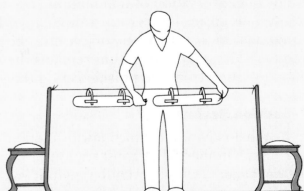

3-4 Balanced and Unbalanced Forces

Objectives

After completing this section you will be able to

A. Explain how a net force acts on a stationary object.

B. Explain how a net force acts on a moving object.

Balanced Forces on Stationary Objects

All the stationary objects around you have at least two forces acting on them. These two forces are the downward force of gravity and an upward, supporting force. Hold this book up off the desk while you read. The force of gravity pulls the book down against your hand as shown in *Figure 3-10.* Your hand pushes up on the book with an equal force. Without this upward force, the book would fall to the floor.

All forces have both size and direction. In the case of the book in your hand, the forces acting on it were equal in size but opposite in direction. Forces that cancel each other completely, like the forces on a book at rest, are **balanced forces.** However, sometimes the forces acting on an object are not balanced. Any force left over when the amount of force in one direction cancels only part of the force in another direction is the **net force.** If the forces on an object are balanced, the net force is zero. Newton's second law deals with the net force.

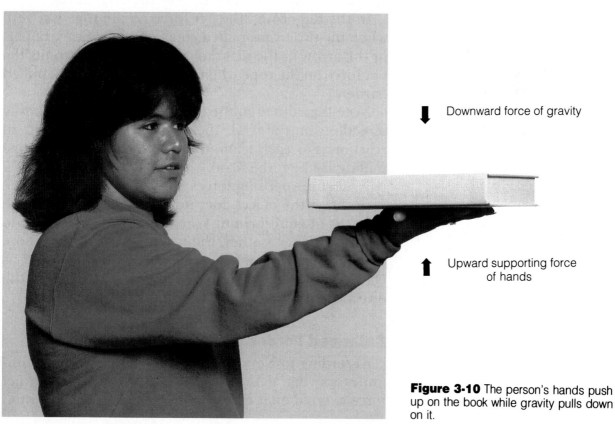

Downward force of gravity

Upward supporting force of hands

Figure 3-10 The person's hands push up on the book while gravity pulls down on it.

No Motion

Net force = 0

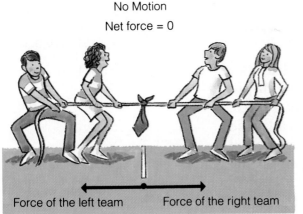

Accelerated motion to the right

Net force ——→

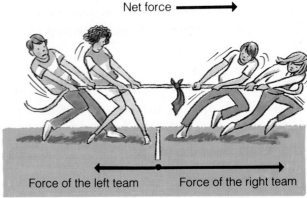

Force of the left team   Force of the right team

Force of the left team   Force of the right team

Figure 3-11 Horizontal forces in a game of tug-of-war

In addition to vertical forces, horizontal forces often act on objects. The diagrams show the horizontal forces in a game of tug-of-war. In the first picture, the people on both teams are pulling on the rope with the same strength but in opposite directions. Because the forces on the rope are balanced, the teams are not moving. In the second picture, the team on the right pulls harder on the rope than the team on the left. The forces are now unbalanced. The net force causes the teams to accelerate to the right. Notice how the flag moves.

In the tug-of-war, the net force on the rope was zero when the two teams pulled equally hard. The extra part of the arrow in the diagram on the right represents the net force on the rope when the team on the right pulled harder.

Note that although the teams are pulling in opposite directions on the rope, their forces are not action and reaction. For each team, the reaction force is the rope pulling back on the team.

When the opposing forces acting on an object balance each other, the object does not change its motion. The object is in **equilibrium.** When the opposing forces do not balance each other, the object changes its motion, as Newton's first law states. In fact, it will accelerate, as Newton's second law states. The object accelerates in the direction of the net force.

Balanced Forces on Moving Objects

According to Newton's first law, a moving object continues moving at the same velocity as long as the net force exerted on it is zero. The object is in equilibrium.

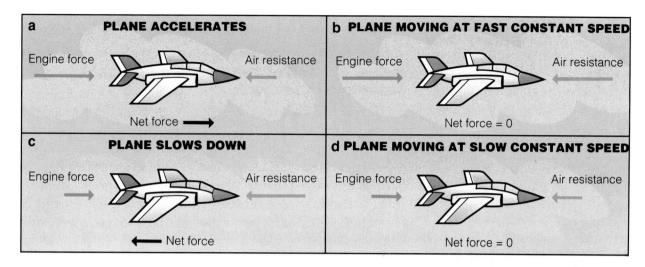

a PLANE ACCELERATES	**b** PLANE MOVING AT FAST CONSTANT SPEED
Engine force →	Air resistance ←	Engine force →	Air resistance ←
Net force →	Net force = 0
c PLANE SLOWS DOWN	**d** PLANE MOVING AT SLOW CONSTANT SPEED
Engine force →	Air resistance ←	Engine force →	Air resistance ←
← Net force	Net force = 0

In the diagrams of the jet plane, the downward force of gravity is balanced by the upward force of the air pushing against the plane's wings. The horizontal forces are the forward thrust from the engine and the friction of air pushing back on the plane, which is air resistance. According to Newton's third law, the forward horizontal force on the plane is the reaction from the backward thrust of the engine.

In *a*, the force of the plane's engine is greater than the force of air resistance. As long as the net force is greater than zero, the plane accelerates. But the faster the plane flies, the greater the air resistance becomes. Eventually, as in *b*, the air resistance pushing backward equals the force of the engine pushing forward. When the two forces balance each other, the net force is zero. The plane is in equilibrium. It then moves at a constant speed in a straight line, as Newton's first law predicts.

Now suppose the pilot decreases the force produced by the plane's engine, as in *c*. Then the force of air resistance becomes greater than the engine's force. The resulting net force causes the plane to slow down. As the plane's speed decreases, the air resistance decreases. In *d*, the two forces again balance each other, and the plane is in equilibrium once again. The plane's speed stays constant at its lower rate.

Figure 3-12 The balanced forces acting upward and downward are not shown in the diagrams. In each diagram, the net force indicates the difference between the horizontal forces. If the plane is moving at a constant speed, the net force is zero. The direction of net force arrows indicates whether the plane is speeding up or slowing down.

Section Review

1. What is net force?
2. How can the forces on a moving object be balanced?

Challenge: What forces act on a bridge? Why must engineers be certain that these forces are balanced?

After completing this section you will be able to

A. State how Newton's laws explain circular motion.
B. Describe how centripetal force causes circular motion.
C. List the factors that determine how fast an object rotates.

Explore!

Find out what the Coriolis force is and whether it is a real force. How is it related to Newton's laws of motion and how does it affect storms on earth?

Figure 3-13 When a car turns, the passengers continue moving straight ahead.

Force Is Needed To Change an Object's Direction of Motion

If you are in a car moving on a straight road, both you and the car go straight ahead. But what happens if the car stops suddenly? Newton's first law predicts the results. If the car were moving slowly, you would be stopped by the friction between the seat and your clothing. If the car were moving more quickly, you would be stopped by the safety belt, by the dashboard, or even by the windshield.

Imagine yourself in the car in the diagram. What happens when the car turns to the left? According to Newton's first law, you still keep moving straight ahead. The car, however, turns to the left under you. You therefore feel as if you are sliding to the right. The faster the car turns, the more you slide over on the car's seat. You actually move in a straight line, but the car follows a curved path. The car and seat are actually moving to the left under you. Eventually, the force of friction between the seat and your clothes links you to the car's curving path. If friction is not strong enough, you will slide over until the car's door pushes back on you.

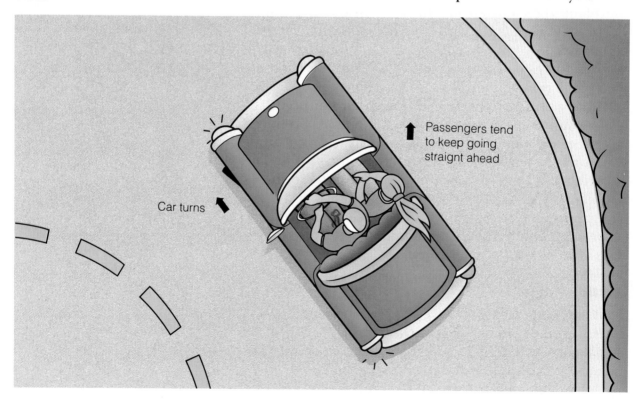

Passengers tend to keep going straignt ahead

Car turns

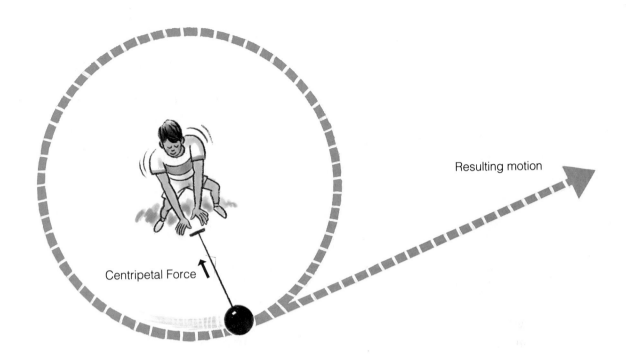

Centripetal Force

Resulting motion

Figure 3-14 Without the inward force of the rope, the sphere moves straight ahead.

Centripetal Force Causes Circular Motion

The hammer thrower in the picture is whirling a sphere at the end of a rope. The rope pulls the sphere inward, causing the sphere to move in a circle. At the instant the athlete releases the sphere, it moves straight ahead, as the arrow shows. How does Newton's first law explain the sphere's motion?

When the sphere moves in a circle, its direction of motion changes. It is therefore accelerating. According to Newton's first law, a force must be acting on the sphere. The hammer thrower exerts this force to keep the sphere from going straight ahead. The force he exerts as he pulls inward on the rope is called **centripetal** (sen tri′pi təl) **force.** This force is the inward force needed to keep an object moving in a circle. When the athlete releases the rope, the centripetal force no longer acts on the ball. As a result, the ball moves straight ahead.

Figure 3-15 shows a ball moving through a spiral tube. The wall of the tube keeps the ball circling by exerting a force on it. When the ball comes out of the tube, the force of the wall stops acting on the ball. Thus, the ball then moves straight ahead. It follows the path shown by the arrow. A force is needed to keep objects moving in a curved path. Without a force, an object always moves straight ahead. The object will not curve.

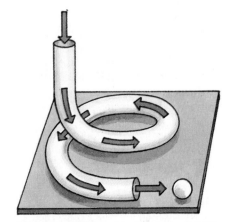

Figure 3-15 An object moves straight ahead unless a force changes its direction.

Bicycle racers frequently change gears so that their feet always turn the pedals at the same rate even though they exert different amounts of torque.

Figure 3-16 The person using the larger wrench is exerting more torque.

Figure 3-17a The distance is measured from the axis to the point where the force is applied. **b** The larger torque makes the bicycle easier to pedal, but makes it slower.

Torque

Just as a force causes an object to move forward, **torque** causes an object to rotate. More torque makes an object spin faster, just as more force makes an object move faster. The photographs show an example of torque. The worker with the shorter tire wrench is unable to loosen the bolt. On the other hand, the worker with the longer wrench exerts the same amount of force and loosens the bolt. The longer wrench allows the worker to exert more torque.

Torque depends on two factors—the amount of force exerted and the distance between the axis and the point where the force is applied. An **axis** is an imaginary line through a rotating object. Find the position of the axis and the force in *Figure 3-17a*. Torque increases as you move the force farther from the axis or as you apply a greater force.

Figure 3-17b shows two gears, such as those on the rear wheel of a 10-speed bicycle. The distance from the axis to the teeth differs for the two gears. When you switch from small to large gear, distance to the axis increases. Thus, torque increases. Using the larger gear makes pedaling easier because you produce a larger torque with the same force you used on the smaller gear. For this reason, people use the larger gear when they ride uphill or against the wind. However, the large torque and easier pedaling result in a slower ride.

Notice the chains around the two gears. The same length of chain turns the large gear once and the small gear twice. Thus, for the same number of turns of the pedals, the small gear moves the bicycle twice as far as the large one does. To attain high speeds, you need a small gear, which produces less torque.

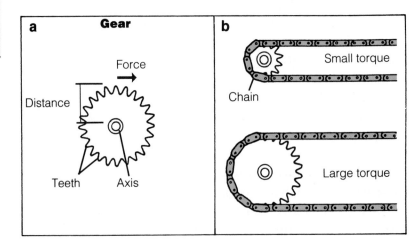

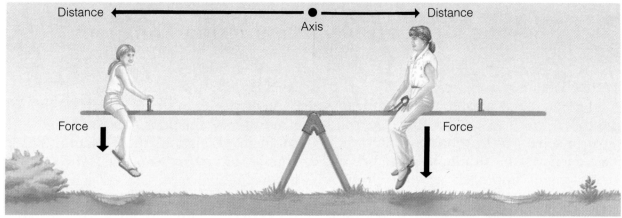

Figure 3-18 When the net torque is zero, neither person moves up or down.

The people in the picture are balancing on a seesaw. They have found the distances from the seesaw's axis that give them equal and opposite torques. In this case, torque depends on the forces acting on the people and on their distances from the axis. The little girl must sit farther from the axis.

The force on each one comes from the pull of gravity. Because gravity pulls more on the woman, she exerts more force on her side of the seesaw. But torque also depends on each person's distance from the axis. The small girl exerts a weaker force. But she applies the force farther from the axis than the woman does. Therefore, the torques on the seesaw are balanced, and the seesaw does not move around its axis.

Torques can cancel each other the way forces do. In the picture, the torque of one person is equal to and acts in the direction opposite to the torque of the other person. Therefore, the net torque is zero.

If one of them moves farther out, her torque increases. The net torque is no longer zero. As a result, the seesaw starts to move around the axis in the direction of the net torque. The net torque is in the direction of the larger torque, so the seesaw drops on the side of the person who moved. Either one could also increase her torque by carrying an extra mass, such as a package.

Explore!

The high wheeler was a type of bicycle people rode in the 1870s. Use library books to find information about the design of this bicycle. Based on your findings, explain how the pedals of this bicycle produced a large torque.

Section Review

1. Why do you slide to the right inside a car that is turning to the left?
2. What force keeps an object moving in a circle?
3. What two factors determine torque?

Challenge: Explain why a screwdriver with a thick handle would be better to use with hard-to-turn screws than a screwdriver with a thin handle.

Science Skills

Solving Word Problems and Using Equations

PART A

Mathematics is a valuable tool for interpreting scientific data. Therefore, learning how to solve word problems is an important science skill. Although 10 science students might approach a word problem from 10 different angles, successful problem-solving usually involves the following, general steps.

1. Read through the problem several times. Look up any any unfamiliar words or phrases.
2. Try to picture in your mind what is happening. If possible, make a simple line drawing or diagram showing the information given in the problem.
3. Identify the information you are to find.
4. Look up any information you need for solving the problem.
5. Plan the step or steps you will follow to solve the problem. Decide which equation or equations you will use.
6. Perform the calculations.
7. Reread the problem. Check to see that you have answered the right question and that your answer is reasonable.

PART B

As discussed in step 5 of Part A, you will need to use equations to solve many word problems. Equations show relationships in science and define concepts. The symbols in an equation represent variables. For example, in the equation $F = ma$, F stands for force, m stands for mass, and a stands for acceleration. However, $F = ma$ is only one way to express the relationship between force, mass, and acceleration. Two other forms of this equaiton are $m = F/a$ and $a = F/m$. Use the three forms of the equation to solve the following word problems.

1. A person swings a croquet mallet so that the head of the mallet accelerates at 3m/s/s. The head of the mallet has a mass of 1.5 kg. What is the force (N) being exerted on the head of the mallet?
2. As the mallet strikes a croquet ball, it exerts a force of 3.2 N on the ball. This force produces an acceleration of 8 m/s/s while the mallet is in contact with the ball. What is the mass (kg) of the ball?
3. A basketball dropped from the balcony of a gym falls with an acceleration of 9.8 m/s/s. Gravity exerts a force of 6.1 N on the basketball. This force causes the ball to accelerate at 9.8 m/s/s. What is the mass of the basketball?

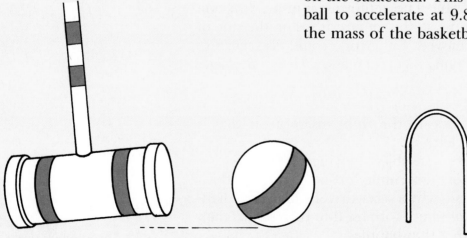

✔️ Summary

3-1 Newton's First Law of Motion

A. Friction is a force that slows down moving objects.

B. Newton's first law of motion states that, as long as no force acts on an object, a moving object will keep going at the same speed and in the same direction, and a stationary object will remain at rest.

3-2 Newton's Second Law

A. Newton's second law of motion states that a force is required to accelerate an object. The more mass an object has, the more force is needed to change its acceleration.

B. Force is measured in newtons. One newton is the force required to accelerate 1 kilogram by 1 meter per second every second.

C. An object's momentum is its mass times its velocity.

3-3 Newton's Third Law

A. Newton's third law of motion states that every action is accompanied by an equal and opposite reaction.

B. According to the law of conservation of momentum, if outside forces do not act on a group of objects, the total momentum of the group does not change.

3-4 Balanced and Unbalanced Forces

A. A stationary object remains stationary when the net force acting on it is zero. A stationary object is accelerated when the net force on the object is greater than zero.

B. A moving object continues to move at the same velocity when the net force acting on it is zero. A moving object is accelerated when the net force acting on it is greater than zero.

3-5 Circular Motion

A. A force is needed to change an object's direction of motion.

B. Centripetal force is an inward force that keeps objects moving in a circle.

C. How fast an object rotates depends on the force applied to the object and the distance the force is applied from the axis.

Vocabulary

For each of the following terms, write a sentence that uses the term correctly.

air resistance	force	newton
axis	inertia	Newton's first law of motion
balanced forces	law of conservation	Newton's second law of motion
centripetal force	of momentum	Newton's third law of motion
equilibrium	momentum	torque
	net force	

Check Your Knowledge

PART I: Matching   Match the definition in Column I with the correct term in Column II.

Column I
1. SI unit for force
2. imaginary line around which an object rotates
3. tendency for an object to resist changes in motion
4. keeps an object moving in a circle
5. force that slows down an object
6. any force left over when the amount of force in one direction cancels only part of the force in another direction
7. strength of an object's motion
8. for every action there is an equal and opposite reaction
9. anything that alters the velocity of a moving object
10. causes an object to rotate

Column II
a. axis
b. centripetal force
c. force
d. friction
e. inertia
f. momentum
g. net force
h. newton
i. Newton's second law of motion
j. Newton's third law of motion
k. torque

PART II: Multiple Choice   Choose the letter of the best answer.
11. Objects traveling along a rough surface slow down because of (a) friction. (b) reaction. (c) action. (d) inertia.
12. If you exert less force on a moving object, the object will accelerate (a) more. (b) less. (c) sooner. (d) later.
13. The mass of an object affects (a) the force needed to accelerate it. (b) its momentum. (c) its inertia. (d) all of these.
14. To change an object's momentum, you must apply (a) friction. (b) force. (c) torque. (d) air resistance.
15. You can increase your momentum as you run by (a) stopping suddenly. (b) slowing down. (c) running faster. (d) sitting down.
16. How does the floor push on you when you do pushups on it? (a) not at all (b) downward (c) upward (d) sideways

17. When the forces acting on an object are balanced, (a) the object accelerates. (b) the net force is not zero. (c) the object is in equilibrium. (d) the object stops.
18. When a bus stops suddenly, the passengers (a) stop immediately. (b) keep moving ahead. (c) move to the left. (d) move to the right.

Part III: Completion   Write the word or words that complete the sentence correctly.
19. If a force acts on an object, the object will _____.
20. The momentum of an object is its mass times its _____.
21. Forces that are equal in strength but opposite in direction are _____.
22. A plane will accelerate as long as the net force is greater than _____.
23. Switching from a small gear to a large gear on a bicycle makes pedaling _____.

✓ Check Your Understanding

1. If Newton's first law of motion is correct, why do moving objects on earth eventually stop moving?
2. If you use similar car engines to exert the same force in two cars with different masses, which car will accelerate more?
3. Which has greater momentum—an athlete with a mass of 100 kg or one with a mass of 90 kg, if both are running at the same velocity?
4. Why does an inflated balloon move forward when the air inside the balloon is released?
5. If you swing a ball on a string in a circle and the string breaks, what happens to the ball?
6. In a game of tug-of-war, when is the net force acting on the rope zero?
7. How are the small gears on a 10-speed bicycle different from the larger ones? Which gears do cyclists use when they want to go fast?

Apply Your Knowledge

1. How does Newton's first law of motion explain the need for headrests on car seats in case of a rear-end collision?
2. How fast can you accelerate a 60-kg object if you push on it with 120 N of force? (Assume no friction opposes you.)
3. Use Newton's third law of motion to explain the direction a boat crew must work the oars to move the boat forward.
4. The planets orbit around the sun. Using this fact, what can you say about the forces acting on them?
5. Explain the forces acting on you during a trip down a spiral waterslide.

Extend Your Knowledge

Research/Projects

1. Cut out magazine pictures showing examples of friction, Newton's three laws of motion, and centripetal force. Explain how each picture shows forces at work. Indicate which forces are balanced and which are unbalanced.
2. Spin a bicycle wheel from a spot near the axle and from a spot near the rim, using the same force. Observe and explain how distance to the axis affects torque. Spin the wheel several times at the same spot, applying different amounts of force. Observe and explain how force affects torque.

Readings

Baggett, James A. "Is Superman a Fraud?" *Scholastic Science World*, April 20, 1987, pages 4–7. Discusses how Hollywood movies violate Newton's laws and other laws of physics.

Laithwaite, Eric. *Force: The Power Behind Movement.* Watts, 1986. A look at the basic principles that bridge the gap between pure science and the everyday world.

"Playing With Pedal Power." *National Geographic World*, October, 1986. A brief look at human-powered vehicles in motion.

CHAPTER 4
Gravitation

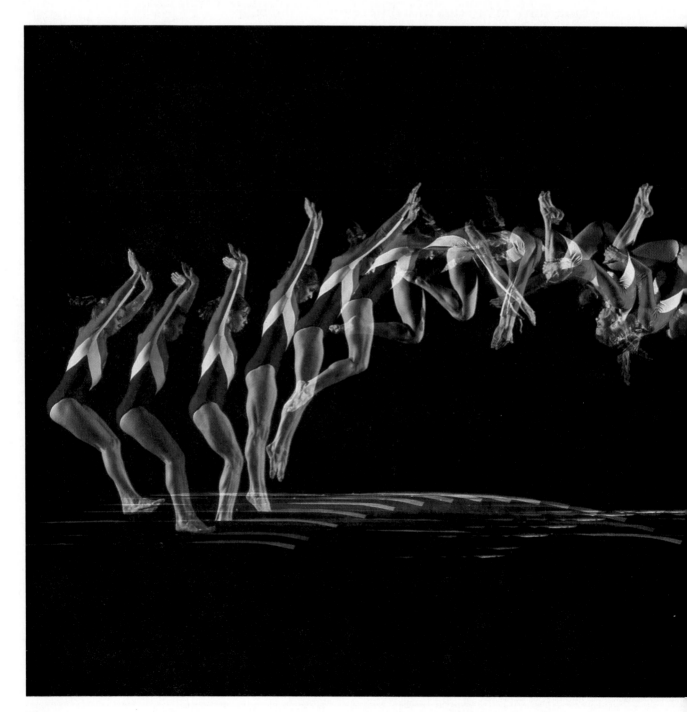

The gymnast runs forward and leaps into the air. Thus launched, she first moves upward and forward as she begins to flip her body over. Then gravity begins to pull her down as she continues to move forward and flip. Finally, gravity causes her to land on the floor of the gymnasium. The path the gymnast's body follows is determined by the physics of motion. Pole vaulters' and divers' bodies follow similar paths.

Organizing Your Study Skills The outline below will help you see how the chapter is organized and what you should learn as you read.

I. Section: 4-1: The Motion of Falling Objects
   A. What force makes falling objects accelerate?
   B. What does acceleration due to gravity mean?
   C. What are projectiles, and how do they move?

II. Section 4-2: Gravity, Mass, and Weight
   A. What is the difference between mass and weight?
   B. What does the term microgravity mean?
   C. How do the center of gravity and the center of mass of an object differ?

III. Section 4-3: The Force of Gravity Affects the Planets
   A. How does the force of gravity affect the motion of planets?
   B. What is a planet's period of revolution?

IV. Section 4-4: The Law of Gravity
   A. What led to the discovery of the law of gravity?
   B. What factors influence the strength of gravitational force?
   C. How are spacecraft able to escape the earth's gravitational attraction?

Objectives

After completing this section you will be able to

A. Name the force that makes falling objects accelerate.
B. Define acceleration due to gravity.
C. Explain what projectiles are and how they move.

4-1 The Motion of Falling Objects

The Force of Gravity Accelerates Falling Objects

Many sports are based on the motion of falling objects. When you leap from a diving board you become a falling object. By understanding the motion of falling objects, you may become better at shooting a basketball, throwing a baseball, or aiming an arrow.

You probably know that the force of gravity keeps you on the surface of the earth. However, you might not realize that the force of gravity also pulls you toward your desk and toward each of your classmates. The same force also draws your desk and your classmates toward you. The force of gravity acts between any two objects because every object has mass, and the force of gravity acts to pull all pairs of masses together.

The more mass an object has, the stronger its gravitational pull on other objects. For example, the earth has so much mass that the gravitational pull between it and a person is extremely strong. In comparison, the force of gravity between two objects on the earth is so weak that you do not notice it. You cannot sense your gravitational pull on another person. But, scientists can measure the pull of gravity between two small masses.

Figure 4-1 shows what happens when the earth's gravitational pull attracts an apple. A bright light flashed every 0.03 seconds to photograph the falling apple. Notice how the apple falls farther and farther between flashes. The apple is accelerating downward. The force of gravity makes the apple accelerate.

The Acceleration Due to Gravity

The **acceleration due to gravity** is the rate at which the velocity of a freely falling object changes as it falls under the influence of gravitational force alone. The force of gravity makes both heavy objects and light objects accelerate at the same rate. At or near the surface of the earth, this acceleration is about ten meters per second each second, directed downward. Ten meters per second each second means that during each second an object is falling freely, its velocity increases by ten meters per second.

Figure 4-1 The apple falls faster and faster.

If nothing slowed falling objects, all matter would drop with the same acceleration. The parachutists shown in *Figure 4-2* are slowed by air resistance as they drop. To understand gravitational attraction, it is easiest to ignore the effect of air, but on the earth you cannot always do so. For example, when you drop a crumpled piece of paper and a flat one, the crumpled piece drops straight down. The flat piece of paper floats around as it drops. Although the earth pulls down with equal force on each piece of paper, air resistance opposes the earth's pull. Because the flat paper has a greater surface area, it runs into more air resistance than the crumpled paper. Thus the flat paper falls more slowly than the crumpled one.

Think about the effects of gravitational force and air resistance on the skydivers in *Figure 4-3*. Though the force of gravity pulls them down, air resistance slows their fall. When the divers first jump, they accelerate downward. But for most of their fall the upward force of air resistance is equal to the downward force of gravity, and they do not accelerate. Because the divers are moving when they stop accelerating, they continue to move at a constant velocity. The velocity that any falling object reaches when air resistance balances the force of gravity is the object's **terminal velocity.**

To prove that the acceleration due to gravity is the same for any object, one of the *Apollo 15* astronauts performed an experiment. On the airless moon, the astronaut dropped a hammer and a feather. The hammer and the feather reached the moon's surface at the same time in spite of their different masses and surface areas. This experiment showed that on the airless moon the acceleration due to gravity is the same for any object.

Explore!

On a two-meter-long rope or string, tie a metal washer every twenty centimeters. Stand on a table and hold the rope by one end so that the other end touches the floor. Let the rope drop and listen to the sound of the washers hitting the floor. Notice that the interval between washers hitting the floor gets shorter. How do you explain this? How might you arrange washers along a rope to make the intervals equal? Try it.

Figure 4-2 These parachutists were pulled downward by the force of gravity but were slowed by air resistance.

Figure 4-3 The skydivers are moving at a constant velocity.

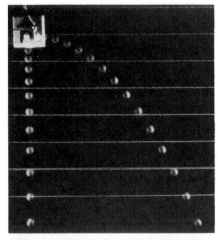

Figure 4-5 Both balls accelerate downward at the same rate. Both balls also move forward at a constant rate. The free-falling ball moves forward at the rate of 0 km/s.

Figure 4-4 The basketball, after being thrown, rises and then falls, while it moves forward at a constant rate.

The Path of Projectiles

Figure 4-4 shows the path of a basketball after a player throws it. The ball rises and then falls, while it moves forward all the time. The ball is a **projectile**, an object that moves freely through space after an initial push. Projectiles may be thrown, hit, or shot forward. All projectiles are pulled down by the force of gravity.

In *Figure 4-5*, the motion of a free-falling ball is compared with the motion of a projectile—a ball that was pushed forward. The photograph as taken with a light that flashed at equal intervals. Notice that each ball falls faster and faster, and each has the same downward acceleration. However, the projectile also moves forward by a constant distance during each time interval because its forward velocity is constant.

Although the projectile moves both forward and downward at the same time, you can study these motions separately. Photography shows that a thrown ball accelerates downward because of the force of gravity. At the same time, it keeps moving forward at a constant velocity because no force acts on it in this direction. In this way, you can study the motions of projectiles such as baseballs, footballs, and golf balls.

Section Review

1. What causes falling objects to accelerate?
2. Express in meters per second each second the acceleration due to gravity near the surface of the earth.
3. Describe the motion of a projectile.

Challenge: Two disks are shot into the air at different angles. Disk A is shot at a 90-degree angle and disk B is shot at a 60-degree angle. The disks are shot at different speeds so that they reach the same altitude at the same time. Which disk will hit the ground first?

The Effects of Gravitational Force and Air Resistance

Purpose

To observe effects of gravitational force and air resistance

Materials

- old newspaper
- clay
- golf ball
- thick book
- 1-m-long plank
- 2 meter sticks
- 3 pieces of note paper
- masking tape
- stopwatch

Procedure and Observations

PART A

1. Spread the newspaper on your desk. Spread the clay on the newspaper so that it forms a 10 cm × 10 cm square that is 1 cm thick. Try to make the top surface smooth.
2. Drop the golf ball into the clay from a height of about 30 cm. Measure the diameter of the dent the ball makes in the clay.
3. Repeat step 2 from heights of 60, 90, and 120 cm.

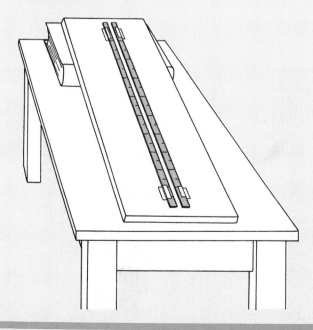

PART B

1. At one end of a table, set up the plank and book, as shown in the picture.
2. Make a track on the plank by taping the meter sticks about 2 cm apart. Release the golf ball from the top of the plank between the sticks. Do not let the ball hit the floor.
3. Use a stopwatch to find the time needed for the ball to reach each of the following marks on the meter stick: 10 cm, 20 cm, 30 cm, 40 cm, 50 cm, 60 cm, 70 cm, 80 cm, 90 cm, and 100 cm. (Let the ball roll down the track as many times as needed to find all the times.) Use the times and the corresponding distances to compute the velocity of the ball at each mark.

PART C

1. Crumple one of the three pieces of note paper and fold the second one in fourths. Leave the third piece of paper flat.
2. Drop the three pieces of paper in different pairs. For each pair, note which has a larger surface area exposed to the air and which hits the floor first.

Analysis and Conclusions

1. In Part A, the diameter of the dent in the clay depended on the ball's velocity as it hit the clay. How did the ball's velocity change in steps 2 and 3?
2. In Part B, how did the distance traveled and the ball's velocity change each second?
3. According to your results from Part C, describe how air resistance affects falling objects.

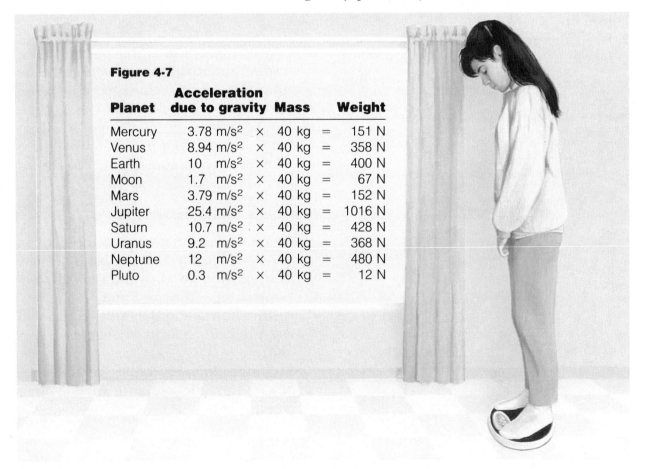

Objectives

After completing this section you will be able to

A. Compare mass and weight.
B. Explain the term microgravity.
C. Describe the difference between center of gravity and center of mass.

4-2 Gravity, Mass, and Weight

Contrasting Weight and Mass

Your body has a certain amount of mass, which is pulled down by Earth's gravitational force. The amount of gravitational force that pulls on a mass is called its **weight.** Because weight is a force, it is measured in newtons, as are other forces.

To find the amount of force that pulls on a mass, use Newton's second law, F = ma. For example, *Figure 4-6* shows a girl weighing herself on a scale on Earth. The girl's mass is 40 kilograms. The acceleration at which the girl would fall at Earth's surface is 10 meters per second each second, or 10 m/s^2. Thus, the amount of force acting on the girl is 40 kg $\times$ 10 m/s^2, which equals 400 newtons.

How does a spring scale measure weight? When you stand on a scale, a spring in the scale stretches. The amount this spring stretches reflects how strongly the force of gravity pulls on you.

Figure 4-6 The girl has the same mass on Earth and on Mars, but would weigh less on Mars, where acceleration due to the force of gravity is weaker.

Figure 4-7

Planet	Acceleration due to gravity		Mass		Weight
Mercury	3.78 m/s^2	$\times$	40 kg	=	151 N
Venus	8.94 m/s^2	$\times$	40 kg	=	358 N
Earth	10 m/s^2	$\times$	40 kg	=	400 N
Moon	1.7 m/s^2	$\times$	40 kg	=	67 N
Mars	3.79 m/s^2	$\times$	40 kg	=	152 N
Jupiter	25.4 m/s^2	$\times$	40 kg	=	1016 N
Saturn	10.7 m/s^2	$\times$	40 kg	=	428 N
Uranus	9.2 m/s^2	$\times$	40 kg	=	368 N
Neptune	12 m/s^2	$\times$	40 kg	=	480 N
Pluto	0.3 m/s^2	$\times$	40 kg	=	12 N

Imagine the same girl and scale on Mars. The acceleration due to gravity on the surface of Mars is weaker than on Earth. Therefore, the girl weighs less on Mars. She weighs less because, although her mass is the same, the force of gravity acting on her mass is less.

Figure 4-7 shows what the girl would weigh on each of the nine planets and on Earth's moon. Acceleration due to gravity on a planet depends both on how much mass the planet has and on how large the planet is.

Microgravity

Suppose that the box in *Figure 4-8* is falling freely—that is, it is accelerating downward due to the force of gravity alone. This would not happen in an ordinary situation but it serves as a useful thought experiment. The force of gravity accelerates the boy, the ball, and the box at the same rate. When the boy releases the soccer ball, it seems to hover near him. To the boy, it seems as if the force of gravity has disappeared. But the correct explanation for the apparent weightlessness of the ball is that the boy, the ball, and the box are all falling freely at the same rate.

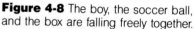

For Practice

Use Figure 4-7 to solve these problems.
● How much would a person who weighed 600 newtons on Earth weigh on Jupiter? on Mercury?
● A person weighs 45 newtons on the moon. How much does that person weigh on Earth? How much would that person weigh on Pluto?

Figure 4-8 The boy, the soccer ball, and the box are falling freely together.

Applying Science

Tightrope walkers keep from falling by keeping their centers of gravity directly above the rope. In this position, the force of gravity causes no torque on them.

Astronauts aboard a spaceship have the same type of experience as the boy in the freely falling box. Unless the astronauts tie themselves down, they find themselves floating as their ship moves through space. To keep from "sleep floating," astronauts zip themselves into sleeping bags attached to the walls of the spacecraft.

An orbiting spacecraft's speed keeps it moving away from the earth on a straight line tangent to the orbit. At the same time, it experiences a falling motion due to the gravitational pull of Earth. The effects of the two motions add to each other putting the spacecraft in orbit. Meanwhile, it is constantly falling freely, and so are the objects in it. This causes the objects to appear to be weightless. The astronauts cannot weigh themselves because any scale they stood on would read zero as it fell with them. The condition in which the force of gravity seems to disappear because a spacecraft and its contents are falling freely at the same rate is called **microgravity**. This condition is shown in *Figure 4-9*.

Figure 4-9 Astronauts Richard H. Truly and Guyon Bluford in microgravity on a Space Shuttle

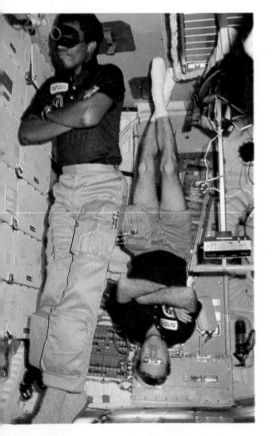

Center of Gravity

Compare the length of the pencil on either side of the finger shown in *Figure 4-10*. Because the eraser side of the pencil is heavier than the other side, the distance between the finger and the side of the pencil without the eraser is longer. The torque produced by the longer side is balanced by that of the eraser side. When the torques are balanced, the pencil does not tip. The point at which the torques on an object are exactly balanced is called the **center of gravity.** For example, the pencil's center of gravity is directly above the finger.

The force of gravity seems to act on an object at its center of gravity. If you hold a pen gently near one end, the force of gravity will pull the pen's center down. The same principle applies to the tilted salt shaker in *Figure 4-11*. The shaker tips over because its center of gravity is to the right of its axis. If the center of gravity were to the left of the shaker's axis, the shaker would return to its normal upright position. If the center of gravity remained directly above the axis, the shaker would balance in that position.

When an object moves freely through the air, its center of gravity always follows a smooth path. In *Figure 4-12*, the hammer's center of gravity moves in a smooth path. The hammer turns around its center of gravity.

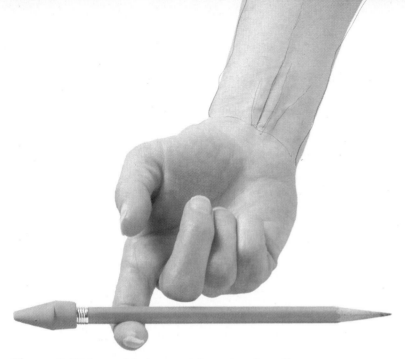

Figure 4-10 A pencil balances at its center of gravity.

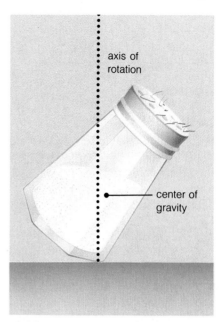

Figure 4-11 A shaker will tip over if its center of gravity is on the right side of its axis of rotation.

The force of gravity pulls on a mass. If the acceleration due to gravity is the same over a whole object, then the object's center of gravity is in the same place as its **center of mass.** The center of mass moves according to Newton's laws of motion. However, an object might be so large that some parts of it are much farther from a large mass, such as the earth, than other parts. Parts of an objects that are farther from a large mass have a lower acceleration due to gravity, and the object's center of mass and the center of gravity are in different places. This would be true for a uniform, mountain-sized cube of stone on the earth. The center of mass would be at the center of the cube. However, the center of gravity would be lower because the bottom part of the cube would be closer to the center of the earth than the top part of the cube.

Section Review

1. What would happen to your mass and weight if you went to the moon?
2. Why does the force of gravity seem to disappear when astronauts are in space?
3. When can an object's center of gravity be in a different location from its center of mass?

Challenge: It is easier to balance on a bicycle that is moving than on one that is standing still. Use your understanding of center of gravity to explain why.

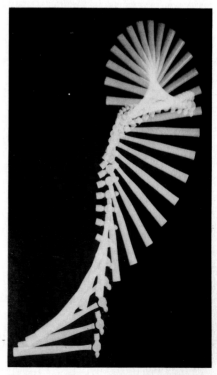

Figure 4-12 The hammer's center of gravity follows a smooth path.

Studying Microgravity and Center of Gravity

Purpose

To observe the effects of the force of gravity on objects falling at the same time and to observe how an object balances at its center of gravity

Materials

- cover goggles
- 2 plastic-foam cups
- 2 coins
- 2 rubber bands, each slightly shorter than the height of the cups
- transparent tape
- 2 paper clips
- water
- sink or wastebasket
- sheet of heavy cardboard
- scissors
- pencil
- masking tape
- 20-cm-long string
- heavy metal washer
- straightedge

Procedure and Observations

PART A

1. Put on your cover goggles. Tape each rubber band to a coin, as in **a.**

   a
   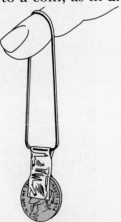

2. Straighten one end of a clip and use it to make a hole in the bottom of one cup.
3. Fit the rubber bands through the hole and attach them with the unopened paper clip, as in **b.** The rubber bands should be stretched slightly.

b
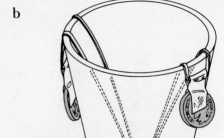

4. Drop the cup from shoulder level to the floor. Notice what happens to the coins.

PART B

1. Use the open paper clip to make two small holes in the bottom of the second cup.
2. Fill the cup half full with water while holding your finger or thumb over the holes, as in **c.**

c
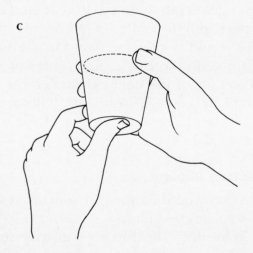

3. Hold the cup high over a wastebasket or sink. Uncover the holes and drop the cup.
4. Notice what happens to the water as the cup falls.

PART C
1. Cut a circle, a rectangle, and an irregularly shaped figure from the cardboard. Make each at least 10 cm across.
2. Use the scissors to make two widely spaced holes near the outside edge of each figure.
3. Tape the pencil to the table so that 1 cm extends over the edge.
4. Tie one end of the string to the washer and make a loop at the other end.
5. Hang the circle on the pencil by one hole.
6. Hang the string on the pencil by the loop.
7. Hold the string against the bottom edge of the circle, as in **d.** Mark the point where the string crosses the circle's edge.

d

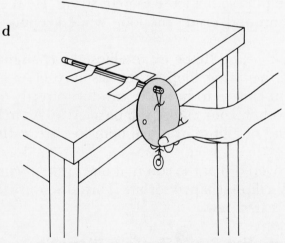

8. Remove the string and circle from the pencil. Use the straightedge to draw a line from the mark to the hole you used to hang the circle. The circle's center of gravity must have been directly below the pencil and so must be on this line.
9. Repeat steps 5–8, hanging the circle from the other hole. Where your two lines meet, mark "CG" for center of gravity.

10. Repeat steps 5–9 with the other shapes.
11. Slowly spin each figure on one finger, as in **e.** Try several positions for your finger until each shape balances. Compare these positions with each figure's center of gravity.

e

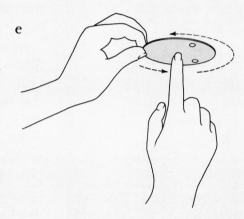

PART D
1. Punch a hole at the center of gravity of the circle and at two other spots nearby.
2. Place the circle on the pencil through the hole.
3. Spin the circle. Notice whether the force of gravity pulls any particular part of the circle downward.
4. Repeat steps 1–3, hanging the circle from each of the two other holes.

Analysis and Conclusions

1. Explain why the coins acted as they did in Part A, step 5.
2. Explain why the water acted as it did in Part B, step 4.
3. Where does an object's center of gravity always lie?
4. What is the effect of the force of gravity on an object when the object is rotating about its center of gravity? What is the effect when the object is rotating about another axis?

Objectives

After completing this section you will be able to

A. Explain how the force of gravity affects the motion of planets.

B. Define a planet's period of revolution.

4-3 Gravity and the Planets

The Force of Gravity Shapes the Planets' Orbits

The planets, like all moving objects, would move straight ahead if no force acted on them. However, the gravitational attraction of the sun pulls on each planet and keeps it moving around the sun in a path called an **orbit.** Just as the gravitational pull of the earth bends the path of a projectile, the sun's gravitational pull bends a planet's path.

In the early 1600s, the astronomer Johannes Kepler discovered three laws about the planets' orbits. After years of study, he realized that the planets do not orbit the sun in circles, but in other ellipses. These ellipses are special kinds of figures that are like flattened circles.

An ellipse has two fixed points, or **foci.** (Each point is called a focus.) The foci in the picture are at the two pins. For any point on an ellipse, the sum of the distances to the two foci is constant. To draw the ellipse in the picture, the boy put two pins in a piece of paper, and linked the pins with a loose loop of string. He then pulled a pen around inside the loop while keeping it taut.

You can change the shape of an ellipse by changing the length of the string loop or the distance between the foci. If you choose to have the two foci directly on top of one another, your ellipse will be a circle. A circle is a special kind of ellipse in which both foci are at the same point.

Kepler discovered that the sun is at one of the foci of each planet's ellipse-shaped orbit. This discovery is called **Kepler's first law.**

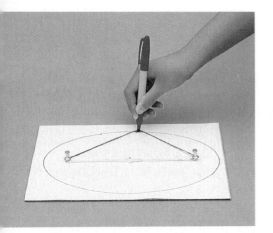

Figure 4-13 Keeping the string taut forces the pen to draw an ellipse.

Distance from the Sun Affects a Planet's Speed

Because a planet's orbit is an ellipse, the distance between a planet and the sun changes. As a planet's distance from the sun changes, so does its speed. **Kepler's second law** shows how much faster a planet moves when it is closer to the sun. It also shows that the line joining a focus and the planet sweeps out the same area each hour no matter what part of its orbit it is in.

The length of time each planet takes to complete one orbit around the sun is called a **period of revolution. Kepler's third law** links a planet's period of revolution and its distance from the sun. Kepler's third law shows how much longer a planet's period of revolution is when its orbit is larger. For example, planets that are farther from the sun travel more slowly. Compare the sizes of the planets' orbits and their periods of revolution in *Figures 4-14* and *4-15*.

Figure 4-14 The orbits of the planets:
a. Mercury
b. Venus
c. Earth
d. Mars
e. Jupiter
f. Saturn
g. Uranus
h. Neptune
i. Pluto

Figure 4-15

Planet	Orbit compared to Earth's	Period of revolution
Mercury	0.4	0.2 year (88 days)
Venus	0.7	0.7 year (243 days)
Earth	1.0	1.0 year
Mars	1.5	2.0 years
Jupiter	5.2	12 years
Saturn	9.5	30 years
Uranus	19.2	84 years
Neptune	30.1	165 years
Pluto	39.5	249 years

Have You Heard?

Pluto is considered to be the outermost planet because the largest distance across the ellipse that is its orbit is greater than the greatest distance across the ellipses of the orbits of the other planets. But Pluto is now on a part of its orbit that takes it inside Neptune's orbit. So Pluto will actually be closer to the sun than Neptune's orbit until 1998.

Section Review

1. What holds the planets in their orbits?
2. What happens to a planet's speed as it nears the sun?

Challenge: Explain how Pluto can have a longer period of revolution than Neptune, even though Pluto will be closer to the sun until 1998.

Objectives

After completing this section you will be able to

A. Describe what led to the discovery of the law of gravity.

B. Name the factors that influence the strength of gravitational force.

C. Explain how spacecraft escape the earth's gravitational pull.

4-4   The Law of Gravity

Newton Stated the Law of Gravity

In 1543, when most people thought that the sun and planets revolved around Earth, the astronomer Nicolaus Copernicus published his theory that the planets circle the sun. In the early 1600s, the scientist Galileo looked at the night sky with a telescope and discovered that four moons circled Jupiter. Galileo's observation proved that not everything circled Earth, which also meant that Earth did have to be the center of everything in the universe. In addition, Galileo's discovery meant that the ancient astronomers did not know everything about the universe and much still remained to be learned.

At about the same time that Galileo was observing the planets with a telescope, Kepler was making his discoveries about planetary motion. Galileo's and Kepler's discoveries supported Copernicus's theory that Earth and other planets orbit the sun. However, why the planets moved around the sun was still unknown.

In the mid-1600s, Isaac Newton began investigating the "why" of Galileo's and Kepler's findings. Newton found the beginnings of his answer when one day he saw an apple fall and he conceived the idea of a force of gravity. As the picture indicates, Newton realized that the force that causes apples to fall also keeps the moon and planets in their orbits. Newton later used his ideas about gravity to explain Kepler's discoveries.

The Force of Gravity Depends on Mass and Distance

Many people had seen apples fall, but only Newton realized that the force of gravity occurs between any two objects. The force of gravity always pulls two objects together. Newton's **law of gravity** states that the force of gravity depends on the mass of each object and on the distance between them. The law of gravity enables you to calculate the force of gravity between any two objects.

Figure 4-16 Newton, seeing an apple fall, realized that the force that makes the apple fall is the same force that keeps the moon and planets in their orbits.

Figure 4-17 shows the relationship among mass, distance, and the force of gravity. Newton discovered that the mass of a uniform, round object acts as though it is at the object's center. The larger the mass of either of two objects, the stronger the attraction between them. Newton's law of gravity states that to find the force of gravity, you must multiply the masses of the objects and divide by the square of the distance between them. Doubling the mass of one object doubles the force of gravity. Doubling the masses of both objects multiplies the force of gravity by four, since $2 \times 2 = 4$. The closer objects are, the stronger the force of gravity between them. Halving the distance between two objects multiplies the force of gravity by four, which is two squared. Doubling the distance reduces the force of gravity to one-fourth, which is one divided by two squared.

Newton's law of gravity has been tested many times. Edmond Halley used this law to predict that a comet would return. When it did return, it proved that Newton's law was correct. The comet that Halley predicted would return is now called Halley's Comet, although it might be equally appropriate to call it Newton's Comet. Currently, Newton's law is used in sending spacecraft to the planets. For example, scientists used Jupiter's gravitational pull to send the *Voyager 2* spacecraft onward to Saturn, Uranus, and Neptune.

Although Newton's law of gravity enables us to determine the strength of gravitational forces, it does not tell us why gravitational force exists. In 1916, however, Albert Einstein explained gravitational force as the result of warping, or distortion, of space. A large mass warps space a lot, and approaching objects tend to fall toward the mass, just as a golf ball rolling on a warped green tends to curve.

For Practice

Use Newton's ideas about gravity to answer the following questions.
● What would happen to the force of gravity between you and some cereal in a box if you added cereal to the box until there was three times as much cereal as it first had?
● What would happen to the force of gravity between Earth and the sun if Earth was twice as far from the sun?

Figure 4-17 Increasing either of the masses or decreasing the distance between the masses increases the force of gravity. Increasing the distance between the masses decreases the force of gravity.

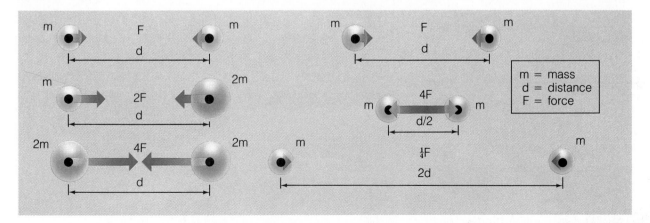

Special Velocities of Rockets

Imagine that you are high above the earth, on the blue dot in the picture. The earth's gravity would pull you straight down. But if you were on the red dot, which is moving forward along the red arrow, the earth would curve away from you. And, if you were moving forward fast enough, the earth would curve away by the exact amount that you would fall. Consequently, you would never get any closer to the earth's surface, but would go around and around. The speed at which you would circle the earth is the **orbital velocity** for your distance from the earth's center. If you circle within a few hundred kilometers of the surface of the earth, you would travel 27 000 km/hour, about 8 km each second.

To escape the earth's gravitational pull, you would have to go faster still. Only if you are going faster than about 37 000 km/hour, about 11 km/second, can you reach the other planets. This speed, directed outward, is the **escape velocity** from the earth. Unless you reach this speed, the earth's gravitational force will pull you back.

Even if you start out moving at the escape velocity, you will only go into orbit around the sun, because all of the escape velocity is used up in getting away from the earth. However, if you start at a faster speed than escape velocity, you will have some velocity left over and can orbit the sun at a higher speed. This orbit could carry your craft to the desired planet.

Figure 4-18 An object orbits the earth when the earth curves away at the same rate that the object falls toward the earth's center.

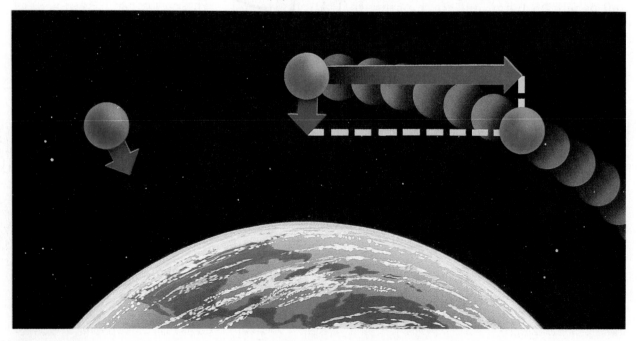

The astronauts who went to the moon kept slowing down until the moon's gravitational pull started speeding them up again. The astronauts reached the moon in four days. The *Voyager* spacecraft to Jupiter, Saturn, Uranus, and Neptune passed the moon in less than one day.

Section Review

1. Describe how Newton said he discovered gravitation.
2. State Newton's law of gravity.
3. Define orbital velocity.

Challenge: On the moon a person can jump higher than a person can jump on the earth. Is the escape velocity higher or lower on the moon than it is on the earth? On which of the planets is the escape velocity highest?

People and Science

Albert Einstein

Born in Germany in 1879, Albert Einstein was three years old before he could talk. It was thought that he might be retarded. When he was five years old and bedfast with an illness, his father gave him a mariner's compass, thinking that the moving needle would amuse him. That compass may have been the intellectual stimulus that Einstein needed. He was fascinated by the idea of invisible forces making the needle spin. The interest it sparked remained throughout his life.

Mathematics was the only subject in which Albert excelled in school. Otherwise he strongly disliked school and did not like to conform to what others expected of him. His genius allowed him to explore new patterns of thought and to follow new directions.

When he was turned down for

a physics teaching position, Einstein took a job as a patent examiner in Berne, Switzerland. In his spare time, he worked on theoretical physics. In 1905, at age 26, he published three important papers in a physics journal. One dealt with light quanta, which he called photons. This work earned him the Nobel Prize in physics several years later.

Four years after his papers

were published, Einstein was recognized as a genius and was awarded a professorship in physics at the University of Zurich. In 1914, he became the director of the Kaiser Wilhelm Physical Institute in Berlin, and in 1916 his General Theory of Relativity was published.

Einstein's general theory deals with gravity. He demonstrated mathematically that light rays traveling near a large mass, such as the sun, are bent or warped. He pointed out also that gravity affects the movement of objects on the earth. For example, clocks run more slowly in a strong gravitational field.

In 1933, Einstein left Germany and went to England. He then moved to the United States and became a professor of physics at the Institute for Advanced Study until his death in 1955.

Making Models

By drawing a series of ellipses, you can better understand the solar system and how the planets orbit.

1. Cut a piece of string so that it is about 20 cm long. Tie the ends of the string together to form a loop.
2. Press two pins or thumbtacks into a piece of paper with a thick cardboard backing. The pins should be about 5 cm apart.
3. Loop the string around the pins. Use the point of a pen or pencil to stretch the string taut, as shown in the picture. Then, keeping the string taut, move the pencil or pen along the string until you have drawn an ellipse.

4. The pins represent the foci of the ellipse. Move one pin 1 cm closer to the other pins and repeat step 3.
5. Repeat step 4 twice.

Use your drawings to answer the following questions.

1. How do the shapes of your ellipses change as the foci are moved closer and closer together?
2. What kind of figure do you get if both foci are in the same spot?
3. Assume that one of the ellipses you drew represents the orbit of a planet around the sun. In what part of its orbit does the planet move fastest? In what part does it move slowest?

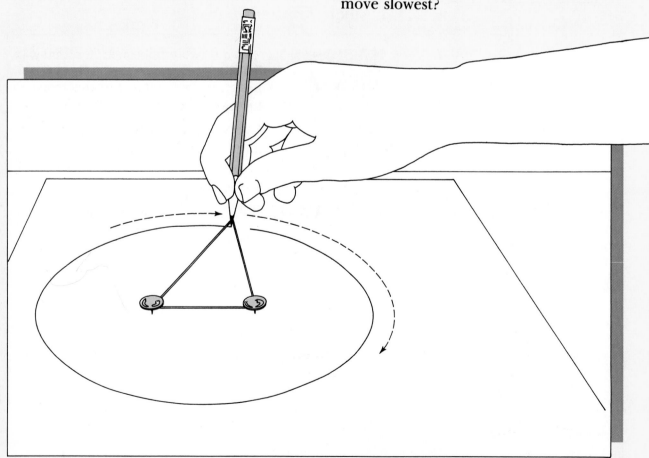

✔ Summary

4-1 The Motion of Falling Objects

A. The force of gravity makes falling objects accelerate.

B. Acceleration due to gravity is the rate at which a freely falling object's velocity changes as the force of gravity acts on it.

C. Projectiles are objects that move freely through space after an initial push. Projectiles move forward at a constant speed as they fall at an accelerating rate.

4-2 Gravity, Mass, and Weight

A. The force of gravity pulls masses together. The amount of gravitational force that pulls on a mass is its weight.

B. Microgravity is a condition in which objects are freely falling, accelerating at the same rate.

C. An object's center of gravity is the point at which the object's torques are exactly balanced. In most cases, an object's center of gravity and its center of mass are both in the same place.

4-3 The Force of Gravity Affects the Planets

A. The sun's gravitational pull bends the planets' paths and keeps them moving around the sun in elliptical orbits.

B. A planet's period of revolution is the length of time it takes for a planet to complete one orbit of the sun.

4-4 The Law of Gravity

A. The theories of Copernicus, Galileo, and Kepler led Newton to discover the law of gravity.

B. Newton discovered that the force of gravity acting between two objects increases if the mass of either object increases or if the distance between the two objects decreases.

C. Spacecraft escape the earth's gravitational pull by traveling at escape velocity, about 37 000 km/hour, or 11 km/second.

Vocabulary

For each of the following terms, write a sentence that uses the term correctly.

acceleration due to gravity	Kepler's second law	period of revolution
center of gravity	Kepler's third law	projectile
center of mass	law of gravity	terminal velocity
escape velocity	microgravity	weight
foci	orbit	
Kepler's first law	orbital velocity	

✔ Check Your Knowledge

Part I: Matching Match the definition in Column I with the correct term in Column II.

Column I

1. opposes a falling object's acceleration
2. makes all matter fall with the same acceleration
3. a falling object's velocity when air resistance balances gravitational pull
4. maintains a constant forward velocity as it falls
5. in 1543, he published his theory that the planets revolve around the sun
6. the first to realize that the force of gravity occurs between any two objects
7. the speed at which an object circles the earth
8. the amount of gravitational force that pulls on a mass
9. the condition in which objects fall freely at the same rate
10. the sun is at one focus of each planet's elliptical orbit

Column II

a. air resistance
b. Copernicus
c. force of gravity
d. Galileo
e. Kepler's first law
f. microgravity
g. Newton
h. orbital velocity
i. projectile
j. terminal velocity
k. weight

Part II: Multiple Choice Choose the letter of the best answer.

11. The larger an object's mass, the stronger its (a) foci. (b) acceleration. (c) gravitational pull. (d) orbit.
12. To make an object a projectile, you could (a) smash it. (b) aim it. (c) hurl it. (d) touch it.
13. Which of these pairs of objects has the greatest gravitational pull between them? (a) a mouse on an elephant (b) a person on Earth (c) a person on Uranus (d) All pairs of objects have the same gravitational pull.
14. Newton's formula for finding the gravitational force acting on an object is (a) F = ma. (b) F = wm. (c) F = wa. (d) F = mv.
15. Gravitational force always acts on an object at its (a) center of mass. (b) center of gravity. (c) torques. (d) ellipse.
16. A girl would weigh most on (a) Mars. (b) Uranus. (c) Earth. (d) Pluto.
17. The sun's gravitational pull causes (a) planets to move straight ahead. (b) mass to increase. (c) planets to orbit. (d) air resistance.

Part III: Completion Write the word or words that complete the sentence correctly.

18. A planet's velocity _____ as it gets closer to the sun.
19. _____ discovered that the force of gravity depends on 2 objects' masses and the distance between them.
20. The sun is at one of the _____ of each planet's elliptical orbit.
21. Parts of an object that are farthest from a large mass have a _____ acceleration due to gravity.
22. Double an object's mass, and you _____ its gravitational force.

Check Your Understanding

1. How does air resistance cause an object to reach terminal velocity?
2. What link is there between a projectile's forward motion and its downward motion?
3. Why does a hammer drop more quickly than a feather on the earth but not on the moon?
4. When you drop one ball and, at the same time, shoot another ball straight forward from the same height, why do both balls hit the ground at the same time?
5. Suppose you drop a brick and a small piece of cloth at the same time. Explain what you observe as they fall and hit the ground.
6. How much would you weigh on a scale in an orbiting spaceship? What would your mass be? Why are these different?
7. What happens to an object supported at its center of gravity?
8. Compare the periods of revolution of the orbits of the planets farthest from the sun with those of the planets nearest to the sun.

 Apply Your Knowledge

1. Use Figure 4-7 on page 81 to find out how much stronger the acceleration due to gravity is on Jupiter's surface than on Earth's surface. How much would a 30-kg person weigh there?
2. Using the term center of gravity, explain how you might balance a broom upright in the palm of your hand.
3. Kepler's laws are also true for comets. How does Kepler's second law explain why Halley's Comet moves within months through the part of the solar system within the earth's orbit and spends the rest of its 76-year period of revolution moving slowly through the outer parts of the solar system?

✔ Extend Your Knowledge

Research/Projects
1. At the same instant that you roll a ball forward off a desk, drop another from the same height. Determine which ball, if either, hits the ground first.
2. Use reference books to find out how the *Apollo* spacecraft switched from the escape velocity necessary to leave Earth to the orbital velocity needed to orbit around the moon, and how it got out of lunar orbit and returned to Earth.

Readings
Ipsen, D. C. *Isaac Newton: Reluctant Genius.* Enslow, 1985. A biography of the famous scientist, including his development of the theory of gravity.
Kilgore, Jim. "The Art and Science of Punting." *Scholastic Science World*, November 20, 1987, pages 28–29. Explains how, in football, a good punter can take advantage of the laws of projectile motion.

Around the World Without Refueling

On its departure from Edwards Air Force Base in California on December 14, 1986, the *Voyager*'s success seemed doubtful. The plane taxied to the very end of the runway before slowly becoming airborne. The tips of its wings dragged limply on the ground. With this menacing takeoff, the *Voyager* started on its history-making flight around the world.

Circling the globe without stopping had been done before. However, the *Voyager* was the first plane to fly around the world without refueling.

To carry enough fuel for such a trip required a plane designed for efficiency. The wings of the *Voyager* are light and flexible, so flexible that they flap, bowing at a 12-meter arc. In rough air the plane pitches and rolls, like a rowboat in heavy swells.

To keep the plane light, the cockpit has only one seat. The crew, made up of Jeana Yeager and Dick Rutan, had to roll over each other to switch off piloting duties. Finally, to maintain maximum efficiency, the plane cannot fly faster than 200 km/hr. On average it goes no faster than a race car in the Indy 500. At this speed, it took nine cramped days to circle the globe. The journey of the *Voyager* was as much a testimony to human endurance as it was to innovative engineering.

The *Voyager*'s route was planned to avoid two hazards: rough weather and unpredictable or hostile countries. Even with the careful planning, the crew ran into both. They had to pass close by a hurricane, at one point doing a 180-degree turn to avoid heavy turbulence. Refused emergency permission to fly over Vietnam, the *Voyager* skirted dangerously close to a wall of thunderstorms, looming more than 25 000 m high. They suffered a broken wing tip before they even left the ground and came uncomfortably close to crashing in the 11th hour.

Limping home on dangerously low fuel tanks, the *Voyager* cruised over Edwards Air Force Base early on December 23, 1986. Thousands of people came out to watch the historic landing.

Today the *Voyager* is on display and the National Air and Space Museum in Washington, D.C. It hangs with planes of other famous and daring pilots who dared to do the undoable.

For Discussion

1. What aspects of the *Voyager*'s design made the plane efficient but uncomfortable to fly?

2. How might the journey of the *Voyager* eventually benefit society?

Fire Sprinkler Systems

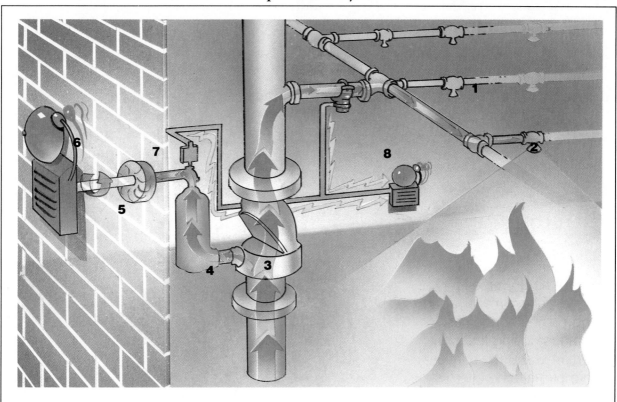

Have you ever noticed small metal disks on the ceilings in schools, stores, or offices? The objects are part of sprinkler systems that are designed to protect the building and the people in it from fire.

If a fire breaks out, water sprays down from the sprinklers onto the fire. An alarm sounds, alerting people to the danger, and allowing them to escape from the building. Usually, another alarm is sent directly to the nearest fire department so they will know where to send fire-fighting equipment.

Not all sprinkler systems work the same way. Some have electronic heat sensors that turn them off as well as on. If the fire is put out by the sprinkler system, the sensors will turn the system off. Other systems spray chemicals rather than water onto a fire. These kinds of systems can be used in places where water pipes might freeze. The diagram shows how the most frequently used sprinkler system works.

1. Water under pressure stays in the pipes all the time.

2. Heat from a fire breaks a seal that holds a cap on the sprinkler head. The pressure of the water forces the cap off.

3. A continuous supply of water comes up from the main valve to replace water that sprays from the sprinkler.

4. Some of the water flowing through the main valve escapes through a side valve.

5. This water flows to a water wheel, causing it to spin.

6. When the wheel spins, a hammer attached to it strikes a bell in a fire alarm outside the building.

7. The water flowing to the water wheel also turns on an electric switch.

8. The switch sets off the fire alarm in the building.

The Structure of Matter

Matter is the stuff of which the universe is made. Taking matter apart and putting it together again, studying the forms of matter and the relationship of matter to energy—these have challenged scientists through the centuries, for knowing about matter is basic to understanding the world in which we live.

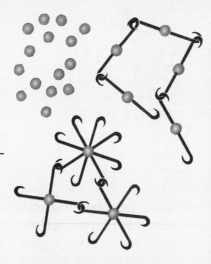

4th Century B.C.

A few of the ancient Greeks believed the world consisted of only two things: atoms and the empty spaces, or voids, between them. Atoms, too small to be seen, could be solid, infinite in number, kind, and shape, and variously joined. Those closely packed formed solids; those spread out and with large amounts of space or voids between them accounted for gases and liquids. They believed also that atoms could not be broken apart. With logic and systematic thinking, the Greeks—most particularly Democritus—had arrived at an astonishingly modern version of the atomic theory.

18th Century

For many years chemistry remained much in the realm of magic. No one really understood what happened when different substances reacted. Then Lavoisier, a French scientist, made an important discovery—that a burned substance weighs more than the original. Oxygen had been added to the total.

Chapter 5 Matter and Its Phases
Chapter 6 Properties of Matter
Chapter 7 The Atom
Chapter 8 The Atomic Nucleus

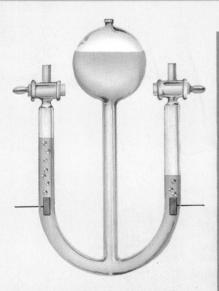

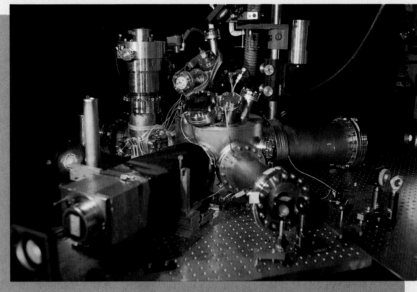

19th Century

Early in the 1800s scientists determined that compounds, such as water, consist of atoms of elements bonded together. Learning how many atoms of each element formed the basic unit of various compounds became a consuming occupation of chemists. Individual atoms could not be counted, of course, but they could be weighed in quantity and thus their proportionate numbers in each compound calculated. Using this knowledge, it is possible to determine that the mass proportion in water are 2.0 grams of hydrogen to 16.0 grams of oxygen.

20th Century

Atoms remained indestructible until this century. Then scientists began to dissect them, discovering that they consist of still smaller particles—a nucleus, made up of protons and neutrons, and electrons. Furthermore scientists succeeded in splitting these small bits of matter, ushering in the Atomic Age. Atomic bombs were used by the United States in World War II. Since then, nuclear power—the release of tremendous amounts of energy when atoms are either split or joined—has provided us with many peaceful uses, mainly in supplying energy but also in medicine and research. Scientists are now using devices called "atom traps" in which laser beams slow down atoms, so that they can be studied more closely.

CHAPTER 5
Matter and Its Phases

The photograph shows balloons used in a Fourth of July celebration. The balloons are filled with helium gas. Because helium is less dense than air, these balloons rise when they are released. This chapter discusses properties of gases, liquids, and solids. After you read this chapter, you will know why objects rise in air and float in water.

Organizing Your Study Skills The outline below will help you see how the chapter is organized and what you should learn as you read.

I. Section 5-1: The Phases of Matter
   A. What is matter?
   B. How do the phases of matter differ?
   C. How are the particles held together in each phase of matter?

II. Section 5-2: Characteristics of Solids
   A. How are the particles arranged in a solid?
   B. What are some characteristics of crystalline solids?
   C. What are some characteristics of amorphous solids?

III. Section 5-3: Characteristics of Liquids
   A. How do the particles in a liquid behave?
   B. What determines the pressure in a liquid?
   C. What is the buoyant force?
   D. How is pressure transmitted through a liquid?

IV. Section 5-4: Characteristics of Gases
   A. How do gases produce pressure?
   B. How do changes in the volume and temperature of a gas affect its pressure?
   C. How does Archimedes' principle apply to gases?
   D. What is Bernoulli's principle?
   E. What is plasma?

V. Section 5-5: Changes in Phase of Matter
   A. What happens when matter changes from one phase to another?
   B. What is meant by the term *latent heat?*

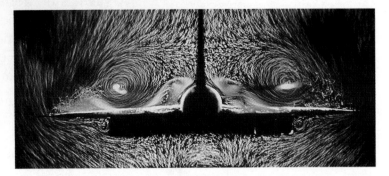

After completing this section, you will be able to

A. Define matter.
B. Describe the phases of matter.
C. Explain how particles are held together in each phase of matter.

Figure 5-1 The sun shines as it converts matter into energy.

Explore!

Use an encyclopedia to find out about the Manhattan Project of the 1940s and how it was related to changing matter into energy.

Defining Matter

What do you have in common with a table, orange juice, and the air? Like you, all of these are made of matter.

In the early 1900s, Albert Einstein discovered that matter can be changed into energy and energy can be changed into matter. In other words, Einstein discovered that energy and matter are different forms of each other. You know that the sun, shown in the picture, gives off a tremendous amount of energy. This energy is produced by the conversion of matter into energy deep within the sun. The sun continuously radiates this energy into space. It provides us with the energy we use every day.

In everyday life, matter is usually considered to be anything that has mass and takes up space. This description of matter applies best to the portions of matter that you can see and work with. These portions of matter are described by their properties.

Solids, Liquids, and Gases

Matter that you can see and touch exists as solids, liquids, and gases. These three different states of matter are called **phases of matter**.

A **solid** has a definite shape and volume. For example, a book is a solid. It has a specific shape and size that can be measured.

A **liquid** has a definite volume but no definite shape. A liquid takes the shape of the container that holds it. For example, water flows to fit the shape of the glass into which you pour it. If you pour the water into a larger glass, its shape changes but its volume remains the same.

A **gas** has no definite shape and no definite volume. Gas takes the shape and volume of its container. For example, a small amount of gas can be contained inside a balloon, or it can expand to fill a room.

In all its phases, matter behaves as if it consists of tiny particles too small to see. Scientists call these particles atoms and molecules.

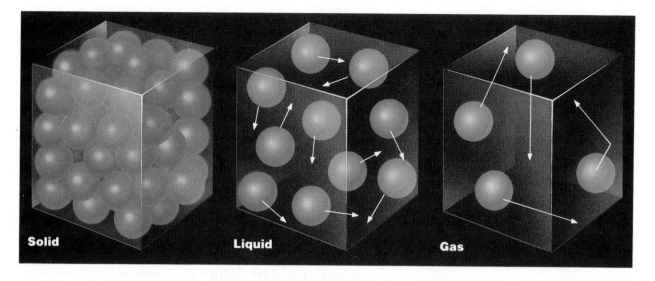

Solid   Liquid   Gas

Phases of Matter Depend on How Particles Are Linked

The phase in which matter exists depends on how strongly its particles are held together. *Figure 5-2* represents particles in a solid, a liquid, and a gas.

In a solid, the particles are held together closely and strongly. Each particle vibrates about a fixed position, but does not move otherwise. As a result, a solid has a definite shape and volume.

In a liquid, the particles are not held together as tightly as in a solid. A liquid's particles are held together loosely and are able to slide past one another. As a result, a liquid can flow. Thus, even though a liquid has a definite volume, it takes the shape of its container.

In a gas, the particles are not held together at all and are free to move quickly in all directions. As a result, a gas does not have a definite shape or volume. Instead, the volume and shape of a gas are determined by its container.

Figure 5-2 Particles are held together most tightly in a solid. In a liquid, particles are able to slide past one another. Gas particles can move about freely.

Applying Science

Very high temperatures occur deep within stars where matter is converted into energy. Scientists are making progress in using this process to generate energy on the earth. They have heated gas to 200 000 000° C as part of their effort.

Section Review

1. What did Einstein discover about how matter and energy are related?
2. List and describe the three phases of matter.
3. How are particles held together in a solid, a liquid, and a gas?

Challenge: A balloon filled with helium bursts in a closed room. What space will the helium occupy? What will be its shape?

After completing this section, you will be able to

A. Describe how particles are arranged in a solid.
B. Name some characteristics of crystalline solids.
C. Name some characteristics of amorphous solids.

5-2 Characteristics of Solids

How Particles Are Arranged in Solids

In the world around you, there are many more different solids than either liquids or gases. In all solids, each particle vibrates about a fixed position. When a solid's particles are arranged in a definite pattern that repeats itself again and again, the solid is crystalline. Crystalline solids are made up of units called **crystals**.

When the particles of a solid are not arranged in an orderly pattern, the solid is **amorphous**. Sulfur can exist as a crystalline solid or as an amorphous solid. In *Figure 5-3*, liquid sulfur changes to an amorphous solid when it is poured into cold water. This yellow, rubbery substance has a texture like chewy taffy.

Characteristics of Crystalline Solids

The ring in *Figure 5-4* contains more than one kind of crystalline solid. Some solids, such as diamonds and rubies, consist of a large, single crystal. Other solids, such as the metal part of the ring, are made up of many tiny crystals.

Crystals may form when a melted substance cools. The size of the crystal depends on how quickly the substance cools. If the substance cools slowly, a large crystal may develop. If the substance cools quickly, many smaller crystals form. Rock candy forms when hot sugar syrup (a mixture of sugar and water) cools slowly and forms crystals.

Figure 5-3 The yellow solid is an amorphous form of sulfur.

Figure 5-4 The ring is made of crystalline solids.

Figure 5-5a Well-developed fluorite crystals **b** Ice crystals in a snowflake

Notice the smooth surfaces of the fluorite crystals in the picture. A crystal has smooth, flat surfaces because the particles in it are arranged in a definite pattern. A crystalline solid breaks evenly along the surfaces of its crystals. *Figure 5-5* also shows the orderly arrangement of ice crystals in a snow flake.

Some substances have several different crystal forms. Carbon, for example, can form diamond crystals, which have six sides. The "lead" in your pencil actually contains graphite. Graphite is a soft, black form of carbon. Diamonds are colorless and are the hardest known natural substance. The differences between graphite and diamond result from the different arrangements of their atoms.

Most crystalline solids change quickly and totally into liquids when they are heated to a certain temperature. Heat causes the orderly arrangement of particles to break apart, destroying the neat arrangement of the solid all at once. This process is called **melting**.

Characteristics of Amorphous Solids

Sometimes a liquid cools so rapidly that crystals do not have time to form. Amorphous sulfur forms when liquid sulfur cools very quickly. Glass is an amorphous solid that forms when melted silicon cools quickly. Atoms in glass have no regularly repeating patterns.

Have You Heard?

Some rocks found on the moon are glassy, amorphous solids. These rocks probably formed after meteorites hit the moon and melted some of its surface. The melted material cooled too rapidly for crystals to form.

Figure 5-7 Some examples of amorphous solids are shown here.

Figure 5-6 Obsidian cooled too quickly for crystals to form.

Some amorphous solids form naturally. The rock in *Figure 5-6* is a type of natural glass that formed when lava from a volcano cooled too quickly for crystals to form.

Figure 5-7 shows other kinds of amorphous solids. For example, the rubber band in the girl's hair, the plastic bag she wraps her lunch in, and her fingernails are all amorphous solids. Particles of rubber, plastics, and fingernails are even less orderly than the particles of glassy materials. These amorphous solids are made of long chains of particles. These chains can be as tangled as the strands in a bowl of spaghetti.

Unlike crystals, which melt suddenly at a given temperature, amorphous solids melt gradually over a temperature range. Ice, which is crystalline, changes directly to a liquid. But candle wax, which is amorphous, gets softer and softer as it melts.

Section Review

1. How do the particles of a solid move?
2. What can determine the size of a crystal?
3. What are two differences between crystalline and amorphous solids?

Challenge: You have 12 liters of graphite. You put 6 liters of the liquid graphite in a refrigerator and leave the other 6 liters at room temperature. After 24 hours, which container of graphite will have larger crystals?

Crystalline Solids

Purpose

To observe the effect of cooling rate on the formation of some solids

Materials

- copper sulfate
- sugar
- water
- bowl or tray
- teaspoon
- metal spoon
- Bunsen burner
- matches
- pot holder
- ring stand and ring
- wire gauze
- 100-mL beaker
- mass
- string
- rubber band
- paper towel
- cover goggles

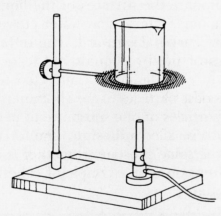

Procedure and Observations

PART A

1. Set up the ring stand, ring, wire gauze, and burner as shown.
2. Put about 50 mL of water in the beaker.
3. *CAUTION: Put on your cover goggles. Keep hair, clothes, and paper away from the burner flame.* Heat and water to make it hot. It does not have to boil.
4. Turn off the burner. Stir about 2 teaspoons of copper sulfate into the hot water. *CAUTION: Copper surface is poison-*

ous. Do not get any of it in your mouth. Wash your hands after using it.

5. Tie the mass to some string. Put the mass in the hot water so that the loose end of the string hangs over the edge of the beaker.
6. When the beaker is cool enough, cover it with a paper towel held in place by the rubber band.
7. Let the beaker stand undisturbed for 1 to 2 days. Then examine the contents and record your observations.

PART B

1. Put some cold water in the bowl.
2. Light the burner and adjust it to produce a very small flame. Slowly heat a spoonful of sugar over the flame. *CAUTION: Hold the spoon with the pot holder and keep hair, clothes, and papers away from the flame.*
3. As soon as the sugar melts, remove the spoon from the burner. If you do not remove the sugar from the flame as soon as it melts, it will burn.
4. Put the spoon and the liquid sugar into cold water so that the sugar will cool quickly.
5. Observe and record in what form the sugar becomes solid again.

Analysis and Conclusions

1. Compare the structure of the solid that formed quickly with the one that formed slowly.
2. Examine the solid copper sulfate attached to the string. Determine whether or not the copper sulfate formed crystals.

5-3 Characteristics of Liquids

After completing this section, you will be able to

A. Describe how particles in a liquid behave.
B. Explain what determines the pressure in a liquid.
C. Define the buoyant force.
D. Describe how pressure is transmitted through a liquid.

How Particles in a Liquid Behave

The particles in a liquid are not held together as strongly as those of a solid. Yet the particles of a liquid do not move about as freely as those of a gas.

Beneath the surface of a liquid, particles are attracted in all directions by other particles. However, on the surface of a liquid, a particle is attracted only by particles that are beneath it and to its sides. Because there are no particles above a surface particle to attract it upwards, particles at the surface of a liquid are attracted into the liquid. For this reason, the surface of a liquid has surface tension. **Surface tension** makes the surface of a liquid act as if it were a stretched elastic sheet. Surface tension makes it possible for the insect shown in *Figure 5-8* to stand on the surface of the pond.

In *Figure 5-9*, compare the surfaces of the liquids in the two glass containers. Notice that water curves upward while mercury curves downward. The difference between the curves of the two liquids has to do with how the particles in each liquid are attracted to one another and to the glass particles in the containers. The force that attracts particles of one substance to particles of another substance is called **adhesion**. The force that keeps particles of the same substance together is called **cohesion**. Surface tension is an example of cohesion at the surface of a liquid.

Water   Mercury

Figure 5-9 Water's surface curves up and mercury's curves down.

Figure 5-8 Example of surface tension

The adhesion of water particles to glass particles is stronger than the cohesion between water particles. Thus, water moves up the glass. But the adhesion of mercury particles to glass particles is weaker than the cohesion between mercury particles. Thus, mercury does not move up the sides of the glass container.

Particles that attract each other strongly do not move past each other readily. Cohesion is one of the factors that can slow liquid flow. A liquid's resistance to flowing is its **viscosity**. Viscous liquids have high viscosities. They are thick and sticky and do not pour easily. Tar is an example of a highly viscous liquid. Roofers heat tar before they spread it because heat makes liquids less viscous, and thus makes the tar easier to work with. The lava in the picture is melted rock. However, the lava is so hot that it has a low viscosity. Therefore it flows.

Density and Depth Determine Liquid Pressure

When you swim underwater, the pressure you feel in your ears is the force of water pressing on your ear drums. In a similar way, a liquid presses against the walls of the container that holds it. **Pressure** is the amount of force acting over a unit of area. Pressure acts in all directions, not only downward.

The pressure that a liquid exerts depends on the depth of the liquid. The deeper you swim under water, the greater the pressure on you. At two meters beneath the surface of a pool there is twice as much pressure on you as at one meter beneath the surface.

Pressure also depends on the density of a liquid. Salt water is denser than fresh water. When you swim at a certain depth, the pressure on you is greater in salt water than in fresh water.

The volume of liquid does not affect pressure. The volume of a large lake is much greater than the volume of a swimming pool. But if you swim at the same depth in both a lake and a swimming pool, the pressure on you is the same in each case.

Special research vessels are made to withstand the great pressures found deep in the ocean. The special construction of these vessels enables them to dive to the ocean floor without being crushed. These vessels can go to depths of about 11 kilometers below the surface. New, strong underwater vessels allowed scientists to find the sunken ship *Titanic* deep under the Atlantic Ocean.

Figure 5-10 Lava is melted rock that flows.

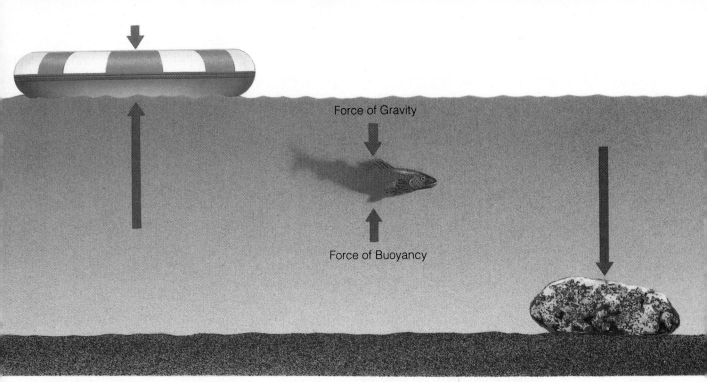

Force of Gravity

Force of Buoyancy

Figure 5-12 Compare the force of gravity and the buoyant force acting on each object in the picture.

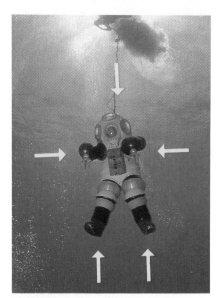

Figure 5-11 Since water pressure increases with depth, the upward pressure on his feet is greater than the downward pressure on his head.

The Buoyant Force and Floating

If you have lifted a heavy object out of water, you have experienced an effect of liquid pressure called buoyancy. Due to buoyancy, an object submerged in a liquid appears to lose weight. For example, when you try to lift a rock underneath the surface of water, it seems light. However, when you lift the rock above the water, it becomes considerably heavier. The rock's lightness below the surface of the water results from the upward force that water exerts on it. This upward force is called the **buoyant force**. This force exists because water pressure increases with depth.

Figure 5-11 shows a diver suspended in water. The arrows represent forces caused by water pressure. The forces acting on the sides of the diver are in balance. The upward force acting on the bottom of the diver is greater than the downward force acting on his head, because his feet are deeper in the water. (Water pressure increases with depth.) Thus, there is a net upward force acting on objects in the water—the buoyant force. This force upward makes the objects seem lighter under water.

If an object weighs less than the buoyant force, it floats. After all, its weight is a downward force and the buoyant force is an upward force, as shown in *Figure 5-12*. If an object weighs more than the buoyant force, it sinks. If an object's weight is equal to the buoyant force, it can remain at any level.

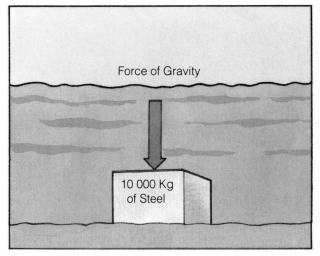

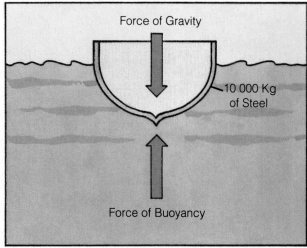

Figure 5-13 The weight of water displaced by the ship is much greater than the weight of water displaced by the block of steel.

The buoyant force is greater in a denser liquid than in a less dense one. Because salt water is denser than fresh water, it is easier to float in salt water.

To further understand the magnitude of buoyant force, it is important to understand the expression "volume of water displaced." For example, if you fill a pan to the very top with water and then put an egg in it, some of the water is pushed out of the pan. The amount of water displaced by the egg equals the egg's volume.

More than 2000 years ago, the Greek mathematician Archimedes figured out that the buoyant force on an object is equal to the weight of the liquid it displaces. **Archimedes' principle** is applied when ships are designed. For example, a ship's volume must be great enough to displace a volume of water of equal weight. *Figure 5-13* shows that a block of steel sinks. But the steel ship floats because the water displaced by the ship's hull weighs as much as the ship does. Archimedes' principle also tells us that an object placed in a liquid seems to lose weight equal to the weight of the fluid it displaces.

How a Liquid in a Container Transmits Pressure

In 1651, the French scientist Blaise Pascal wrote about the behavior of liquids. Pascal's theories can be used to explain how liquid pressure is used in all sorts of familiar objects, from car brakes to airplane landing gear. Pascal theorized that if the pressure of a liquid in one part of a container changes, the pressure changes throughout the container. This theory is known as **Pascal's principle**. Pascal's principle applies for gases as well as liquids.

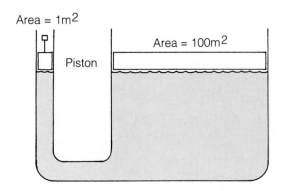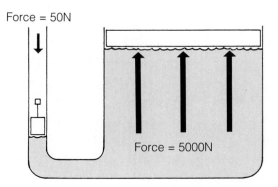

Figure 5-14 The force increases as it moves through the water from the small cylinder to the large cylinder.

Have You Heard?

The brake pedal in a car is connected to pistons. When the driver presses on the brake pedal, the pressure is transmitted through a liquid. This forces the brake linings to rub against the spinning brake drums or discs on the wheels.

Explore!

Find out what hydraulic pumps are and how they are used in elevators.

To help you understand how Pascal's principle works, look at the diagram. A small cylinder and a large cylinder that are connected at the bottom are filled with water. The larger cylinder has 100 times the cross-sectional area of the smaller one. At the top of each cylinder is a piston.

Suppose you press down on the piston on top of the small cylinder. The pressure is transmitted throughout the water. If you remember that pressure = force/area, you will see that force = pressure × area. Pascal's principle tells us that the pressure is the same in both places.

However, since the area of the larger cylinder is 100 times the area of the smaller cylinder, the pressure creates a force on the larger piston that is 100 times larger than that on the smaller piston. For example, if you push down on the smaller piston with a force of 50 newtons, the force exerted by the larger piston will be 100 times greater—5000 newtons. When the area of the larger cylinder is many times greater than that of the smaller cylinder, a machine like this can lift very heavy objects.

Section Review

1. Why do mercury and water curve differently in a beaker?
2. Which does not affect liquid pressure: volume, density, or depth?
3. Why can a steel ship float while a steel block sinks?
4. What is Pascal's principle?

Challenge: Two submarines of equal weight and volume are at the same depth, one in fresh water and one in salt water. To get to the surface, each submarine will need to get rid of some weight. Which submarine will need to drop more weight?

5-4 Characteristics of Gases

How Gases Produce Pressure

The picture shows particles of gas in a bicycle tire. The gas particles bump into and bounce off one another as they fly about. When the particles hit the tire wall, they press against it. This force of gas particles that press against the tire causes pressure.

The gases of the air that surround our planet are kept from escaping outwards by the force of gravity, which acts like a container. The air's gas particles bump into and bounce off one another as they fly about the earth's atmosphere. These particles produce pressure on everything they hit, including your body. However, the cells of your body push out with the same pressure that the air around you pushes in. Therefore, you do not feel pressure from the air.

You may have noticed changes in air pressure, however. Air pressure changes with altitude. As you go higher in the atmosphere, air pressure is less because there is less air above you to push down. When you go up in a speedy elevator or when you ride in a car over a steep mountain road, you may feel your ears pop. Your ears pop as they adjust to the change in air pressure.

Air pressure varies from place to place. Air pressure can even change at the same location. To keep track of air pressure changes, a standard is needed to express air pressure. The standard for air pressure on earth is expressed in terms of the average weight of air at sea level. Standard sea level air pressure is a little over 100 000 newtons per square meter. In SI, 1 pascal (symbol: Pa) is 1 newton per square meter, so standard sea level pressure is a little over 100 000 pascals.

Figure 5-15 The arrows indicate the movement of air molecules in the bicycle tire.

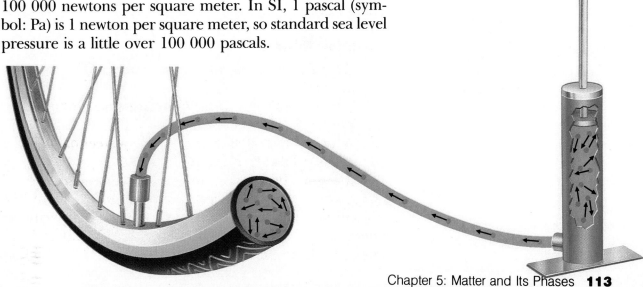

Changes in Volume and Temperature of Gases

Figure 5-16 shows how the pressure of a gas changes as its volume changes. In these pictures, the temperature of the gas is constant. When you reduce the volume of a container by half, the same amount of gas takes up only half as much space as before. The change in volume forces the gas particles together. The pressure of the gas then increases, because more particles bounce against each square centimeter of the container's walls each second. Scientists have found, when temperature is constant, that the pressure of a gas doubles when the volume of its container is halved.

On the other hand, if you double the volume of a container, fewer particles bounce against each area of the container's walls each second, and pressure drops. Experiments show that doubling the volume of a container of gas halves the pressure.

Tires that are filled with a gas at high pressure hold up heavy objects and make a vehicle's ride smoother. When a car travels over a bump, the volume of the tire decreases briefly, and the pressure of the gas inside increases.

Figure 5-17 shows how the pressure of a gas changes as temperature changes, while its volume stays the same. An increase in temperature causes the energy of gas particles to increase. As gas particles gain energy, they move more quickly. They bounce against the container's walls more often and with greater force. Therefore, as you heat a gas, its pressure increases. If you cool a gas, the particles move more slowly and the pressure drops.

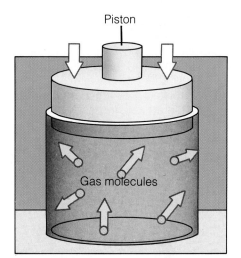

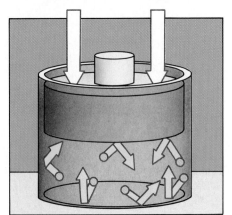

Figure 5-16 At a constant temperature, the pressure of a gas increases when the volume of its container decreases.

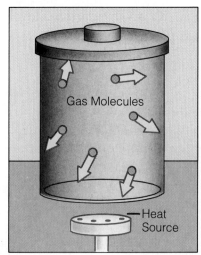

Figure 5-17 As a gas is heated, its pressure increases, provided its volume is unchanged.

114

Archimedes' Principle and Gases

In the photograph on pages 100 and 101, some helium-filled balloons are rising through the air. Helium-filled balloons rise in air for the same reason that a cork floats in water. According to Archimedes' principle, the cork is held up by a buoyant force equal to the weight of the water it displaces. The upward force on the cork is greater than the downward force on the cork. In the same way, a balloon is held up by a buoyant force equal to the weight of the air it displaces. A volume of helium weighs less than the same volume of air. Thus, because helium is less dense than air, it is used to lift balloons and airships.

Hot air balloons also depend on buoyant force. When the gas inside a balloon is heated, its pressure increases. As a result, the balloon expands and rises. The volume of the balloon increases, but its mass does not. Thus, the balloon displaces more air, and the buoyant force is greater. The balloon continues to expand until the pressure inside equals the air pressure outside.

Bernoulli's Principle

While taking a shower, you may have noticed that a heavy flow of water sometimes causes the shower curtain to move in. The moving water makes the air inside the shower move, too. However, moving air exerts less force against the shower curtain than still air outside the curtain does. Thus, pressure on the inside of the shower curtain drops. The greater air pressure from outside the shower stall pushes the curtain in.

The Swiss scientist Daniel Bernoulli, who lived in the 18th century, studied how the velocity of a liquid or gas is related to pressure. According to **Bernoulli's principle**, as the velocity of a gas or liquid increases, the pressure it exerts decreases. As the velocity decreases, the pressure increases.

Figure 5-18 shows the Bernoulli principle at work. The student has set a cylinder of posterboard over some puffed rice. She uses a vacuum cleaner hose attached to the back of a vacuum cleaner to blow air across the top of the cylinder. The moving air creates a low pressure in the cylinder, which results in a higher pressure below the cylinder than above it. This difference in air pressure causes air carrying cereal to rise in the cylinder.

Applying Science

Even though hydrogen is less dense than helium, it is not used to fill airships because it explodes too easily.

Figure 5-18 Demonstrating Bernoulli's principle.

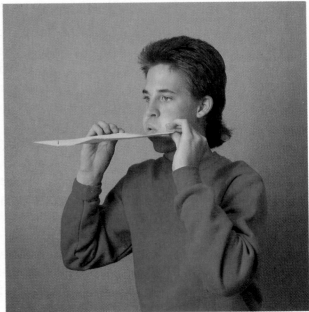

Figure 5-19 Air pressure is higher below the paper than above it, so the paper moves upward toward the lower air pressure.

Explore!

The picture of the airplane in the wind tunnel on page 101 shows how air moves around an airplane's wings. Try to find out what role Bernoulli's principle plays in the design of airplane wings.

Figure 5-20 The glowing gas in a neon sign is an example of a plasma.

You can demonstrate Bernoulli's principle using a sheet of paper, as shown. Hold the paper near your mouth. Blow along the top of the paper. As the velocity of the air above the paper increases, the pressure drops. Air pressure along the upper surface of the paper is then lower than air pressure below the paper. This difference in pressure pushes the paper upward.

Bernoulli's principle explains why passing ships may collide sideways. The velocity of the water between the ships is greater than the velocity of water on their opposite sides. Therefore, the pressure against the near sides of the ships' hulls drops. The greater pressure on the outer sides of the ships can force the ships together if the captains do not adjust their steering.

Plasma—A Special Kind of Gas

At very high temperatures, the particles in gases break up into their parts. A gas broken up into negatively and positively charged particles is called **plasma**. All stars, including the sun, are balls of plasma. Among gases, plasmas are special because electricity passes through them and magnetism affects them. Magnetism shapes the outer layer of the sun—a plasma that extends millions of kilometers into space.

The glowing gas in a neon sign, such as the one in *Figure 5-20,* is an example of a plasma on the earth. Fluorescent lights also contain plasmas.

Inside the sun and the other stars, plasma is very dense. The sun and stars get energy as these dense plasmas undergo a process called fusion. Scientists are trying to reproduce this process on earth. Many scientists think that most of our energy will come from fusion one day. Scientists are trying to learn how to control plasmas as they control solids, liquids, and regular gases.

Have You Heard?

Layers of plasma surround the earth. You can tune in distant radio broadcasts when radio waves from the earth bounce off these layers.

Section Review

1. How can the atmosphere create pressure even though it is not in a container?
2. How do changes in volume and temperature affect the pressure of a gas?
3. What force keeps a balloon floating in the air?
4. What does Bernoulli's principle say about the pressure in a moving liquid or gas?
5. How does plasma differ from regular gas?

Challenge: A balloon filled with helium moves from sea level to an altitude of 1000 meters. Where is the balloon's acceleration greater, closer to sea level or near 1000 meters? Why?

People and Science

Shirley Ann Jackson, Theoretical Physicist

Shirley Ann Jackson was valedictorian of her class at Roosevelt High School in Washington, D.C. Four years later, she got her bachelor of science degree at Massachusetts Institute of Technology (MIT). After graduation, she was accepted in the graduate schools at Harvard University, Brown University, and the University of Chicago. However, she decided to stay at MIT. In 1973, she became the first American black woman to be granted a Ph. D. from that institution.

As a professional scientist, Dr. Jackson worked first in high-energy physics. This field deals with the acceleration of subatomic particles to high speeds.

Later, she became interested in solid-state physics, which involves the behavior of particles in solids.

For two years, Dr. Jackson served as a research associate at the Fermi Laboratory in Batavia, Illinois. She was also a visiting scientist in the theoretical division of the *European Organization for Nuclear Research* in Geneva, Switzerland. Currently, she works as a research physicist in the AT&T Bell Laboratories. She has published numerous articles in scientific journals and gives speeches regularly at scientific meetings. She also spends much of her time encouraging young people to study physics.

After completing this section, you will be able to

A. Describe how matter changes from one phase to another.

B. Explain the term *latent heat*.

5-5 Changes in Phase of Matter

How Matter Changes from One Phase to Another

How does a rain puddle on a sidewalk disappear? Why does a lake freeze over in winter and melt back into water in spring? These changes take place because matter changes from one phase to another when its temperature changes enough.

Temperature affects the way particles in a substance are held together. At low temperatures, particles move slowly and become closely linked. At high temperatures, particles gain energy and move more quickly and more freely.

Many materials can exist as solids, liquids, or gases, and can change from one phase to another and back again. Iron, for example, is a solid at room temperature. In the outer core of the earth, however, iron is molten—a liquid. In the stars, iron exists as plasma—a gas.

Water is a familiar example of matter that exists in different phases in the range of temperatures found on earth. The picture shows solid water—ice.

Melting is the change of phase from solid to liquid. Ice and other solids melt when their particles gain enough energy. In the picture, the energy from sunlight can melt the ice. The temperature at which a solid melts is its **melting point**. Each pure substance has a specific melting point. For example, the melting point of water is 0° C at normal atmospheric pressure. That of iron is 1525° C.

Freezing is the change of phase from liquid to solid. Water freezes into ice. The temperature at which a liquid changes into a solid is its **freezing point**. The freezing point of a substance is the same as its melting point.

Figure 5-21 The ice will change phase when it reaches its melting point temperature.

The temperature at which a liquid boils is its **boiling point**. At its boiling point, a liquid changes into a gas in a process called **vaporization**. Water in the gaseous phase—water vapor—is an invisible gas.

The boiling point of a substance depends on air pressure. Under air pressure at sea level, water reaches its boiling point at 100° C. Air pressure at high altitudes is lower than air pressure at sea level. It is easier for particles of liquid water to escape into the air at lower air pressures. Thus, water boils at lower temperatures at high altitudes.

Water can **evaporate**—change from a liquid to a gas— even when its temperature is below the boiling point. This process is called **evaporation**. At any temperature, some particles in a liquid move faster than others. The fastest particles can escape from the liquid. In this way, water evaporates little by little.

Water vapor can change into a liquid—or **condense**— in a process called **condensation**. If the temperature of a gas is lowered enough, the gas can become a liquid. The water drops on the outside of the cold glass are condensed water vapor from the air.

Natural gas for heating is often condensed to a liquid. This fuel takes up 600 times less space as a liquid than it does as a gas. So, it is easier, although more dangerous, to transport and store as a liquid. Raising the temperature returns the fuel to its vapor form.

Ice can become a gas without going through a liquid phase. This process is called **sublimation.** A comet's tail, shown in *Figure 5-23*, develops through the process of sublimation. The comet's head is made of ice and dust. When the comet passes near the sun, the energy from the sun turns some of its ice directly into a gas. In other words, some of the ice **sublimes**.

Figure 5-22 Water vapor in the air was chilled when it touched the cold surface of the glass. This chilling caused the water vapor to condense, forming drops of water on the outside of the glass.

Figure 5-23 The comet's head and tail are visible in this infrared photograph.

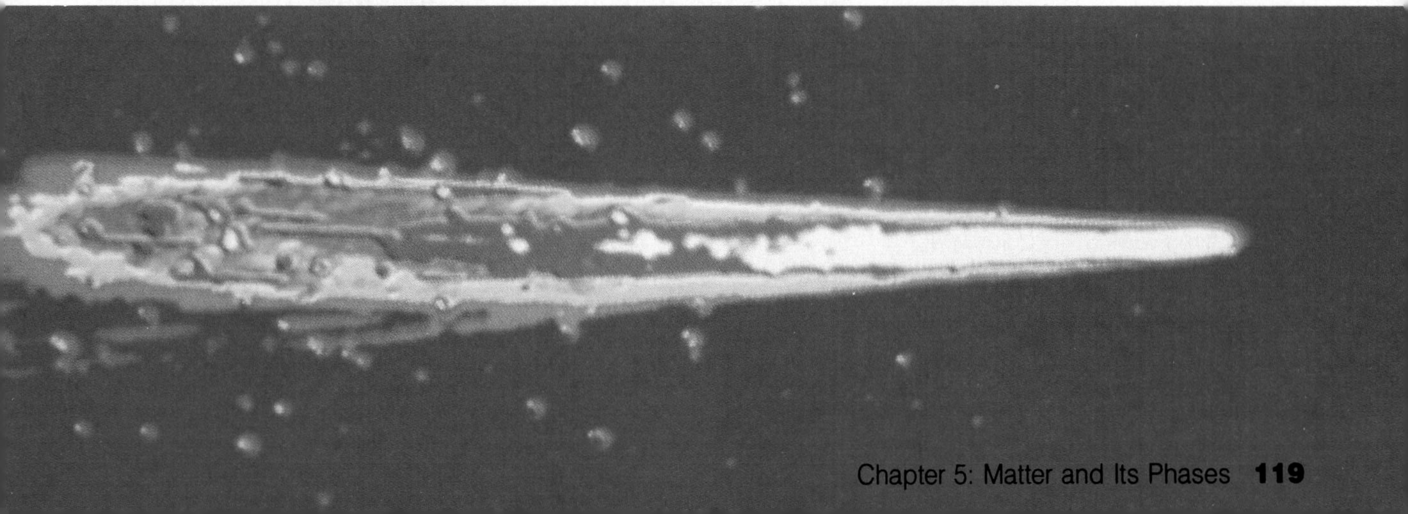

Figure 5-24 Liquid water and ice can exist side by side at zero degrees Celsius.

Explore!

Find out how some power plants use a tube in which water changes to steam and back again to water.

Applying Science

Liquid crystals are substances that flow like liquids but have some properties of solids. When ordinary solids melt, their particles move in all directions. Before a liquid crystal melts completely, its particles line up side by side in groups that can move past one another only in certain directions. Small temperature changes cause many types of liquid crystals to change color.

Temperature Does Not Change During Phase Changes

The pictures show ice melting in a beaker. A thermometer measures the temperature of the ice-water mixture. The temperature does not change as long as the melting continues. At normal atmospheric pressure, the temperature remains at the melting point of water—0° C—as long as there is any ice present. Instead, the heat, which is called **latent heat**—or hidden heat—makes the ice change phase. The temperature of the water in the beaker will not start to rise until all the ice has melted.

In melting ice, latent heat provides the energy that breaks up the orderly arrangement of particles in the ice crystals. In boiling water, latent heat provides the energy needed to separate one water particle from another and change the water into vapor.

Understanding latent heat can help you understand why water vapor burns you more seriously than water at the same temperature. When water vapor condenses, energy from the latent heat is released. If water vapor at 100° C touches your skin, the vapor gives off a large amount of latent heat as it condenses. Even after you are burned by the latent heat of the vapor changing to water, you still have water at 100° C, which also burns you.

Section Review

1. How does water change phase when it evaporates and condenses?
2. Explain the meaning of latent heat.

Challenge: Explain why it takes longer to cook food in Denver, which is at a high elevation, than in New Orleans, which is at sea level.

Changing Phases

Purpose

To observe the effects of latent heat

Materials

- 250-mL beaker
- hot plate, or Bunsen burner, ring, ring stand, wire gauze, and matches
- thermometer that includes 0° C and 100° C
- water
- ice
- watch or clock, to measure half-minutes
- cover goggles
- stirring rod

Procedure and Observations

1. Fill the beaker about two-thirds full of ice.
2. Set up your equipment as shown in **a.** *CAUTION: Handle the thermometer with care so that you do not break it.*

a
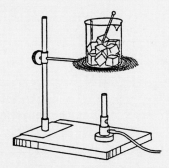

3. Add enough water to the beaker to cover the bulb of the thermometer.
4. Put on your cover goggles. Stir the ice-water mixture very gently, using the stirring rod (*not* the thermometer). When the temperature has stayed at 0°C for 2 minutes, light the burner. *CAUTION: Keep clothes, hair, and paper away from the flame.*

5. Heat the beaker with a steady, low flame, and record the temperature of the water every half-minute. Stir gently to distribute heat evenly.
6. Record the temperature at which the ice has completely melted. Continue to heat the water until it boils, recording the temperature every half-minute.
7. Record the temperature at which the water starts to boil. Continue to record it every half-minute for 3 minutes more. *CAUTION: When boiling water, remember that steam and hot water can cause burns.*
8. Copy the grid in **b,** plot your data, and draw a graph by connecting the plotted points. Extend the grid as much as needed. Mark on the graph the time at which the melting of the ice was completed and the time at which the water started to boil.

b
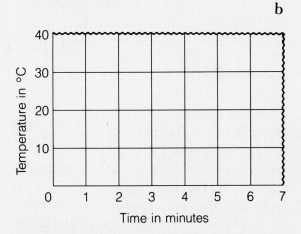

Analysis and Conclusions

1. What happened to the temperature of the water while the ice was melting? Explain in terms of latent heat.
2. What happened to the temperature of the water while it was boiling? Explain in terms of latent heat.

Science Skills

Interpreting a Graph that Shows Temperature-Time Relationships

Interpreting time-temperature changes can help you understand how heat energy affects different substances. In this activity, you will use a graph to show how the temperature of each of two liquids changes over time when the liquids are heated.

In a certain experiment, two beakers, one half full of water and one half full of wood alcohol, were placed in a large container of hot oil. After one minute, an experimenter began to collect the data given in the table. Use this data to draw a graph line for each liquid. Use the grid below the table as a model for your graph. Answer the questions below, referring to your completed graph.

1. Which liquid, according to your graphs, shows a greater rate of increase in temperature during any interval of time between 0 and 6 minutes?
2. What are the temperatures of the water and alcohol after 3 minutes?
3. At what specific time is the temperature of the water the same as the temperature of the alcohol?
4. Describe what happens to the water between 20° C and 100° C.
5. Describe what happens to the alcohol between 20° C and 65° C.
6. Describe what is happening to the water in the time interval during which its temperature is 100° C.
7. Describe what is happening to the alcohol in the time interval during which its temperature is 65° C.
8. Explain how the graph illustrates latent heat.

Time in minutes	Water	Temperature °C Wood Alcohol
0	20	20
1	25	27
2	30	34
3	35	41
4	40	48
5	45	55
6	50	62
7	55	65
8	60	65
9	65	65
10	70	65
11	75	65
12	80	
13	85	
14	90	
15	95	
16	100	
17	100	
18	100	
19	100	
20	100	

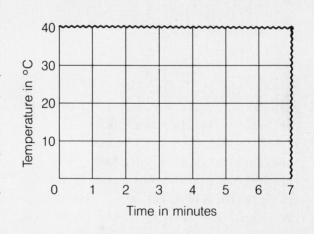

 Summary   18¹ ⁶

5-1 The Phases of Matter

A. Matter is every living and nonliving thing.

B. The phases of matter are solid, liquid, and gas.

C. The phase of a substance is determined by how strongly its particles are held together.

5-2 Characteristics of Solids

A. Each particle in a solid vibrates about a fixed position.

B. In crystalline solids, the particles are arranged in definite patterns that repeat themselves.

C. Particles in an amorphous solid are not arranged in an orderly pattern.

5-3 Characteristics of Liquids

A. A liquid's particles are not held together as strongly as those of a solid, and they are not as free to move around as those of a gas.

B. Pressure is force per unit area. In a liquid, pressure is determined by depth and density.

C. Pascal's principle states that pressure is transmitted through a liquid.

5-4 Characteristics of Gases

A. According to Archimedes' principle, the buoyant force on an object is equal to the weight of the gas or liquid that is displaced.

B. Bernoulli's principle relates the pressure of a gas or liquid to its velocity.

C. Plasma is gas broken up into positively and negatively charged particles.

5-5 Changes in Phase of Matter

A. Solids, liquids, or gases can change from one phase to another and back again.

B. Temperature does not change during a change of phase. Energy gained or lost during a phase change is known as latent heat.

Vocabulary

For each of the following terms, write a sentence that uses the term correctly.

adhesion	condense	liquid	sublimation
amorphous	crystals	melting	sublime
Archimedes' principle	evaporate	melting point	surface tension
Bernoulli's principle	evaporation	Pascal's principle	vaporization
boiling point	freezing	phase of matter	viscosity
buoyant force	freezing point	plasma	
cohesion	gas	pressure	
condensation	latent heat	solid	

Check Your Knowledge

Part I: Matching. Match the definition in Column I with the correct term in Column II.

Column I
1. results from cohesion
2. greater in salt water than in fresh water
3. ice changes directly to gas
4. definite volume, indefinite shape
5. tend to form when a substance cools slowly
6. amorphous solid
7. crystalline solid
8. viscous
9. solid to liquid
10. gas made up of charged particles

Column II
a. buoyant force
b. crystals
c. glass
d. ice
e. liquid
f. melting
g. plasma
h. sublimation
i. surface tension
j. syrup
k. vaporization

Part II: Multiple Choice. Choose the letter of the best answer.

11. Albert Einstein discovered that (a) matter can be changed into a liquid. (b) matter can be changed into a gas. (c) matter can be changed into energy. (d) energy *cannot* be changed into matter.

12. A crystalline solid (a) is a rubber band. (b) forms when a substance cools rapidly. (c) breaks unevenly along its surface. (d) melts quickly and totally into a liquid.

13. Adhesion (a) keeps particles of the same substance together. (b) causes surface tension. (c) causes water to curve upward in a glass tube. (d) causes mercury to curve downward in a glass tube.

14. Depth and density affect (a) melting point. (b) boiling point. (c) condensation. (d) pressure.

15. What causes a heavy object to be lifted more easily in water than in the air? (a) air pressure (b) a downward force (c) buoyant force (d) Pascal's principle

16. As the velocity of a gas or liquid decreases, its pressure increases. This is part of (a) Archimedes' principle. (b) Pascal's principle. (c) Bernoulli's principle. (d) buoyant force.

17. The process in which a liquid changes to gas is (a) evaporation. (b) condensation. (c) sublimation. (d) melting.

Part III: Completion. Write the word or words that complete the sentence correctly.

18. The _____ _____ of water is 0° C.
19. The boiling point of a liquid depends on the _____ pressure.
20. A substance's melting point is also its _____ _____.
21. The energy released by melting ice is known as _____ _____.
22. When the volume of a container of gas is doubled, the _____ is reduced by half, if the temperature remains constant.

✔ Check Your Understanding

1. Describe the two main types of solids.
2. What makes it possible for an insect to stand on the surface of a pond?
3. Which is more viscous, honey or milk?
4. Where is the pressure greatest in a liquid?
5. What is the buoyant force?
6. Explain how a small force can be used to lift a very heavy object.
7. Explain what happens inside a closed container of a gas as the temperature is raised.
8. What happens to the pressure exerted sideways by a flowing gas when the velocity of the gas increases.
9. How may a better understanding of plasmas affect our energy supply on earth?
10. Compare and contrast evaporation and vaporization.
11. Explain what happens to the particles of a liquid as the liquid freezes.

✔ Apply Your Knowledge

1. You find a large crystal of quartz in some rocks. Describe some conditions under which that crystal formed.
2. How does heating a liquid make it less viscous?
3. Is there a greater pressure at the bottom of a vase filled to a depth of 40 centimeters or at the bottom of a wading pool filled to a depth of 30 centimeters?
4. Compare the water pressure at the bottom of a 10-meter tube of water with the water pressure 10 meters below the surface of a 100 000-liter reservoir.
5. A ship enters the ocean from a river. During which part of its trip does it ride higher in the water? Explain.
6. Use the words volume and weight to describe buoyant force.
7. Use Bernoulli's principle to explain why an umbrella sometimes turns inside out on a windy day.

✔ Extend Your Knowledge

Research/Projects

1. Place wooden, plastic, and brass buttons in a glass of water to see which float.
2. To show that a denser liquid has a greater buoyant force, place an egg in fresh water and then in salt water.
3. Press the sharp edge of a table knife on an ice cube. How does pressure affect the melting point of ice? Find out how this process explains how ice skates and sleds work.

Readings

Arnov, Boris. *Water: Experiments to Understand It.* Lothrop, Lee, and Shepard. 1980. Demonstrations that point out the properties of water.

Zubrowski, Bernie. *Messing Around with Water Pumps and Siphons.* Little, Brown, 1981. Experiments and demonstrations. (Be sure to ask a parent's permission before doing any experiments at home.)

CHAPTER 6
Properties of Matter

The photograph shows silver metal that was produced by passing an electric current through a solution containing silver. The photograph is enlarged 80 times to show the pattern of ridges that developed on the surface of the silver. Red dots in the picture are tiny laser beams used to highlight the ridges.

Organizing Your Study Skills The outline below will help you see how the chapter is organized and what you should learn as you read.

I. Section 6-1: The Elements
 A. What is an element?
 B. How were the elements discovered?
 C. What are chemical symbols?
 D. How can you describe an element?

II. Section 6-2: Physical Properties and Changes
 A. How can you describe physical properties?
 B. How are physical changes produced?

III. Section 6-3: Chemical Properties and Changes
 A. How can you identify chemical properties?
 B. How are chemical changes produced?

After completing this section, you will be able to

A. Define an element.
B. Describe the discovery of some elements.
C. Explain the use of chemical symbols.
D. Describe some elements.

6-1   The Elements

Elements Are Basic Substances

Only ten numerals are used to write even the biggest numbers. In a similar way, everything in the world is made of combinations of about 100 different substances. These substances that form all matter are called elements. An **element** is a substance that cannot be broken down into other substances by heat, light, or electricity. *Figure 6-1* shows some important elements.

An element contains only one kind of atom. Copper is made of only copper atoms, and iron is made of only iron atoms. An **atom** is defined as the smallest particle of an element that has the properties of the element. Water, for example, is not an element. Water can be broken down into two elements—hydrogen and oxygen—by passing electricity through it.

Your body contains many of the elements. The most abundant elements in your body are oxygen, hydrogen, carbon, and nitrogen. In addition, calcium and phosphorus are important parts of your teeth and bones. Zinc keeps your taste buds working properly. Copper helps your nerves function. Iron is essential in the blood cells that carry oxygen from your lungs to the muscles and organs of your body. Still other elements are needed for the proper functioning of your body.

Figure 6-1a Titanium **b** Calcium
c Copper **d** Zinc
e Chromium **f** Mercury

Discovering the Elements

We know of 109 elements. Ninety of them are found in easily identifiable quantities in nature. Two exist in nature for only short periods of time. Seventeen others do not occur naturally but can be made by scientists in laboratories. These artificially made elements exist only for short periods of time.

The discovery of all the elements took thousands of years. In ancient times, people worked with nine elements, even though they did not know they were elements. Gold and silver were used in jewelry. Mercury was used as a medicine. Copper and tin were used for cooking utensils and were combined to make bronze for weapons. As time went by, people learned to use iron for making tools and weapons. They also discovered carbon, lead, and sulfur.

By the time of the American Revolution, about twenty elements were known. By the end of the Civil War, more than sixty elements had been discovered. The world was excited in 1898 when Marie Curie and her husband Pierre found two elements, which they named radium and polonium. The discovery of these elements, which are radioactive, and the study of their properties led eventually to the technology used in making nuclear weapons and nuclear reactors. By 1900, 85 elements had been found. Today most scientists agree that all naturally occurring elements have been found.

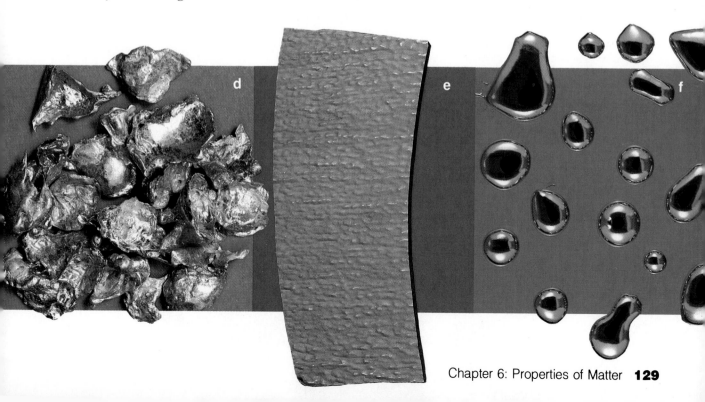

Chemical Symbols

When you want to save time, you may write your initials instead of your full name. When you address a letter, you may use a standard two-letter code instead of writing out the full name of a state. In a similar way, scientists have assigned a chemical symbol for each element.

A **chemical symbol** is a shorthand form of the element's name. It always begins with a capital letter. As the chart shows, the chemical symbols for some elements are the first letters of their names. Thus, hydrogen's symbol is H, carbon's is C, and nitrogen's is N. Symbols for other elements use the first two letters of their names. Helium's symbol is He, cobalt's is Co, and nickel's is Ni. Other elements have two-letter symbols that clearly come from their names but are not the first two letters. The words chlorine and chromium both begin with *ch*. To make it easy to identify each element by its symbol, chlorine's symbol is Cl and chromium's is Cr.

The symbols for some other elements seem confusing. Why is gold's symbol Au and lead's Pb? The symbols for these and some other elements are based on their Latin names. In Latin, gold is *aurum* and lead is *plumbum*. Plumbers got their name from the fact that the first water pipes were made of lead.

Describing Elements

Scientists group elements according to their properties. Most elements are **metals**, or metallic elements. Tin, lead, iron, and aluminum are examples of metallic elements.

Figure 6-2 Names and symbols of some elements

Hydrogen	H
Carbon	C
Nitrogen	N
Helium	He
Cobalt	Co
Nickel	Ni
Chlorine	Cl
Chromium	Cr
Gold	Au
Mercury	Hg
Lead	Pb

Figure 6-3 Chromium was used in the trim on older cars because this element resists corrosion.

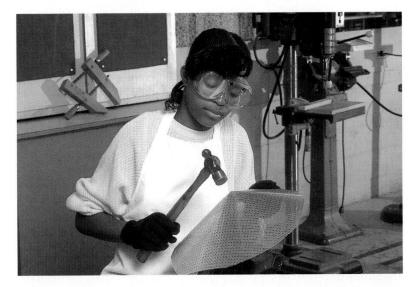

Figure 6-4 A metal worker can hammer a piece of copper into the desired shape.

Metals have a **luster**, which means they are shiny. The ancient Romans polished sheets of silver to a high luster and used them as mirrors. Chromium, which has a high luster, has been used on car bumpers, door handles, and trim, as the picture shows.

Metals conduct heat well. Some cooking utensils are made of copper, iron, or aluminum. A pot made of one of these elements heats quickly and distributes heat evenly. Handles on most metal pots are not made of metal. A metal handle would conduct heat from the pot to your hand.

Metals also conduct electricity. Gold is used in some batteries because it is one of the best conductors. Electricians use copper and aluminum in electrical wiring. Copper, aluminum, platinum, and some other metals are **ductile**, which means that they can be drawn into a wire. Most wiring in houses is made of copper. Covered copper wires are used for electric cords in electrical appliances. Most power lines are made of aluminum, which is less expensive than copper.

Some metals can be hammered, rolled, or shaped without being broken, as shown in the picture. These metals are **malleable**. Jewelers can pound copper, gold, and silver into jewelry because they are malleable elements. Aluminum foil folds easily around a sandwich because aluminum is malleable.

Most metals are solids at room temperature under ordinary pressure. Mercury is an exception. It is a liquid at room temperature.

Have You Heard?

Metals are found in nature in rocks called ores. Ores are found in different parts of the world. For example, platinum ores are found in only three or four locations in large enough quantities to be mined economically.

Sulfur, carbon, and helium are examples of another group of elements—the **nonmetals,** or non-metallic elements. These elements are called nonmetals because their properties are not like those of metals. Fewer than two dozen elements are nonmetals. At room temperature under ordinary pressure, most nonmetals are solids or gases. Sulfur and iodine, shown here, are crystalline solids. Iodine is a dark purple crystal. At room temperature, some iodine changes into purple vapor, as the picture shows. Another solid nonmetal, phosphorus, is a soft, white solid, but it also occurs as a red solid. Some of the gaseous nonmetals are nitrogen, oxygen, and fluorine. Bromine is the only liquid nonmetal.

Metals and nonmetals have opposite properties. Nonmetals have low luster. They conduct heat and electricity poorly, and they are not ductile or malleable.

Figure 6-5 The Iodine has sublimated, producing a purple vapor.

Figure 6-6a Sulfur

b A sulfur mine

A few elements have properties in between those of metals and nonmetals. They conduct electricity less efficiently than metals but more efficiently than nonmetals. They are called **metalloids**. Two of these elements, silicon and germanium, are used in electronics. Computers contain tiny pieces of silicon in their electric circuits. The photograph shows crystals of silicon.

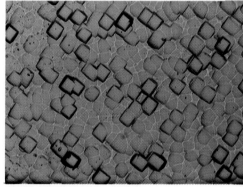
Figure 6-7 Silicon crystals

Section Review

1. Use the word "atom" to define the word "element."
2. Why were the Greeks wrong in thinking that water was an element?
3. Why are chemical symbols useful?
4. What are three differences between metallic and nonmetallic elements? How do metalloids differ from metals and nonmetals?

Challenge: Why do you think all the elements were not discovered at the same time?

Careers in Physical Science

Assayer

Suppose you are panning for gold and discover a large piece of yellow metal. How can you find out if it is gold? An assayer can tell you the value and composition of your find.

Assayers work in laboratories to analyze metal. They try to discover the type, weight, and purity of metal samples using careful tests and measurements. Often, the assayer looks at many samples from one place to predict the metal content of that area.

Assayers receive science degrees when they graduate from college. They study both chemical and physical properties of metals, and learn methods for doing experimental tests.

Applying Science

A gas with a distinctive odor is added to natural gas used for cooking and heating. Natural gas by itself has no odor, so it would not be noticed if it were escaping from a furnace or stove.

Figure 6-8 The diamond embedded in the rock was discovered in a mine in South Africa.

6-2 Physical Properties and Changes

Describing Physical Properties

When a new student comes to your school, you might describe your new classmate as tall, brown-eyed, dark-haired, and thin. In the same way, chewing gum can be described as sticky and stretchable. Like a person and chewing gum, each sample of matter can be described by listing its properties. No single property can be used to distinguish one substance from another. Several properties must be used. For convenience, we classify properties into two types—physical and chemical.

A **physical property** is a property that makes a substance identifiable. For example, at room temperature sulfur is a yellow solid and iodine is a purple, crystalline substance. The properties of metals (luster and the ability to conduct heat and electricity) are also physical properties. Each element has many characteristic physical properties. Chemists use a variety of these properties to identify a substance.

Distinctive tastes and odors are physical properties of some substances. Even if you were blindfolded, you would not be likely to mistake onions for oranges, for example. Similarly, some elements have a distinctive odor. The element bromine gets its name from the Greek word *bromos*, which means "stench," or "bad smell."

Hardness is another physical property. The harder the substance, the more difficult it is to scratch the surface of the substance. Geologists use hardness, among other properties, to identify rocks and minerals. Diamond is the hardest naturally occurring substance. A diamond, such as the one in *Figure 6-8*, will scratch any other surface.

If you heat a silver spoon to a high enough temperature, it will melt and change shape, but the silver remains silver. The temperature at which a substance melts or boils is called its melting point temperature or boiling point temperature. The melting point and boiling point of an element or other substance are physical properties. Each element has its own characteristic boiling point and melting point. Chlorine boils at $-34.6°$ C. The metal gallium, shown here, melts in your hand because its melting point is $29.5°$ C, and your body temperature is $37°$ C.

Color is another physical property. Chlorine is a yellowish-green gas at room temperature. It gets its name from the Greek word for light green. The photograph on page 127 shows chlorine, bromine, and iodine.

Crystalline solids have a special physical property—the crystal shape. Geologists identify many minerals, such as the quartz in the photograph, by their crystal shapes.

Magnetic properties are also physical properties. Iron is the most magnetic element. Nickel and cobalt are somewhat magnetic. *Figure 6-11* shows that magnetite, a mineral containing iron, is attracted to a magnet.

Figure 6-10 Geologists can identify the mineral quartz by the shape of its crystals.

Figure 6-11 Magnetite, a mineral containing iron, is attracted to a magnet.

Figure 6-9 Gallium is a metal that melts in a person's hand.

Figure 6-12 How Archimedes discovered the property of density

Density is an important physical property used to identify substances. A scientist named Archimedes is said to have discovered the concept of density (density = mass/volume). According to the story, King Hieron of Sicily gave a jeweler some gold to be formed into a crown. When the crown was delivered, it weighed as much as the gold the king had given the jeweler. Nevertheless, the king suspected that the jeweler had kept part of the gold for himself and had added some silver to the gold in the crown.

King Hieron asked Archimedes to find out whether or not the crown was pure gold. For weeks Archimedes puzzled over this problem. One day as he stepped into a tub at the public baths, he noticed that the more his body sank into the water, the more the water overflowed. Also, his body seemed to press down—or weigh less—when he was submerged in the water.

After some thought, Archimedes proposed that the volume of his body was equal to the volume of water displaced when he sank into the tub. Also, a submerged object, such as his body, lost as much weight as the weight of the water it displaced.

Archimedes applied what he had learned about the displacement of water to the problem of the king's crown. He knew that a mass of silver has a larger volume than an equal mass of gold. Therefore, the silver displaces more water than the gold. He found that the submerged crown displaced more water than an equal mass of gold. He concluded that the crown contained silver as well as gold. Archimedes had discovered that density—the ratio of mass to volume—can be used to distinguish between two metals.

You can expand the concept of buoyant force discussed on pages 110 and 111 to include density. An object floats if it is less dense than water, and it sinks if it is more dense than water. However, a heavy object floats if its volume is large enough to displace a volume of water of equal mass.

Identifying Physical Changes

Iron can be hammered into sheets, molded into a radiator, or bent into a chain. During each change, the iron remains iron. A **physical change** is any change that does not alter the chemical identity of a substance.

Sawing wood, shredding paper, and crushing a sugar cube produce physical changes. In each case, the composition of the substance remains unchanged.

In a physical change, the size, shape, or phase of the substance changes. For example, under most conditions, carbon dioxide is a gas. When it is cooled, however, carbon dioxide becomes the white solid, "dry ice." Although the white solid looks different from the colorless gas, both are carbon dioxide.

In some cases, a substance looks completely different after it changes phase. For example, at room temperature and at ordinary pressures, phosphorus is a white solid. If phosphorus is heated to 250° C in the absence of air, it turns red. The red substance is still the element phosphorus, but its color changes. The color changes because the atoms of the phosphorus move into a different crystal shape. But the crystals are still atoms of phosphorus. Thus, a physical change has taken place.

A physical change also occurs when a substance dissolves in water. When sugar dissolves in tea, the sugar is no longer a solid, but it is still sugar. If you boil away the water in the tea, the sugar remains.

Figure 6-13 The match tips contain phosphorus.

Section Review

1. List three physical properties of an element.
2. Describe three physical changes of elements.
Challenge: What is true of a substance both before and after a physical change?

Activity 6-1

Physical Properties

Purpose

To observe physical properties of substances

Materials

- aluminum foil
- copper wire
- sulfur crystals
- zinc strips
- small hammer
- nail
- balance
- 50-mL graduated cylinder
- water
- cover goggles

Procedures and Observations

1. Copy the table shown. Put on your safety goggles.
2. Examine each substance. Describe its color, state (or phase), and luster.
3. Record your observations in the table.
4. Scratch the surface of each substance with a nail. Record "yes" if the nail scratches it, or "no" if the nail does not scratch it.
5. Try to reshape each substance by bending, hammering, or folding it. Record your results.
6. Use the balance to find the mass of each of the samples of the elements. Record the masses.
7. Half-fill the graduated cylinder with water, and record the height of the water.
8. Drop the zinc into the water. Record the new height of the water.
9. Subtract the water levels you measured in steps 7 and 8. The difference is equal to the volume of the zinc.
10. Calculate and record zinc's density using: density = mass/volume. Write the units g/mL for each density value you find.
11. Repeat steps 7–10 for the other substances.
12. Classify the substances you tested, according to their properties, as metals or nonmetals.

Analysis and Conclusions

1. What kinds of substances were you able to reshape?
2. How are properties useful in classifying substances?
3. How have people used knowledge of the properties of elements to design nails, wire, and foil?

Data chart

Element	Shape	Color	State	Luster	Scratch	Malleability	Density
Aluminum							
Copper							
Sulfur							
Zinc							

6-3 Chemical Properties and Changes

After completing this section, you will be able to

A. Identify chemical properties.
B. Describe chemical changes.

Identifying Chemical Properties

Your friends look different from one another. They also differ from each other in the ways they interact with other people. In a similar way, matter has not only physical properties but it also has chemical properties. A **chemical property** describes how a substance reacts with other substances.

Chemical properties can be used to distinguish between two substances. Gold prospectors sometimes mistook iron pyrite for the element gold. Iron pyrite looks so much like gold that it is called "fool's gold." However, the chemical properties of gold and iron pyrite are different. When gold is put in nitric acid, the gold remains unchanged. When fool's gold is put in nitric acid, a chemical change occurs, and a smelly, poisonous gas, hydrogen sulfide, is produced. The iron pyrite changes chemically when it is put in nitric acid.

If you ignite a piece of wood in a fireplace, the wood burns. An iron fireplace tool does not burn when it is used to move the hot coals. When iron is heated to a high temperature, it becomes red-hot. At high enough temperatures, iron melts to form a liquid. On the other hand, at lower temperatures, iron reacts with the oxygen in damp air to form rust—a new substance.

Figure 6-14 Iron pyrite (FeS) and gold (Au) often look similar, but they have different chemical properties.

Explore!

Use an encyclopedia or chemistry book to find out how to prevent rust and tarnish.

Figure 6-15 The physical science student creates a chemical change when he combines vinegar and baking soda.

Producing Chemical Changes

Reacting with air and water are chemical properties. A nail turns rusty because iron in the nail reacts with oxygen and water. A silver dish tarnishes because silver reacts with oxygen in the air. The copper skin of the Statue of Liberty turned dull green because copper reacts with gases in the air.

Rust, tarnish, and the coating on copper are new materials with new properties. They result from **chemical changes**, which are changes that form new substances with new properties.

Many substances react with water or air. When an antacid tablet is dropped into water, it reacts with the water. The bubbling and fizzing indicate that a chemical change has occurred.

Reacting with acid also produces a chemical change. In *Figure 6-15*, a student is pouring vinegar on baking soda. The acid in the vinegar is reacting with the baking soda, and bubbles of carbon dioxide are forming.

After a chemical change, the original substances are no longer present. Burning wood is a chemical change in which wood reacts with oxygen in the air. The new substances formed by this change are ashes, carbon dioxide gas, and water vapor. Neither its powdery ashes nor its two gases resemble the original substances.

Section Review

1. What are two chemical properties?
2. How can you tell whether a chemical change has occurred?

Challenge: Describe a substance before and after a chemical change.

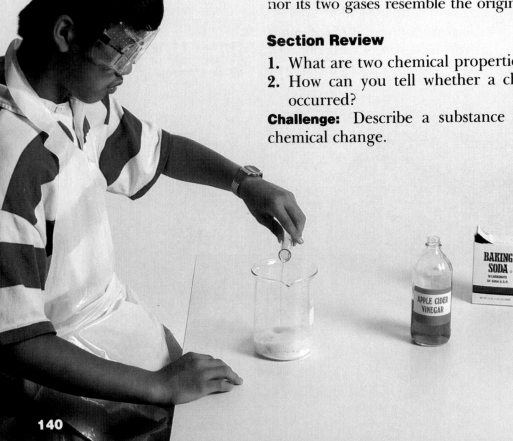

A Chemical Change

Purpose

To observe what happens during a chemical change

Materials

- several wooden splints
- ring stand with test tube clamp
- test tube
- 1-hole stopper, with glass tubing inserted, for test tube
- Bunsen burner
- matches
- cover goggles

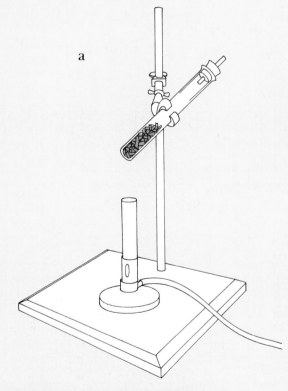

Procedures and Observations

1. Break the wooden splints into small pieces.
2. Fill the test tube about one-fourth full with wood.

3. Stopper the test tube, using a 1-hole stopper with glass tubing in it.
4. Clamp the test tube to the ring stand. The test tube should be slanted, as in **a**.
5. *CAUTION: Do not point the test tube toward your face, another person, or the aisle. Wear your cover goggles.* Heat the lower one-fourth of the test tube slowly for about 10 minutes, as in **b**.

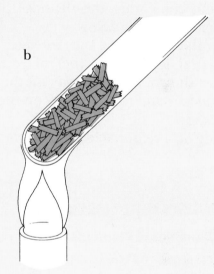

6. Observe and record any changes in the wood.
7. Note and record whether any material escapes from the test tube or appears on the sides of the test tube.
8. Turn off the burner and let everything cool before you put the equipment away.

Analysis and Conclusions

1. What evidence for a chemical change did you see?
2. What can you say about the substances before and after the chemical change took place?

Using a Bar Graph to Compare Densities

Bar graphs are useful for comparing measurements or properties, such as density. All graphs should contain a title, labels, and axes—lines that intersect at a right angle. The title and labels show the items that are being compared and the units used for the comparison. In a density bar graph, one axis shows the names of the substances and the other shows units of density. Follow the instructions to make a bar graph comparing the densities of the elements in the table below.

1. Draw the two axes so they intersect near the lower left-hand corner of your paper, as shown. Show density on the horizontal axis and the elements on the vertical scale.

2. Decide on a reasonable scale for the density values. Notice that the range of values for the thirteen elements is 2.0 to 19.3 g/cm^3.

3. List the elements along the vertical axis with equal spaces between the elements' names.

4. For each element, draw a horizontal line that ends even with the value for its density along the horizontal axis. Since most of the given values are not whole numbers, estimate where the horizontal line should stop.

5. Use the horizontal lines to draw bars for each of the elements. Make each bar the same thickness. Use pencils or markers to shade the bars.

6. Give your graph a title.

Densities of Elements

Element	Density (g/cm^3)
aluminum	2.7
copper	8.8
gold	19.3
iron	7.7
lead	11.3
mercury	13.5
nickel	8.9
silver	10.5
sulfur	2.0
tin	7.3
uranium	18.7
zinc	7.1

Summary

6-1 The Elements

A. An element is a substance that cannot be broken down into other substances by heat, light, or electricity. An element contains only one type of atom. An atom is the smallest particle of an element with the chemical properties of the element.

B. Ancient people knew of nine elements. By 1776, about twenty elements were known. By the end of the Civil War, sixty elements were known. Now more than one hundred elements have been discovered or artificially made.

C. A chemical symbol is a shorthand form of an element's name. Often the first letter of the name is the symbol. For other elements a combination of letters is used.

D. Elements are grouped into three categories based on their properties—metals, nonmetals, and metalloids. Metals have luster and are conductors of heat and electricity. Some metals are malleable and ductile. Nonmetals and metals have opposite properties. Metalloids have properties between metals and nonmetals.

6-2 Physical Properties and Changes

A. Physical properties of substances include density, color, hardness, odor, ability to conduct heat or electricity, the melting point temperature and the boiling point temperature.

B. A physical change can result in a change in size, color, or phase of a substance. A physical change does not result in the formation of a new substance.

6-3 Chemical Properties and Changes

A. The chemical properties of a substance describe the way it interacts with other substances.

B. A chemical change results in the formation of one or more new substances.

Vocabulary

For each of the following terms, write a sentence that uses the term correctly.

atom	**element**	**nonmetal**
chemical change	**luster**	**physical change**
chemical property	**malleable**	**physical property**
chemical symbol	**metal**	
ductile	**metalloid**	

Check Your Knowledge

PART I: Matching Match the definition in Column I with the correct term in Column II.

Column I
1. produces new substances
2. temperature at which a substance changes from a liquid to a gas
3. short form of an element's name
4. does not produce new substances
5. poor conductor of electricity and heat
6. element with magnetic properties
7. good conductor of heat and electricity
8. smallest particle of an element
9. cannot be broken down by heat, light, or electricity
10. brightness

Column II
a. atom
b. boiling point
c. chemical change
d. chemical symbol
e. element
f. iron
g. luster
h. melting point
i. metal
j. nonmetal
k. physical change

Part II: Multiple Choice Choose the letter of the best answer.
11. Rust forms on iron because of (a) physical change. (b) electricity. (c) density. (d) chemical change.
12. Electric wires are made of (a) metalloids. (b) nonmetals. (c) metals. (d) graphite.
13. How many elements did ancient people use? (a) 100 (b) 92 (c) 60 (d) 9
14. What group of elements includes important components of computers? (a) metalloids (b) gases (c) nonmetals (d) radioactive elements
15. Which property is common to non-metals? (a) high luster (b) easily made into wires (c) poor conductors of electricity (d) easily rolled into sheets
16. During a chemical change (a) a substance changes from a liquid to a gas. (b) a new substance forms. (c) a substance changes shape. (d) nothing happens.

17. Which is an example of a chemical change? (a) boiling water (b) melting iron (c) measuring density (d) iron rusting
18. Which group of elements is used to make many cooking utensils? (a) metalloids (b) nonmetals (c) metals (d) all of these elements

Part III: Completion Write the word or words that complete the sentence correctly.
19. A new substance is NOT formed during a _____ change.
20. A _____ change occurs when a substance changes phase.
21. Metals and nonmetals have _____ properties.
22. Hardness is an example of a _____ property.
23. The fizzing of baking soda when vinegar is poured on it is an example of a _____ change.

Check Your Understanding

1. Explain why rust is not an element.
2. What is the chemical symbol for oxygen?
3. Is the ductility of copper a physical or a chemical property?
4. Compare the change that produces sawdust with the change that produces wood ashes.
5. How could the copper sheets on the Statue of Liberty be kept from turning green?
6. Sugar that you eat and oxygen that you breathe combine to form carbon dioxide and water. What kind of change is this?
7. Why are metals rather than nonmetals used for making jewelry?
8. If you drop an object into nitric acid and bubbles began to form, what kind of change has occurred?

 Apply Your Knowledge

1. Name the property of copper which causes people to use it for: (a) wire (b) cooking utensils (c) jewelry.
2. Which of the following statements about the element sodium refer to physical properties? (a) It reacts violently with water. (b) It is a shiny metal. (c) It is so soft that a knife can cut it. (d) It tarnishes quickly in air.
3. A car gets hot when it stands in the sun. Is this a physical change or a chemical change?
4. Name each of the following events as a physical or chemical change: apple spoiling; ice melting; gasoline burning in a car's engine; egg cooking; bread being toasted.
5. Name five elements in the human body and state their importance.
6. Why would a cooking utensil made of graphite NOT be a useful item?
7. List six physical properties of substances.

 Extend Your Knowledge

Research/Projects

1. Gold is a very soft metal. Talk with a local jeweler to find out what is added to gold to make it stronger.
2. Refer to an encyclopedia to find the names of the elements each of the following scientists discovered: Sir Humphrey Davy, Clemens Alexander Winkler, William Ramsey, Carl Wilhelm Scheele.

Readings

Gardner, Robert. *Kitchen Chemistry: Science Experiments to Do at Home*. Julian Messner, 1982. Describes experiments that can be done with readily available materials.

Ley, Willy. *The Discovery of the Elements*. Delacorte Press, 1968. Describes the circumstances surrounding the discovery of the elements.

CHAPTER 7
The Atom

The ancient Greeks speculated about the ultimate structure of matter. Some thought that all matter was made up of small particles called atoms. Now, more than 2000 years later, scientists study atoms, using devices like the one shown. In this device, laser light is used to create an "optical molasses" to slow down individual atoms for further study.

Organizing Your Study Skills The outline below will help you see how the chapter is organized and what you should learn as you read.

I. Section 7-1: Theories About the Atom
  A. What were some early ideas about the atom?
  B. How did scientists learn that an atom is mostly empty space?
  C. What happens to an atom when it gains or loses energy?
  D. What are the basic ideas of present atomic theory?

II. Section 7-2: How Atoms Differ
  A. How are atoms of the same element alike?
  B. How are atoms of the same element different?
  C. What does its mass number reveal about an element?

III. Section 7-3: Classifying Elements
  A. On what basis were elements arranged in the first periodic table?
  B. On what basis are elements arranged in modern periodic tables?
  C. What are the names of the groups and periods in the periodic table?
  D. What are some of the characteristics of the groups in the periodic table?
  E. What is special about the two rows of elements below the main part of the periodic table?

After completing this section, you will be able to

A. Describe some early ideas about the atom.
B. Explain how scientists learned that an atom is mostly empty space.
C. Describe what happens to an atom when it gains or loses energy.
D. State the basic ideas of present atomic theory.

Figure 7-1 Some of Dalton's chemical symbols for elements

7-1   Theories About the Atom

Early Ideas About the Atom

The term *atom* comes from the ancient Greek word meaning "that which cannot be further cut." More than two thousand years ago, the Greek thinker Democritus suggested that matter was made of tiny particles. He called the tiny particles atoms because he thought they could not be broken up into smaller particles.

In 1808, the English schoolteacher John Dalton offered the first modern theory about the atom. He described atoms as solid particles that cannot be divided. Dalton believed that each element has its own kind of atoms. The drawing shows the chemical symbols Dalton used for some elements.

In the 1890s, the English scientist J. J. Thomson discovered that atoms contain tiny particles with negative electric charges. These particles are called **electrons**. Thomson knew that ordinary matter has no charge—it is neutral. Consequently, he reasoned that positive charges must also exist in atoms to balance the negative electrons. Thomson, however, was unable to detect positive charges. Thus, he thought that atoms consisted of electrons scattered through a thin, positive material. Thomson compared his idea about atoms to English plum pudding, which has small "plums" (electrons) spread throughout it.

Many questions remained. Where are the positive charges in an atom? Are positive charges evenly spread throughout the atom as Thomson thought? Or, are there small, positively charged objects in atoms?

Atoms Are Mostly Empty Space

In the early 1900s, in England, Ernest Rutherford tested the Thomson model of the atom. He shot high-speed, positively charged particles at a thin sheet of gold foil. Since Thomson's atom was uniformly positive, except for the light, singly charged electrons, Rutherford expected the positive particles to sail through the foil with little deflection. Just in case Thomson was wrong, Rutherford placed detecting screens around the gold foil to see if some positive particles would bounce back. *Figure 7-2* shows Rutherford's arrangement of the foil and screens.

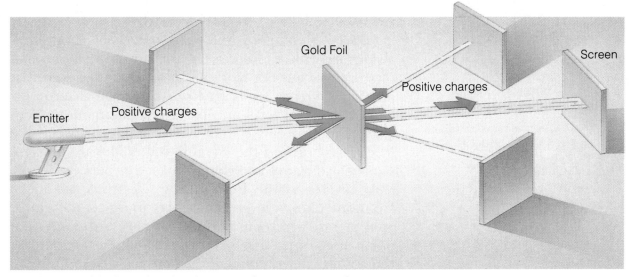

Figure 7-2 Rutherford's gold foil experiment

The result of Rutherford's experiment amazed everyone. Even though most of the positive "bullets" passed through the foil, a few *did* bounce back. Rutherford used these results to form a new atomic model. Because most charges passed through foil, he reasoned that the atom must be mainly empty space. Because like charges repel (push away) each other, he reasoned that whatever caused the positive bullets to bounce back also must have a positive charge. Thus, Rutherford theorized that each atom contains a small, positively charged object, which he called the **nucleus.** Compared to electrons, the nucleus has a large mass.

Because unlike charges attract, Rutherford expected the positive nucleus to attract the negative electrons. Rutherford compared his model of the atom with the solar system. Electrons whirled around the nucleus, just as planets orbit the sun.

Rutherford's model raised the question of why the negative electrons in an atom are not pulled directly into the positive nucleus. In 1913, Niels Bohr suggested that perhaps electrons do not fall into the nucleus because they can move around the nucleus only in certain fixed paths. According to Bohr, each path is a certain distance from the nucleus. Electrons in those paths, which are called **energy levels,** have only certain amounts of energy.

Bohr's model of a hydrogen atom is shown in *Figure 7-3*. The hydrogen atom has one electron that moves around the nucleus. In Bohr's model, this electron can be on any of the paths, but never between them. In the picture, it is on the innermost path, where the electron has the least amount of energy in the atom.

Proton

Positively charged

Electron

Negatively charged

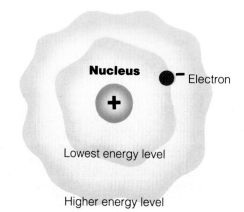

Figure 7-3 The Bohr model of a hydrogen atom

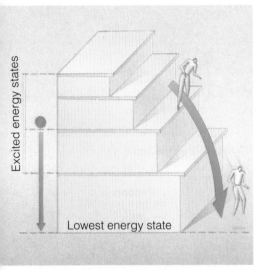

Excited energy states

Lowest energy state

Figure 7-4 Compare the energy levels to uneven risers on a staircase. The person has jumped down two energy levels.

Figure 7-5 From top to bottom, the continuous spectrum, and the spectra for hydrogen, helium, and calcium

Electrons Have Certain Energies

Figure 7-4 compares the energy levels of an atom to a staircase with uneven risers. You can stop on one step or the next, but not between steps. Bohr believed that an atom's energy levels are like steps. Each electron occupies a certain level and has a certain amount of energy. The electrons cannot have energies between the levels. And, just as the risers in the model are uneven, so are the distance and change in energy between levels.

According to the Bohr model, electrons can move from one energy level to another. To do so, they must gain or lose a certain amount of energy. Shining light on an atom or passing electricity through it can increase the atom's energy. If an atom gains exactly enough energy to move one of its electrons to a higher level, the electron jumps to that higher level. An atom that has one or more electrons in higher energy levels is said to be in an **excited state.** To return the atom to its usual state of lower energy, the high-energy electrons must release exactly enough energy to move to lower energy levels. The released energy may produce visible light.

An atom of each element has a particular set of energy levels. For example, energy levels for hydrogen are different from energy levels for carbon. An element can be recognized by the energy its excited atoms release. The energy pattern, called a **spectrum,** is the "fingerprint" of an element. No two elements have the same spectrum. The spectra for hydrogen, helium, and calcium, in that order, are shown in *Figure 7-5.* A continuous rainbow of color is shown, too, so that you can see more clearly the colors of the spectra of the different elements. Each element's spectrum has many lines because each element has many different energy levels. Scientists accepted Bohr's model for the atom because it predicted why the spectrum of hydrogen looks the way it does.

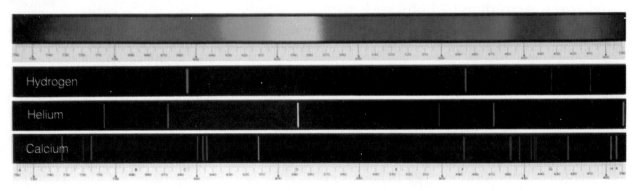

Hydrogen

Helium

Calcium

The Atom Today

At first, scientists did not know what an atom's nucleus contains. They knew only that a nucleus has a positive charge. By 1920, they found that the nucleus contains particles with positive charges exactly as strong as the negative charge on an electron. These positively charged particles, called **protons**, are shown in *Figure 7-6*. Although a proton's charge is the same strength as an electron's, a proton has 1836 times more mass.

In 1932, James Chadwick discovered another particle in the nucleus, a neutron. The particles are called **neutrons** because they have no charge—they are neutral. A neutron has about the same mass as a proton.

By 1926, Erwin Schroedinger, Werner Heisenberg, and others had looked at evidence about atoms in a new way, using mathematical models. They learned that at any one instant the location of an electron is unknown, but the probability that an electron is at any one place can be known. The diagram of the present atomic model reflects the evidence of this knowledge.

An electron cloud model for the hydrogen atom is shown in *Figure 7-7*. Each dot represents a possible location of the electron. The cloudlike regions—where the dots are closest together—show where the electron is most likely to be.

In the lowest energy state of the hydrogen atom, the electron is in the lowest energy level. The electron is most likely to be near the nucleus, as the dot pattern indicates. The model also shows higher energy levels, which are farther from the nucleus.

The current model is able to predict the energy states for more complicated atoms, as well as for hydrogen. It predicts how the electrons are distributed among energy levels in an atom. The first energy level can hold no more than 2 electrons, the second no more than 8, the third no more than 18, and so on.

Section Review

1. What was Thomson's model of the atom?
2. What was Bohr's model of the atom?
3. How does an atom produce a spectrum?
4. What is the present model of the atom?

Challenge: If an atom has 6 protons, how many electrons does it have? Why?

Proton

Neutron

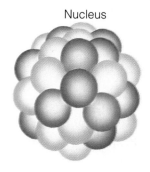

Nucleus

Figure 7-6 The nucleus contains protons and neutrons. A proton has a positive charge. A neutron has no charge.

Figure 7-7 The dark, cloudy region that surrounds the nucleus indicates where electrons in the lowest energy level are most likely to be found. Each higher energy level is farther from the nucleus.

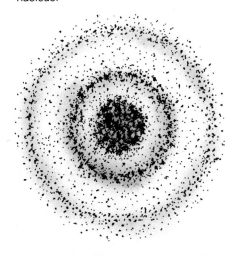

Activity 7-1

Inside an Atom

Purpose

To simulate scientific models

Materials

- marble or ball bearing
- enough small bits of cardboard, each 2 mm square, to total the same volume as the marble or the ball bearing
- narrow stick or knitting needle
- clay

Procedure and Observations

PART A

1. Mix the small bits of cardboard throughout a sphere of clay, about 5 cm in diameter.
2. Try to push the narrow stick through the clay.
3. Push the narrow stick through the clay 10 times in different directions, and note how many times it hits a piece of cardboard. Note also how hard the cardboard resists being pushed.

PART B

1. Put the marble in the center of the lump of clay.
2. Shape the clay into a sphere that has a diameter of about 5 cm. Be sure that the marble is still in the center.
3. *CAUTION: Do not hit your partner's hand with the stick in this step.* Push the stick through the clay as shown. The stick does not have to pass through the center of the sphere.
4. Record what happens to the stick as it passes through the clay.
5. Repeat steps 3 and 4 nine times. Each time, push the stick through a different part of the sphere.
6. Note how hard the sphere resists being pushed when you hit it.

Analysis and Conclusions

1. Did the cardboard bits resist being pushed more or less than the marble?
2. What do the marble, the clay, and the cardboard bits represent?

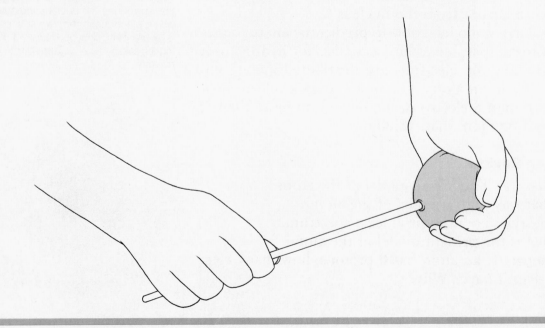

7-2 How Atoms Differ

Atomic Number

During the early 1900s, scientists determined the number of electric charges on the nuclei of many types of atoms. They found that all the atoms of a given element have the same number of positive charges on their nuclei, or the same **atomic number.** The atomic number was found to correspond to the number of protons in the nucleus. Thus an iron atom, which has an atomic number of 26, has 26 protons in its nucleus. Similarly, a cobalt atom has an atomic number of 27 and 27 protons in its nucleus.

The number of electrons in an atom is the same as the number of protons. An oxygen atom, shown in *Figure 7-8*, has 8 protons in its nucleus. The nucleus is surrounded by 8 electrons in the atom's electron cloud. Because the number of positive charges just balances the number of negative charges, the atom as a whole is neutral. Similarly, the sulfur atom, which has 16 protons in its nucleus, has 16 electrons in its electron cloud.

Isotopes of an Element

You and your classmates may have much in common, but there are also important differences among you. For example, each of you is a member of the class, yet your birthdays, physical characteristics, and personalities differ. Similarly, even though atoms of an element act alike, they can have different traits.

Earlier in this lesson you learned that all atoms of an element have the same number of protons. However, the number of neutrons in the atoms and thus the masses of the atoms may be different.

Objectives

After completing this section, you will be able to

A. Describe how atoms of the same element are alike.

B. Describe how atoms of the same element may differ.

C. Explain what the mass number tells about an element.

Have You Heard?

Antimatter is made of particles that are the opposite of regular atomic particles. The opposite particles are called antiparticles. For example, the electron's antiparticle—the positron—has the same mass as an electron but a positive electric charge. When an electron and a positron collide, they destroy each other completely. All of their mass is changed into energy. Both matter and antimatter are types of matter.

Figure 7-8 All oxygen atoms (O) have 8 protons per nucleus. All sulfur atoms (S) have 16 protons per nucleus.

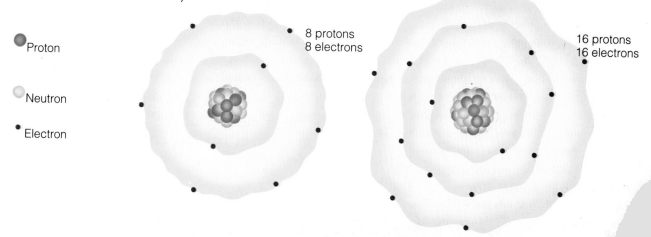

Proton

Neutron

Electron

8 protons
8 electrons

16 protons
16 electrons

Hydrogen

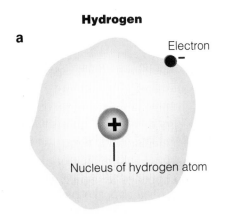

a

Deuterium

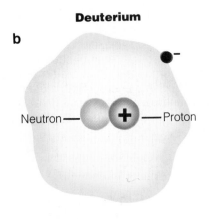

b

Tritium

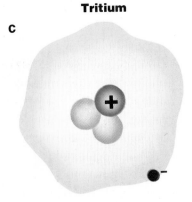

c

Figure 7-9 a Hydrogen atom **b** Deuterium atom **c** Tritium atom

Atoms of an element that contain different numbers of neutrons are called **isotopes** of the element. The mass of each isotope of an element is slightly different.

For example, study the models of the three isotopes of hydrogen shown in *Figure 7-9*. Notice that each nucleus has only one proton. But each nucleus has a different number of neutrons. Although the masses of the three isotopes are not the same, their chemical properties vary only slightly.

However, the most common isotope of hydrogen, shown in *a*, has no neutrons. **Deuterium** is a form of hydrogen with one proton and one neutron. **Tritium** is another isotope of hydrogen. It has one proton and two neutrons. Tritium does not occur naturally on the earth, but is made artificially.

Scientists use the differences in mass to separate isotopes of an element. For instance, three methods are used to change the natural mixture of the two major isotopes of uranium. The fraction of the less massive isotope must be increased for use in nuclear power plants. In one method, the mixture of naturally occurring isotopes is placed in a device called a centrifuge, which spins at high speed in a circle. The more massive isotope settles near the outer portion of the device faster than the less massive one, resulting in a separation of the isotopes. In another method, gas containing uranium is sent through small holes. The more massive isotope goes through at a different rate from the less massive isotope. Thus, the isotopes are separated.

A newer method of separating isotopes is based on the fact that the different isotopes have slightly different energy levels. This method uses a laser to excite the atoms of only one uranium isotope in a mixture. Then, another laser knocks the electrons in the excited isotopes out of the atoms. This process produces positively charged atoms that can be separated from the other atoms.

Mass Number

The total number of protons and neutrons in an atom is called the **mass number** of the atom. Because each isotope of an element has a specific number of neutrons, the element's isotopes have different mass numbers.

All isotopes of hydrogen, for example, have an atomic number equal to 1. The mass number of the most common form of hydrogen is also 1, because it has 1 proton and no neutrons. Deuterium, with 1 proton and 1 neutron, has a mass number of 2. Tritium, with 2 neutrons and 1 proton, has a mass number of 3.

You can figure out the number of neutrons that an atom has by subtracting its atomic number from its mass number. Tritium's mass number is 3 and its atomic number is 1. Because $3 - 1 = 2$, tritium has 2 neutrons.

Figure 7-10 shows the naturally occurring isotopes of carbon. The atomic number of all three isotopes is 6. But the mass numbers of the isotopes differ. The most common carbon atom has a mass number of 12 because it has 6 protons and 6 neutrons. Some carbon atoms are a little more massive. One isotope of carbon has 6 protons and 7 neutrons, so its mass number is 13. A still more massive isotope has 6 protons and 8 neutrons, which gives it a mass number of 14.

The weighted average of the masses of all an element's isotopes is called the **atomic mass** of the element. The weighted average of masses is based on the percentage of each isotope in nature. For example, the atomic mass of carbon is 12.01115. This value is close to the mass number of the most common isotope because that isotope occurs in nature much more than the others. Every few years, an international committee meets to review and update the atomic masses of the elements, based on the latest measurements.

Scientists identify an isotope of an element in writing by giving its symbol, its atomic number, and its mass number. The atomic number appears at the lower left of the symbol. The mass number appears at the upper left. For example, hydrogen is ^1_1H, deuterium is ^2_1H, and tritium is ^3_1H. The three carbon isotopes are $^{12}_6\text{C}$, $^{13}_6\text{C}$, and $^{14}_6\text{C}$. Scientists also identify an isotope by its name and its mass number—carbon-13, hydrogen-1, and so on.

Carbon-12

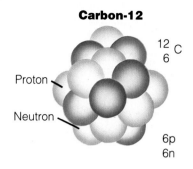

$^{12}_6\text{C}$

Proton

Neutron

6p
6n

Carbon-13

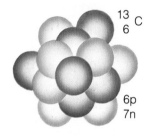

$^{13}_6\text{C}$

6p
7n

Carbon-14

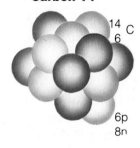

$^{14}_6\text{C}$

6p
8n

Figure 7-10 Three carbon isotopes

Section Review

1. What does an element's atomic number represent?
2. How do isotopes of the same element differ?
3. What data is given by a mass number?

Challenge: Do all isotopes of the same element have identical chemical and physical properties? Explain in terms of separating isotopes.

For Practice

1. How many protons, electrons, and neutrons are there in one atom of $^{235}_{92}\text{U}$?
2. How many protons, electrons, and neutrons are there in one atom of $^{238}_{92}\text{U}$?

Activity 7-2

Isotopes

Purpose

To study the isotopes of common atoms

Materials

- blue clay
- red clay
- yellow clay
- notebook paper
- pen or pencil
- pipe cleaners
- scissors

Element	Symbol	Protons	Neutrons	Electrons
Hydrogen	$_1^1$H			
	$_2^1$H			
	$_3^1$H			
Carbon	$_6^{13}$C			
	$_6^{14}$C			
	$_8^{12}$C			

Procedure and Observations

1. Copy the table into your notebook. Complete the table as you go through steps 1-8.
2. For each isotope, make enough blue clay balls to equal the number of protons and enough red clay balls to equal the number of neutrons. Each clay ball should be about 1 cm in diameter.
3. For each isotope listed, pick up the blue and red clay balls. Between your hands, put them together lightly into a nucleus, as in **a.**

a

4. Label the paper with the symbols for each of the isotopes. Place all the hydrogen isotopes together and all the carbon isotopes together. Display your models of isotopes above their symbols.
5. For each of the isotope models, make enough yellow clay balls to represent the electrons. Each yellow clay ball should be about 3 mm across.
6. For each isotope, decide how many electrons are in each energy level. (The first energy level of an atom can contain a maximum of 2 electrons. The second energy level, a maximum of 8.)
7. Cut the pipe cleaners into lengths of 1 cm to represent the first energy level and lengths of 2 cm to represent the second energy level.
8. Add the proper number of electrons to each of the isotope models by placing the electrons on one end of a piece of a pipe cleaner and placing the other end of the pipe cleaner in the clay nucleus, as in **b.**

b

Analysis and Conclusions

1. How are the nuclei of the isotopes of each element similar to each other?
2. Are the arrangements of electrons for the isotopes of each element similar or different? Explain.

7-3 Classifying Elements

The History of the Periodic Table

During the 1860s and 1870s, about 60 elements were known. John Newlands, an English chemist, found that a pattern appeared if the elements were listed by increasing atomic mass. He noticed that properties of the first element are like those of the eighth; those of the second element are like those of the ninth; and so on. He had discovered that the same properties appear for every eighth element in the list.

A few years later the Russian chemist Dmitri Mendeleev listed the elements according to their atomic masses, as in *Figure 7-11*. Mendeleev left spaces between some elements to make the known elements fall into groups with similar properties. He noticed that similar chemical properties appeared at regular intervals—or periodically. Mendeleev's table was called the **periodic table of the elements.**

Mendeleev believed that the spaces in his table indicated elements yet unknown. Mendeleev predicted that when scientists discovered the unknown elements, they would have properties similar to the other elements in their columns.

Within 15 years after Mendeleev made his predictions, three such elements were found. A French scientist found the first unknown element, which he named gallium after the Latin word for France. Gallium's properties matched perfectly with those of the element Mendeleev had predicted. The photograph on page 134 shows a picture of gallium.

Mendeleev also predicted that two more elements would be discovered. He predicted that one would have an atomic mass between the atomic masses of calcium and titanium, and one would have properties similar to silicon. A Swedish scientist discovered the first element, which he named scandium because Sweden is a Scandinavian country. A German scientist found the element with properties similar to those of silicon, which he named germanium in honor of his country.

The discoveries of gallium, scandium, and germanium seemed to confirm the theory on which the periodic table was based.

Objectives

After completing this section, you will be able to

A. Describe how elements were arranged in the first periodic table.

B. Describe how elements are arranged in modern periodic tables.

C. Name the groups and periods in the periodic table.

D. Name some characteristics of groups in the periodic table.

E. Explain what is special about the two rows of elements below the main part of the periodic table.

TABLE II.
The Atomic Weights of the Elements
Distribution of the Elements in Periods

Groups	Higher Salt-forming Oxides	Typical or 1st Small Period	Large Periods				
			1st	2nd	3rd	4th	5th
I.	R_2O	Li = 7	K 39	Rb 85	Cs 133	–	–
II.	RO	Be =9	Ca 40	S 87	Ba 137	–	–
III.	R_2O_3	B =11	Sc 44	Y 89	La 138	Yb 173	–
IV.	RO_2	C =12	Ti 48	Zr 90	Ce 140	–	Tb 232
V.	R_2O_5	N =14	V 15	Nb 94	–	Ta 182	–
VI.	RO_3	O =16	Cr 52	Mo 96	–	W 184	Ur 240
VII.	R_2O_7	F =19	Mn55	–	–	–	–
VIII.	{		Fe 56	Ru 103	–	Os 191	–
			Co 585	Rh 104	–	Jr 193	–
			Ni 59	Pd 106	–	Pt 196	–
I.	R_2O	H=1.Na=23	Cu 63	Ag 108	–	Au 198	–
II.	RO	Mg= 24	Zn 65	Cd 112	–	Hg 200	–
III.	R_2O_3	Al =27	Ga 70	Jn 113	–	Tl 204	–
IV.	RO_2	Si =28	Ge 72	Sn 118	–	Pb 206	–
V.	R_2O_5	P =31	As 75	Sb 120	–	Bi 208	–
VI.	RO_3	S =32	Se 79	Te 125	–	–	–
VII.	R_2O_7	Cl =355	Br 80	J 127	–	–	–
		2nd Small Period	1st	2nd	3rd	4th	5th
			Large Periods				

Figure 7-11 Mendeleev's periodic table

The Periodic Table Is Based on Atomic Numbers

When Mendeleev drew his periodic table, scientists had not yet discovered electrons and protons. But scientists had measured the atomic masses of many elements. It seemed reasonable to them that the elements' chemical behavior should be related to atomic mass. Arranging the known elements in order of atomic mass led to some problems, however. For example, based on its atomic mass, argon should be in the same group as lithium and sodium. However, lithium and sodium are chemically active solids, and argon is a gas that does not react easily with other elements.

The problem of arranging elements was solved in 1913 by physicist Henry Moseley. He found that an element's properties are more closely related to its atomic number than to its atomic mass. Since Moseley's discovery, the periodic table has been based on the atomic numbers of elements. Mendeleev's periodic table worked so well because, for the most part, atomic masses increase in the same order as atomic numbers.

The present periodic table appears on pages 160–161. The table contains the 109 elements presently known. About 90 of these elements occur naturally on the earth. The other elements are made artificially in the laboratory. Some elements exist for only a fraction of a second.

Each box in the periodic table contains an element's chemical symbol and name as shown in *Figure 7-12*. The atomic number appears above the symbol. Atomic mass appears below the name. When all the isotopes of an element are short-lived, the atomic mass of one of them is given in parentheses. The small numbers to the right of the atomic number indicate the number of electrons in each energy level. The top number tells how many electrons are in the energy level closest to the nucleus.

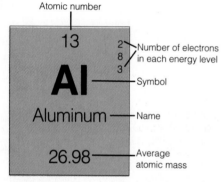

Figure 7-12 Information given in each box of the periodic table

Figure 7-13 How the periodic table would look if it were expanded to include the two rows below the main table.

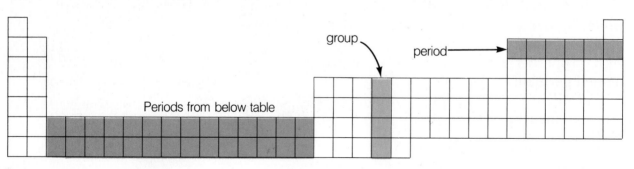

Aluminum, for example, has atomic number 13 and atomic mass 26.98. Its 13 electrons are arranged with 2 electrons in the energy level closest to the nucleus, 8 in the next level, and 3 in the outermost level.

The two rows of elements below the main table are usually shown there to save space. *Figure 7-13* shows where these rows fit into the table.

Using the Periodic Table

An element's position in the periodic table tells much about the element. Each of the table's horizontal rows is called a **period.** Along a period, a gradual change in chemical properties occurs from one element to another. For example, metallic properties decrease and nonmetallic properties increase as you go from left to right across a period. Changes in the properties occur because the number of protons increases from left to right across the row. The number of electrons also increases by one. This increase is important because the outer electrons determine the element's chemical properties.

The table consists of seven periods. The periods vary in length. The first period is very short and contains only 2 elements, hydrogen and helium. The next two periods contain 8 elements each. Periods 4 and 5 each have 18 elements. The sixth period has 32 elements. The last period is not complete because new elements are still being made in laboratories.

Each vertical column is called a **group.** The table contains 18 groups. Elements in a group have similar properties because they have the same number of outer electrons. Elements in a group are like members of a family—each is different, but all are related by common characteristics.

Notice that each group is headed by a number. For many years, groups were referred to by Roman numerals and the letters *a* and *b*. However, scientists in the United States and Europe used different letters to refer to the same groups. To avoid confusion, groups are now designated by a number from 1 to 18. The Roman numerals and the letters are eliminated.

The middle section of the periodic table contains the transition elements. Transition elements are metals. Chemical changes of the transition elements produce colorful new substances, as *Figure 7-14* shows.

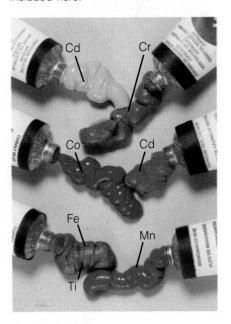

Figure 7-14 The transition metals produce bright-colored substances, such as paints. The transition metals in period 5 end with silver (Ag). The next element to the right of silver, cadmium (Cd), is not a transition metal. Because cadmium has many chemical properties similar to those of the transition elements, paint containing cadmium is included here.

Periodic Table of the Elements
(Based on Carbon-12 = 12.00)

1

1
1 1
H
Hydrogen
1.008

2

2
3 2 1
Li
Lithium
6.941

4 2 2
Be
Beryllium
9.012

11 2 8 1
Na
Sodium
22.99

12 2 8 2
Mg
Magnesium
24.31

3	**4**	**5**	**6**	**7**	**8**	**9**
19 2 8 8 1 **K** Potassium 39.10	**20** 2 8 8 2 **Ca** Calcium 40.08	**21** 2 8 9 2 **Sc** Scandium 44.96	**22** 2 8 10 2 **Ti** Titanium 47.88	**23** 2 8 11 2 **V** Vanadium 50.94	**24** 2 8 13 1 **Cr** Chromium 52.00	**25** 2 8 13 2 **Mn** Manganese 54.94
37 2 8 18 8 1 **Rb** Rubidium 85.47	**38** 2 8 18 8 2 **Sr** Strontium 87.62	**39** 2 8 18 9 2 **Y** Yttrium 88.91	**40** 2 8 18 10 2 **Zr** Zirconium 91.22	**41** 2 8 18 12 1 **Nb** Niobium 92.91	**42** 2 8 18 13 1 **Mo** Molybdenum 95.94	**43** 2 8 18 13 2 **Tc** Technetium 98.91
55 2 8 18 18 8 1 **Cs** Cesium 132.9	**56** 2 8 18 18 8 2 **Ba** Barium 137.3	**71** 2 8 18 32 9 2 **Lu** Lutetium 175.0	**72** 2 8 18 32 10 2 **Hf** Hafnium 178.5	**73** 2 8 18 32 11 2 **Ta** Tantalum 180.9	**74** 2 8 18 32 12 2 **W** Tungsten 183.9	**75** 2 8 18 32 13 2 **Re** Rhenium 186.2
87 2 8 18 32 18 8 1 **Fr** Francium 223.0	**88** 2 8 18 32 18 8 2 **Ra** Radium 226.0	**103** 2 8 18 32 32 9 2 **Lr** Lawrencium (260)	**104** 2 8 18 32 32 10 2 **Unq** Unnilquadium (261)	**105** 2 8 18 32 32 11 2 **Unp** Unnilpentium (262)	**106** 2 8 18 32 32 12 2 **Unh** Unnilhexium (263)	**107** 2 8 18 32 32 13 2 **Uns** Unnilseptium (262)

8	**9**
26 2 8 14 2 **Fe** Iron 55.85	**27** 2 8 15 2 **Co** Cobalt 58.93
44 2 8 18 15 1 **Ru** Ruthenium 101.1	**45** 2 8 18 16 1 **Rh** Rhodium 102.9
76 2 8 18 32 14 2 **Os** Osmium 190.2	**77** 2 8 18 32 15 2 **Ir** Iridium 192.2
108 2 8 18 32 32 14 2 **Uno** Unniloctium (265)	**109** 2 8 18 32 32 15 2 **Une** Unnilennium (266)

57 2 8 18 18 9 2 **La** Lanthanum 138.9	**58** 2 8 18 19 9 2 **Ce** Cerium 140.1	**59** 2 8 18 21 8 2 **Pr** Praseodymium 140.9	**60** 2 8 18 22 8 2 **Nd** Neodymium 144.2	**61** 2 8 18 23 8 2 **Pm** Promethium 144.9	**62** 2 8 18 24 8 2 **Sm** Samarium 150.4	**63** 2 8 18 25 8 2 **Eu** Europium 152.0
89 2 8 18 32 18 9 2 **Ac** Actinium 227.0	**90** 2 8 18 32 18 10 2 **Th** Thorium 232.0	**91** 2 8 18 32 20 9 2 **Pa** Protactinium 231.0	**92** 2 8 18 32 21 9 2 **U** Uranium 238.0	**93** 2 8 18 32 22 9 2 **Np** Neptunium 237.0	**94** 2 8 18 32 24 8 2 **Pu** Plutonium 239.1	**95** 2 8 18 32 25 8 2 **Am** Americium 243.1

Solid
Liquid
Gas
Made artificially

18

| 2
He
Helium
4.003 | 2 |

| **13** | **14** | **15** | **16** | **17** |

| 5
B
Boron
10.81 | 2 3 | 6
C
Carbon
12.01 | 2 4 | 7
N
Nitrogen
14.01 | 2 5 | 8
O
Oxygen
16.00 | 2 6 | 9
F
Flourine
19.00 | 2 7 | 10
Ne
Neon
20.18 | 2 8 |

⟵ **Metals**

| **10** | **11** | **12** |

| 13
Al
Aluminum
26.98 | 2 8 3 | 14
Si
Silicon
28.09 | 2 8 4 | 15
P
Phosphorous
30.97 | 2 8 5 | 16
S
Sulfur
32.07 | 2 8 6 | 17
Cl
Chlorine
35.45 | 2 8 7 | 18
Ar
Argon
39.95 | 2 8 8 |

| 28
Ni
Nickel
58.69 | 2 8 16 2 | 29
Cu
Copper
63.55 | 2 8 18 1 | 30
Zn
Zinc
65.39 | 2 8 18 2 | 31
Ga
Gallium
69.72 | 2 8 18 3 | 32
Ge
Germanium
72.59 | 2 8 18 4 | 33
As
Arsenic
74.92 | 2 8 18 5 | 34
Se
Selenium
78.96 | 2 8 18 6 | 35
Br
Bromine
79.90 | 2 8 18 7 | 36
Kr
Krypton
83.80 | 2 8 18 8 |

| 46
Pd
Palladium
106.4 | 2 8 18 18 | 47
Ag
Silver
107.9 | 2 8 18 18 1 | 48
Cd
Cadmium
112.4 | 2 8 18 18 2 | 49
In
Indium
114.8 | 2 8 18 18 3 | 50
Sn
Tin
118.7 | 2 8 18 18 4 | 51
Sb
Antimony
121.8 | 2 8 18 18 5 | 52
Te
Tellurium
127.6 | 2 8 18 18 6 | 53
I
Iodine
126.9 | 2 8 18 18 7 | 54
Xe
Xenon
131.3 | 2 8 18 18 8 |

| 78
Pt
Platinum
195.1 | 2 8 18 32 17 1 | 79
Au
Gold
197.0 | 2 8 18 32 18 1 | 80
Hg
Mercury
200.6 | 2 8 18 32 18 2 | 81
Tl
Thallium
204.4 | 2 8 18 32 18 3 | 82
Pb
Lead
207.2 | 2 8 18 32 18 4 | 83
Bi
Bismuth
209.0 | 2 8 18 32 18 5 | 84
Po
Polonium
210.0 | 2 8 18 32 18 6 | 85
At
Astatine
210.0 | 2 8 18 32 18 7 | 86
Rn
Radon
222.0 | 2 8 18 32 18 8 |

| 64
Gd
Gadolinium
157.3 | 2 8 18 25 9 2 | 65
Tb
Terbium
158.9 | 2 8 18 27 8 2 | 66
Dy
Dysporsium
162.5 | 2 8 18 28 8 2 | 67
Ho
Holmium
164.9 | 2 8 18 29 8 2 | 68
Er
Erbium
167.3 | 2 8 18 30 8 2 | 69
Tm
Thulium
168.9 | 2 8 18 31 8 2 | 70
Yb
Ytterbium
173.0 | 2 8 18 32 8 2 |

| 96
Cm
Curium
247.1 | 2 8 18 32 25 9 2 | 97
Bk
Berkelium
247.1 | 2 8 18 32 27 8 2 | 98
Cf
Californium
252.1 | 2 8 18 32 28 8 2 | 99
Es
Einsteinium
252.1 | 2 8 18 32 29 8 2 | 100
Fm
Fermium
257.1 | 2 8 18 32 30 8 2 | 101
Md
Mendelevium
256.1 | 2 8 18 32 31 8 2 | 102
No
Nobelium
259.1 | 2 8 18 32 32 8 2 |

Characteristics of Some Groups

If you know something about one element in a group, you know something about all the elements in the group. For example, the elements in group 1 are the most metallic elements. Each element is a soft, shiny, silvery metal that reacts readily with oxygen and water. These metals undergo chemical changes easily and sometimes violently, as shown in *Figure 7-15.*

Elements to the left of the stairstep line in the periodic table are metals and elements to the right of the line are nonmetals. However, the change from metal to nonmetal occurs gradually across a period.

The elements in group 3 to group 11 are called *transition metals*. Most of the elements used to make the metal objects we use everyday come from this block of elements. Transition metals are less reactive than group 1 metals, which makes them very useful. For example, many resist corrosion.

Group 11 includes copper (Cu), silver (Ag), and gold (Au), which are often called the **coinage metals.** They have been used for centuries to make coins. All three coinage metals are rather durable, because they do not undergo chemical changes easily.

Group 17 contains the most nonmetallic element—fluorine. Chlorine and fluorine are gases. Bromine and iodine easily become gases. These elements also undergo chemical changes easily.

Figure 7-15 The elements in group 1 are the most reactive metals. In the photograph, potassium reacts violently with water.

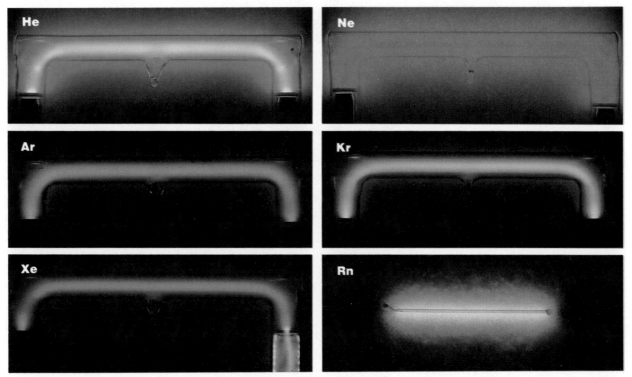

The elements in group 18 are all gases. They are the most stable of the elements. They do not naturally undergo chemical changes because their outer energy level contains eight electrons—the maximum number for that level. When excited, these elements give off light as shown in *Figure 7-16*. These elements are often used in what people call neon signs. Such signs may also contain other elements to create different colors.

Figure 7-16 The group 18 elements, which are called the noble gases, do not react readily with other elements.

The Two Rows of Elements Below the Main Table

In the periodic table on pages 160–161, a space separates barium (atomic number 56) from lutetium (atomic number 71). The elements with atomic numbers 57–70 are called **rare earth elements.** The rare earths actually belong in period 6 between barium and lutetium. The periodic table would have to be very wide to show 32 elements in one period. So the rare earths are placed at the bottom of the table. Rare earths are often called *lanthanides* to show their relationship to lanthanum.

Rare earth elements have similar properties. They are silvery metals that combine well with nonmetals. Rare earths are not really rare. Most are found in nature—in rocks and stars—combined with nonmetallic elements.

Explore!

Find out why the elements in group 18 are called the noble gases.

Figure 7-17 Rare earth elements are used in picture tubes, such as the one shown here inside a computer. These elements help produce the bright colors you see in the computer graphic image.

Rare earth elements are used to polish telescope mirrors and to make lenses for cameras, binoculars, and eyeglasses. Some rare earths are used to produce strong colored light on television screens, as illustrated in the photograph. When rare earth elements are mixed with oxygen and heated, they emit a strong white light that resembles sunlight. Consequently, the rare earths are often used in lights for the movie industry, in streetlights, and in searchlights. Rare earths are also used to make lasers and to produce X-ray pictures, such as those used to examine teeth and bones.

Directly beneath the rare earth elements in the table is a row of elements beginning with actinium. These elements follow 88, radium, and are called *actinides*. Uranium is the most familiar actinide. Uranium and several other actinides occur in nature. All elements with atomic numbers higher than that of uranium are made artificially. Two of the actinides, uranium and plutonium, are used in nuclear energy plants.

Section Review

1. How is the table of elements periodic?
2. How did Moseley improve on Mendeleev's table?
3. Give the period and group that each of these elements belongs to: mercury, chromium, tin, and platinum.
4. What are the elements in group 18?
5. What is one use of the rare earth elements and one use of elements in the actinide group?

Challenge: Which element, chlorine (Cl) or helium (He), will react more violently when exposed to metals in group 1 or 2? Refer to the periodic table.

People and Science

Rosalyn Yalow, Medical Researcher

At age 19, Rosalyn Yalow graduated from Hunter College with honors in physics. She was granted a teaching assistantship at the University of Illinois, and earned her Ph. D. in physics in 1945.

Dr. Yalow began teaching at Hunter College, but at the same time she was doing research part-time at the Bronx Veterans Administration Hospital. In a janitor's closet she set up a radioisotope laboratory. She designed, built, and calibrated apparatus for measuring radioactive substances. Within two years, she and her associates produced eight scientific publications.

In 1950, Dr. Yalow resigned her teaching job and began full-time research at Bronx Veterans Hospital with Dr. Solomon A. Berson. They developed the technique of radioimmunoassay, which is called RIA. For this work, Dr. Yalow was awarded the Nobel Prize in 1977.

RIA proved to be over 1000 times more sensitive than any other method for assessing levels of insulin in the blood. Some have compared its sensitivity to being able to find a lump of sugar in a body of water the size of Lake Erie. RIA is also used to measure trace amounts of hormones, viruses, vitamins, drugs, and other chemicals in the body. Today, Dr. Yalow's process is used in thousands of laboratories throughout the world.

Interpreting the Periodic Table

The periodic table summarizes information about the elements. You can use the periodic table to learn more about individual elements. In this activity, you will interpret the periodic table and organize information in a table.

On a separate piece of paper, copy the table below, allowing 16 lines below the heads. Then fill it in using the periodic table on pages 160-161.

Arrange the elements listed below by their atomic numbers. The element with the lowest atomic number should appear at the top of the table. Refer to pages 153–155 to determine the number of protons, electrons, and neutrons in an atom.

After you fill in the blank for atomic mass, round the number given in the periodic table to the nearest whole number. For example, the atomic mass of the element *scandium* is 44.96. Round this number to 45.

Use your rounded atomic mass values as mass numbers. (The mass number is needed to calculate the number of neutrons in one nucleus.)

Answer the following questions.

1. Some elements in your table have chemical symbols that are not based on the English name of the element. List these elements and their symbols.
2. In the periodic table on pages 160-161, which two elements are liquids at room temperature?
3. List the elements in the periodic table that belong to group 1. Among these elements, what similarities do you notice? Differences?
4. Which elements belong to group 17? What similarities and differences do you notice among these elements?
5. For the elements in period 3, find a pattern in the number of electrons in the outer energy level. What pattern do you notice? How does this pattern differ from the outer electron pattern for periods 4, 5, 6, and 7?

fluorine	chlorine	zinc	radon
sodium	argon	bromine	europium
magnesium	potassium	silver	uranium
silicon	copper	mercury	plutonium

Name of Element	Chemical Symbol	Number of Protons	Atomic Mass	Number of Neutrons	Number of Electrons	Electrons in outer energy level	Period	Group	Phase at room temperature

 Summary

7-1 Theories About the Atom

A. Originally, atoms were thought to be particles that could not be divided.

B. Rutherford discovered that an atom is mostly empty space.

C. When an electron in an atom gains energy, it jumps to a higher energy level. When the electron moves to a lower level, the atom releases energy.

D. Present atomic theory states that atoms consist of a nucleus, which contains neutrons and protons, and electrons, which can appear at specific different places within the atom.

7-2 How Atoms Differ

A. All atoms of the same element have the same number of protons and electrons.

B. Atoms of the same element can have different numbers of neutrons and thus different masses. Isotopes of an element are nuclei that have the same number of protons, but different numbers of neutrons.

C. The mass number of an atom is the total number of protons and neutrons in the nucleus of an atom.

7-3 Classifying Elements

A. Mendeleev, a Russian scientist, proposed that elements be arranged in order of increasing mass. This arrangement resulted in a pattern of repeating properties.

B. In the modern periodic table, elements are arranged according to their atomic numbers.

C. Periods are the horizontal rows in the periodic table. Groups are the vertical columns in the periodic table.

D. Group 1 elements are very metallic. Group 11 elements are coinage metals. Group 17 elements are nonmetallic. Group 18 elements are very unreactive gases. Transition metals are located in the middle of the periodic table.

E. The two rows below the main periodic table contain the rare earth and actinide elements.

Vocabulary

For each of the following terms, write a sentence that uses the term correctly.

atomic mass	excited state	period
atomic number	group	periodic table of the elements
coinage metals	isotope	proton
deuterium	mass number	rare earth elements
electron	neutron	spectrum
energy level	nucleus	tritium

Check Your Knowledge

Part I: Matching Match the definition in Column I with the correct term Column II.

Column I
1. listed elements by atomic masses
2. has properties similar to silicon's
3. vertical columns in the periodic table
4. arranged elements by atomic numbers
5. produce bright-colored substances
6. number of protons in an atom
7. tritium
8. particles with negative charges
9. energy pattern
10. total number of protons and neutrons

Column II
a. atomic number
b. Dmitri Mendeleev
c. electrons
d. germanium
e. groups
f. Henry Moseley
g. hydrogen isotope
h. mass number
i. periods
j. spectrum
k. transition elements

Part II: Multiple Choice Choose the letter of the best answer
11. Electrons jump to a higher energy level when they (a) release energy. (b) gain protons. (c) gain energy. (d) are a certain distance from the nucleus.
12. A neutral atom has (a) more neutrons than protons. (b) same number of protons and electrons. (c) same number of protons and neutrons. (d) more neutrons than electrons.
13. All atoms of an element have (a) same number of neutrons. (b) same mass number. (c) different numbers of protons. (d) same atomic number.
14. Isotopes can be separated because of their different (a) masses. (b) atomic numbers. (c) numbers of protons. (d) numbers of electrons.
15. The present periodic table contains (a) 90 elements. (b) 20 elements. (c) 109 elements. (d) 120 elements.
16. An element's chemical properties are determined by the (a) number of its neutrons. (b) number of its electrons. (c) its number of energy levels. (d) the color of its spectrum.
17. Elements with atomic numbers higher than that of uranium are (a) gases. (b) made artificially. (c) rare earth elements. (d) in Period 1 of the periodic table.

Part III: Completion Write the word or words that complete the sentence correctly.
18. The periodic table is arranged according to the _____ _____ of the elements.
19. In the periodic table, the small numbers to the right of the atomic number indicate the number of _____ in each energy level.
20. _____ _____ elements rarely react chemically.
21. The various isotopes of an element have different _____ _____.
22. Rutherford compared his model of the atom to the _____ _____.

Check Your Understanding

1. Compare Dalton's atomic model with the present model.
2. What experimental evidence convinced Rutherford that the atom is mainly empty space?
3. What is an electron cloud?
4. Define atomic number, mass number, and atomic mass.
5. Which element does not belong to the same *group* in the periodic table as the other two elements: titanium, manganese, or zirconium?
6. Which element does not belong to the same *period* in the periodic table as the other two elements: potassium, cesium, or iron?
7. What factor determines how easily the atoms of an element undergo chemical changes?

Apply Your Knowledge

1. Draw a Bohr diagram of fluorine (F).
2. What is the mass number of the lead isotope that contains 125 neutrons?
3. How many outer electrons does chlorine (Cl) have?
4. How many protons, electrons, and neutrons does an atom of $^{90}_{38}Sr$ contain?
5. How is it possible to predict the properties of an element from its position in the periodic table?
6. How are elements in group 18 alike?
7. Fluorine (F) is the most active nonmetal and francium (Fr) is the most active metal. Use the periodic table to explain what these facts reveal about group properties.
8. Based on your answer to the last question, compare the reactivities of: fluorine (F) and iodine (I); lithium (Li) and francium (Fr).

Extend Your Knowledge

Research/Projects

1. Choose an element that interests you. Find out the following information about it: (a) when, how, and by whom it was discovered; (b) its physical and chemical properties; and (c) some of its uses.
2. Make your own three-dimensional model of an atom. Choose a smaller element, because smaller elements are simpler to model. You might use cotton batting, coat hangers, polystyrene, and rubber balls to represent the parts of an atom.

Readings

Emsley, John and Edwards, Peter. "Elements Show They're Metal." *New Scientist*, April 9, 1987, pages 32–35. Describes some peculiar properties of metals when they are subjected to high pressures and temperatures.

Hamilton, J. H. and Maruhn, J. A. "Exotic Atomic Nuclei." *Scientific American*, July, 1986, pp. 80–89. An interesting look at some atomic nuclei that have unusual shapes.

CHAPTER 8
The Atomic Nucleus

The photograph shows the tracks of tiny atomic particles traveling through liquid helium. In this chapter you will be studying about the particles that make up the atom and the energy contained in an atomic nucleus.

Organizing Your Study Skills The outline below will help you see how the chapter is organized and what you should learn as you read.

I. Section 8-1: The Structure of the Nucleus
  A. How is the atomic nucleus held together?
  B. What smaller particles make up protons and neutrons?
  C. What are the six kinds of quarks?

II. Section 8-2: Radioactivity
  A. What is radioactivity?
  B. How is radioactivity detected and measured?
  C. In what ways does radioactivity affect people?

III. Section 8-3: Mass, Energy, and the Speed of Light
  A. What was Einstein's theory about the relationship between mass and the speed of light?
  B. What is the relationship between mass and energy?

IV. Section 8-4: Nuclear Fission
  A. How does nuclear fission produce energy?
  B. In what ways can the energy from nuclear fission be used?

V. Section 8-5: Nuclear Fusion
  A. How do elements combine to form larger elements and produce energy?
  B. How are all the elements in the universe formed by nuclear fusion?

Objectives

After completing this section you will be able to

A. Describe the force that holds the particles of a nucleus together.

B. Describe the characteristics of protons and neutrons.

C. Name the six different kinds of quarks.

8-1 The Structure of the Nucleus

The Force That Holds the Nucleus Together

The nucleus of an atom is so tiny that, if all the atomic nuclei in your body could be packed together, they would fit on the tip of a little finger. Forcing all the atomic nuclei in your body into a tiny space would be very difficult, however. All nuclei have positive electric charges, so they repel one another. You could not push hard enough to make nuclei touch.

Although particles in a nucleus repel each other, the particles still do not fly apart. Some stronger, attracting force must hold the particles in a nucleus together. This force is called the **strong force.** It holds together nuclear particles that are extremely close to one another. The strong force works only over a very short range. At distances greater than the size of the nucleus, the strong force has no effect.

The strong force, like the forces of gravity and electromagnetism, is one of nature's major forces. To the left in *Figure 8-1,* the electromagnetic force, coming from the protons in the nucleus, repels a proton that passes near the nucleus. However, the proton to the right is moving fast enough to overcome the electromagnetic force. Thus, it can get close enough to the nucleus to be captured by the strong force.

Neutrons add to the strong force holding a nucleus together. Without this added strong force, the nuclei of large atoms would break up. Only the nucleus of ordinary hydrogen ¦H does not need neutrons in addition to protons. The nucleus of this form of hydrogen is a single proton.

Figure 8-1 The electric force repels a proton that passes near a nucleus. The strong force captures a proton that is moving fast enough to get close to the nucleus.

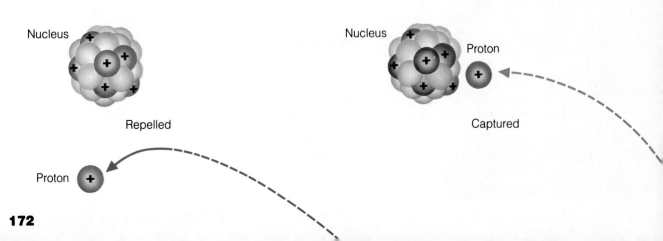

Nucleus

Repelled

Proton

Nucleus

Proton

Captured

The Building Blocks of Protons and Neutrons

Physicists use very large machines called particle accelerators to explore the nuclei of atoms. In particle accelerators, such as the one in *Figure 8-2*, highspeed beams of atomic particles are shot at each other and at nuclei. In the resulting collisions, the particles and nuclei split apart. The parts that result cannot be seen with the eye, but they make tracks in liquid helium, as shown on pages 170-171. The tracks led physicists to discover more than 100 nuclear particles in addition to protons and neutrons. Scientists found so many particles that they began to talk about the "particle zoo."

In 1963, two scientists suggested that all the different types of particles in the zoo were really made of smaller objects. According to their theory, nuclear particles consist of basic units called **quarks**. At first, physicists believed three kinds of quarks could be enough to form all the known nuclear particles. In a spirit of fun, they said that quarks came in three "flavors": up, down, and strange. They assigned the up quark an electric charge of $+2/3$, down quark $-1/3$, and strange quark $-1/3$.

Ordinary matter is made of only up quarks and down quarks. As *Figure 8-3* shows, protons consist of two up quarks and one down quark. Neutrons are made of one up quark and two down quarks. The strange quark is found in some of the other particles that scientists find when they smash nuclei apart.

Figure 8-2 An aerial photograph of Fermi Lab Accelerator ring in Batavia, Illinois.

Proton and neutron quarks			
Particle	**Quark parts**	**Quark charges**	**Total charge**
Proton	up, up, down	$+\frac{2}{3} + \frac{2}{3} - \frac{1}{3}$	$+1$
Neutron	up, down, down	$+\frac{2}{3} - \frac{1}{3} - \frac{1}{3}$	0

More Kinds of Quarks

There are several ways of putting quarks of flavors "up," "down," and "strange" together. Each way makes a different particle. But scientists found more particles than could be explained by the existence of only three kinds of quarks.

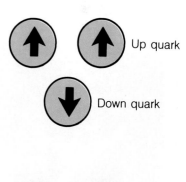
Up quark
Down quark

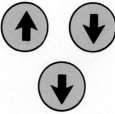

Figure 8-3 Different combinations of up and down quarks make up protons and neutrons.

Positive and negative electric charges are used to get the particles in particle accelerators moving at speeds approaching the speed of light. The charges push or pull charged particles in a beam, speeding them up until they are going almost as fast as light. In many accelerators, magnets are used to deflect the particles into a circular path, so that they travel hundreds of kilometers in a circle of only a few kilometers across.

To explain the new particles, physicists needed three more kinds of quarks, which they named charm, truth, and beauty. Again, the names are just labels. They have nothing to do with the everyday meaning of the words *charm, truth,* and *beauty.*

We cannot study single quarks. In fact, most physicists think that they may never separate quarks from the particles they form. However, the theory that quarks are the basic building blocks of the nucleus does explain the evidence. Physicists continue to study nuclear particles in search of quarks. Whether or not the quarks are themselves made up of still smaller particles is an unanswered question.

Section Review

1. What is the name of the force that binds nuclear particles?
2. What are quarks?
3. Name the six kinds of quarks.

Challenge: Describe what might happen if the strong force worked at a much greater distance.

People and Science

Luis Alvarez, Physicist (1911–1988)

Luis Alvarez distinguished himself as a physicist at the University of California where his primary research involved the study of subatomic particles. He did his research using a "bubble chamber," which is a steel tank with strong glass windows. The chamber is cooled to $-200°$ Celsius and then filled with liquid hydrogen. When particles are shot through the liquid, they leave tracks. Each particle forms a tiny bubble when pressure in the bubble chamber is slightly reduced. By studying the bubble tracks, hundreds of new subatomic particles have been discovered.

The research initiated by Alvarez opened up a whole new world for scientists—a menagerie of new particles. For his work, he received the Nobel Prize in physics in 1968.

Alvarez is best known for his theory about mass extinctions of many kinds of life on earth. Alvarez, his son Walter, and other scientists hypothesized that an asteroid collided with the earth about 65 million years ago. This collision caused many years of dust-darkened skies. During this time, plants could not carry on photosynthesis and provide basic food. As a result, many animals including the dinosaurs became extinct.

8-2 Radioactivity

Radiation Results from the Breakdown of Nuclei

In 1895, scientists discovered a new kind of radiation called an X ray. It could penetrate paper and even the human body. The following year, the French scientist Henri Becquerel stored some of his samples of chemicals near photographic film. To his surprise, the film next to some uranium salts changed, just as if it had been exposed to X rays. In this way, he discovered that uranium gives off powerful invisible rays similar to X rays.

One of Becquerel's students, Marie Curie, shown here, continued work on these invisible rays. Together with her husband, Pierre, Madame Curie discovered two elements that gave off even more powerful rays than uranium. They named one of these new elements radium. They named the other element polonium, after Poland, Madame Curie's birthplace. For their work, Becquerel and the Curies won the Nobel Prize for physics in 1903. In the years that followed, scientists discovered other elements that behaved like uranium, polonium, and radium.

The nuclei of uranium and of some other elements are unstable. They decay (break apart) into the nuclei of elements with smaller atomic masses. The Curies used the name **radioactivity** for this decay. Measurement of radioactive decay is one way scientists use to estimate the effects of a second force that operates inside the nucleus—the **weak force.** The weak force is involved in the interactions that allow nuclei to undergo radioactive decay. The force of electromagnetism, the strong force, the weak force, and gravity are the four basic forces in nature.

The nuclei in a given amount of radioactive element steadily decay until few are left. No one can predict when any particular nucleus will decay. But we can predict how many will decay in a certain time. For example, as *Figure 8-5* shows, half the nuclei in a sample of $^{235}_{92}U$ will decay in 713 million years. The time it takes half the nuclei in a sample of radioactive isotope to decay is that isotope's **half-life.**

Objectives

After completing this section you will be able to

A. Define and describe radioactivity.
B. Describe methods for detecting and measuring radioactivity.
C. Describe some effects and uses of radioactivity.

Figure 8-4 Marie Curie (1867-1934)

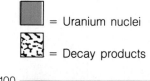

☐ = Uranium nuclei

▨ = Decay products

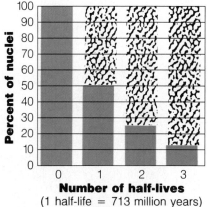

Number of half-lives
(1 half-life = 713 million years)

Figure 8-5 Every 713 million years, half the nuclei in a $^{235}_{92}U$ sample decay.

The half-life of a radioactive isotope is constant. For example, the half-life constant of $^{235}_{92}U$ is 713 million years. If a sample of $^{235}_{92}U$ contains 1000 nuclei, 500 of those nuclei would remain after 713 million years. After another 713 million years, 250 nuclei would remain. The decaying nuclei form nuclei of lighter elements, some of which are also radioactive. *Figure 8-6* gives the half-lives of some other radioactive isotopes.

Figure 8-6 The half-lives of some radioactive isotopes		
Element	**Isotope**	**Half-life**
Polonium	$^{214}_{84}Po$	0.0001 seconds
Iodine	$^{131}_{53}I$	8 days
Strontium	$^{90}_{38}Sr$	28 years
Carbon	$^{14}_{6}C$	5730 years
Uranium	$^{238}_{92}U$	4.5 billion years

As nuclei decay, they release particles and rays called **radiation.** Decaying nuclei give off three kinds of radiation, which were named after the first letters of the Greek alphabet: *alpha*, *beta*, and *gamma*. At first they were all called rays, but scientists soon learned that two of the rays were really particles. An alpha particle is a helium nucleus. It consists of two protons and two neutrons. A beta particle is a rapidly moving electron.

The third type of radiation is really a ray. A gamma ray is a bundle of light energy similar to, but more powerful than, an X ray. A gamma ray is much more powerful than a bundle of visible light energy.

Figure 8-7 Comparing the penetrating power of alpha, beta, and gamma radiation

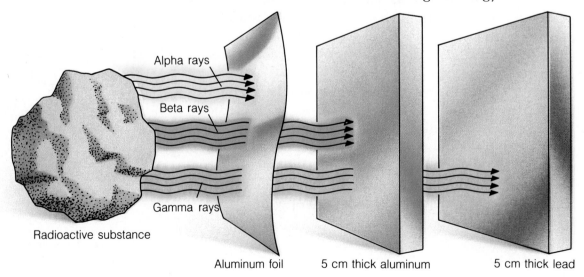

Alpha rays

Beta rays

Gamma rays

Radioactive substance

Aluminum foil

5 cm thick aluminum

5 cm thick lead

Alpha particles, beta particles, and gamma rays occur naturally. For example, nuclei of unstable ^3_1H release beta particles. Nuclei of unstable $^{235}_{92}U$ and $^{238}_{92}U$ give off both alpha particles and gamma rays.

The different kinds of radiation vary in their ability to pass through substances. *Figure 8-7* shows that an alpha particle can penetrate only a thin sheet of aluminum foil. A beta particle can penetrate 5 centimeters of aluminum. A gamma ray can penetrate one meter of concrete or 5 centimeters of lead.

Alpha particles, beta particles, and gamma rays that travel through outer space are called cosmic rays. Most cosmic rays from outer space, though, cannot travel through the earth's atmosphere. The earth's atmosphere protects us from them so that only a small percentage of the cosmic rays reach the ground. The cosmic radiation that reaches the earth is one kind of **background radiation.**

Detecting and Measuring Radioactivity

The first instrument to detect radiation from radioactive material was the **Geiger counter.** Hans Geiger developed the instrument in 1908. *Figure 8-8* shows a Geiger counter. Radiation from the radioactive source enters the window and gives an electric charge to the gas inside the tube. Electric current then flows from the gas to the wire to the metal cylinder. Usually, the pulse of current causes a loudspeaker to click. The more frequent the clicks, the more radiation is present.

Figure 8-8 In a Geiger counter, radiation from the radioactive substance causes eleric current to flow through the tube. The current causes a click when it is amplified to the speaker.

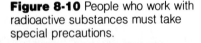

Figure 8-9 A Geiger counter enables the geologist to detect radioactivity in rocks.

Figure 8-10 People who work with radioactive substances must take special precautions.

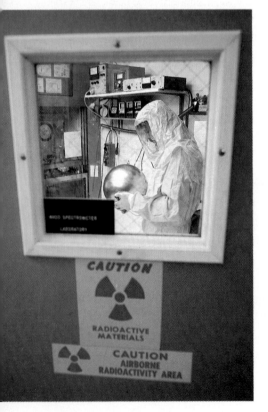

The geologist in the picture is using a Geiger counter to locate radioactive isotopes. Today, most scientists searching for radioactive substances use a smaller device. This type of radiation counter can measure low levels of radioactivity more efficiently than a Geiger counter. It contains a substance called a *scintillator* that gives off flashes of light when exposed to certain types of energy. Alpha radiation from radioactive materials makes the substance flash.

Ways of detecting the amount of radiation that an object absorbs have also been developed. For example, workers in atomic plants carry radiation meters with them. A simple radiation meter is a piece of photographic film, which is sealed in black paper to prevent light from exposing it. Tiny black specks on the developed film reveal how much radiation the person carrying the meter has absorbed.

Scientists use a unit called the rad to measure the amount of energy an object has absorbed from radiation. Different types of radiation affect the human body differently. For example, alpha particles do more damage than beta particles. The rem, which is short for rad equivalent in man, provides a measure for the effects of radiation a person receives, whether the radiation is in the form of X rays or gamma rays. One rem of radiation of any type does the same amount of damage to a human being.

People who work with or near radioactive materials, as shown, must be careful not to be exposed to the harmful radiation. Radiation is invisible, and a person will not be aware that he or she has been injured by radiation until the damage has been done.

The Effects and Uses of Radioactivity

Radioactivity occurs normally all around us. Some nuclei in all matter continually decay. Natural radiation also reaches us in the form of cosmic rays from beyond the earth's atmosphere. A person living at sea level absorbs about 40 millirems (40/1000 rem) a year from cosmic rays. For each increase in altitude of 30.5 meters, a person is exposed to one additional millirem per year. Each year the average American receives about 130 millirems from natural sources of radioactivity and another 1 millirem from human activities. The United States government recommends that people be exposed to no more than 500 millirems per year.

Exposure to large doses of radiation can cause radiation sickness, which can be fatal. Radiation also can produce changes in genes, which determine inherited traits. In places where radioactive materials are used, workers shield themselves from the rays given off by the radioactive materials. In nuclear reactors, for example, thick concrete shields protect the workers from radioactivity, and workers use remote-control devices to handle the radioactive materials that are produced.

Radiation can be helpful when it is controlled. For example, the cancer patient in *Figure 8-11* is being treated with radiation because it can kill diseased cells. But radiation can also kill healthy cells. It must be aimed carefully to hit only the diseased cells.

Scientists use $^{14}_{6}C$, a radioactive isotope of carbon called carbon–14, to determine ages of fossils, which are the preserved remains of dead plants and animals. All living organisms maintain the same proportion of $^{14}_{6}C$ in their bodies in relation to other isotopes of carbon. After an organism dies, it stops taking in any kind of carbon. Years later, if the fossil is found, scientists can measure the amount of $^{14}_{6}C$ that has decayed and determine how long ago the organism died.

Section Review

1. Explain the meaning of half-life.
2. What do the units rad and rem measure?
3. Describe one medical use of radioactivity.

Challenge: The half-life of a radioactive isotope is 2 years. A sample of this isotope contains 800 atoms (nuclei). How many years must pass before there will be only 25 nuclei of this isotope left?

For Practice

Campers found a bone buried in a field. Scientists did tests that showed 50 percent of the $^{14}_{6}C$ isotope was gone. The half-life of $^{14}_{6}C$ is 5730 years. About how long ago did the animal die?

Figure 8-11 Using radioactive isotopes in the diagnosis and treatment of disease

Activity 8-1

Radioactive Decay

Purpose

To understand the process of radioactive decay

Materials

- 64 red beans
- 136 white beans
- 64 pieces of shell macaroni
- shoebox
- graph paper

Procedures and Observations

PART A

1. Red beans represent atoms of a radioactive isotope and white beans a nonradioactive isotope of the same element.
2. Put red and white beans in a shoebox, and mix them up. Copy the table shown here. Record the total number of atoms (beans) present.
3. Assume the half-life of red beans is 2 minutes and 2 minutes have passed. Take out half the red beans. Replace them with macaroni shells to represent atoms of the decay product.
4. Record how many red beans you removed.
5. Repeat steps 3 and 4 five more times.
6. After each "half-life", record how many red beans you have removed, how many red beans remain in the shoebox, the number of half-lives that have passed since you began, and the total number of atoms (beans plus macaroni) present.

PART B

1. Draw a graph with the number of half-lives that have passed on the horizontal axis and the number of red beans remaining on the vertical axis.
2. Connect the points with a solid line.

3. On the same graph paper, plot the number of half-lives that have passed on the horizontal axis and the total number of atoms (beans plus macaroni shells) in the box on the vertical axis.

	Starting number	Number of trials					
		1	2	3	4	5	6
Red beans							
White beans							
Macaroni							

4. Connect the points with a dotted line.
5. To see how old the material in the box would be if you found 25 red beans in it, draw a horizontal line from 25 on the vertical axis until it hits the curve drawn with a solid line. Then draw a line downward from this intersection to the horizontal axis. This point marks the amount of time passed in numbers of half-lives.

Analysis and Conclusions

1. How does the number of red beans (radioactive atoms) decaying change as time goes on?
2. How does the number of macaroni shells (the atoms that result from the decay) change as time goes on?
3. Would the answers to 1 and 2 be different if you started out with twice as many atoms of each type? Which of the quantities described in 1 and 2 is most useful for estimating ages of earth materials?
4. What else, in addition to the decay product element, is produced during radioactive decay?

8-3 Mass, Energy, and the Speed of Light

Mass Becomes Greater as Speed Increases

As scientists discovered that matter was made up of subatomic particles, they started to rethink many ideas about the nature of matter. Some scientists began to see a relationship between mass and space, time, and energy. One scientist, Albert Einstein, proposed a definite relationship between mass, the speed of light, and time.

Einstein explained the relationship between mass and speed this way. Imagine you have unlimited strength and that you have a bicycle with hundreds of higher gears. Your goal is to ride your bicycle until you reach the speed of light. As you keep increasing your speed, your mass becomes greater. At nine-tenths the speed of light, your mass becomes about twice as large as it was at the start. Even though you have unlimited energy and a perfect bicycle, you are unable to reach the speed of light.

Einstein was the first person to propose that mass increases as speed increases. This growth is shown in *Figure 8-12*. The idea that mass is linked to speed is part of Einstein's "special theory of relativity." In this theory, Einstein also stated that the new mass is created from the energy used to make the original mass go faster. When an object nears the speed of light, its mass increases greatly. Since the amount of energy needed to make a mass accelerate is directly related to the size of the mass, more energy is needed to accelerate a faster object. In other words, the faster an object is moving, the greater the amount of energy needed to cause an increase in speed.

Applying Science

Television and radio signals can travel at the speed of light because they have no mass. However, these signals still take time to travel from one place to another. For example, signals bounced to local television stations from satellites overhead must travel 45 000 km up to the satellite and back down. They arrive about 1/6 second later than if they came directly to us. Signals from the *Voyager* spacecraft near Uranus took 2 hours 45 minutes to reach the earth.

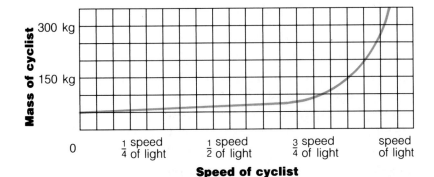

Figure 8-12 The graph shows how mass varies with speeed.

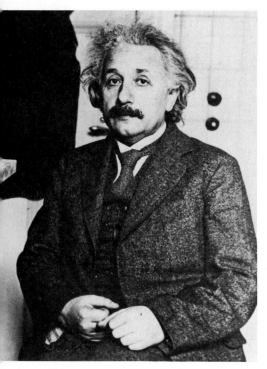

Figure 8-13 Albert Einstein (1879-1955)

Einstein's theory predicts that no object with mass can go as fast as the speed of light. The object's mass would keep increasing indefinitely as more energy was supplied in an effort to increase the speed of the object. Even humans with unlimited strength cannot produce enough energy to make an object move at the speed of light.

Riding a bicycle fast enough to test Einstein's theory is not possible. However, physicists can test the theory in particle accelerators. As atomic particles accelerate nearly to the speed of light, more and more energy is needed to make them go faster, just as Einstein predicted.

The Conservation of Mass-Energy

Einstein realized that matter is more than something that has mass and occupies space. He concluded that matter and energy are interchangeable. In other words, matter can be converted to energy, and energy converted to matter. The energy *(E)* in matter is equal to the mass *(m)* of the matter multiplied by the speed of light squared *(c²)*. Because the speed of light is three hundred million (3×10^9) meters per second, the speed of light squared is an incredibly large number (9×10^{18}). Einstein's famous equation $E = mc^2$, means that a tiny amount of mass can be changed into a huge amount of energy.

Einstein also realized that the total amount of energy and matter never changes. Energy can be changed into matter, and matter can be changed to energy, but nothing is ever lost in the change. This idea is called the **law of conservation of mass-energy.**

Einstein's idea seemed strange when he first suggested it, but now it is universally accepted. The theory has been supported many times by research in laboratories around the world.

Section Review

1. Describe what would happen to objects traveling near the speed of light.
2. Explain the law of conservation of mass-energy.

Challenge: How much energy could be formed if one milligram $(1 \times 10^{-6}$ kg$)$ of matter was converted to energy? (*E* is expressed in units of energy called joules, *m* in kilograms, and *c* in meters per second.)

8-4 Nuclear Fission

What Happens During Fission

Long before people knew about atoms and nuclei, some people hoped to change less valuable metals into gold. They never succeeded. However, some elements do change into other elements all the time due to radioactive decay. Physicists now know how to make some heavy nuclei break apart to form nuclei of lighter elements. The process by which one type of nucleus changes into another is called a **nuclear reaction.**

In 1939, scientists found that certain heavy nuclei split into lighter nuclei when they absorb slowly moving neutrons. The splitting of a nucleus in this way is **nuclear fission.**

Figure 8-14 shows a typical nuclear reaction when a slow neutron splits a uranium nucleus ($^{235}_{92}$U). In this particular example, three neutrons and two isotopes that have lower atomic masses than uranium are formed. The isotopes in this case are barium ($^{141}_{56}$Ba) and krypton ($^{92}_{36}$Kr).

The number of protons after fission occurs (56 + 36 = 92) is the same as the number of protons before fission. The total number of neutrons and protons afterwards is 141 + 92 + (3 x 1) = 236. This number is the same as the original number of particles, 1 + 235 = 236. The total mass of the two nuclei and three neutrons at the end, though, is slightly less than the total mass of the uranium nucleus and neutron at the beginning.

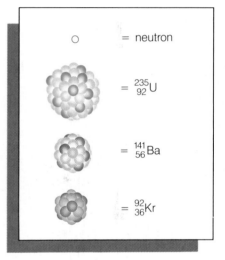

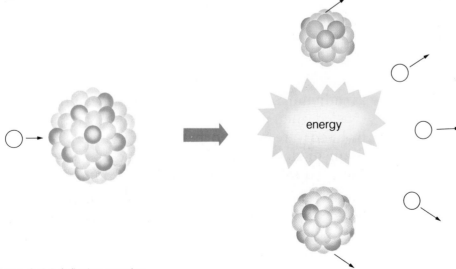

energy

Figure 8-14 A fission reaction

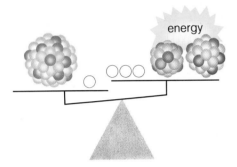

energy

Figure 8-15 The fission of a nucleus produces smaller nuclei, neutrons, and energy.

Following the law of conservation of mass-energy, the missing mass changed into energy. Some of the energy was used in accelerating the nuclei and the neutrons as they sped away from each other. The energy of the speeding nuclei can be converted to heat energy when the nuclei collide with molecules and atoms in the materials around them.

In addition to the isotopes of lower atomic mass and the neutrons, nuclear fission produces radiation that can be converted to heat.

The amount of energy produced in a fission reaction can be found using Einstein's formula, $E = mc^2$. Remember that c^2 is a huge number. So only a tiny amount of mass has to change into energy for fission to produce a large amount of energy.

Once nuclear fission starts, it can continue in a **chain reaction** if enough of the right nuclear fuel is present. *Figure 8-16* demonstrates how a chain reaction works. First, a neutron enters a $^{235}_{92}$U nucleus. Next, the nucleus splits and releases neutrons and energy. Then, one or two of these neutrons enter and break up another nuclei. Still more neutrons are produced. They collide with and split other nuclei. Each splitting nucleus releases neutrons and more energy. Thus, the products of a fission reaction are smaller nuclei, neutrons, and energy.

If a large number of uranium-235 nuclei are available for fission, the chain reaction continues to grow. The radiation and fast-moving nuclear particles produce a huge amount of energy. Whenever more than about four kilograms of uranium nuclei are packed together, so much energy is released so fast that it acts like a bomb. A nuclear bomb is an uncontrolled chain reaction.

Nuclear chain reactions can be controlled by spreading out the uranium so that a runaway chain reaction cannot occur. "Control rods," made from such materials as cadmium or boron, can capture some of the neutrons created when nuclei split. In a nuclear power plant, control rods are inserted between containers of the uranium to slow down the chain reaction. The neutrons captured by the control rods cannot hit other uranium nuclei, so the reaction is slowed. By capturing some—but not all—of the neutrons, scientists maintain a chain reaction at a steady rate.

The neutrons in a chain reaction split uranium better if they move slowly. So in a nuclear power plant, the uranium is usually surrounded by a material, called a moderator, that slows the neutrons. In most American power plants, the moderator is ordinary water.

Power plants can use only the $^{235}_{92}U$ isotope of uranium. Since most natural uranium is the $^{238}_{92}U$ isotope, which is not capable of fission, uranium ores must be purified. Complex purification processes have been developed to produce uranium that contains high concentrations of the $^{235}_{92}U$ isotope.

Uses of Nuclear Fission

Energy from nuclear fission can be helpful or harmful. The most dramatic use of nuclear fission is nuclear weapons. A fission bomb easily can destroy a whole city.

Nuclear power plants are another application of nuclear fission. In nuclear power plants, the energy produced during fission is used to heat water into steam. Once the steam is produced, the production of electricity in nuclear power plants is the same as it is for power plants that run on other fuels. The steam turns the blades in a turbine, which then turn a generator to produce electricity.

Nuclear power plants have many advantages over coal-burning plants. Energy for many homes and factories can be supplied without the air and water pollution resulting from burning coal, oil, and gas.

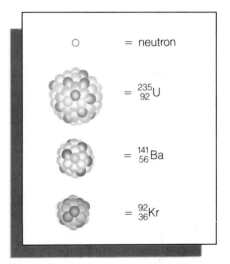

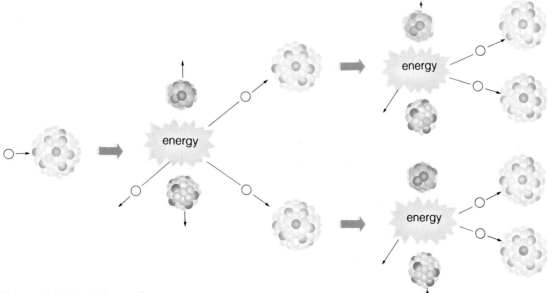

Figure 8-16 A chain reaction

Find out why $^{238}_{92}U$, which is more abundant in nature than $^{235}_{92}U$, is not a good fuel for nuclear reactors.

Figure 8-17 The fission power plant aboard the *Voyager* spacecraft is in the white cylinders.

In fact, a properly functioning nuclear power plant gives off less radioactivity than a coal-fueled power plant. Nuclear power plants also produce huge amounts of electricity from small amounts of fuel.

However, nuclear power plants, like all power plants, have problems. Dangerous radioactive wastes from nuclear plants must be stored somewhere. In addition to the radioctive wastes produced at nuclear power plants, radioactive wastes are produced during the mining and purification of uranium-containing ores. Also, accidents can occur. In 1986, a serious accident occurred at a nuclear power plant at Chernobyl in the Soviet Union. Dozens of people were killed and hundreds more were seriously injured.

Nuclear power also can be used on a smaller scale. Submarines using nuclear energy can travel underwater for long periods. Spacecraft can be supplied with energy for very long periods from the fission of a radioactive element. The fission power plant in the *Voyager* spacecraft, shown in *Figure 8-17*, is in the three white cylinders. The power has run the radios and computers since its launch in 1977. *Voyager* visited Neptune, which is nearly 3 billion miles from the sun, in 1989.

Section Review

1. How does a chain reaction work?
2. How does nuclear fission make electricity?

Challenge: Use an enclyclopedia to find the isotopes that are formed when uranium–235 undergoes radioactive decay.

Chain Reactions

Purpose

To show how a chain reaction works

Materials

- 24 dominoes
- paper and pencil

Procedure and Observations

PART A

1. Set up 10 dominoes about 10 cm from one another, as in *a*.
2. Knock over 2 or 3 of the dominoes. Note what happens to the others.

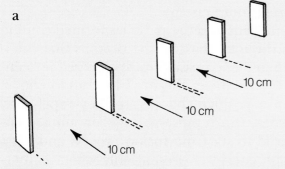

a

10 cm

10 cm

10 cm

PART B

1. Set up 24 dominoes in a line, as in *b*. Space the dominoes about 1 cm apart.
2. Knock down the first domino. Note how it affects other dominoes and how many dominoes fall. This situation resembles a nuclear chain reaction.
3. Repeat steps 1-2 a few more times.

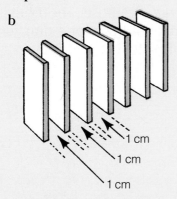

b

1 cm

1 cm

1 cm

PART C

1. Set up 3 dominoes as in *c*. When the first domino falls, it knocks down the other two. This situation represents a situation in which the fission of one uranium nucleus causes the fission of two uranium nuclei.

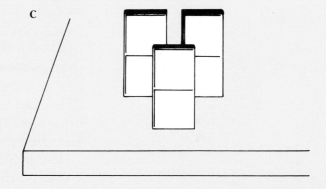

c

2. Set up one, two, and four dominoes so that one domino knocks over two, which in turn knock over four.
3. Set up 24 dominoes so that the first domino can fall and cause the other 23 to fall. The setup should have as many opportunities as possible for one domino to cause two other dominoes to fall. This will result in the fastest chain reaction.
4. Make a drawing of the setup that resulted in the fastest chain reaction.

Analysis and Conclusions

1. How can you speed up, slow down, or stop a chain reaction of dominoes?
2. How can you make the chain reaction include all the dominoes but take the longest time? How can you make the chain reaction include all the dominoes but take the shortest time?
3. How could scientists slow down or speed up a chain reaction of uranium nuclei?

8-5 Nuclear Fusion

After completing this section you will be able to

A. Define and describe nuclear fusion.

B. Describe the process by which the elements in the universe formed.

How Nuclear Fusion Happens

Stars shine by changing mass into energy in a process different from fission. In fission, a heavy nucleus breaks into lighter particles. In **nuclear fusion,** two or more light nuclei combine to produce a heavier nucleus. Both processes convert mass into energy.

Figure 8-18 shows how fusion takes place in the sun. In step 1, two hydrogen nuclei, each ^1_1H, undergo fusion to make the hydrogen isotope ^2_1H, which is known as "deuterium." Some energy is given off. In step 2, a third hydrogen nucleus fuses with the ^2_1H deuterium to make the helium isotope ^3_2He. Energy is given off again. After this process occurs two times, the two helium nuclei (^3_2He) can fuse, as seen in step 3. The result is the ordinary helium nucleus, ^4_2He, two hydrogen nuclei (^1_1H), and the release of more energy.

The helium nucleus and the particles formed contain less mass than the total mass of the protons that originally formed them. The missing mass changed into energy. This energy produces the sun's heat and light.

All nuclei have positive charges, so they repel each other. To overcome this repulsion, large amounts of energy are required to start the fusion process and keep it going. Enough energy is present only when temperatures reach millions of degrees. At such high temperatures, nuclei move very rapidly. Some come close enough to each other for the strong force in the nuclei to capture them, resulting in fusion.

Fusion occurs continually inside the sun and other stars. On earth, however, no container can hold matter at fusion-level temperatures for long. Fusion bombs have been developed, but fusion has not yet been used successfully for energy. Scientists are trying to contain the hot material in a laboratory for a time long enough to produce a controlled fusion reaction.

Figure 8-18 Fusion reactions which provide the energy for the sun to shine.

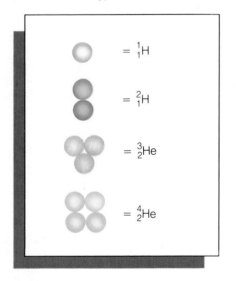

$= \,^1_1H$

$= \,^2_1H$

$= \,^3_2He$

$= \,^4_2He$

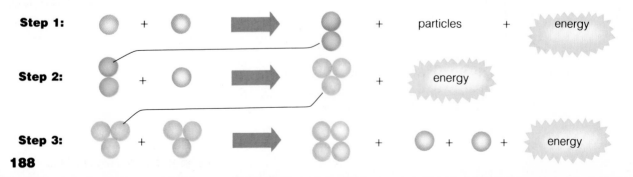

Step 1: ○ + ○ ⟶ ◐ + particles + energy

Step 2: ◑ + ○ ⟶ ◒ + energy

Step 3: ◓ + ◓ ⟶ ◈ + ○ + ○ + energy

Scientists have reached a temperature of 200 million degrees Celsius in the laboratory. They are using magnetism to hold the hot gas in place. Now they are trying to reach the high temperature in a denser gas and to hold the gas in place longer. These are all steps toward making a fusion power plant.

Fusion Forms the Elements

Astronomers believe that about 15 billion years ago, soon after the universe was formed, only protons and other particles existed. Within a few minutes, fusion began and produced deuterium and then helium nuclei. Scientists think that nuclear reactions occur continually in stars when they reach temperatures above 4 billion degrees Celsius. The neutrons produced by the nuclear reactions are fused with existing nuclei and, over time, the nuclei of all the elements are formed.

Similar processes continue today in most stars. Deep inside them, hydrogen atoms are fusing to make helium. In the sun, this process has gone on for about 5 billion years. Enough hydrogen is left in the center of the sun for another 5 billion years or so. After all the hydrogen has been used up, the helium will start fusing to make carbon.

In stars that contain many times more mass than the sun, the carbon will fuse to make still heavier elements. The combining of lighter elements within stars produces all the elements in the periodic table before iron. After iron is formed inside very massive stars, the stars collapse and then explode. In the explosion, elements heavier than iron are formed and shot out into space. *Figure 8-19* shows the remains of a star that exploded thousands of years ago.

When solar systems such as ours are formed, the matter in them is made up of the debris of stars that exploded earlier. The iron, carbon, and other elements in your body were once parts of shining stars.

Section Review

1. How does fusion differ from fission?
2. How do elements heavier than hydrogen form?

Challenge: Compare fission and fusion reactions. What are the starting materials? What happens during fission and fusion? What is left over after fission and fusion?

Explore!

Use a library to find out how a *tokomak* may help provide fusion energy on earth.

Applying Science

Studying which elements and forms of elements are present in the universe tells scientists what the universe was like long ago, soon after it formed. If the universe was dense about 10 minutes after it was formed, then all the heavy isotopes of hydrogen (^2_1H) underwent fusion to become helium. If the universe was not dense, these heavy isotopes of hydrogen would be left over. Scientists are studying gas in space to find out how much of these heavy isotopes of hydrogen are still present.

Figure 8-19 The colorful Veil Nebula is made up of the remains of a star that exploded long ago. In the explosion, the heaviest elements were formed. All the heavy elements in your body were once parts of exploding stars.

Interpreting and Making Pie Graphs

In this activity you will interpret and make a series of pie graphs to represent the radioactive decay of two isotopes.

These isotopes are identified by the name of the element followed by the mass number of the isotope. For example, $^{14}_{6}C$ is written carbon–14. Similarly, $^{40}_{19}K$ is potassium–40; $^{14}_{7}N$ is nitrogen–14; and $^{40}_{18}Ar$ is argon–40.

PART A

The series of pie graphs below represent the radioactive decay of carbon-14. Nitrogen–14 results when carbon–14 decays. Look at the pie graphs and answer the questions.

1. What percentage of carbon–14 atoms are found in the first sample?
2. In how many years is the percentage of carbon–14 reduced by half?
3. According to the pie graph, what percentage of carbon–14 remains after 11 460 years?
4. Use the pie graphs to determine the half-life of carbon–14.
5. What percentage of carbon–14 would you expect to find in a piece of wood that is 28 650 years old?

PART B

Potassium–40 has a half-life of 1.3 billion years. Argon–40 is produced when potassium–40 decays. Follow the steps below to make a series of pie graphs for the radioactive decay of potassium–40.

1. On a separate piece of paper, trace the five circles shown in Part A.
2. Choose two colors. One color represents potassium–40, the other argon–40.
3. The first circle represents the sample of potassium–40. Fill in the circle with the potassium–40 color. Label your graph.
4. To show one half-life of potassium–40, shade half the second circle with the color for potassium–40 and the other half with the color for argon–40. Indicate the number of years the pie graph represents and label the parts of the graph.
5. Fill in the next three pie graphs, showing the percentages of potassium–40 and argon–40 for the next three half-lives. Use a protractor to mark the sections, if necessary. Label each graph and indicate the number of years represented.

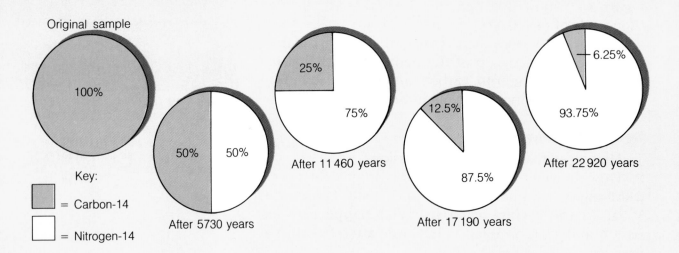

Original sample

100%

Key:

= Carbon-14

= Nitrogen-14

50% 50%

After 5730 years

25%

75%

After 11 460 years

12.5%

87.5%

After 17 190 years

6.25%

93.75%

After 22 920 years

✓ Summary

8-1 The Structure of the Nucleus

A. The strong force is one of nature's major forces. The strong force holds together nuclear particles that are close to one another.

B. More than 100 nuclear particles have been discovered. The basic nuclear particles are called quarks.

C. In addition to "up" and "down" quarks, scientists have discovered "strange" quarks and quarks named "charm," "truth," and "beauty."

8-2 Radioactivity

A. Radioactivity is the process during which nuclei of one element decay into nuclei of other elements with smaller masses.

B. Radioactivity can be detected using a Geiger counter. The amount of radiation is measured by radiation meters.

C. Radiation is used in medicine, in manufacturing processes, and to help determine the ages of fossils.

8-3 Mass, Energy, and the Speed of Light

A. Albert Einstein discovered that the mass of an object increases as its velocity (speed) increases. The mass of an object traveling at nine-tenths the speed of light is about twice the mass of the object at rest.

B. Energy can be changed into matter and matter into energy, but nothing is ever lost in the change.

8-4 Nuclear Fission

A. During nuclear fission, the nuclei of certain heavy elements split when they absorb slowly moving neutrons.

B. Nuclear fission is used to make nuclear weapons, to generate electricity, and to power submarines.

8-5 Nuclear Fusion

A. In fusion, two or more nuclei combine, producing a heavier nucleus.

B. The fusion of hydrogen nuclei has produced all atoms in the universe.

Vocabulary

For each of the following terms, write a sentence that uses the term correctly.

background radiation
chain reaction
Geiger counter
half-life
law of conservation of
   mass-energy

nuclear fission
nuclear fusion
nuclear reaction
quark
radiation

radioactivity
strong force
weak force

Check Your Knowledge

Part I: Matching   Match the definition in Column I with the correct term in Column II.

Column I
1. holds protons and neutrons together in atomic nuclei
2. means for detecting radioactivity
3. splitting of heavy nuclei after they absorb slowly moving neutrons
4. decay of unstable nuclei into smaller nuclei
5. process during which radioactive decay results in the release of two or more neutrons which cause additional nuclei to break up
6. energy and mass are equivalent
7. basic building block of the atom
8. includes nuclear fusion and fission
9. time required for half the atoms in a sample to decay
10. combining of two or more light nuclei to form a heavier nucleus

Column II
a. chain reaction
b. Geiger counter
c. half-life
d. law of conservation of mass-energy
e. nuclear reaction
f. nuclear fission
g. nuclear fusion
h. quark
i. radioactivity
j. strong force
k. weak force

Part II: Multiple Choice   Choose the letter of the best answer.
11. Cosmic rays (a) come from outer space. (b) are made in laboratories. (c) come from deep inside the earth. (d) cannot be detected.
12. What is the basic building block of matter? (a) electron (b) proton (c) quark (d) neutron
13. During nuclear fusion (a) heavy nuclei break apart. (b) light nuclei combine to form heavy nuclei. (c) mass increases greatly. (d) quarks are formed.
14. The major force that holds a nucleus of an atom together is (a) gravitation. (b) strong force. (c) weak force. (d) electromagnetism.
15. A radiation meter measures (a) heat. (b) light. (c) alpha, beta, and gamma radiation. (d) radio waves.

16. During nuclear fission (a) heavy nuclei break apart. (b) light nuclei combine to form heavy nuclei. (c) mass increases greatly. (d) quarks are formed.

Part III: Completion   Write the word or words that complete the sentence correctly.
17. The process by which elements are formed in stars is _____ _____.
18. Albert Einstein discovered the relationship between the speed of light and _____.
19. The spontaneous decay of heavy nuclei to form lighter nuclei is called _____.
20. The types of radiation from radioactive materials are _____, _____, and _____.
21. The process during which nuclear fission continues after it has once started is a _____ _____.

Check Your Understanding

1. Name the four major forces of nature.
2. Name the six kinds of quarks.
3. Describe the properties of the three types of radiation that are emitted from radioactive isotopes.
4. Describe three uses of radioactivity.
5. Describe the use of radioactivity in determining the age of a fossil.
6. What does the law of conservation of mass-energy state?
7. What are two advantages and two disadvantages of using nuclear fuel to produce electricity?
8. How are fission and fusion processes different? How are they similar?
9. Why are neutrons more easily captured by the strong force in a nucleus than protons are?

Apply Your Knowledge

1. Strontium–90 is a radioactive isotope formed during nuclear fission. This isotope is dangerous because it interferes with the absorption of calcium in the body. Calcium is needed for bone formation. If testing showed that soil concentrations of strontium–90 were 4 times the safe level, how long must a farmer wait to grow crops if the half-life of strontium–90 is 28 years?
2. Carbon–14 has a half-life of 5730 years. Suppose scientists found that one-half of the original amount of carbon-14 was present in a fossil. How old is the fossil?
3. A person at sea level absorbs about 40 millirems of radiation from cosmic rays each year. Each increase of 30.5 meters above sea level results in exposure to one additional millirem per year. If a person lived 3000 meters above sea level, about what would be his or her level of exposure to radiation?
4. A sample of a radioactive isotope with a half-life of 3 years contains 32 000 nuclei. How many nuclei of this isotope will be left at the end of 12 years?

Extend Your Knowledge

Research/Projects
1. Use the library to learn about the use of radioactive isotopes in medicine. Write a paragraph describing the way each of three isotopes is used in medicine.
2. Health experts are warning about the danger of radon gas in houses. Where does radon gas come from and why is it dangerous?

Readings
Baggett, James A. "The Chernobyl Disaster." *Scholastic Science World*, September 22, 1986, pages 12–15. Describes the cause and effects of the worst nuclear accident.

McGowen, Tom. *Radioactivity: From the Curies to the Atomic Age*. Watts, 1986. Describes what radioactivity is, and how it was discovered.

Irradiated Foods—Will They Sell?

For may years scientists have known that foods can be preserved by irradiation. In fact, since the 1960s irradiation has been used to stop insects from infesting wheat and to prevent potatoes from sprouting.

Irradiation is a popular way to preserve a variety of supermarket items in European countries. In the United States, the use of irradiation may soon become commonplace.

Gamma rays, X rays, and electron beams can be employed to preserve foods. Because these forms of radiation do not heat up the food, losses in nutritional value are very low. In addition, irradiation causes no changes in flavor, odor, color, or texture of most foods.

The process of irradiation is extremely efficient. Crates of potatoes, sacks of flour, and whole hams and turkeys can be treated all at once.

Irradiated foods can be shipped without freezing. They have a longer shelf life than fresh foods that have not been treated with radiation.

Despite the benefits of preserving foods by irradiation, many food distributors are reluctant to begin using this technology. They fear that the public simply will not buy irradiated foods. Though these foods do not give off harmful radiation, some people are confused by the terminology. They mistakenly believe that

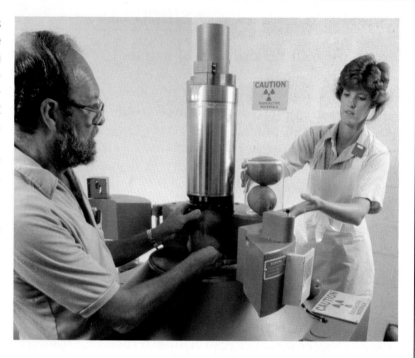

irradiated foods are radioactive. For this reason, food distributors believe that educating the consumer about the safety of irradiated foods might be a massive and expensive task.

Food distributors and other people are also concerned about the indirect effects of using radiation to preserve foods. They think that factory workers in charge of irradiating the food might be exposed to unsafe levels of radiation.

Another cause for concern is the buildup of radioactive wastes from the spent fuel rods in the irradiating machines. Until scientists find a safe way to dispose of these wastes, many people are reluctant to expand the uses of radiation. Finally, increased

use of radiation may produce mutant forms of bacteria, molds, and insects. These new pathogens may pose a worse health threat than those in existence today.

Whether the benefits of food irradiation outweigh the risks, at this point, is an ongoing debate. In the end, the American consumer will make the final decision.

For Discussion

1. What are some advantages of preserving food by irradiation?

2. What are some of the concerns people have about irradiated foods and the technology associated with food irradiation?

3. Would you buy food that has been irradiated? Give reasons for your answer.

Neon Signs

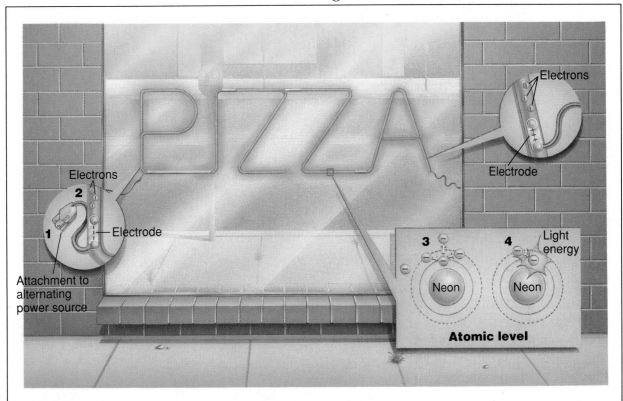

You see them in every town and city—glowing neon signs with bright, flashy messages. Their shapes and colors are unlimited. They advertise movies, restaurants, car lots, and many other places people need to find.

They are called neon signs because they were first made using the rare gas neon. A French chemist, Georges Claude, discovered a way to remove neon from the other gases in the atmosphere and place it in a glass tube used for lighting. Neon is still used in signs today, but so are other elements including argon and mercury. Combined in measured amounts, these elements give the signs dif-ferent colors and degrees of brightness. Neon gas gives lights a bright red-orange color. Argon gas produces a pale lavender light.

The signs are made by heating glass tubes and bending them into shapes or letters. Then electrodes for conducting electricity are fit into the ends of the tubes. Before the tubes are sealed, the air inside is pumped out and replaced with neon or other gases. Follow the diagram above to learn how the neon light works.

1. The electrodes in the ends of the tubes are attached to an alternating current source, and so they switch from being positive to being negative and back again. Each electrode alternates charge every $\frac{1}{120}$th of a second.

2. Free electrons from the electrode that has a negative charge are pushed into the neon gas. These electrons move rapidly toward the positively-charged electrode.

3. The moving electrons strike the electrons in the neon atoms. The collisions "bump" the orbiting electrons into wider orbits.

4. Each bumped electron quickly drops back to its original orbit. As it drops back, it gives off a burst of light energy. The light energy released from billions of neon atoms creates the glowing light of the neon sign.

UNIT 3
Changes in Matter

Technology *in Perspective*

Learning the components of matter, putting pieces of matter together to make new forms or kinds—this is the fascinating work of chemists and physicists. It has brought about our world of modern ways and materials.

16th Century

People have practiced chemistry of a sort since early times. Making wine, dying cloth in vats, making soap, tanning leather—all of these and others involve chemical reactions that in some manner change matter. In cooking, too, compounds and mixtures are concocted to arrive at desired tastes. The alchemists of ancient times concerned themselves mainly—and fruitlessly—with trying to make gold from substances of lesser value or in mixing magical potions. They did little to promote better living.

18th Century

Robert Boyle provided a near-modern definition of elements in the 17th century, getting rid of the belief inherited from the Greeks that there were only four elements: earth, air, fire, and water. Armed with this new approach, chemists of the 18th century throughout Europe began putting this knowledge to work. Soap making moved out of the home and became an industry. Glass, textiles, and other products were also industrialized. As chemists learned their composition and arrived at ways to put them into large-scale production, the chemical industry was born.

Chapter 9 Compounds and Mixtures
Chapter 10 Holding Atoms Together
Chapter 11 Chemical Reactions
Chapter 12 Acids and Bases

19th Century

Numerous chemical processes, many still in use today, came into being during the 1800s. Manufacture of chemical fertilizers, vulcanized rubber, rayon, synthetic dyes, and celluloid—the first plastic— were among the industries spawned by the knowledge of how to put chemicals to work for people. Each basic process produced spinoff products, too, such as saccharin from the coal tar used in making dyes. Each process also demanded raw materials, some calling for establishment of still other kinds of factories. In making synthetic dyes, for example, great quantities of sulfuric acid had to be supplied.

20th Century

Chemical products, such as plastic bags, are so commonplace in our world today that people are most awed by those few products that are natural. Clothing, automobiles, furniture, the endless variety of plastic products literally have people living in a synthetic world. Chemistry has become so sophisticated that products are tailor-made to fit specific needs. This is particularly important in the world of medicine where chemical products are used to save millions of lives each year.

CHAPTER 9
Compounds and Mixtures

The food on the table is made of substances whose elements have been combined in a variety of ways. Some of the foods are pure chemical substances, while others are mixtures of pure chemical substances. The food you eat, the air you breathe, the building you live in, and even your own body are made of such compounds and mixtures.

Organizing Your Study Skills The outline below will help you see how the chapter is organized and what you should learn as you read.

I. Section 9-1: Identifying Compounds
   A. What is a compound?
   B. What are some characteristics of compounds?
   C. What are some common compounds?

II. Section 9-2: Identifying Mixtures
   A. What is a mixture?
   B. How can substances in mixtures be separated?

III. Section 9-3: Solutions—One Kind of Mixture
   A. How does a solution form?
   B. What are the different types of solutions?
   C. How do scientists describe the strength of solutions?

IV. Section 9-4: Suspensions—Another Kind of Mixture
   A. How do suspensions differ from solutions?
   B. What are some kinds of suspensions?

After completing this section you will be able to

A. Define the term compound.
B. Explain how compounds differ from elements.
C. List some common compounds.

9-1 Identifying Compounds

Elements Combine to Form Compounds

The pair of scissors in the picture was left outside in the rain. A rough, brown material appeared on the blades after several days. Where did the material come from? Is it part of the metal? Did the rain cause it?

The rust on the blades is a new substance that formed from two other substances. One of the substances is iron, the main element in the steel scissors. The other substance is oxygen, a gas in the air. Iron and oxygen combine to form rust when water is present.

A substance formed by the chemical combination of two or more elements is a **compound.** Iron and oxygen join chemically to form a compound commonly known as rust.

Although elements combine chemically, they cannot be broken down into simpler substances by ordinary chemical means. Oxygen is a colorless, tasteless gas. Iron is a gray, malleable, ductile solid. The compound rust is unlike either of the elements that joined to form it. It is brown and breaks apart easily. The chemical change that occurred when the scissors rusted produced a substance with different properties.

Figure 9-1 The pair of scissors rusted when it was left outside. Rust forms because iron in the scissors combines with oxygen and water.

When a particular compound forms, it always contains the same elements and the atoms of the elements are in the same ratios. For example, rust contains iron and oxygen. The ratio of atoms required to form rust is: two iron atoms for three oxygen atoms. Similarly, a molecule of water forms when two hydrogen atoms and one oxygen atom combine chemically.

A **chemical formula** represents a chemical compound. A formula includes symbols of elements and numbers to show the ratios of atoms. For instance, H_2O is the chemical formula for water. H is the symbol for the element hydrogen and O is the symbol for oxygen. The small number 2 is called a subscript. It shows that each molecule of water contains two atoms of hydrogen. If an element symbol has no subscript, the subscript is understood to be one. Therefore, each H_2O molecule has one oxygen atom.

NaCl represents the compound you know as table salt. Its chemical name is sodium chloride. Na stands for sodium and Cl for chlorine. What ratio of sodium and chlorine atoms are required to form a sample of salt?

Compounds Can Be Broken Down

Most compounds look different from the elements they contain. For example, the compound rust looks different from iron, which is gray, and from oxygen, which is an invisible gas. Also, rust crumbles if you handle it, but iron can be shaped.

Because the elements in a compound are chemically joined, a chemical process is necessary to separate them. Compounds can be broken down by various methods. Heating breaks down some compounds. The iron in rust can be separated from the oxygen by heating the compound with the element carbon. In the heating process, the oxygen combines with the carbon, producing carbon dioxide gas. Pure iron remains after the reaction.

Electrolysis is another process used to separate elements in a compound. In electrolysis, an electric current is passed through the compound. During electrolysis, water breaks down into hydrogen gas and oxygen gas. Note that the two elements are pure substances that cannot be broken down chemically. Thus, hydrogen and oxygen are not affected by electrolysis.

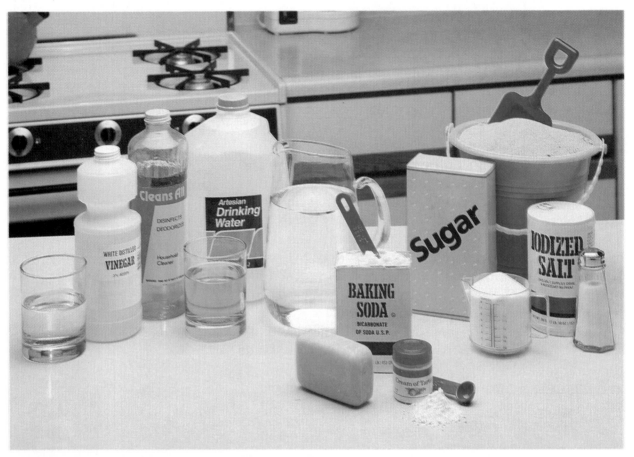

Figure 9-3 These common substances are compounds.

Name	Formula
Sugar	$C_{12}H_{22}O_{11}$
Salt	NaCl
Water	H_2O
Ammonia	NH_4OH
Cream of Tartar	$KHC_4H_4O_6$
Soap	$C_{17}H_{35}COONa$
Baking Soda	$NaHCO_3$
Sand	SiO_2

Figure 9-2 Chemical formulas of the compounds shown in the photograph

Formulas for Common Compounds

Many millions of compounds exist. You probably know the names of very few of them. *Figure 9-2* lists the formulas of some common compounds, which are also shown in the picture.

Table salt and sugar look alike, but compare their formulas in the table. Salt has a simple chemical formula. Equal numbers sodium and chlorine atoms are required to form salt. Sugar's chemical formula is much more complex. The most common type of sugar molecule contains twelve carbon atoms, twenty-two hydrogen atoms, and eleven oxygen atoms.

Section Review

1. How is a compound formed?
2. How are compounds different from elements?
3. Give the formulas of two compounds and tell what the formulas represent.

Challenge: Explain why samples of pure elements are hard to find in nature.

Forming a Compound

Purpose

To observe the formation of a compound

Materials

- 50 mL of warm vinegar in a paper cup
- 2 large test tubes
- 2 wads of coarse steel wool about 3 cm in diameter
- baking pan
- metric ruler
- clock or watch to measure minutes
- water
- cover goggles

Procedure and Observations

PART A

1. *CAUTION: Wear your cover goggles during this activity.* Pour water into the baking pan to a depth of 0.5 cm.
2. Soak one wad of steel wool in the cup of vinegar for one minute. Remove the wad and gently squeeze out the vinegar.
3. Push the wet steel wool into the bottom of a test tube. Push the other wad of steel wool into the second test tube.
4. Stand both tubes upside down in the water, as in **a.** The steel wool must stay in place.
5. Measure the height of the water in each test tube, as in **b.** Record the height of the water.

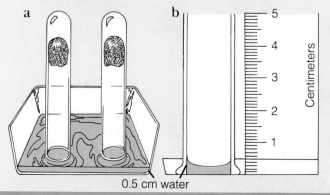

0.5 cm water

6. Measure and record the height of the water in each tube at the end of 4, 8, 12, 16, and 20 minutes.
7. Make a copy of the graph shown in **c.**
8. Plot each height with its time for the wet steel wool. Connect your points with a solid line. On the same grid, plot the times and heights for the dry steel wool. Connect these points with a dashed line.

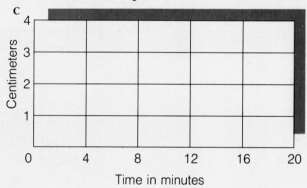

c

Centimeters

Time in minutes

PART B

1. Turn each test tube right side up. Leave the steel wool inside.
2. Fill each test tube half full with water.
3. Cover the mouths of the test tubes with your thumbs. Shake the test tubes five or six times.
4. Record any color changes you observe.

Analysis and Conclusions

1. How much did the water level in each tube change during the 20 minutes? What do these results show?
2. Use your observations to explain what happened in the two test tubes during the 20-minute period.
3. What compound formed in this chemical reaction? What elements were necessary and where did they come from?

Identifying Mixtures

After completing this section you will be able to

A. Describe what a mixture is.
B. Describe how substances in a mixture can be separated.

Substances in a Mixture Do Not Combine Chemically

You may have eaten a snack made from a mixture of different kinds of nuts. Each ingredient in this nut mixture keeps its own taste and shape. In a similar way, some substances can mix physically with other substances without joining chemically.

If you mix iron dust with powdered sulfur, the result is not a compound. The iron remains a gray metal, and the sulfur remains a yellow powder. The elements in this iron and sulfur combination can be separated by using a magnet. However, iron and sulfur will form a compound if heat is added to cause a chemical reaction.

Two or more substances that are mixed together but not joined chemically form a **mixture.** Substances in a mixture can be either elements or compounds. Iron dust and sulfur powder form a mixture of two elements. Sand and sugar form a mixture of two compounds. In some mixtures you can see the individual substances, as shown in the picture of the paint mixture. Another example of a mixture is soil, which consists of materials such as sand, rock, clay, and decaying leaves.

Figure 9-4 A mixture of paints

Air is a mixture of gases, but you cannot see any of the gases. Some of the gases in air are elements, while others are compounds. Milk is a mixture of water, fats, sugars, and other compounds. Perfumes, crayons, and toothpaste are also mixtures, but their individual components cannot be distinguished.

Unlike a compound, a mixture does not necessarily contain a specific amount of each substance. For example, the compound iron sulfide, FeS, always has one iron atom for every sulfur atom. However, a mixture of iron and sulfur can have any number of each kind of atom.

Separating Substances in a Mixture

You can easily separate the ingredients in some mixtures. For example, you can remove solid particles from a liquid by using a filter. The liquid flows through the filter, but the solid particles do not. Filters in an air conditioner remove bits of dust from the air. *Figure 9-5* shows a mixture of water and soil being poured into a funnel that contains a piece of filter paper. Notice that the water that has passed through the filter is clear. The soil is separated from the water and remains on the filter paper in the picture on the right.

Figure 9-5 Some mixtures, such as soil and water, can be separated by pouring the mixture through a filter.

Figure 9-6 A mixture containing water and vegetable oil separates into two layers.

Substances in some mixtures separate naturally. *Figure 9-6* shows how water and oil separate if the mixture is left standing. The particles of water are denser than the particles of oil. The water gradually sinks to the bottom of the container.

Section Review

1. How can you tell the difference between a mixture and a compound?
2. Why do water and oil separate?

Challenge: Are the properties of a compound always the same? Are the properties of a mixture always the same? Explain.

People and Science

Marjorie Smigel, Conservation Activist

In 1980, Marjorie Smigel of Bethesda, Maryland, discovered a worker from a commercial lawn care service spraying trees in her backyard. When she questioned him, she found out that he was at the wrong address. She wondered how often this mistake had happened before.

Marjorie Smigel and some of her friends did research about the use of chemical pesticides on lawns, trees, and shrubs. They learned that federal, state and local laws were totally inadequate to deal with new industries that apply pesticides in

urban/suburban areas.

Smigel created an educational program for communities and enlisted support for a pesticide "right to know" ordinance that was enacted by Montgomery County, Maryland, in 1986. Since then, five states have started to regulate commercial pesticide application.

Because of Marjorie Smigel's efforts, companies that take care of lawns, trees, and shrubs now must provide homeowners with information on health risks. They also must post signs on freshly treated areas.

9-3 Solutions—One Kind of Mixture

Objectives

After completing this section you will be able to

A. Describe what happens when one material dissolves in another.

B. Name the different types of solutions.

C. Explain solubility curves.

How Substances Dissolve

Lemon juice, water, and sugar form a uniform mixture when stirred together. Each substance cannot be seen because it has broken into very small particles. This kind of mixture is a **solution.** Even though you no longer see the sugar, it makes the solution taste sweet, and the lemon flavor still remains. Neither the sugar, the lemon juice, nor the water has changed into a new substance.

The most common kind of solution is a solid dissolved in a liquid, such as sugar in water. The sugar dissolves in the water. The diagram shows that sugar dissolves when individual particles break away from a sugar cube. The particles of water attract the sugar particles, which spread into spaces between water particles. After a while, all the particles are evenly mixed. The different substances do not settle in layers. Instead, they stay mixed. Although the sugar particles do not combine chemically with the water particles, they are too tiny to be seen. The sugar particles are even small enough to pass through a filter.

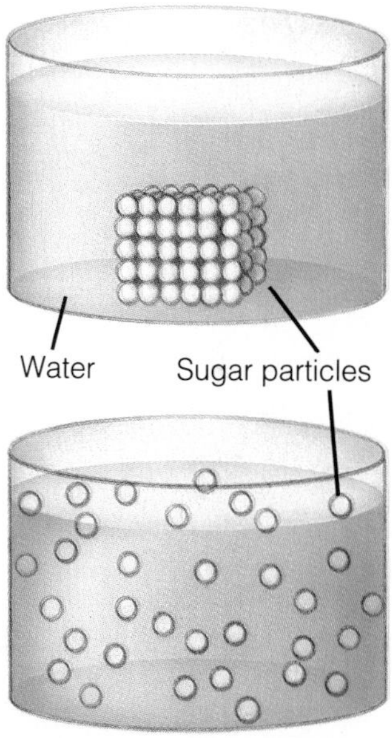

Figure 9-7 Particles in a cube of sugar spread evenly throughout water, forming a solution.

Some solutions consist of one liquid dissolved in another liquid. Water and glycol form such a solution. Glycol is used in car radiators to keep water from freezing. Other solutions, such as carbonated soft drinks, contain a gas dissolved in a liquid. The picture shows bubbles of gas in a glass of carbonated water. The dissolved gas, carbon dioxide, gives the water its fizz.

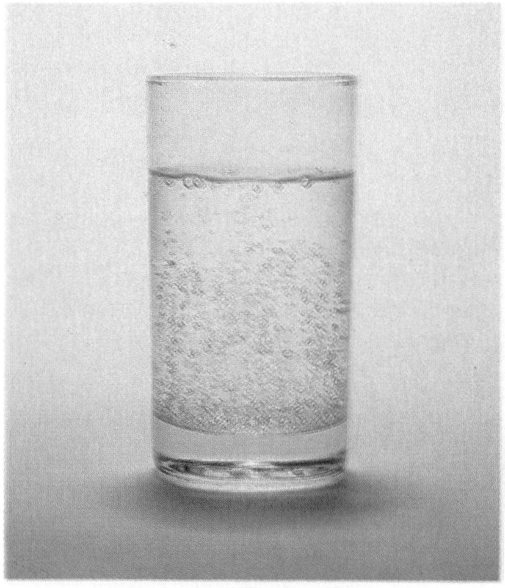

Figure 9-8 Carbonated water contains dissolved carbon dioxide gas.

If one substance can be dissolved in another substance, it is said to be **soluble** in that substance. Sugar is soluble in water. If a substance cannot be dissolved in another substance, it is insoluble in that substance. Sand is insoluble in water.

A substance that dissolves other materials is a **solvent.** The substance being dissolved is a **solute.** In a solution of sugar and water, sugar is the solute and water is the solvent.

Water is the most common solvent, but not all materials dissolve in water. For example, water does not dissolve oil-based paints, but turpentine does.

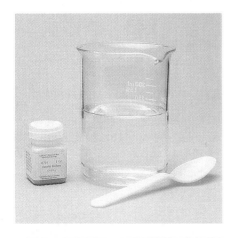

Figure 9-9 Dissolving blue copper sulfate crystals (the solute) in water (the solvent) produces a blue copper sulfate solution.

Describing Solutions

A solution can contain various amounts of solute. Solutions with a small amount of solute are described as **dilute.** Weak coffee is a dilute solution. A solution with a large amount of solute is **concentrated.** Strong coffee is a concentrated solution.

If you stir sugar into cold water and gradually add more sugar, the solution becomes more and more concentrated. Eventually, no more solute can be dissolved at that temperature and pressure. The solution is **saturated.** If you add any more sugar to this saturated solution, the added sugar will sink to the bottom. However, if you heat the solution, still more sugar can dissolve. Usually, as a solution's temperature rises, more solid solute can dissolve in a liquid solvent.

The opposite situation is true for gases dissolved in a liquid. Usually, more gas can dissolve in a liquid solvent as the solution's temperature decreases. If you set a glass of cold water on a table, it will warm up to room temperature. As the water warms, you will be able to see small bubbles appear in the water. These bubbles are formed by gases from the air that can no longer remain dissolved in the warm solution.

Determining Solubility

The **solubility** of a solution describes the amount of solute necessary to saturate a definite amount of a solvent at a given temperature.

The graph in *Figure 9-10* shows the solubility curves of two potassium compounds in water. KNO_3 is the formula for potassium nitrate. KCl is potassium chloride, which is used as a substitute for table salt by people on low sodium diets. Although both compounds contain potassium, water does not dissolve the same amount of each at all temperatures. You can see on the graph that at 50°C, about 40 grams of KCl can dissolve in 100 grams of water. But notice that at the same temperature, about 90 grams of KNO_3 can dissolve in 100 grams of water. At what temperature is the solubility of both compounds the same?

For many solids, solubility increases as temperatures rise and solubility decreases as temperatures drop. With an increase in temperature, a solid's particles move faster and spread farther apart. This process allows more room in a liquid for dissolved particles.

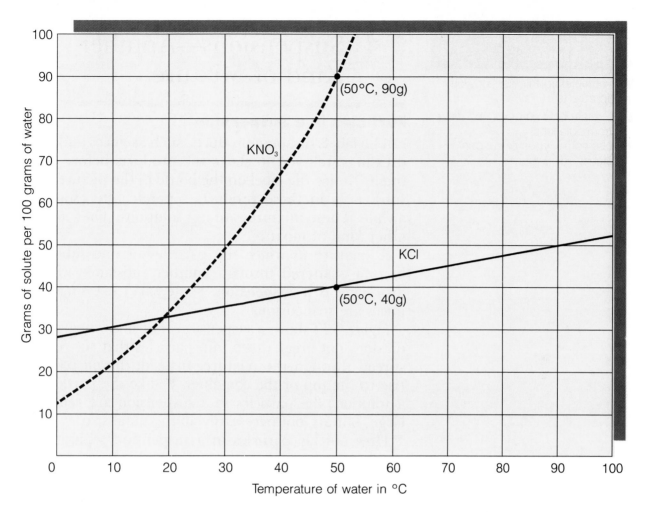

On the other hand, an increase in temperature decreases the solubility of a gas in a liquid. When the solution's temperature increases, the speed of the dissolved gas particles increases. As the dissolved gas particles gain energy, they tend to leave the solution. The next time you heat a pan of water on a stove, notice that bubbles of dissolved air escape long before the water boils. The water is able to hold less air in solution as its temperature increases.

Figure 9-10 The solubilities of potassium chloride (KCl) and potassium nitrate (KNO_3) increase as temperature goes from 0°C to 100°C.

Section Review

1. How do solutions differ from other mixtures?
2. What are dilute, concentrated, and saturated solutions?
3. What does a solubility curve tell you about a solute and solvent?

Challenge: A student mixes a saturated solution of sugar in water on a Friday. On Monday morning, the open container has particles of sugar on the bottom. Suggest several reasons to explain why this happened.

After completing this section you will be able to

A. Explain how suspensions differ from solutions.
B. List some types of suspensions.

9-4 Suspensions—Another Kind of Mixture

Particles in a Suspension

The labels on some products, such as juices and salad dressings, tell you to shake the products before using them. Notice the label on the bottle in the picture. The substances in these products separate after standing awhile. These mixtures are not solutions. They are another kind of mixture.

A mixture in which the particles of one substance become scattered through another substance without dissolving is a **suspension.** Some salad dressings and juices are suspensions.

Figure 9-11 shows a suspension of oil and vinegar. The oil does not break down into particles that stay evenly spread through the mixture. Instead, the oil particles rise to the top of the container. Unlike the particles in a solution, the particles in a suspension are relatively large, but are not necessarily all the same size.

How quickly particles in a suspension separate depends mainly on their size and weight. In most cases, large or heavy particles separate more quickly than small or light particles.

Figure 9-11 The substances in a suspension separate after standing awhile.

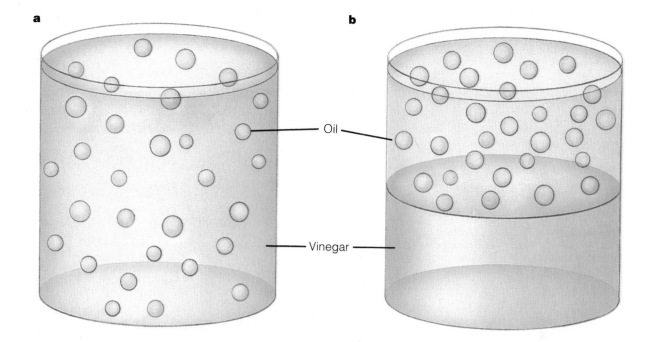

a

b

Oil

Vinegar

Kinds of Suspensions

Just as there are several types of solutions, there are also several types of suspensions. One type of suspension contains solid particles suspended in a liquid, such as sand mixed with water. If this mixture stands awhile, sand settles out of the water.

Another type of suspension contains solid particles scattered throughout a gas. Smoke is a suspension of solid dirt and dust particles in the gases of air. After a while, the solid particles fall to the ground.

A third type of suspension contains gas molecules scattered throughout a liquid. Shaving cream is a suspension of a gas in a liquid. The gas is air, and the liquid is a creamy fluid. After standing a short time, shaving cream flattens because the air escapes. Similarly, whipped cream is a suspension of air in cream.

On the other hand, gases are never suspended in other gases. A mixture of gases is always a solution, never a suspension. When two or more volumes of gases combine, gas molecules mix evenly, just as solute and solvent do in a solution.

The particles in solutions are molecular in size and they remain in solution. The particles in suspensions are much larger, and they settle out of the suspension. However, some suspensions, called colloids, contain very small particles. Such mixtures have properties of both solutions and suspensions.

Figure 9-12 a Drops of oil are suspended in vinegar. **b** The suspension separates into two layers. Oil, which is less dense, rises to the top.

Explore!

Some of the ingredients in foods, cosmetics, and drugs are compounds and suspensions. Check the labels of these products for such ingredients. Then use an encyclopedia or chemistry book to learn more about these ingredients.

Figure 9-13 The light beam passes directly through the solution on the left, but it scatters particles in the colloid on the right.

Figure 9-14 In mayonnaise, egg yolk is an emulsifier that keeps oil and vinegar particles from separating.

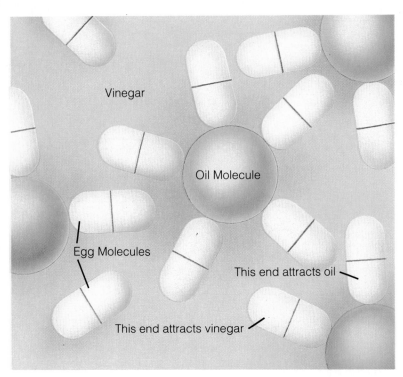

Vinegar

Oil Molecule

Egg Molecules

This end attracts oil

This end attracts vinegar

A suspension of small particles that remain mixed in a gas, liquid, or solid is a **colloid.** A colloid only appears to be a solution. Even though the particles in a colloid are too small to be seen, they are larger than the particles in a solution. Milk, blood, fog, and some paints are examples of colloids. As the pictures show, the particles in a colloid are big enough to scatter a beam of light. The particles in a solution are not as big and do not scatter the light beam.

A colloid that consists of one liquid suspended in another liquid is an **emulsion.** For example, mayonnaise is an emulsion made from vinegar and oil, plus egg yolks. The egg yolk is an emulsifier. An **emulsifier** is a substance that keeps the particles of one liquid mixed in another liquid.

In *Figure 9-14*, the emulsifier holds the particles of the two liquids in the mixture. One end of the emulsifier attracts vinegar, and the other end attracts oil. Many, but not all, emulsions have emulsifiers.

Section Review

1. How do the particles in a suspension differ from the particles in a solution?
2. What is a colloid? What is an emulsion?

Challenge: Explain how a mixture can be both a solution and a suspension at the same time.

Investigating Suspensions, Solutions, and Emulsions

Purpose

To identify various types of mixtures

Materials

- 50 mL of garden soil
- 50 mL of sugar
- 50 mL of vegetable oil
- 5 mL of liquid soap
- water
- 6 test tubes
- test tube rack
- medicine dropper
- 2 filter papers
- metal spoon
- Bunsen burner
- hot pad
- funnel
- matches
- cover goggles

Procedure and Observations

PART A

1. Fold the filter paper, as in **a.** Place it in the funnel, as in **b.**
2. Pour soil into a test tube to a depth of 0.5 cm. Pour sugar into another test tube to the same depth. Add water to both test tubes until they are about two-thirds full.
3. Shake the test tubes to mix the ingredients.
4. Allow the test tubes to remain still for 5 minutes. Observe and record what happens to the contents.
5. Place the funnel containing the filter paper in an empty test tube.

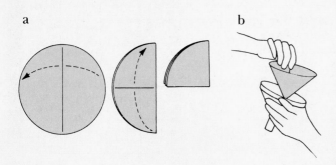

a   b

6. Shake the soil and water mixture well and pour it through the funnel. Record what you observe.
7. Place some of the substance that passed through the filter paper in the spoon.
8. Put on your cover goggles. Using a hot pad, hold the spoon over a lighted Bunsen burner, as in **c,** until most of the liquid boils away. Record your observations. *CAUTION: Be sure long hair is tied back and kept clear of the flame and do not touch the hot spoon.*
9. Repeat steps 1 and 5-8 for the sugar and water.

c

PART B

1. Fill two test tubes half full with water.
2. Add oil to both tubes until they are three-fourths full.
3. Add a few drops of soap to one of the test tubes.
4. Cover both tubes with your thumbs and shake them for 10 seconds.
5. Allow both test tubes to remain still for 5 minutes. Observe what happens to the contents. Record your observations.

Analysis and Conclusions

1. Name and describe the kinds of mixtures you made in Parts A and B.
2. What did the soap do to the oil and water mixture?
3. In Part B, which test tube was the control?

Graphing and Interpreting Data

You have learned that line graphs show relationships between two quantities or factors. For example, a line graph can show how the solubility of a substance changes as the temperature changes. In this activity you will graph the solubility of two different salts, table salt (NaCl) and potassium chloride (KCl). Then, use your graph to answer the questions.

Copy the grid shown below. Note the range of data in the table and determine appropriate scales for both the horizontal and vertical axes. Plot the data for KCl and connect the points with a line. Using a different color, plot the data for NaCl and connect the points with a line. Title your graph.

Next, study the graph and answer the following questions.

1. What quantity is plotted on the vertical axis of the graph?
2. What quantity is plotted on the horizontal axis of the graph?
3. What temperature is required to dissolve 36 grams of sodium chloride in 100 grams of water?
4. How many grams of potassium chloride dissolve in 100 grams of water at 60°C?
5. How many grams of potassium chloride dissolve in 100 grams of water at 90°C?
6. At what temperature could you dissolve equal amounts of both compounds?
7. What does the graph tell you about the relationship of solubility to temperature for these two substances?

Temp. in °C	NaCl in grams	KCl in grams
0	34	29
20	35	34
40	36	39
60	37	44
80	38	49
100	39	54

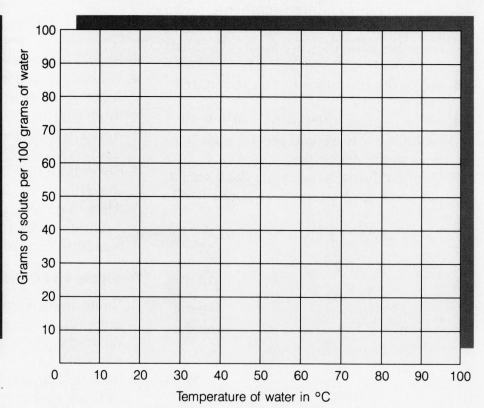

✔ Summary

9-1 Identifying Compounds

A. A compound is formed by the chemical combination of two or more elements.

B. The number and kind of atoms joined in a specific compound are always the same.

C. A compound has properties that are different from the properties of the elements.

9-2 Identifying Mixtures

A. A mixture consists of two or more substances mixed together, but not joined chemically.

B. A mixture does not have a definite number of each type of atom. Substances in mixtures maintain their own individual properties. The substances in a mixture can be separated. Filtering is a common way to separate solids from a liquid mixture.

9-3 Solutions—One Kind of Mixture

A. A solution is a mixture in which the dissolved substances break down into tiny particles and mix evenly.

B. Dilute solutions contain a small amount of solute in a solvent. Concentrated solutions contain a large amount of solute in a solvent. Saturated solutions contain all the solute that a solvent can hold at a given temperature.

C. Solubility describes how much solute can be dissolved in a given amount of solvent at a certain temperature. Often, the solubility of a solid in liquid increases with an increase in temperature. The solubility of a gas in liquid decreases with an increase in temperature.

9-4 Suspensions—Another Kind of Mixture

A. A suspension is a mixture in which particles of one substance are scattered evenly throughout another substance. The particles may settle out of a solution. Large particles will settle before smaller particles.

B. Colloids are suspensions in which the particles are larger than those in solutions. An emulsion is a colloid of one liquid in another liquid.

Vocabulary

For each of the following terms, write a sentence that uses the term correctly.

chemical formula	dilute	saturated	solution
colloid	emulsifier	solubility	solvent
compound	emulsion	soluble	suspension
concentrated	mixture	solute	

✔ Check Your Knowledge

Part I: Matching   Match the definition in Column I with the correct term in Column II.

Column I
1. containing a small amount of solute
2. a substance that dissolves other substances
3. two or more elements chemically joined in definite amounts
4. two or more substances mixed but not chemically joined
5. a suspension in which the particles stay mixed
6. a substance that is dissolved by another substance
7. containing a large amount of solute
8. a colloid of one liquid in another
9. a mixture in which the substances break into separate particles and one dissolves in the other
10. a mixture in which the particles are scattered but not dissolved

Column II
a. colloid
b. compound
c. concentrated
d. dilute
e. emulsion
f. mixture
g. saturated
h. solute
i. solution
j. solvent
k. suspension

Part II: Multiple Choice   Choose the letter of the best answer.

11. The substances in a mixture (a) are always evenly spread. (b) are joined chemically. (c) are not joined chemically. (d) must be in definite amounts.
12. The solute in a solution (a) settles out. (b) can be filtered out. (c) can be seen. (d) breaks down into tiny particles.
13. Without heating, saturated solutions usually (a) can dissolve more solute. (b) do not stay mixed. (c) cannot dissolve more solute. (d) do not mix.
14. Adding more solvent to a solution makes the solution more (a) saturated. (b) emulsified. (c) concentrated. (d) dilute.
15. The particles in a suspension (a) never separate. (b) stay mixed. (c) are chemically joined. (d) are not dissolved.
16. Emulsifiers cause emulsions to (a) separate. (b) stay mixed. (c) dissolve. (d) become solutions.
17. The particles in a colloid (a) remain mixed. (b) separate. (c) dissolve easily. (d) are very large.
18. You boil away a clear liquid until a solid remains. The liquid and solid were (a) a solution. (b) a suspension. (c) an emulsion. (d) a colloid.

Part III: Completion   Write the word or words that complete the sentence correctly.

19. An abbreviation for the names and number of atoms that combine to form a compound is called a _____.
20. The substances in a mixture can be either elements or _____.
21. The solvent used most commonly is _____.
22. A beam of light is scattered by the particles in a _____.
23. In mayonnaise, egg yolk is the _____ that keeps the oil and vinegar mixed.

Check Your Understanding

1. What does the formula of a compound tell you about the particles of that compound? Give an example.
2. Rust—or iron oxide—is a compound. What does this tell you about the substance?
3. State three characteristics of a solution.
4. What does it mean when you say that a substance is soluble or insoluble in another substance?
5. What is a solvent? Name three solvents.
6. How are the particles in a suspension different from the particles in a solution?
7. Can a gas ever be suspended in another gas? Explain your answer.
8. Define mixture. Name two mixtures not described in this chapter and list the substances in each.
9. If you stirred sugar and sand together, would you make a mixture or a compound? Explain.

 Apply Your Knowledge

1. Explain the formulas in the chart on page 202. List the elements in each compound and the relative number of atoms of each.
2. When a hot sugar solution cools, some sugar drops out of the solution. Was this solution saturated before or after cooling? Explain.
3. Suppose you were given a bottle that contained a mixture of a liquid and a solid. How could you tell whether the mixture was a solution or a suspension?
4. The water in the ocean contains salt. Explain why a layer of salt does not form on the ocean floor.
5. Why do stream beds gradually fill up with soil and gravel?
6. Hard water contains dissolved minerals. Could you soften hard water by filtering out the minerals? Explain your answer.

 Extend Your Knowledge

Research/Projects

1. Visit a water treatment or sewage treatment plant to find out how the plant removes solid substances from water.
2. Make some lemon soda water. Use a clean plastic 1- or 2-liter bottle with a screw top. Put about one spoonful of baking soda and about 250 mL of water into the bottle. Add about 10 mL of lemon juice and quickly screw on the top.

Readings

Cobb, Vicki. *Chemically Active!* Lippincott, 1985. Describes how to make solutions, and how to separate mixtures.

Ponte, Lowell. "Dawn of the New Stone Age." *Reader's Digest,* July, 1987, pages 128-133. Discusses the applications of new ceramic compounds that can be used in everything from tableware and car engines to false teeth.

CHAPTER 10
Holding Atoms Together

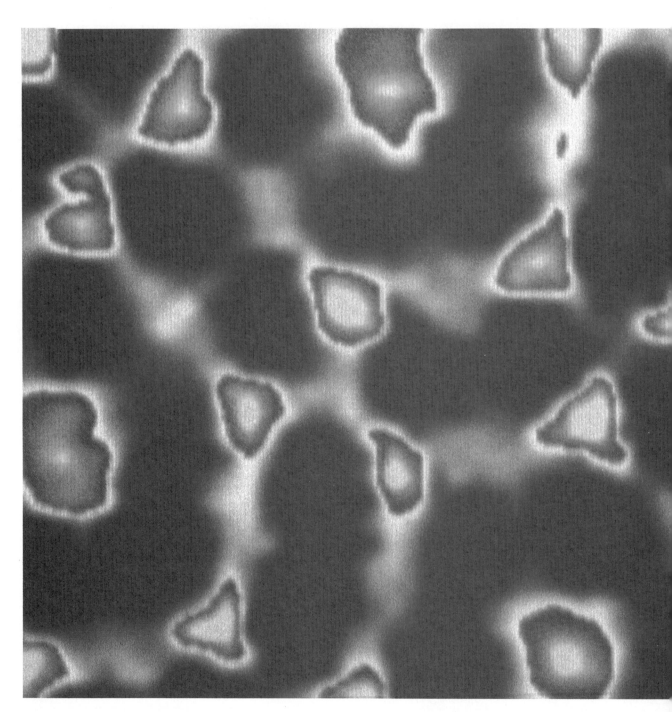

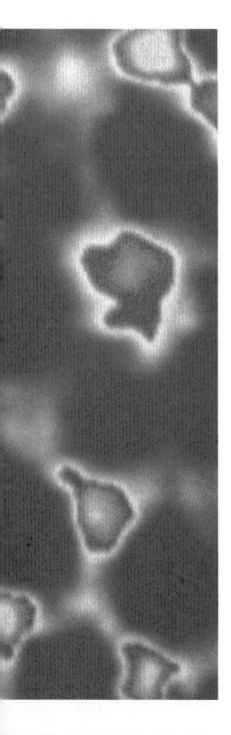

The photograph shows silicon atoms magnified about 10 million times. The nuclei are red and yellow. The faint, cloudy links between the nuclei are the outermost electrons in each atom. Scientists call them "sticky" electrons because they help hold the silicon nuclei together.

Organizing Your Study Skills The outline below will help you see how the chapter is organized and what you should learn as you read.

I. **Section 10-1: Bonding Atoms**
   A. How are chemical bonds defined?
   B. How do electrons affect bonding?
   C. What characteristics in a substance do bonds determine?

II. **Section 10-2: Ionic Bonding**
   A. How are ions defined?
   B. What are some of the properties of ionic compounds?

III. **Section 10-3: Covalent Bonding**
   A. What is a covalent bond?
   B. What are covalent compounds like?
   C. How are carbon compounds linked?
   D. How are the hydrocarbons in crude oil separated?

IV. **Section 10-4: Chemical Equations and Dot Diagrams**
   A. What do chemical equations represent?
   B. How does the conservation of mass law apply to chemical reactions?
   C. How are dot diagrams used to show ionic bonding?
   D. How are dot diagrams used to show covalent bonding?

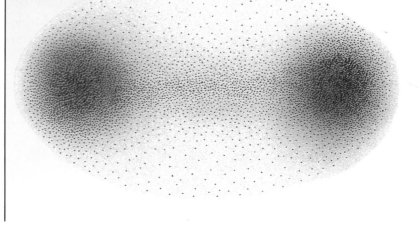

10-1 Bonding Atoms

After completing this section, you will be able to

A. Define chemical bonds.
B. Describe how electrons affect bonding.
C. Name some characteristics that bonds determine in a substance.

Chemical Bonds Hold Atoms Together

Elements differ in their tendencies to form compounds. The differences depend on how strongly electrons are held by an atom's nucleus, and on how strongly electrons are attracted by other atoms.

Electrons and protons attract each other because they have opposite charges. The attraction between electrons and protons holds an atom together. These attractions extend outside the atom, as the drawing shows. If two atoms come near each other, the attraction between them may be strong enough to hold the two atoms together. The attraction that holds two atoms together is a **chemical bond**. A compound is produced by the formation of many chemical bonds.

Bonds and an Atom's Outer Electrons

Each energy level holds a certain number of electrons. The outer energy level in most atoms holds a maximum of eight electrons. (In hydrogen and helium, the maximum number is two.) Electrons in the outer energy level are called an atom's outer electrons. The noble gases in group 18, which have eight outer electrons per atom, show little tendency to react with other elements. Thus, scientists conluded that an atom with a filled outer energy level is **chemically stable**. Most atoms, however, do not contain eight outer electrons.

Chemical bonds result from the tendency of an atom to fill its outer energy level. A chemical bond forms when one or more outer electrons are transferred from one atom to another or are shared by two atoms. A chemical bond is a stable arrangement of atoms, not a physical link between them.

Figure 10-1 a Two protons repel each other, and two electrons repel each other. **b** Protons are strongly attracted to their own electrons and to neighboring electrons.

a

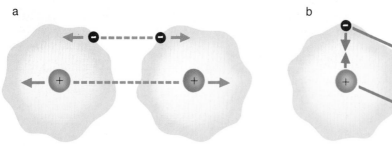

Repellant forces

b

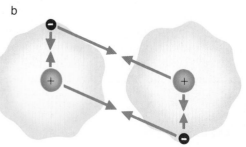

Attractive forces

The periodic table on pages 160-161 tells the number of outer electrons for the atoms of each element. In each box, this number is listed at the bottom of the column showing electrons. For example, the number of outer electrons for a chlorine atom (Cl) is 7.

Note that the number of outer electrons for metals in groups 1 and 2 are 1 and 2, respectively; for elements in groups 13-17, the number is 3 to 7, respectively. The number of outer electrons for metals in groups 1 and 2 is the same as the group number. The number of outer electrons for elements in groups 13-17 is the group number minus ten. This relationship does not apply to the transition metals in groups 3-12.

The number of outer electrons—sometimes called *valence electrons*—indicates whether atoms give up, take on, or share electrons when they form chemical bonds. Atoms can become more stable by attaining an electron arrangement like that of the noble gases, which have 8 outer electrons. For instance, if a chlorine atom gains one electron, it attains an electron arrangement like that of argon (Ar). By losing its one valence electron, a sodium (Na) atom attains an electron arrangement like that of neon (Ne). In forming bonds, metallic elements tend to lose electrons, and nonmetallic elements tend to gain electrons, as shown in *Figure 10-2*.

When bonds form between two nonmetals, such as carbon and oxygen, the outer electrons are generally shared between atoms of the two elements.

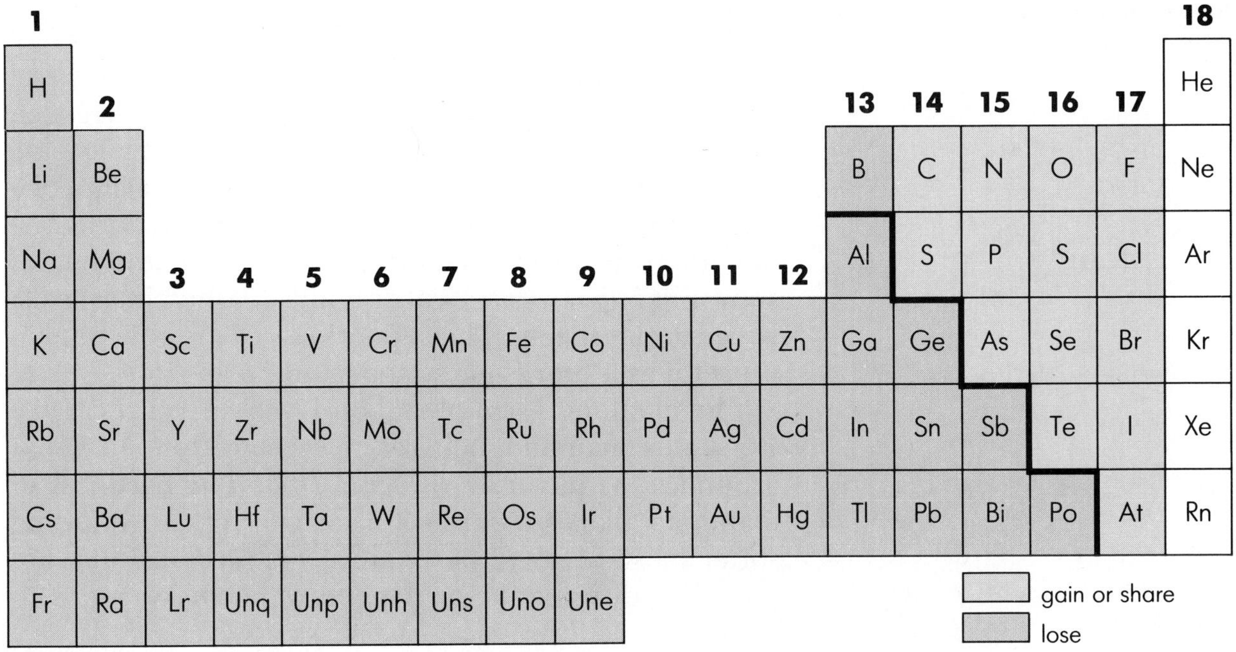

Figure 10-2 Metals are to the left of the stairstep line and nonmetals are to the right. When a compound forms between a metal and a nonmetal, metal atoms give up electrons to nonmetal atoms

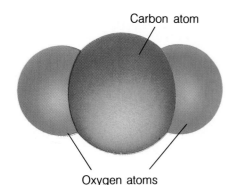

Carbon atom

Oxygen atoms

Figure 10-3 A carbon dioxide molecule

Within a group of elements, the tendency to lose electrons increases from top to bottom. In larger atoms, which are at the bottom of the group, the valence electrons are farther from the nucleus. The greater the distance, the weaker the attraction between the nucleus and the outer electrons. Thus, valence electrons are more easily lost than inner electrons.

Within a period the tendency to gain electrons increases from left to right. The number of protons—or positive charges—increases from left to right. Thus, the valence electrons are held more tightly in each succeeding element to the right.

Atoms can bond in many different combinations. *Figure 10-3* shows a model of a carbon dioxide molecule. This molecule forms when an atom of carbon and two atoms of oxygen combine. Carbon has four valence electrons and oxygen has six. By sharing electrons, both atoms can have a complete outer energy level. Each bond consists of two pairs of electrons, one pair from each element.

Atoms of elements combine with one another in various ratios. For example, a hydrogen atom has one valence electron, and a chlorine has seven. If the two atoms share electrons, they have eight electrons between them. Therefore, atoms of hydrogen and chlorine combine in a one-to-one ratio. A calcium atom with two outer electrons, combines with two chlorine atoms, for a ratio of two chlorine atoms to one calcium atom.

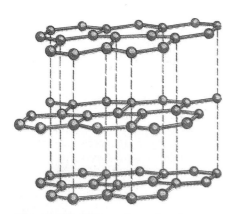

Figure 10-4 The pattern of carbon atoms in graphite

Bonds Determine a Compound's Properties

Chemical bonds account for many of the physical properties of compounds. Bonds exist not only between the atoms in a molecule, but also throughout a crystal. For example, the graphite form of carbon is a slippery, black solid. The strong bonds in graphite hold the carbon atoms in sheets that can slide over one another, as shown in *Figure 10-4*. Weaker bonds (dashed lines) exist between the sheets. The slipperiness of graphite makes it useful as a lubricant, as shown in *Figure 10-6*.

The diamond form of carbon is a clear, hard crystal. Bonds in diamond hold each carbon atom to those around it, as pictured in *Figure 10-5*. The hardness of diamonds makes them useful for cutting and grinding softer substances. In the two forms of carbon, atoms are joined by different arrangements of chemical bonds.

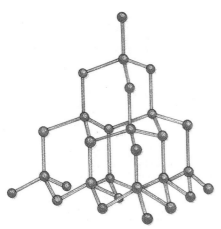

Figure 10-5 The pattern of carbon atoms in diamond

Figure 10-6 Graphite keeps windows from sticking.

Applying Science

The properties of graphite make it useful in pencil leads. The "lead" in pencils is usually a mixture of graphite and some other material, such as clay. Different mixtures give different degrees of softness to the "lead."

Another difference in crystal structure occurs when white phosphorus is heated to 250°C in the absence of air. The phosphorus turns red because the bonds between the phosphorus atoms rearrange to form a different structure. Yet both substances are phosphorus. In white phosphorus, four atoms form a molecule (P_4) with a tetrahedral shape, as shown in *Figure 10-7*. Red phosphorus is amorphous. That is, it has no regularly repeating arrangement of atoms.

Melting point is another property that bonds determine. You can heat and melt sugar in a pan on your stove. However, you have to heat quartz to 1600°C before it melts. Bonds within a sugar molecule or a quartz crystal are strong. But the bonds in quartz extend throughout the crystal. As in diamond, all the atoms are linked by chemical bonds. These bonds must break before quartz can melt. When sugar melts, only the weak forces of attractions between the molecules are broken. Therefore, quartz has a higher melting point than sugar.

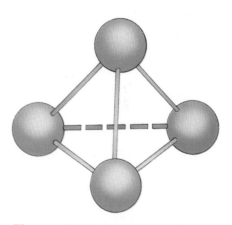

Figure 10-7 A phosphorus molecule

Section Review

1. Why are chemical bonds important?
2. Why is the number of outer electrons in an atom important for bonding?
3. How do bonds account for a compound's properties?

Challenge: The earth's atmosphere contains mostly nitrogen and oxygen. Why would an atmosphere made up mostly of hydrogen and oxygen not be possible?

Activity 10-1

Comparing Bonds

Purpose

To observe the properties of compounds that have different types of bonds

Materials

- a small amount of table salt
- a small amount of table sugar
- 3 teaspoons
- tongs
- magnifying glass
- 2 matches
- cover goggles

Procedure and Observations

1. Copy the table in **a** for your data.
2. Rub a few grains of salt between your fingers. Do the same with a few grains of sugar. Record which type of grain feels rougher.
3. Place a few grains of salt in one teaspoon and a few grains of sugar in another teaspoon.
4. Examine the grains with the magnifying glass. Compare the shapes of the salt and sugar grains. Record your observations.
5. Use the third spoon to crush the grains in the other two spoons as in **b**. Record which substance is harder to crush.

a

Data Table

Characteristics	Table salt	Sugar
Roughness		
Grain shape		
Hardness		
Melting point		

6. Put on your goggles. Light a match and hold it, using tongs, above and near the salt in the spoon. Let the match burn for about 10 seconds. Note whether any salt melts.
7. Repeat step 6 with the sugar.
8. Record which substance has the higher melting point.

Analysis and Conclusions

1. Summarize the differences in the properties of salt and sugar.
2. Think of each substance as made of atoms locked to one another. Which substance has stronger locks—or bonds? Explain.

b

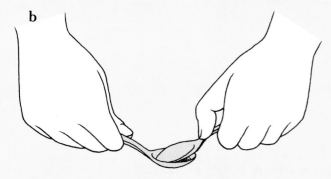

10-2 Ionic Bonding

Ions Form Ionic Bonds

An atom is electrically neutral. When an atom loses or gains one or more electrons, the atom becomes a charged particle called an **ion**. When one atom pulls an electron from another atom, both atoms become ions. The atom that gained the electron becomes a negatively charged ion. The atom that lost the electron becomes a positively charged ion.

Sodium and chlorine atoms become ions easily because of their electron arrangments. The diagram shows how atoms of sodium (Na) and chlorine (Cl) become ions. The sodium atom readily gives up the only electron in its outer energy level. This leaves the sodium atom with a new outer energy level, which is filled. The electron joins the outer energy level of the chlorine atom. This transfer gives the chlorine atom a filled outer energy level.

When a sodium atom loses its outer electron, a positively charged ion, Na^+, forms. The plus sign indicates that the net charge on this ion is $+1$. The chlorine atom gains an electron and becomes a negatively charged ion, Cl^-. The negative sign indicates a net charge of -1. The oppositely charged ions attract each other, forming an **ionic bond**. NaCl is the formula that describes this *ionic compound*. The compound's name is sodium chloride.

The reaction between sodium and chlorine is a vigorous one, giving off both light and heat. The compound, sodium chloride, is more stable than the elements from which it formed.

After completing this section, you will be able to
A. Define ions.
B. Name some properties of ionic compounds.

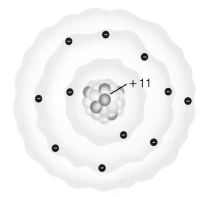

Figure 10-8 A neutral sodium atom has 11 protons and 11 electrons.

Figure 10-9 A neutral chlorine atom has 17 protons and 17 electrons.

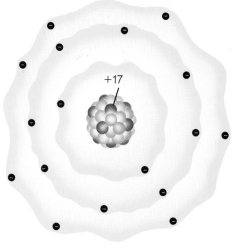

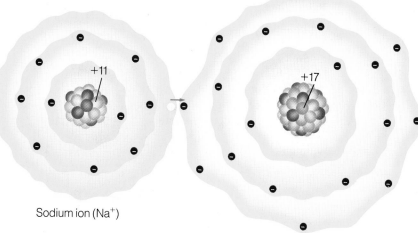

Sodium ion (Na$^+$)

Chloride ion (Cl$^-$)

Figure 10-10 The two atoms become ions when sodium gives up an electron to chlorine.

Many ionic compounds do not have a one-to-one ratio of ions. Notice in *Figure 10-12* that a calcium atom has two valence electrons. Calcium easily loses these two electrons, and forms a calcium ion with a positive charge of two. Each fluorine atom needs just one electron to complete its outer energy level. Each fluorine atom gains one electron, forming an ion with a negative charge of one. Each calcium atom reacts with two fluorine atoms, forming the ionic compound calcium fluoride. This ionic compound is represented by the formula CaF_2.

Many ionic compounds form when an ion of one element is attracted to a complex ion containing several elements. Some common examples of such ions—called *polyatomic ions*—are shown in *Figure 10-11*. These groups of elements act as single ions when they react with other elements. For example, one oxide ion (O^{2-}) and one hydrogen ion (H^+) combine to form a hydroxide ion. A hydroxide ion has a charge of -1. The formula for the hydroxide ion is OH^-. The negative sign indicates the net charge on the ion. Hydroxide ions combine with sodium ions to form the ionic compound sodium hydroxide, NaOH. Hydroxide ions combine with calcium ions in a ratio of two to one to form calcium hydroxide, $Ca(OH)_2$. The subscript following the parentheses shows that there are two hydroxide ions for each Ca^{2+} ion in the compound.

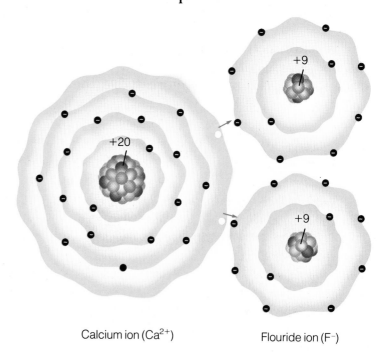

Figure 10-12 When a calcium atom gives up its two outer electrons to two flourine atoms, three ions form.

Calcium ion (Ca^{2+})

Flouride ion (F^-)

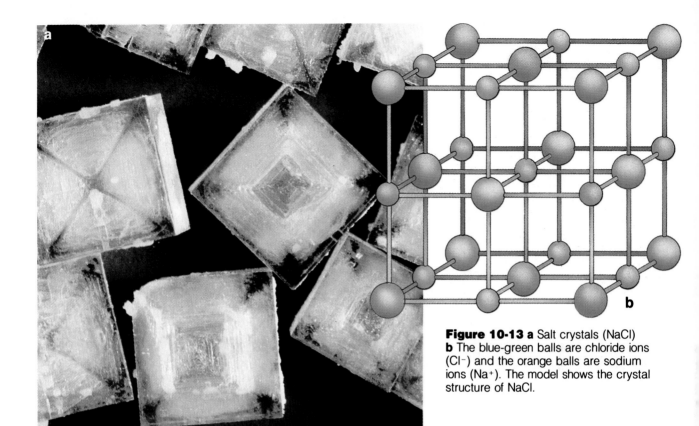

Figure 10-13 a Salt crystals (NaCl) **b** The blue-green balls are chloride ions (Cl⁻) and the orange balls are sodium ions (Na⁺). The model shows the crystal structure of NaCl.

Properties of Ionic Compounds

The properties of sodium chloride differ from those of sodium and chlorine. Sodium is a silvery metal that reacts violently with water. Chlorine is a yellow-green, poisonous gas. The ionic compound sodium chloride is a white, nonpoisonous solid that dissolves easily in water. You use sodium chloride as table salt. Similarly, calcium fluoride, CaF_2, has properties that are different from both calcium and fluorine. The bonded ions are quite unlike the atoms from which they formed.

The ions in a compound are arranged in an orderly way to form a crystal. *Figure 10-13* shows the arrangment of the ions in sodium chloride. The orange balls represent sodium ions. The blue-green balls are chloride ions. The photograph shows sodium chloride crystals. Each crystal contains billions of ions. However, no two oppositely charged ions can be singled out as the basic unit of the NaCl crystal.

Ionic bonds are especially strong because they extend throughout the entire crystal. Therefore, most ionic compounds are hard solids at room temperature, and they have high melting points. For example, sodium chloride melts at about 800°C.

In the solid form, ionic compounds do not conduct electricity. However, when NaCl is melted or is dissolved in water, the ions separate, move about freely, and conduct electricity well.

Section Review

1. How do atoms form ionic bonds?
2. What are three properties of ionic compounds?

Challenge: What charge would you expect to find on ions of the following elements: sodium, potassium, magnesium, barium, aluminum, and sulfur?

People and Science

Gilbert Newton Lewis, Chemist and Physicist

G. N. Lewis (1875-1946) is one of the most renowned chemists in American history. He received his bachelor's degree from Harvard in 1896. He taught school for one year, and then returned to Harvard to get his Ph. D. in 1899. Lewis worked in the laboratory of the U.S. Bureau of Weights and Measures at Manila in the Philippines. In 1907, he became an assistant professor at Massachusetts Institute of Technology (MIT) in Boston. Four years later, he became a full professor.

In 1912, Dr. Lewis was appointed chairman of the small chemistry department at the University of California at Berkeley. He immediately began building a powerful and creative department. Nobel prize winners from his department include Linus Pauling, Melvin Calvin, and Harold Urey. He also attracted outstanding graduate students. Before his arrival, the chemistry department had granted only four Ph. D. degrees in chemistry. During his years as chairman, 290 Ph. D. degrees were given.

As chairman, he continued to do research. In 1916, he published a paper called "The Atom, and the Molecule." In this paper, he explained covalent bonding, which is the sharing of electrons by atoms. His theories became the basis for the electron theory of chemical structure. He summed up his work in the 1923 book entitled *Valence and the Structure of Atoms and Molecules.*

Lewis was noted for his inspiring lectures, particularly those given at seminars for graduate students. Lewis blazed paths followed by chemists throughout the world.

10-3 Covalent Bonding

Objectives

After completing this section you will be able to

A. Describe a covalent bond.
B. Describe covalent compounds.
C. Describe how carbon compounds are linked.
D. Describe how the hydrocarbons in crude oil are separated.

How Covalent Bonds Form

When two atoms share a pair of electrons, they are held together by a chemical attraction called a **covalent bond**. A covalent bond links the two hydrogen atoms in a hydrogen molecule (H_2). Each hydrogen atom has one electron. When the two atoms come together, their electrons pair up. Since the two atoms share the electron pair, the two electrons are attracted by the nuclei of both atoms. This attraction holds the atoms together.

The pair of electrons is in an energy level that both nuclei share. The electron-cloud drawing on page 219 shows a hydrogen molecule. The large number of dots indicates that the two electrons are not fixed in any one position. A hydrogen molecule is more chemically stable than a single hydrogen atom is.

Molecules Result from Covalent Bonding

Two or more atoms joined by covalent bonds make up a **molecule**. A molecule can contain atoms of one element, such as hydrogen, or of different elements.

A hydrogen molecule is called a **diatomic molecule** because it contains two atoms. Fluorine, chlorine, oxygen, nitrogen, bromine, and iodine commonly exist as diatomic molecules.

A *covalent compound* is one that contains atoms held together by covalent bonds. A molecule is the smallest unit in a covalent compound. In general, covalent compounds are made of two or more nonmetals. For example, hydrogen and chlorine combine to form molecules of hydrogen chloride, HCl. Hydrogen atoms have one valence electron, and chlorine atoms have seven. When these two atoms unite, each contributes an electron to form an electron pair that is shared by both atoms. Neither atom can exert enough force to pull an electron away from the other atom. Thus, they share electrons.

Water is probably the most common covalent compound. In the water molecule shown in *Figure 10-14*, two hydrogen atoms share their electrons with one oxygen atom. This arrangement completes the outer energy level of all three atoms: two electrons for each hydrogen atom and eight electrons for the oxygen atom.

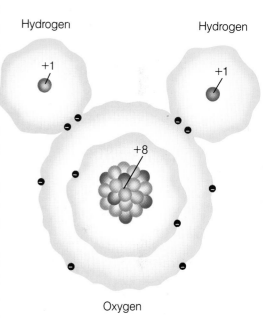

Hydrogen

Hydrogen

Oxygen

Figure 10-14 In a water molecule, covalent bonds hold two hydrogen atoms and one oxygen atom together.

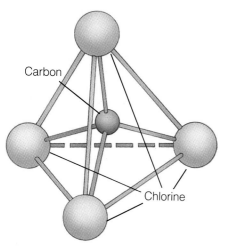

Figure 10-15 In a carbon tetrachloride molecule (CCl₄), a carbon atom has four covalent bonds with four chlorine atoms.

Most covalent substances do not conduct electricity. Some covalent substances, such as diamond, are very hard because the covalent bonds between their atoms are very strong and extend throughout the crystal. Others, such as sugar, are soft and melt at low temperatures because the attractions linking sugar molecules are weak.

Carbon, hydrogen, and silicon form more covalent compounds than other elements do. Carbon forms very many covalent compounds because its atoms have four outer electrons to share with other atoms, including other carbon atoms. Each of a carbon atom's four electrons can form part of one covalent bond.

Figure 10-15 shows one carbon atom with bonds to four chlorine atoms. The carbon atom completes its outer energy level by sharing its four electrons with four chlorine atoms. This arrangement also fills the outer energy level of the chlorine atoms. The result is one molecule of carbon tetrachloride, CCl₄, a covalent compound.

Forming Carbon Compounds

Carbon atoms join easily to form many compounds. Sugars, plastics, and fuels are carbon compounds. Chemically, you are a collection of carbon compounds because every cell in your body is made of molecules that contain carbon atoms.

Figure 10-16 Carbon compounds

The elements carbon and hydrogen combine to form **hydrocarbon** compounds. Natural gas used for cooking and heating is a mixture of hydrocarbons. Methane is the main compound in natural gas. *Figure 10-17* shows the arrangement of atoms in a methane molecule. Each of carbon's four electrons pairs up with a hydrogen electron. A covalent bond containing one pair of electrons is called a *single covalent bond*.

Figure 10-18 shows another way to represent a methane molecule—a structural formula. One dash (—) represents one pair of electrons in a bond. The four dashes around *"C"* stand for four single covalent bonds.

Most natural gas also contains some propane. In a propane molecule, (C_3H_8), three carbon atoms bond to each other and to eight hydrogen atoms. The structural formula for propane is shown in *Figure 10-19*.

Carbon occurs in so many compounds for two reasons. One reason is that carbon forms four strong covalent bonds. The other is that a carbon atom readily forms bonds with other carbon atoms. The linking of carbon atoms leads to many stable compounds.

Hydrocarbon Fuels

Most fossil fuels are made from carbon compounds that are the remains of organisms which lived on the earth millions of years ago. These remains have become today's coal, oil, and gas.

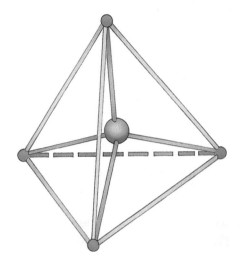

Figure 10-17 A methane molecule

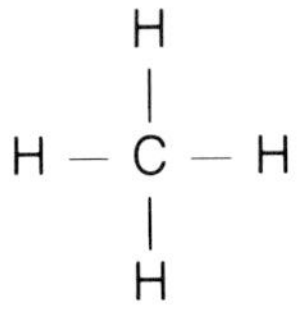

$$H - C - H$$

Figure 10-18 The structural formula for methane (CH_4)

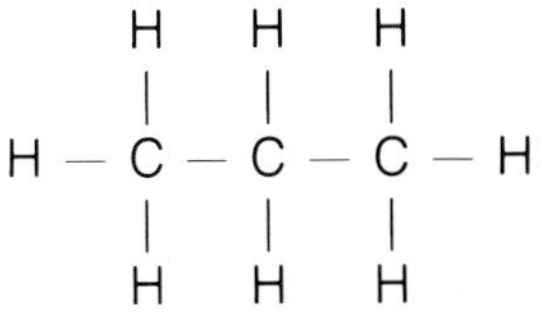

Figure 10-19 The structural formula for propane (C_3H_8)

Figure 10-20 Fossil fuels are carbon compounds.

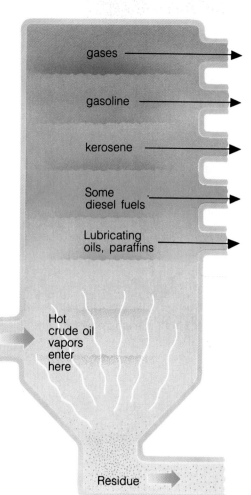

Figure 10-21 A petroleum fractionating tower

Labels on figure (top to bottom):
gases
gasoline
kerosene
Some diesel fuels
Lubricating oils, paraffins
Hot crude oil vapors enter here
Residue

Figure 10-22 Description of some important products that come from crude oil

Hydrocarbon	No. carbon atoms in each molecule	Boiling points range (°C)	Uses
Gases	1–5	−160 to 30	Heating and torches
Petroleum, ether, light naptha	5–7	20–100	Industrial and cleaning solvents
Gasoline	6–12	60–200	Automobile fuel
Kerosene, fuel oil	12–18	180–400	Diesel fuel, oil for heating
Lubricating oil	16 or more	above 350	Motor oil, grease, petroleum jelly
Paraffins	20 or more	low-melting solids	Candle wax
Asphalt, tar	36 or more	gummy solid residues	Roofing & road construction

Crude oil—or petroleum—is a mixture of hydrocarbons. Before crude oil can be used, it must be separated into its components, called *fractions*. The separation process depends on each hydrocarbon's boiling point. The fractions with most carbon atoms have the highest boiling points, as shown in the table.

Crude oil vapors are heated and enter the tower at the bottom, as shown in the drawing. As the hot vapors rise, the hydrocarbons with the highest boiling points cool, condense, and are removed from the tower first. Hydrocarbons with lower boiling points rise higher before they cool and condense. Fractions with the lowest boiling points rise to the top. The process of separating substances by their boiling points is called **fractional distillation.**

Section Review

1. How do covalent bonds form?
2. How are covalent compounds formed?
3. Why does carbon form so many compounds?
4. How can the compounds in petroleum be separated?

Challenge: Why are the bonds in a H_2 molecule covalent rather than ionic?

10-4 Chemical Equations and Dot Diagrams

Objectives

After completing this section, you will be able to

A. Explain what chemical equations represent.
B. Relate the conservation of mass to chemical equations.
C. Explain how ionic bonding is represented using dot diagrams.
D. Explain how covalent bonding is represented using dot diagrams.

Chemical Equations Describe Chemical Reactions

A baker uses a recipe to combine ingredients for a cake. The scientist shown in *Figure 10-23* uses a kind of recipe to produce new substances. The new substances have properties unlike those of the elements and compounds from which they came.

Often a chemical change consists of many different steps. A **chemical reaction** is one of these individual steps. What happens during a chemical change can be described by a sentence for each reaction. For example, to describe the formation of sodium chloride, you might say: "Sodium and chlorine react, forming the compound sodium chloride."

The most efficient way to describe a reaction is a chemical equation. A **chemical equation** is a statement that uses symbols, formulas, and numbers to describe a chemical reaction. An equation tells the *relative* number of atoms, ions, or molecules that react to form new substances. The following equation shows what happens when sodium and chlorine atoms combine.

$$2Na + Cl_2 \rightarrow 2NaCl$$

In all equations, the arrow means "produces." The number in front of a symbol or formula describes the relative number of units (atoms, ions, or molecules) of a substance involved in the reaction. If no number appears before a symbol or formula, the number *one* is understood.

Figure 10-23 A chemist at work in the laboratory

The equation for the formation of water is below.

$$2H_2 + O_2 \rightarrow 2H_2O$$

The equation says that two hydrogen molecules react with one oxygen molecule to make two water molecules.

The equations for the formation of table salt and the formation of water tell nothing about the conditions necessary for the formation of salt or water. When hydrogen and oxygen are mixed at room temperature, no chemical change takes place. Although a spark is enough to start the reaction, the temperature of the substances must be raised to keep the chemical reaction going. Methods of starting and controlling reactions are discussed in the next chapter.

The Conservation of Mass in a Chemical Reaction

During a chemical reaction, bonds are broken and created, but the number of atoms remains the same. This principle follows the **law of conservation of mass**, which states that matter cannot be created or destroyed during ordinary chemical reactions.

Chemical equations must be balanced because the number of atoms does not change during a chemical reaction. A balanced equation has equal numbers of each kind of atom on both sides of the arrow.

In the photograph, the woman is cooking food over a propane stove. The balanced equation below describes the burning of propane gas.

$$C_3H_8 + 5O_2 \rightarrow 3CO_2 + 4H_2O$$

Figure 10-24 Propane combines with oxygen to produce carbon dioxide gas and water.

Using Dot Diagrams to Represent Ionic Bonding

Scientists often use dot diagrams to show how electrons are transferred or shared and how compounds are held together. Each dot represents one valence electron. Dot diagrams for sodium and for chlorine are below.

$$\text{Na}\cdot \qquad \cdot\ddot{\underset{\cdot\cdot}{\text{Cl}}}\!:$$

Notice that only the valence electrons are represented by the dots surrounding the symbol for each element. The element symbol represents the nucleus and all of the inner electrons. *Figure 10-25* shows the dot diagrams for elements in the second period of the periodic table.

Dot diagrams can be used to represent the transfer of electrons involved in forming ionic compounds. The formation of sodium chloride can be represented by the following equation.

$$\text{Na}\cdot + \cdot\ddot{\underset{\cdot\cdot}{\text{Cl}}}\!: \rightarrow [\,\text{Na}\,]^{+} + [:\!\ddot{\underset{\cdot\cdot}{\text{Cl}}}\!:]^{-}$$

Sodium's outer electron is shown by a red dot. The transfer of the electron is shown by the curved arrow. To the right of the arrow, sodium has lost its electron, and the chloride ion is surrounded by eight electrons, which completes its outer energy level.

Calcium has two valence electrons and combines with two atoms of chlorine to form calcium chloride, $CaCl_2$. The formation of $CaCl_2$ is shown here.

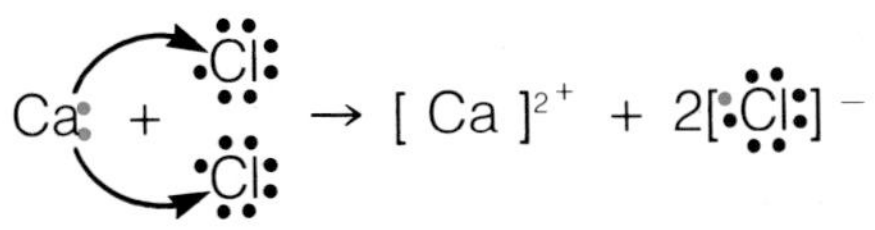

$$\text{Ca}\cdot + \begin{matrix} \cdot\ddot{\underset{\cdot\cdot}{\text{Cl}}}\!: \\ \cdot\ddot{\underset{\cdot\cdot}{\text{Cl}}}\!: \end{matrix} \rightarrow [\,\text{Ca}\,]^{2+} + 2[:\!\ddot{\underset{\cdot\cdot}{\text{Cl}}}\!:]^{-}$$

In summary, the rules for representing the formation of ionic compounds in dot diagrams are:

1. Determine the number of valence electrons from each element's group number.

2. Use arrows and dots to represent transferred electrons.

3. Show the charges of the ions formed.

Figure 10-25 Elements in period 2 of the periodic table

Element	Element symbol	Number of valence (outer) electrons	Dot diagram
Lithium	Li	1	Li·
Beryllium	Be	2	Be·
Boron	B	3	Ḃ·
Carbon	C	4	·Ċ·
Nitrogen	N	5	·Ṅ·
Oxygen	O	6	:Ö:
Fluorine	F	7	·F̈:
Neon	Ne	8	:N̈ë:

For Practice

Represent the formulas for the following compounds, using dot diagrams:
1. Na_2S (ionic compound)
2. HCl (covalent compound)
3. KCl (ionic compound)
4. SO_2 (covalent compound)

Using Dot Diagrams to Represent Covalent Bonding

Dot diagrams also can be used to represent the formation of covalent compounds. The formation of water, a covalent compound, is represented as shown.

$$2H\cdot \; + \; \cdot \ddot{O}\!: \; \rightarrow \; H \; \underset{H}{\overset{}{:}}\ddot{O}\!:$$

Notice that each hydrogen atom has one electron to share, but also needs one electron to complete its energy level. Thus, each hydrogen atom shares an electron pair with the oxygen atom. Including the shared electrons, the oxygen atom is surrounded by eight electrons.

Carbon dioxide is another covalent compound. Each molecule of carbon dioxide contains one atom of carbon and two atoms of oxygen. Carbon has four electrons to share. Each oxygen atom can share two electrons with the carbon atom. A dot diagram for the formation of a carbon dioxide molecule is shown below.

$$:C: \; + \; 2:\ddot{O}\!: \; \rightarrow \; :\ddot{O}\!::C::\ddot{O}\!:$$

The diagram shows that each oxygen atom shares *two pairs* of electrons with each carbon atom. Such bonds are known as *double covalent bonds*. Because of double bonds, each atom attains a stable arrangement of eight electrons.

Some rules for drawing dot diagrams showing covalent compounds are:

1. Determine the number of valence electrons from each element's group number.

2. Place the shared electron pairs between the symbols of the elements so that each atom attains eight electrons (or two for hydrogen).

Section Review

1. What do chemical equations describe?
2. What is the law of conservation of mass?
3. What do the curved arrows indicate in dot diagrams showing the formation of an ionic compound?
4. In a dot diagram, what does an electron pair placed between atoms indicate about the compound?

Challenge: Draw a dot diagram to show a carbon tetrachloride molecule (CCl_4), which has covalent bonds.

A Chemical Reaction and Its Equation

Purpose

To balance the chemical equation for an observed chemical reaction

Materials

- 10 mL of vinegar
- 2 cm³ (2 mL) baking soda
- graduated cylinder
- 200-500 mL beaker or water glass
- 4 matches
- tongs
- cover goggles

b

Procedure and Observations

1. Put on your cover goggles. The "empty" beaker contains air. Light a match and hold it deep in the beaker with the tongs, as in **a.** Does the match continue to burn, or does it go out? Record what happens to the match.
2. Place the baking soda in the beaker.
3. Pour the vinegar into the beaker. Do not disturb the beaker or its contents. Record your observations of the contents of the beaker.
4. Repeat step 1. Do not let the match touch the contents of the beaker.

a

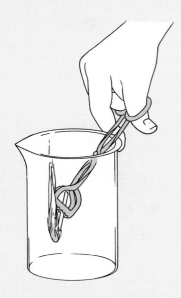

5. Gently tip the beaker, as in **b.** Return it to its normal position. Light another match and slowly move it deeper into the beaker with the tongs. Record your observations.

Analysis and Conclusions

1. Compare the properties of air to the properties of gas produced during the reaction. Is the new gas heavier or lighter than air? Did the match burn in the new gas? Is the new gas visible, or is it as invisible as air?
2. The chemical formula for baking soda is $NaHCO_3$. Vinegar is a mixture of water and acetic acid. The acetic acid reacts with baking soda. The chemical formula for acetic acid is $HC_2H_3O_2$. The chemical equation for the reaction shows that sodium acetate ($NaC_2H_3O_2$), carbon dioxide gas (CO_2), and water form during the reaction.

$$NaHCO_3 + HC_2H_3O_2 \rightarrow NaC_2H_3O_2 + CO_2 + H_2O$$

Count the number of each kind of atom on each side of the equation. Is the equation balanced? If not, suggest a way to balance it.

Dot Diagrams and Ionic Compounds

This activity will give you some practice in drawing dot diagrams for the formation of ionic bonds. You will also examine some similarities in properties and formulas that are characteristic of ionic compounds. Refer to the drawings below and the dot diagrams on page 235 to help you complete this activity.

1. You have seen dot diagrams showing how calcium and chlorine form calcium chloride ($CaCl_2$). Draw dot diagrams for a similar reaction. Show the formation of magnesium fluoride, MgF_2, from magnesium and fluorine.

2. Draw dot diagrams for:

   a. $2Mg + O_2 \rightarrow 2MgO$
   b. $4K + O_2 \rightarrow 2K_2O$.

3. How many valence electrons are in one atom of the following: magnesium, potassium, fluorine, and oxygen?

4. How many electrons are included in the element symbol for: magnesium, fluorine, oxygen, and potassium?

5. Which of the four elements listed above form positive ions? Which ones form negative ions? Explain your answer.

6. Write chemical formulas for the following compounds: lithium and oxygen; barium and chlorine.

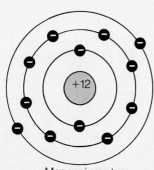

Magnesium atom

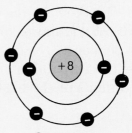

Oxygen atom

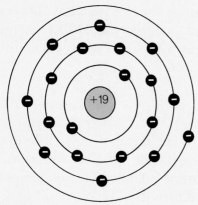

Potassium atom

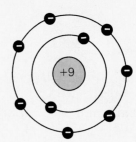

Fluorine atom

 Summary

10-1 Bonding Atoms

A. The attractive force that holds two atoms together is a chemical bond. Chemical bonds result from the tendency of an atom to fill its outermost energy level.

B. Electrons in the outermost energy level of an atom are often called valence electrons.

C. Chemical bonds account for many of the physical properties of substances.

10-2 Ionic Bonding

A. When an atom loses or gains one or more electrons, it becomes a charged particle called an ion. Oppositely charged ions are held together by an ionic bond.

B. The ions in an ionic compound are arranged in an orderly, repeating pattern.

10-3 Covalent Bonding

A. When two atoms share a pair of electrons, they are held together by an attraction called a covalent bond.

B. A molecule contains two or more atoms held together by covalent bonds.

C. Carbon atoms join easily to form many compounds.

D. Most fossil fuels are compounds called hydrocarbons. Petroleum is a mixture of hydrocarbons.

10-4 Chemical Equations and Dot Diagrams

A. Chemical equations use symbols and formulas to describe chemical changes. In any chemical equation, the arrow means "produces."

B. Equal numbers of each kind of atom must appear on both sides of the arrow in a chemical equation.

C. Dot diagrams are used to represent nuclei and valence electrons.

D. Dot diagrams show how valence electrons are transferred or shared during bonding.

Vocabulary

For each of the following terms, write a sentence that uses the term correctly.

chemical bond	**covalent bond**	**ion**
chemical equation	**diatomic molecule**	**ionic bond**
chemical reaction	**fractional distillation**	**law of conservation of mass**
chemically stable	**hydrocarbon**	**molecule**

Review Chapter 10

✔ Check Your Knowledge

Part I: Matching Match the definition in Column I with the correct term in Column II.

Column I
1. substances that contain only hydrogen and carbon
2. particle made of covalently bonded atoms
3. particle formed when an atom gains or loses an electron
4. formulas and symbols that describe a chemical reaction
5. drawing used to show valence electrons of an atom
6. bond formed with shared electrons
7. having a filled outer energy level
8. attractions that hold a compound together
9. bond formed between electrically charged atoms
10. one step in a chemical change

Column II
a. chemical bonds
b. chemical equation
c. chemically stable
d. chemical reaction
e. covalent bond
f. dot diagram
g. fractional distillation
h. hydrocarbon
i. ion
j. ionic bond
k. molecule

Part II: Multiple Choice Choose the letter of the best answer.

11. The maximum number of electrons that can be held in the outermost energy level of most atoms is (a) two. (b) six. (c) eight. (d) ten.
12. Ionic compounds stay together because (a) opposite charges attract. (b) like charges attract. (c) opposite charges repel. (d) electrons are shared.
13. Carbon forms strong bonds with (a) itself and other elements. (b) itself only. (c) other elements only. (d) no other elements.
14. The number of bonds an atom can form depends on the number of (a) atoms. (b) protons. (c) neutrons. (d) outermost electrons.
15. Fluorine will most probably form a covalent bond with (a) fluorine. (b) neon. (c) helium. (d) argon.
16. Lithium will most probably form an ionic bond with (a) beryllium. (b) helium. (c) chlorine. (d) sodium.

17. Choose the element that occurs as a diatomic molecule. (a) sodium (b) neon (c) oxygen (d) calcium
18. Which is a property of ionic compounds? (a) low melting point (b) usually gaseous at room temperature (c) poor electrical conductors when dissolved (d) usually hard and solid
19. Choose the balanced equation.
    (a) $O_2 + H_2 \rightarrow H_2O$
    (b) $CaCO_3 \rightarrow CaO + CO_2$
    (c) $C + Cl_2 \rightarrow CCl_4$
    (d) $H_2 + Cl_2 \rightarrow HCl$

Part III: Completion Write the word or words that complete the sentence correctly.
20. Petroleum is a mixture of _____.
21. Fractional distillation takes place in a fractionating _____.
22. Water is one of the most common _____ compounds.
23. Two or more atoms joined by covalent bonds form a _____.
24. An atom with its outer energy level filled is chemically _____.

Check Your Understanding

1. What evidence shows that atoms usually combine with other atoms?
2. Why must two atoms of hydrogen bond with one atom of oxygen to form one molecule of water?
3. How does knowing the number of electrons in an atom's outer energy level help predict how it combines with other atoms?
4. Explain what happens to two atoms as an ionic bond forms between them.
5. Explain how a covalent bond can form without either atom losing an outermost electron. Include a description of what happens to each atom's electron cloud.

6. What does a chemical equation tell a chemist about making a compound?
7. Explain how the law of conservation of mass governs chemical reactions.
8. What accounts for the large number and the many kinds of carbon compounds?
9. One kind of gasoline molecule contains 10 carbon atoms. One kind of kerosene molecule contains 16 carbon atoms. Which molecule has a higher boiling point? Which molecule condenses first during fractional distillation?

Apply Your Knowledge

1. In what ratio would you expect potassium (K) to combine with sulfur (S)?
2. Explain why positive ions in an ionic crystal are surrounded by negative ions rather than positive ions.
3. How are dot diagrams of atoms related to an element's position in the periodic table?
4. Butane is a hydrocarbon that contains 4 carbon atoms and 10 hydrogen atoms per molecule. Draw a structural formula for this covalent compound.

Extend Your Knowledge

Research/Projects
1. Write to a petroleum company and ask for information on refining crude oil.
2. Use clay or plastic balls and toothpicks to construct models of different crystals. You can find diagrams of the crystal arrangements of atoms in many high school chemistry books.
3. Visit a chemical factory or a pharmaceutical company in your area. Find out about the work a chemist does and how chemists experiment to produce new substances.

Readings
Weiss, Malcom E. *Why Glass Breaks, Rubber Bends, and Glue Sticks.* Harcourt, 1979. Explains how the structure of molecules determines such properties as electrical conductivity and stickiness.

Zubrowski, Bernie. *Messing Around with Baking Chemistry.* Little, Brown, 1981. Explains what happens as you bake bread and cake, especially the effects of baking powder and baking soda.

CHAPTER 11
Chemical Reactions

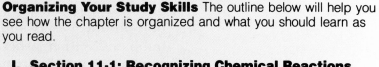

The colorful design in the photograph was produced when an electric current passed through a copper sulfate solution containing a piece of zinc metal. Copper left the solution and crystallized into the treelike structures. The vivid yellow-red color in the picture is characteristic of colloidal-size pieces of copper.

Organizing Your Study Skills The outline below will help you see how the chapter is organized and what you should learn as you read.

I. Section 11-1: Recognizing Chemical Reactions
   A. What are some characteristics of a chemical reaction?
   B. How is energy involved in a chemical reaction?
   C. How can the speed of a chemical reaction be controlled?
   D. What are the parts of a chemical equation?

II. Section 11-2: Synthesis and Decomposition Reactions
   A. What is a synthesis reaction?
   B. What is a decomposition reaction?

III. Section 11-3: Single-Replacement and Double-Replacement Reactions
   A. What is a single-replacement reaction?
   B. How are single-replacement reactions used to compare the reactivities of elements?
   C. What is a double-replacement reaction?

IV. Section 11-4: Oxidation-Reduction Reactions
   A. Why are reactions classified in more than one way?
   B. What takes place during an oxidation-reduction reaction?
   C. What oxidation-reduction reaction is used to produce iron?

V. Section 11-5: Chemistry of Carbon Compounds
   A. What is a polymer?
   B. How is the element carbon important to living organisms?

After completing this section, you will be able to

A. Describe some characteristics of chemical reactions.
B. Explain how energy is involved in a chemical reaction.
C. Describe how the speed of a chemical reaction can be controlled.
D. Identify parts of a chemical equation.

11·1   Recognizing Chemical Reactions

Characteristics of Chemical Reactions

A chemical change takes place during a chemical reaction. Chemical reactions produce new substances with properties different from those of the original materials. In the pictures, chemical reactions occur as paper burns and an antacid tablet fizzes. One chemical reaction produces ashes and the other reaction produces gas bubbles. Neither ashes nor gas bubbles look like the starting materials, paper and an antacid tablet. The original substances in a chemical reaction are called **reactants**. The sheet of paper, water, and the antacid tablet are reactants. Substances formed by the chemical reaction are known as **products**. Ashes and gas bubbles are products of the reactions.

Color changes often indicate that a chemical reaction has occurred. The dark surface on toasted bread and the tarnish on silver are products of chemical reactions. The outside of the Statue of Liberty changed to a green color when copper in the building materials reacted with air. The green is a compound of copper, oxygen, carbon, and hydrogen.

Reactions that continue on their own until one or more reactants are gone are called **spontaneous reactions**. Adding an antacid tablet to water produces a spontaneous reaction. The tablet keeps fizzing in water until the tablet disappears and the reaction appears to stop. Rusting is a slow spontaneous reaction.

Figure 11-1 The antacid tablet is a reactant.

Figure 11-2 The ashes are a product.

When iron is left in moist air, it continues to rust until the iron is "used up."

Above a certain temperature, the burning of paper is a fast spontaneous reaction. Thus, a match or other heat source is used to raise the temperature of the paper just enough to start the reaction. Once started, the chemical reaction keeps going until the paper changes to ashes.

Energy in Chemical Reactions

Energy changes accompany chemical reactions. Many chemical reactions give off energy. When fuels burn, they give off large amounts of energy in the form of heat and light. Chemical reactions that release energy are called **exothermic reactions.** Since the reactants give off energy the products of exothermic reactions contain less energy than the reactants

You can predict that a reaction is exothermic if it gives off heat. The burning of coal, wood, and paper are exothermic reactions. However, some exothermic reactions give off heat very slowly. For instance, the rusting of iron is an exothermic reaction, but heat is produced so slowly it is not noticeable.

On the other hand, some chemical reactions absorb energy. Reactions that absorb energy are known as **endothermic reactions.** Products of an endothermic reaction contain more energy than the reactants.

The industrial production of chlorine gas, Cl_2, from sodium chloride, NaCl, is an endothermic reaction. Because sodium chloride, or table salt, is abundant, it is a good source of both sodium metal and chlorine gas. However, the ionic bonds between sodium and chlorine are very strong. Therefore, the separation of the two elements does not happen by itself. In industry, chlorine and sodium are produced by passing electric energy through melted sodium chloride. Energy must be added to get this endothermic reaction started and to keep it going.

The Speed of a Chemical Reaction

What happens to milk when you forget to put the carton in the refrigerator? You know that milk turns sour faster when it is warm than when it is cold. The souring of milk is a chemical reaction. By refrigerating milk after each use, you are controlling the speed of a chemical reaction.

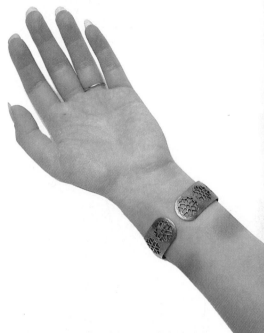

Figure 11-3 The dark band on the girl's arm is evidence that copper in the bracelet has reacted with the chemicals in her body.

Manufacturers add substances to foods to prevent unwanted chemical reactions. For example, calcium propionate is added to bread to slow the chemical reactions in which molds grow. Sodium benzoate prevents the growth of yeast and molds. This compound occurs naturally in some foods and is added to others.

Figure 11-4 Some colorful industrial catalysts

Generally, lowering the temperature of reactants slows down a chemical reaction. The reverse also is true. Raising the temperature of the reactants usually speeds up a chemical reaction.

In order to understand how temperature affects reaction speed, consider a reaction in terms of molecules. A very tiny chemical reaction can take place only when two unlike molecules, each with a given amount of energy, bump into each other. For a significant chemical change to take place, many, many molecules must collide. Adding heat or another form of energy gives molecules more energy and causes them to move faster. The faster they move the more they bump into each other, and the faster a reaction takes place.

Adding certain substances to a reaction also can change the speed of the reaction. A **catalyst** is a substance that speeds up a reaction without itself being changed by the reaction. A catalyst can be a solid, a liquid, or a gas. Catalysts, such as those in the photograph, are extremely important in industry.

Catalysts are essential for living organisms as well. In plants, for example, a substance called chlorophyll acts as a catalyst to trap sunlight and split water molecules during photosynthesis.

Catalysts are vital to your health. Conditions in your body do not favor chemical reactions. Body solutions are dilute—or weak—and your body temperature is low. In your body, many chemical reactions either would not take place or would not be fast enough without catalysts. *Enzymes* are the body's catalysts. Enzymes enable even a simple cell to perform hundreds of chemical reactions. They can cause many reactions to occur at one time, and can speed up slow reactions. Enzymes are more efficient than any known laboratory catalyst!

Your saliva, for instance, contains an enzyme that causes large starch molecules to break down into smaller ones. As a result, the digestion of starch begins as soon as food gets into your mouth. Vitamins and hormones also act as catalysts for chemical reactions in your body.

Examining Chemical Equations

Suppose you need to describe the reaction that takes place when charcoal, a form of carbon, burns in a grill. The chemical equation for the reaction follows.

$$C(s) + O_2(g) \rightarrow CO_2(g)$$

The equation reads: carbon reacts with oxygen to produce carbon dioxide gas. Notice that the chemical equation is read from left to right. The reactants, carbon and oxygen, are to the left of the arrow. The product, carbon dioxide, is to the right of the arrow.

Sometimes small letters in parentheses follow a formula or a symbol. These letters tell the state of a substance: (s) for solid, (g) for gas, and (l) for liquid. In addition, (aq) means a substance dissolved in water. (Aq) means *aqueous*, a Latin word referring to water. In the equation below, aluminum chloride and hydrochloric acid are followed by (aq) because they are in a water solution; aluminum is a solid; and hydrogen is a gas.

$$2Al(s) + 6HCl(aq) \rightarrow 2AlCl_3(aq) + 3H_2(g)$$
aluminum   hydrochloric   aluminum   hydrogen
acid   chloride

Small numbers, called subscripts, are written after and slightly lower than an element symbol. A subscript gives the number of atoms of an element. For example, the *2* after *O* in CO_2 means two oxygen atoms.

Numbers also are written before compound formulas and element symbols. These numbers, called coefficients, tell the *relative* number of atoms, ions, or molecules involved. Thus, the equation above says: 2 atoms of Al react with 6 molecules of HCl. The reaction produces 3 molecules of H_2 and the ions in $AlCl_3$ times 2. The coefficient *one* is not written, as *Figure 11-5* shows.

The same number of atoms of each element must appear on both sides of an equation. To the right and to the left in the balanced equation above are: 2 atoms of Al, 6 atoms of H, and 6 atoms of Cl. To count atoms, remember that the subscript applies only to the atom it follows. Cl_3 means 3 Cl atoms. However, a coefficient applies to all elements in the compound. Thus $2AlCl_3$ means 2 Al atoms and 2 × 3—or 6—Cl atoms.

Section Review

1. What is a spontaneous reaction?
2. Compare exothermic and endothermic reactions.
3. How does temperature affect reaction speed?
4. What information is given by this equation?

$$Cu + Cl_2 \rightarrow CuCl_2$$

Challenge: Would you describe the melting of ice as an exothermic or endothermic process? Explain.

Choose the balanced equation.
1. $Na + F_2 \rightarrow 2NaF$

2. $4Fe + O_2 \rightarrow 2Fe_2O_3$

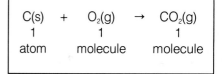

$C(s)$	+	$O_2(g)$	$\rightarrow$	$CO_2(g)$
1		1		1
atom		molecule		molecule

Figure 11-5 If no number is written before an atom, ion, or molecule, the number *one* is understood.

Controlling the Speed of Chemical Reactions

Purpose

To observe how temperature affects the speed of a chemical reaction

Materials

- 50 mL of vinegar
- two spoonfuls of baking soda
- 1 teaspoon
- 100-mL graduated cylinder
- two large beakers (250-mL)
- two wood splints
- shallow aluminum pan
- thermometer
- hot plate or Bunsen burner, metal tripod, wire gauze, and matches
- five or six ice cubes
- 1 piece of black paper
- gloves or hot pads
- fine-point marking pen
- cover goggles

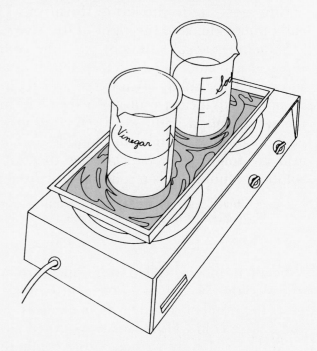

Procedure and Observations

1. *CAUTION: Do not touch anything hot. Put on your cover goggles.* In a beaker, combine 1 spoonful of baking soda and 100 mL of water. Stir well with a splint. Label beaker *baking soda*.
2. In another beaker, combine 25 mL of vinegar with 75 mL of tap water. Stir and label *vinegar*.
3. Place both beakers in a pan containing water 3-cm deep.
4. Set up your heating equipment as shown in the picture.
5. Handle the thermometer carefully. Heat until the temperature of the pan water is 70° C.

6. Remove both beakers and set them on black paper. Slowly pour the vinegar solution into the baking soda solution. Record your observations. Throw out the solution.
7. Repeat steps 1 to 3. Use clean beakers, clean splint, and cold tap water in the pan.
8. Add ice cubes to the water in the pan. Wait five minutes, then record the water temperature.
9. Repeat step 6.

Analysis and Conclusions

1. At which temperature did the substances react more rapidly? How do you know?
2. Make a statement about the effect of temperature on the speed of this chemical reaction.

11-2 Synthesis and Decomposition Reactions

Objectives

After completing this section, you will be able to

A. Identify a synthesis equation.
B. Identify a decomposition equation.

Synthesis: Substances Combine

Millions of different chemical reactions are possible among the known elements. Even chemists cannot learn all these reactions. Instead, they have devised ways to classify reactions into distinct groups. One classification groups reactions according to their chemical equations. In this chapter, you will learn to identify four types of reactions by looking at their chemical equations.

The reaction that darkens silver is a synthesis reaction. The bowl in the picture tarnishes because silver in the bowl combines with sulfur in the air to form silver sulfide, a compound. A **synthesis reaction** is one in which two or more substances combine to form a more complex substance. Study the equation for the reaction in which silver tarnishes. All equations for synthesis reactions show simple substances combining to form a more complex substance.

The combining of oxygen, O_2, and hydrogen, H_2, to form water, H_2O, is a synthesis reaction. Similarly, the rusting of iron is a synthesis reaction. When moisture is present, oxygen from the air combines with iron metal to form iron rust.

A synthesis reaction occurs inside the catalytic converter of an automobile. A car without a catalytic converter gives off carbon monoxide, CO, and other poisonous gases. Adding a catalytic converter, such as the one in the picture, cuts down on the release of the harmful gases. Inside a catalytic converter, carbon monoxide combines with oxygen to form carbon dioxide, CO_2, which is not poisonous. Thus, the exhaust of a well-maintained car gives off more CO_2 than CO.

$$2CO + O_2 \rightarrow 2CO_2$$
carbon monoxide   oxygen   carbon dioxide

The corrosion of metals is a synthesis reaction. In corrosion, a metal combines with oxygen in the air, forming an oxide. Moisture acts as a catalyst for this reaction. The catalytic effect of moisture increases if salt, NaCl, is present too. As a result, the adding of salt to keep roads from icing up during winter storms causes automobiles to rust.

$$2Ag + S \rightarrow Ag_2S$$
silver   sulfur   silver sulfide

Figure 11-6 Silver tarnishes easily

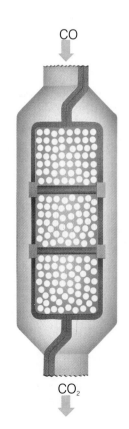

Figure 11-7 The beads inside this catalytic converter contain platinum metal, which acts as a catalyst.

Figure 11-8 Gold resists corrosion

Decomposition Reactions: Compounds Break Down

The second reaction type is the reverse of a synthesis reaction. A **decomposition reaction** occurs when a compound breaks down into two or more simpler substances. Many compounds break down when they are heated. For example, wood is a complex carbon compound. When it burns, the compound breaks down into carbon (ashes), carbon dioxide gas, and water.

The bonds in some compounds are so strong they do not break when the compound is heated. Water is a very stable compound. That is, water does not decompose—or break down—easily. Instead, heating water produces water vapor, water in the gaseous state.

However, passing an electric current through water breaks water into hydrogen gas and oxygen gas. The decomposition of a compound by electric current is known as *electrolysis* (i lek'trol'ə sis). The equation below represents the electrolysis of water. The equation also shows a compound breaking down into two elements.

$$2H_2O \rightarrow 2H_2 + O_2$$
water   hydrogen oxygen

A decomposition reaction provides people with lime, CaO. Lime, which comes from limestone rock, is used to make plaster and cement. The equation below shows that both products are compounds, but both are simpler substances than limestone.

$$CaCO_3 \rightarrow CaO + CO_2$$
limestone   lime   carbon dioxide

Some compounds are so unstable that they break down without adding heat or electricity. Hydrogen peroxide, shown in the picture, is used as a bleach or a mild antiseptic. Many people keep hydrogen peroxide in their medicine cabinets. The chemical formula for hydrogen peroxide is H_2O_2, which is similar to the formula for water. Unlike water, however, hydrogen peroxide is very unstable. As a result, it decomposes readily into water and oxygen.

$$2H_2O_2 \rightarrow 2H_2O + O_2$$

hydrogen peroxide   water   oxygen

Light acts as a catalyst in the decomposition of hydrogen peroxide, because it speeds up the reaction.

Section Review

1. What happens during a synthesis reaction?
2. What happens during a decomposition reaction?

Challenge: Suggest a reason why hydrogen peroxide is sold in brown bottles.

Figure 11-9 Hydrogen peroxide, H_2O_2, is a mild antiseptic and a bleach.

People and Science

Jacqueline K. Barton, Chemist

Jacqueline Barton is a chemist who works with biological materials. She has produced mirror-image molecules, which bind to DNA, a feat that has applications in many sciences.

Chemists use her technique to examine DNA structure. Pharmacists might one day employ her method to make drugs that selectively affect parts of genes. Biologists might apply her findings to pinpoint specific genetic structures.

As an elementary student, Jacqueline Barton became interested in molecular structure. Her interest in molecular shapes and symmetry continues to this day.

Jacqueline Barton finished graduate school at Columbia University with a Ph. D. in chemistry. Then for several years, Dr. Barton taught and did research. Jacqueline Barton is now a professor of chemistry and a director of chemical research at Columbia University. She and her group are studying the chemical structure associated with genetic expression. Dr. Barton has received a number of scientific awards for her outstanding work in chemistry. Among these is the National Science Foundation's *Alan T. Waterman Award*. She is the first woman chemist to win this honor.

A. Identify a single-replacement reaction.
B. Compare the reactivities of some elements.
C. Identify a double-replacement reaction.

11-3 Single-Replacement and Double-Replacement Reactions

Single-Replacement Reactions

The earliest metal workers made gold and copper articles because these metals are found free in nature. However, few metals exist alone in nature. Instead, they are found in rocky materials called ores.

An ore is composed of one compound or a mixture of compounds. As a result, the desired metal is chemically combined with the other elements in a compound. **Single-replacement reactions** have been used for thousands of years to separate a metal from its ore. A single-replacement reaction is one in which one element replaces another element that is in a compound.

Early metal workers learned to produce metals by heating an ore with charcoal, a form of carbon. Among these metals were copper, lead, silver, and later, iron. The picture shows workers making iron just as their ancestors did. The ore is iron oxide, Fe_2O_3, a major source of iron.

Figure 11-10 These people are making iron by ancient methods.

The extraction of iron took place in furnaces where temperatures topped 1000° Celsius. These workers had found that, at high temperatures, carbon replaced the metal in the compound. The single-replacement reaction for producing iron takes place in two steps. The following equation summarizes this reaction.

$$2Fe_2O_3(s) + 3C(s) \rightarrow 4Fe(s) + 3CO_2(g)$$
$$\text{iron oxide} \qquad \text{carbon} \qquad \text{iron} \qquad \text{carbon}$$
$$\text{dioxide}$$

Notice what the equation tells you. Carbon takes the place of iron in the compound. The products are a carbon compound (CO_2) and iron.

Today, many elements are produced commercially by single-replacement reactions. An inexpensive, abundant element is used to replace the desired element, which is locked in a compound.

Comparing the Reactivities of Elements

What causes one element to replace another element in a compound? For the answer, you must compare the elements. During a single-replacement reaction, a more active metal replaces a less active metal. Also, a more active nonmetal replaces a less active nonmetal.

How do people know whether one element will replace another? At first, workers learned by trial-and-error how elements reacted. In time, chemists gathered this experimental data and used it to make tables listing elements by their reactivities. Some common metals are listed in the short table shown here. The most active metal in the list is at the top, potassium. Going down the list, each metal is less reactive.

Look again at the picture on pages 242 and 243. The table indicates that copper is *less* reactive than zinc. Therefore, copper does not replace zinc in solution. In order to get copper crystals, electrical energy is added to the solution.

You can use the periodic table to make some general predictions. The most active metals are in group 1 at the left of the table. Metal activity increases down the group. Francium, at the bottom of group 1, is the most active metal. Similarly, the most reactive nonmetals are in group 17 toward the right of the table. Nonmetal reactivity increases up the group, as shown. Fluorine is the most reactive nonmetal.

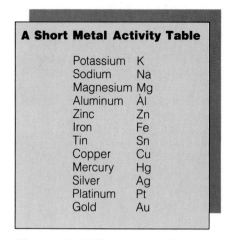

A Short Metal Activity Table

Potassium	K
Sodium	Na
Magnesium	Mg
Aluminum	Àl
Zinc	Zn
Iron	Fe
Tin	Sn
Copper	Cu
Mercury	Hg
Silver	Ag
Platinum	Pt
Gold	Au

Figure 11-11 The most reactive metal in this list is potassium.

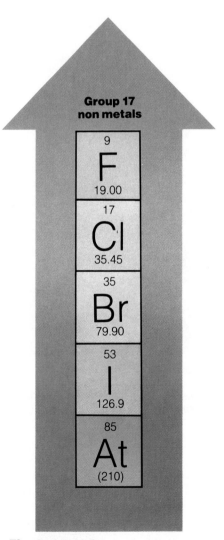

Group 17 non metals

9
F
19.00

17
Cl
35.45

35
Br
79.90

53
I
126.9

85
At
(210)

Figure 11-12 Fluorine is the most reactive nonmetal.

Explore!

Write a chemical equation showing a decomposition, a single-, and a double-replacement reaction. Instead of chemical symbols, use letters, such as A, B, C, and D, to represent elements. For example, you might write a synthesis equation such as the one shown below.

$$A + B \rightarrow AB$$

Figure 11-13 When the yellow solution (sodium chromate) mixes with the clear solution (silver nitrate), a red precipitate (silver chromate) forms.

You can apply this information to a single-replacement reaction used to produce bromine. Bromine has many uses, one of which is to make photographic film. The ocean contains abundant bromine compounds, so seawater is a good source of bromine. The problem is how to get the bromine out of sodium bromide, NaBr, or another bromine compound in seawater.

Which elements might be used to free bromine? Since fluorine and chlorine are above bromine in group 17, they are more active nonmetals than bromine. Thus, either will replace bromine.

However, fluorine is so active that it attacks most laboratory containers. As a result, the less reactive chlorine generally is used to extract bromine. The equation below shows that chlorine replaces bromine, forming sodium chloride.

$$2NaBr(aq) + Cl_2(g) \rightarrow Br_2(l) + 2NaCl(aq)$$
sodium   chlorine   bromine   sodium
bromide   chloride

Double-Replacement Reactions

In a **double-replacement reaction,** two compounds "switch partners." The picture shows the results of a double-replacement reaction between two compounds dissolved in water. The arrows in the equation below show how the parts of each compound exchange places.

$$BaCl_2 + Na_2SO_4 \rightarrow BaSO_4 + 2NaCl$$
barium   sodium   barium   sodium
chloride   sulfate   sulfate   chloride

Both compounds to the left of the arrow are soluble in water. NaCl to the right of the arrow also is soluble in water. However, $BaSO_4$, the second product, is insoluble—or not soluble—in water. A substance, such as $BaSO_4$, that settles to the bottom of the container during a reaction between two solutions is called a **precipitate.**

Section Review

1. What is a single-replacement reaction?
2. Which metals in the table will replace iron in a compound?
3. What is a double-replacement reaction?

Challenge: When a student combines two liquids, a yellow solid appears in the solution. Explain.

Single-Replacement Reactions with Metals

Purpose

To compare the reactivities of four metals

Materials

- 75 mL of $CuSO_4$ solution
- 75 mL of $ZnSO_4$ solution
- 10 cm of copper wire
- 10 cm of zinc strip
- two 10 cm strips of magnesium ribbon
- two large iron nails
- six 100-mL beakers
- 25-mL graduated cylinder
- small piece steel wool
- 2 pieces white paper
- fine-point marking pen
- cover goggles

Procedure and Observations

1. Copy the table. Put on cover goggles.

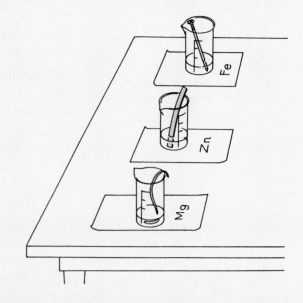

	Original appearance	Final appearance
$CuSO_4$		
$ZnSO_4$		
Zn		
Cu		
Mg		
Fe		

2. Put 25 mL of $CuSO_4$ solution in each of three 100-mL beakers. Label each beaker $CuSO_4$. Set the beakers on white paper.

3. Note the color of the nail, zinc strip, and magnesium ribbon after they are rubbed with steel wool.

4. Place one metal in each beaker. Write the metal's name on the paper, near the beaker in which it was placed, as shown in the drawing.

5. Repeat steps 2, 3, and 4 using $ZnSO_4$ solution, instead of $CuSO_4$ solution, and copper wire in place of the zinc strip.

6. Observe all beakers for the rest of the period. Record any changes you see in the solutions and metals.

Analysis and Conclusions

1. Which metal is most reactive? Least reactive?

2. Explain how you determined your answers above.

3. Use your observations to make an activity table for zinc, copper, iron, and magnesium. Order the metals so reactivity increases down the list.

After completing this section, you will be able to

A. Explain why chemical reactions are classified in more than one way.

B. Describe what happens in an oxidation-reduction reaction.

C. Describe the production of iron as a redox reaction.

11-4 Oxidation-Reduction Reactions

Classifying Chemical Reactions

Most things can be classified in more than one way. For example, an elephant belongs to the group of mammals, but it also belongs to the group of animals with tusks. Being a member of one group does not exclude the elephant from the other group.

Similarly, chemical reactions are classified in more than one way. Classifying a reaction by its chemical equation tells you how the formulas of reactants compare with the formulas of products. However, this information does not adequately describe a chemical reaction. As a result, chemists have other, more descriptive ways to classify chemical reactions. For example, one large group includes the reactions of acids with certain compounds. You will read about this group in the next chapter.

Another group of chemical reactions includes precipitation reactions. This classification focuses on how soluble compounds are in water. In all **precipitation reactions,** an insoluble product forms when two solutions mix. The picture on page 254 showed a red precipitate. Typically, precipitation reactions are double-replacements that take place in a water solution.

Note, however, that two solutions can mix without producing a precipitate. As a result, chemists have devised tables that list soluble and insoluble compounds. People use these tables to predict whether a precipitation reaction will occur when two solutions mix.

Oxidation-Reduction Reactions

A large, important group of reactions focuses on what is happening at the atomic level during a reaction. With the discovery of atomic particles, scientists soon learned that the activities of electrons play an important part in chemical reactions. In fact, more than half of all chemical reactions involve an exchange of electrons. An **oxidation-reduction reaction** is a chemical reaction in which one substance gains electrons given off by another substance. Oxidation-reduction sometimes is shortened to "redox," a term that includes a part of both words.

The pictures show some products of oxidation-reduction reactions. These products are quite diverse. For example, they include rotten apples, rusty metal, ashes from a wood fire, pure metals, the aging of cells in living organisms, and so on! A redox reaction can be represented by a single-replacement, a synthesis, or a decomposition equation.

Originally, *oxidation* referred to a reaction in which a substance combines with oxygen. The oxidation of potassium produces potassium oxide.

$$4K(s) \quad + \quad O_2(g) \quad \rightarrow \quad 2K_2O(s)$$
potassium   oxygen   potassium oxide

By definition, the potassium atoms are oxidized when they combine with oxygen. What is happening at the atomic level during oxidation? Potassium is a metal. In forming compounds, neutral metal atoms form bonds with atoms of other elements. When neutral metal atoms form bonds, they change to positive metal ions. They become positively charged because they give up electrons, which are the negatively charged particles in the atom. **Oxidation,** then, is a reaction in which a substance loses electrons.

Figure 11-14 Each picture shows a product of an oxidation-reduction reaction.

During the oxidation of potassium, oxygen atoms gain the electrons given off by potassium. Gaining the electrons changes the neutral oxygen atoms shown at the left of the arrow to negative ions in the compound to the right of the arrow. **Reduction** is a reaction in which a substance gains electrons. Notice that oxidation and reduction occur at the same time, as electrons move from one substance to another.

Now look at the equation showing potassium reacting with chlorine. The potassium chloride, KCl, in the picture forms in this reaction.

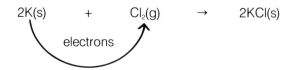

$$2K(s) \quad + \quad Cl_2(g) \quad \rightarrow \quad 2KCl(s)$$

electrons

Once again, neutral potassium atoms are oxidized when they give up electrons, and neutral chlorine atoms are reduced when they gain those electrons. Thus, oxidation and reduction take place, regardless of whether or not oxygen is present.

Figure 11-15 The mineral *sylvite* is potassium chloride (KCl), a compound.

The Reduction of Iron from Its Ore

An oxidation-reduction reaction occurs when an element is extracted from a compound. The iron in iron oxide, Fe_2O_3, is "reduced" in huge blast furnaces. The picture shows molten iron going into a blast furnace. Look again at the single-replacement equation that summarizes this reaction.

assigned electric charges:

$$\overset{+\ -}{2Fe_2O_3} + \overset{0}{3C} \rightarrow \overset{0}{4Fe} + \overset{+\ -}{3CO_2}$$

Because electrons have negative charges, you can think of the transfer of electrons as changes in electric charge. You can assign fictitious charges to each substance by writing 0, +, and − symbols above each. Assign a zero charge to neutral atoms of free elements. In the equation above, both the reactant carbon atoms and the product iron atoms have a zero charge.

The signs also can show that a compound's formula represents a neutral compound. For each formula, write a positive sign above the element on the left and a negative sign above the element on the right, as shown above.

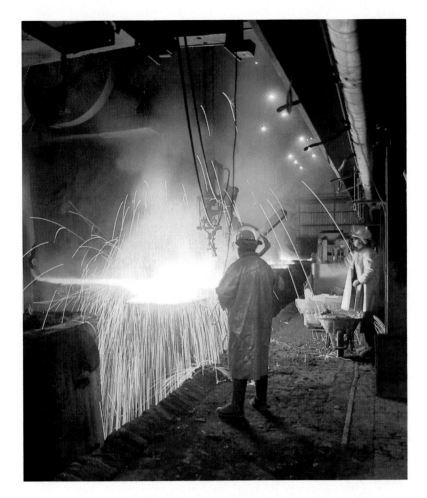

Explore!

Use a chemistry book or an encyclopedia to learn more about the reduction of iron ore in a blast furnace. Make a diagram showing the inside of a blast furnace. Explain the function of limestone in this process.

Figure 11-16 Molten iron going into the blast furnace

Therefore, reading from left to right, the positive sign above the iron ions changes to a zero charge above the iron atoms. This change indicates that iron has gained electrons and is reduced. Note that iron's charge changes from a positive value to zero when it is reduced.

Reading from left to right, carbon's 0 sign changes to a positive sign. Carbon's fictitious charge changes because the carbon atoms have lost electrons. Thus, carbon is oxidized. In this reaction, the oxygen is neither oxidized nor reduced. Like people watching a ball game, oxygen is a "spectator" in this redox reaction.

Section Review

1. What is a precipitate?
2. How are oxidation and reduction related?
3. Which substances are oxidized and reduced when iron is removed from iron oxide?

Challenge: Why are both oxidation and reduction called half-reactions?

After completing this section, you
will be able to

A. Define polymerization.
B. Explain why carbon is so important to living things.

11-5 Chemistry of Carbon Compounds

Reactions of the Hydrocarbons

Hydrocarbons and other carbon compounds undergo many types of chemical reactions. Recall that hydrocarbons are compounds composed of carbon and hydrogen. One important hydrocarbon reaction is combustion—or burning. The combustion of hydrocarbons produces most of our energy.

In general, reactions of carbon compounds are described according to changes in the bonds linking carbon atoms. For instance, consider the change that occurs when propane, C_3H_8, is heated.

propane   propylene

At 460^0 Celsius, hydrogen gas is released, and propane changes to propylene, $CH_3CH:CH_2$. Propane is a heating fuel and propylene is used to make items such as carpet fibers and unbreakable bottles.

Compare the carbon bonds in propane and propylene, shown in the diagram. Each dash represents a bond composed of one pair of shared electrons—a single-covalent bond. Notice that propylene has a double dash between two of its carbon atoms. The double dash represents a bond composed of two pairs of electrons. Such a bond is called a double-covalent bond. The heating of propane is an example of a cracking reaction. A process in which large hydrocarbon molecules are changed into smaller hydrocarbon molecules is called **cracking.**

Although hydrocarbon compounds are composed mostly of carbon and hydrogen atoms, they can contain atoms of other elements as well. Atoms of elements such as chlorine, oxygen, and nitrogen are added to hydrocarbon molecules during substitution reactions. A **substitution reaction** is one in which atoms of other elements substitute for—or replace—atoms of hydrogen. The non-stick material used to line cooking pans is created when fluorine atoms replace hydrogen atoms in a substitution reaction.

In **polymerization reactions,** carbon molecules combine in long chains, forming giant molecules. The giant molecules are known as **polymers**. A polymer can contain many thousands of atoms. The chainlike structure shown in *Figure 11-17* is a small part of a nylon polymer. The dots mean that the pattern continues to repeat on both sides. A diagram showing every atom in one molecule would cover many pages!

Explore!

Make a list of synthetic polymer products found in your home. Use a resource book to find as many names of these polymers as you can.

$$\cdots\!\!\cdot\;\; \overset{\displaystyle O}{\overset{\|}{C}}-NH-(CH_2)_6-NH-\overset{\displaystyle O}{\overset{\|}{C}}-(CH_2)_4-\overset{\displaystyle O}{\overset{\|}{C}}-NH-(CH_2)_6-NH-\overset{\displaystyle O}{\overset{\|}{C}}-(CH_2)_4-\overset{\displaystyle O}{\overset{\|}{C}}-NH\;\;\cdots\!\!\cdot$$

Figure 11-17 A small part of a nylon polymer

Synthetic polymers are those produced in factories or laboratories. Scientists have designed a wide variety of synthetic polymers with different properties. Plastics are synthetic polymers. The picture shows some useful polymer products. Rayon, polyester, phonograph records, paint, glue, and thousands of other items we use are created in polymerization reactions.

Figure 11-18 Useful polymer products

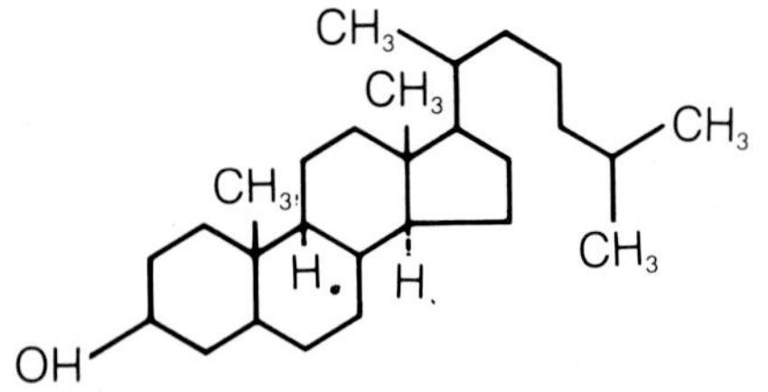

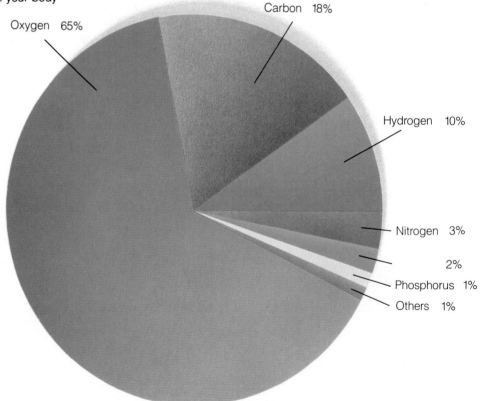

Figure 11-19 Only part of the carbon atoms in a cholesterol molecule are shown in the diagram above. In addition, one carbon atom is present wherever a line bends.

Carbon and the Compounds of Life

The cells of living organisms are composed of carbon compounds. The graph shows that in addition to carbon, the cells of your body contain hydrogen, oxygen, nitrogen, small amounts of phosphorus and calcium, and even smaller amounts of many other elements. Notice that about one-fifth of your mass is carbon.

Living organisms exist because of carbon's unusual bonding properties. That is, carbon atoms readily bond to other carbon atoms, forming molecules with a variety of shapes and sizes. Your body is a factory that manufactures molecules of carbon compounds. For example, your cells produce giant molecules containing long chains of carbon atoms with other elements attached. These huge molecules are natural polymers. Your cells also make structures with rings of carbon atoms, such as the cholesterol molecule shown here.

Proteins are the most complex carbon compounds in living things. Proteins are natural polymers that form when amino acid molecules join. Since amino acids combine in many different ways, different protein molecules are possible. The production of protein in your body is controlled by a very complex molecule called deoxyribonucleic (dē ok'sə rī'bō nü klē'ik) acid—or DNA.

Figure 11-20 The relative amounts of some important elements in your body

Oxygen 65%

Carbon 18%

Hydrogen 10%

Nitrogen 3%

2%

Phosphorus 1%

Others 1%

Figure 11-21 DNA molecule model

Applying Science

Special bacteria are present in the digestive tracts of certain animals, such as termites and cattle. These bacteria can break down plant cellulose into sugar. Humans cannot digest cellulose. A high-fiber diet refers to a diet that is high in cellulose.

The DNA molecule is a natural polymer that contains up to 100 million smaller units joined together! *Figure 11-21* shows a piece of a DNA molecule. The small units in the diagram are groups of atoms containing carbon, hydrogen, oxygen, nitrogen, and phosphorus. The order in which the units are lined up provides a code containing your hereditary information. Your cells use the code to make new cells.

Living organisms also manufacture carbohydrates. Carbohydrates are carbon compounds containing hydrogen and oxygen. Sugar, starch, and the cellulose found in plants are carbohydrates. Sugar molecules are the simplest carbohydrate molecules. Both cellulose and starch are natural polymers that form when sugar molecules join.

When you eat foods containing starch, the sugar polymer is digested into individual sugar molecules. Then the sugar changes into even simpler compounds. These reactions provide energy for your activities and energy to keep your body warm. If your body does not need all its sugar, it changes the excess sugar back into polymers. The excess sugar is stored either as body fat or in your liver. In the liver, the polymerized sugar, called glycogen, quickly changes back into sugar molecules when it is needed for energy.

Only a few natural polymers are mentioned above. A complete description of the chemistry of living organisms would fill many large volumes.

Section Review

1. What is a synthetic polymer?
2. Give three examples of natural polymers in your body.

Challenge: Write one or two sentences describing the equation for photosynthesis below. $C_6H_{12}O_6$ represents sugar.

$$6CO_2 + 6H_2O \rightarrow C_6H_{12}O_6 + 6O_2$$

Classifying and Analyzing Chemical Reactions

On a clean piece of lined paper, copy the table. Write your answers to *Part A* and *Part B* in the two columns provided in this table.

PART A

Classify each equation below as a synthesis, decomposition, single-replacement, or double-replacement reaction. Write the name of each type beside the corresponding number on your paper, in the column for Part A.

1) $2HgO \rightarrow 2Hg + O_2$
2) $S + O_2 \rightarrow SO_2$
3) $4Fe + 3O_2 \rightarrow 2Fe_2O_3$
4) $2KI \rightarrow 2K + I_2$
5) $2KCl + F_2 \rightarrow 2KF + Cl_2$
6) $2HgO \rightarrow 2Hg + P_4 + 5O_2 \rightarrow P_4O_{10}$
7) $Ca + Br_2 \rightarrow CaBr_2$
8) $Mg + 2HCl \rightarrow MgCl_2 + H_2$
9) $Cu + 2AgNO_3 \rightarrow Cu(NO_3)_2 + 2Ag$
10) $2H_2O_2 \rightarrow 2H_2O + O_2$
11) $CaCO_3 \rightarrow CaO + CO_2$
12) $3Li + AlI_3 \rightarrow 3LiI + Al$
13) $2Al + 6HCl \rightarrow 3H_2 + 2AlCl_3$
14) $CaO + SiO_2 \rightarrow CaSiO_3$
15) $Ca(OH)_2 + Na_2CO_3 \rightarrow CaCO_3 + 2NaOH$
16) $CaF_2 + Na_2SO_4 \rightarrow CaSO_4 + 2NaF$

PART B

Equations 1 to 8 are oxidation-reduction reactions. Identify the oxidized and reduced substances in each equation. First, assign fictitious charges to each substance in an equation. Atoms of a free element are given a zero charge. For compound formulas, the element on the left is +, and the element on the right is −. "Read" the charges on an element from left to right in each equation.

The direction of change for assigned charges

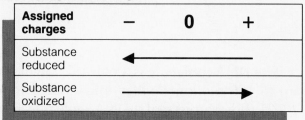

Assigned charges	−	0	+
Substance reduced	←		
Substance oxidized			→

Equation 1 is done for you. In the compound, assign a + charge to Hg, and a − charge to O. Assign 0 to atoms of both Hg and O_2 to the right of the arrow (free elements). Note that the charge of Hg goes from + on the left to 0 on the right, so Hg is reduced. (Its charge is reduced.) The charge of O goes from − on the left to zero on the right, so O is oxidized. (Its charge becomes more positive.)

If an element's charge is the same on both sides of the arrow, it is neither oxidized nor reduced. The arrows in the small table above show how signs change as elements are oxidized or reduced. If the sign changes from − to 0 or from 0 to +, the element is oxidized; if the sign changes from + to 0 or from 0 to −, it is reduced.

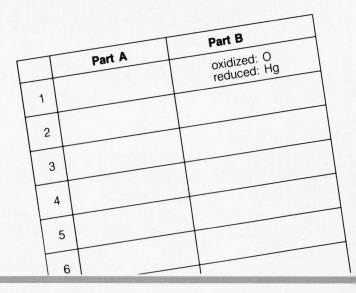

	Part A	Part B
1		oxidized: O reduced: Hg
2		
3		
4		
5		
6		

Summary

11-1 Recognizing Chemical Reactions

A. During a chemical reaction, reactants undergo a chemical change that results in the formation of products.

B. Chemical reactions either give off energy or absorb energy.

C. A person can control the speed of a chemical reaction by changing the temperature of the reactants or by adding a catalyst.

D. A chemical equation is an arrangement of symbols and numbers used to describe a chemical reaction.

11-2 Synthesis and Decomposition Reactions

A. Substances combine to form a more complex substance during a synthesis reaction.

B. A complex substance breaks down into simpler substances during a decomposition reaction.

11-3 Single and Double-Replacement Reactions

A. One element replaces another element combined in a compound during a single-replacement reaction.

B. Single-replacement reactions can be used to determine the reactivities of elements.

C. In a double-replacement reaction, substances in two compounds switch places.

11-4 Oxidation-Reduction Reactions

A. Chemists have more than one way to classify chemical reactions.

B. In an oxidation-reduction reaction, electrons are transferred from one substance to another.

C. Iron and other metals are extracted from their ores during oxidation-reduction reactions.

11-5 The Chemistry of Carbon Compounds

A. The focus of most hydrocarbon reactions involves changes in bonds between carbon atoms.

B. Living organisms produce a wide variety of carbon molecules.

Vocabulary

For each of the following terms, write a sentence that uses the term correctly.

catalyst
cracking
decomposition reaction
double-replacement reaction
endothermic reaction
exothermic reaction

oxidation
oxidation-reduction
　reaction
polymer
polymerization reaction
precipitate

precipitation reaction
product
reactant
reduction
single-replacement
　reaction
spontaneous reaction
substitution reaction
synthesis reaction

✓ Check Your Knowledge

Part I: Matching   Match the definition in Column I with the correct term in Column II.

Column I
1. reaction that gives off energy
2. original substance in a chemical reaction
3. substance that speeds up a chemical reaction without being changed itself
4. substances composed of hydrogen, carbon, and oxygen
5. breaking down compounds into simpler substances
6. electrons are given up during this process
7. combining elements or compounds to make a new substance
8. reaction that absorbs energy
9. newly formed substance in a chemical reaction
10. formation of one very large molecule from smaller molecules

Column II
a. carbohydrates
b. catalyst
c. decomposition
d. endothermic
e. exothermic
f. hydrocarbons
g. oxidation
h. polymerization
i. product
j. reactant
k. reduction
l. synthesis

Part II: Multiple Choice   Choose the letter of the best answer.

11. Large molecules that are made of smaller molecules are (a) reactants. (b) polymers. (c) fractions. (d) catalysts.
12. A polymerized sugar that is stored in plants is (a) glycogen. (b) cellulose. (c) rayon. (d) nylon.
13. What substance deposits on zinc in a copper sulfate, $CuSO_4$, solution? (a) copper atoms (b) sulfur atoms (c) sulfate ions (d) oxygen atoms
14. Plastics result from (a) cracking. (b) substitution. (c) polymerization. (d) combustion.
15. Starch and cellulose are (a) synthetic polymers. (b) natural polymers. (c) DNA. (d) amino acids.
16. Raising the temperature during a reaction results in (a) fewer molecular collisions. (b) slower-moving molecules. (c) slower reaction speed.
(d) faster reaction speed.
17. Sodium replaces zinc, copper replaces mercury, and zinc replaces copper. Which is the most reactive metal? (a) sodium (b) zinc (c) copper (d) mercury
18. When lead is separated from its ore, lead is (a) oxidized. (b) reduced. (c) neither oxidized nor reduced. (d) a spectator.

Part III: Completion   Write the word or words that complete the sentence correctly.
19. A catalyst _____ a chemical reaction.
20. A protein is composed of small molecules that are called _____.
21. During a _____ two chlorine atoms replace two hydrogen atoms in a hydrocarbon molecule.
22. _____ are compounds containing hydrogen and carbon.
23. The product of a _____ is an insoluble compound.

The agricultural worker in the photograph is picking ripe oranges in an orange grove in California. Oranges, grapefruit, lemons, and limes are valuable citrus crops grown in this country. All citrus fruits are members of one of the two groups of compounds discussed in this chapter.

Organizing your Study Skills The outline below will help you see how the chapter is organized and what you should learn as you read.

I. Section 12-1: Properties of Acids and Bases
   A. What is an acid?
   B. What is a base?
   C. What are some important uses of acids and bases?

II. Section 12-2: Acids and Bases in Solution
   A. How are acids alike?
   B. How are bases alike?

III. Section 12-3: Indicators and the pH Scale
   A. How are indicators used?
   B. What is the pH scale?

IV. Section 12-4: Neutralization Reactions
   A. What is a neutralization reaction?
   B. What is the end-point of a neutralization?

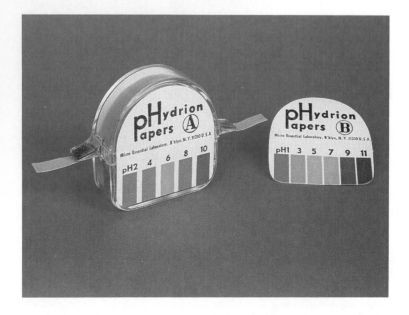

After completing this section you will be able to

A. Describe some properties of an acid.
B. Describe some properties of a base.
C. List some important uses for acids and bases.

12-1 Properties of Acids and Bases

Acids

Grapefruit, lemons, vinegar, and many other foods taste sour because they contain weak acids. The sour taste is a characteristic property of compounds called acids. Citric acid gives grapefruit and lemons their sour taste. Acetic acid makes vinegar taste sour. Milk sours when lactose, the sugar in milk, changes to lactic acid. The word *acid* comes from the Latin word *acidus*, which means "sour." The table lists some common acids. How are the chemical formulas for these acids similar?

Acids have their own set of characteristic properties. The picture shows that acids turn blue litmus paper red. Litmus paper contains a blue dye taken from lichens, which are funguslike organisms. Acids also change the color of certain vegetable dyes produced by plants. When vinegar is added to red cabbage juice, the red cabbage juice turns a bright pink.

Acids release hydrogen gas when they react with active metals, such as iron and zinc. What kind of reaction is shown by the equation below?

$$Zn(s) + HCl(aq) \rightarrow ZnCl_2(aq) + H_2(g)$$

zinc — hydrochloric acid — zinc chloride — hydrogen

Figure 12-1 Some common acids

Common Acids	
Hydrochloric Acid in your stomach	HCl
Acetic Acid in vinegar	$HC_2H_3O_2$
Carbonic Acid in carbonated water	H_2CO_3
Citric Acid in citrus fruits	$H_3C_6H_5O_7$
Sulfuric Acid in batteries	H_2SO_4

Figure 12-2 Litmus paper is red in an acidic solution and blue in a basic solution.

Bases

Soap and detergent feel slippery. The slippery feeling is a property of compounds called *bases*. Some familiar bases are lye, baking soda solutions, milk of magnesia, and ammonia water. *Figure 12-3* lists other useful bases. How are their chemical formulas similar?

Like acids, bases have many similar properties. Soap, milk of magnesia, and other bases have a bitter taste. A base turns red litmus paper blue again, as shown. As *Figure 12-4* suggests, many bases are good household cleaners. However, strong bases also are harmful to your body. Touching lye, for example, causes severe burns and destroys cells.

A reaction between a strong acid and a strong base destroys the acidic and basic properties of the two compounds. For this reason, people can take an antacid tablet to relieve an acid-upset stomach. The antacid dissolved in water contains a base that reacts with excess acid in the stomach. The reaction eliminates—or neutralizes—the excess acid, which makes the person feel better.

Similarly, you can clean up an acid spill by pouring baking soda on it. The acid and the baking soda neutralize each other. The acetic acid in vinegar aids in neutralizing a base spill.

Have You Heard?

A base feels slippery to you because the oil in your skin is reacting with the base. Manufacturers use the same reaction to produce soap! A chemical reaction between a base, such as sodium hydroxide, and either animal fat or plant oil produces soap.

Figure 12-3 Some common bases

Common Bases	
Sodium Hydroxide in drain cleaner; soap making	$NaOH$
Calcium Hydroxide in mortar	$Ca(OH)_2$
Ammonium Hydroxide household cleaner	NH_4OH
Potassium Hydroxide soap and glass making	KOH
Magnesium Hydroxide in milk of magnesia	$Mg(OH)_2$
Aluminum Hydroxide in water purification	$Al(OH)_3$

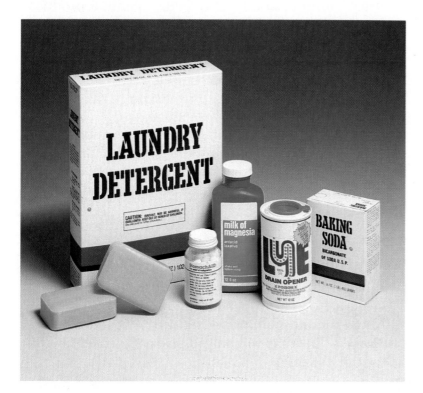

Figure 12-4 Many household products are basic solutions.

The Importance of Acids and Bases

Acids and bases make up two large and important groups of compounds. You have learned that strong acids and strong bases are poisonous. Both also are caustic to living cells and to clothing. That is, splattering strong acids or bases can produce burns on your skin and make holes in your clothing. Nevertheless, these compounds are extremely useful.

Acids and bases have a direct effect on your health. Your body must contain the correct concentrations of acids and bases to function properly. Blood and many body fluids are slightly basic. However, some parts of your body are slightly acidic. The digestive enzymes alone operate in a variety of conditions. The enzyme in saliva is most efficient when saliva is neutral—neither acidic nor basic. Gastric juice in the stomach contains enzymes that function best in an acidic solution. The acidic solution produced in the stomach is hydrochloric acid. On the other hand, enzymes in the small intestine require a basic solution. The results of even slight changes in the "acid-base balance" of any part of the body can result in serious health problems.

Acids and bases also make important contributions to our everyday lives. Our homes, clothing, and food depend on the production of important acids and bases in industry. Sulfuric acid, H_2SO_4, is the chemical produced in largest amounts throughout the world. This acid is needed for the production of metals, fertilizers, petroleum, plastics, paper, and thousands of other products. Nitric acid, HNO_3, and hydrochloric acid, HCl, also are valuable industrial chemicals. The worker in the picture is using hydrochloric acid to clean stone.

Bases are used to manufacture soap, paper, household cleaners, petroleum products, and many other items. Sodium hydroxide, calcium hydroxide, and ammonium hydroxide are among the most widely used bases.

Figure 12-5 The worker is using hydrochloric acid to clean the building.

Section Review

1. What are three properties of acids?
2. What are three properties of bases?
3. Name the most abundant industrial chemical.

Challenge: In what way might acids and bases be considered opposites?

12-2 Acids and Bases in Solution

Objectives

After completing this section you will be able to

A. Explain how acids are alike.
B. Explain how bases are alike.

Hydronium Ions and Acid Properties

How is the acid in the car battery, shown in *Figure 12-6*, similar to the acid in your stomach? Although the two acids have similar properties, they are different compounds, as their chemical formulas show. Battery acid is H_2SO_4 and stomach acid is HCl. Both formulas begin with an *H*. The behavior of these hydrogen atoms in a water solution is the key to the properties of acids.

Hydrochloric acid in your stomach helps you digest the food you eat. Pure HCl is a gas. The equation below shows what happens to HCl in water.

$$HCl(aq) \rightarrow H^+(aq) + Cl^-(aq)$$
$$\text{hydrogen} \quad \text{choride ion}$$
$$\text{ion}$$

Hydrogen chloride molecules in water produce **hydrogen ions** and chloride ions. Consider what has happened. In water, the bonds between the atoms in many acid molecules break. The atoms change to H^+ ions and Cl^- ions. The presence of H^+ ions in water causes litmus to turn red, acids to taste sour, and all other acid properties. An **acid** is a substance that produces hydrogen ions, H^+, in a water solution.

Figure 12-6 An automobile's battery contains sulfuric acid.

Figure 12-7 The label on the container explains some hazards involved in using a strong acid such as HCl.

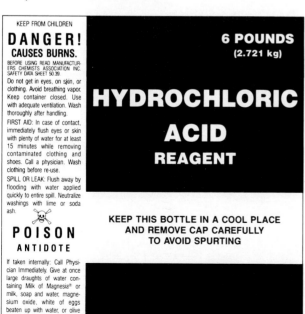

KEEP FROM CHILDREN

DANGER!
CAUSES BURNS.
BEFORE USING READ MANUFACTUR-
ERS CHEMISTS ASSOCIATION INC.
SAFETY DATA SHEET 50.39
Do not get in eyes, on skin, or clothing. Avoid breathing vapor. Keep container closed. Use with adequate ventilation. Wash thoroughly after handling.
FIRST AID: In case of contact, immediately flush eyes or skin with plenty of water for at least 15 minutes while removing contaminated clothing and shoes. Call a physician. Wash clothing before re-use.
SPILL OR LEAK: Flush away by flooding with water applied quickly to entire spill. Neutralize washings with lime or soda ash.

POISON
ANTIDOTE
If taken internally: Call Physi-
cian Immediately. Give at once large draughts of water containing Milk of Magnesia* or milk, soap and water, magne-
sium oxide, white of eggs beaten up with water, or olive oil. Avoid Carbonates. Give No Emetics.

6 POUNDS
(2.721 kg)

HYDROCHLORIC ACID
REAGENT

KEEP THIS BOTTLE IN A COOL PLACE
AND REMOVE CAP CAREFULLY
TO AVOID SPURTING

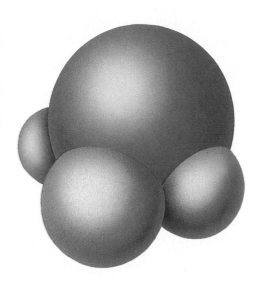

Figure 12-8 In the hydronium ion model, the large sphere is an oxide ion (O^{-2}). The three small spheres are hydrogen ions (H^+).

Figure 12-9 A strong acid contains more ions than molecules. A weak acid contains more molecules than ions.

A hydrogen ion is a hydrogen atom that has lost its electron. However, a hydrogen atom has only one proton and one electron. As a result, a hydrogen ion is the same as one proton. Often, the term *proton* is used when referring to a hydrogen ion.

However, H^+ ions do not stay alone for very long in water. H^+ ions are strongly attracted to the oxygen part of a water molecule. As a result, each H^+ ion combines chemically with one water molecule. The **hydronium ion,** H_3O^+, is a positively charged ion that forms when a H^+ ion and a water molecule combine. The drawing shows a model of the hydronium ion. All acids react similarly in water. They produce H_3O^+ ions.

The strength of an acid is determined by the number of H_3O^+ (or H^+) ions it produces. A weak acid is one that produces few H_3O^+ ions in solution. Acetic acid, the weak acid in vinegar, produces few H_3O^+ ions. Acids in foods generally are weak. *Figure 12-9* indicates that a water solution of a weak acid contains more acid molecules than ions. Hydrochloric acid and sulfuric acid are strong acids because they produce many H_3O^+ ions in water. A strong acid solution has more ions than acid molecules. Compare the relative number of ions and molecules in the acids shown in *Figure 12-9*.

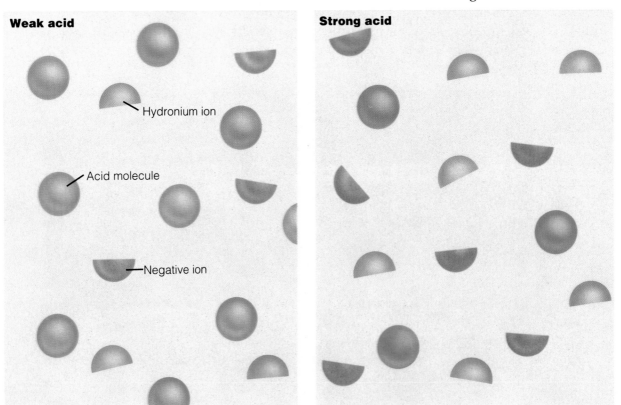

Weak acid

Hydronium ion

Acid molecule

Negative ion

Strong acid

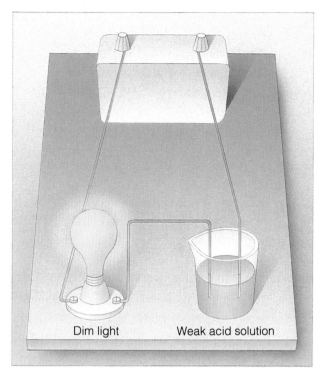
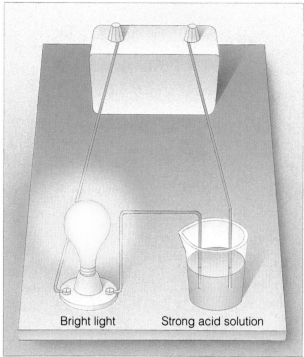

Dim light   Weak acid solution

Bright light   Strong acid solution

In Chapter 10, you read that an electric current can pass through water containing ions. The lighted bulbs in the pictures are evidence that acid solutions contain ions, and they conduct electric current. The brightness of the bulb is related to the number of ions in solution. The more ions, the brighter the light. Notice that the bulb connected to the strong acid solution glows brightly. Less current moves through the weak acid solution, resulting in a dimmer light.

The strength of an acid also determines how it reacts with other substances. A strong acid reacts more vigorously with an active metal than a weak acid does. A strong acid is a better conductor of electricity than a weak acid. You eat food containing weak acids, but you cannot touch a strong acid, such as H_2SO_4. Accidents with strong acids can result in severe burns on the skin and ruined clothing or furniture.

Figure 12-10 A strong acid solution transmits more electric current and, thus, produces a brighter light than does a weak acid solution.

Explore!

Use a high-school chemistry book to identify these acids as strong or weak.
1. $HC_2H_3O_2$, acetic acid
2. HNO_3, nitric acid
3. HF, hydrofluoric acid
4. H_2SO_4, sulfuric acid
5. HCl, hydrochloric acid
6. H_3PO_4, phosphoric acid
7. $HClO_4$, perchloric acid

Hydroxide Ions and Base Properties

Recall that formulas for the bases listed in the table all ended in OH. The O and H together represent the hydroxide ion, OH^-. In a **hydroxide ion**, one ion of oxygen and one of hydrogen behave as one negatively charged ion. The hydroxide ion in solution gives a base its characteristic properties. Thus, a **base** is a substance that produces OH^+ ions in a water solution.

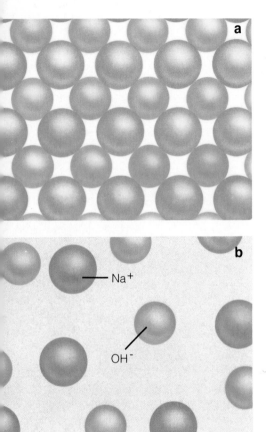

Figure 12-11 a The closely packed spheres in the upper diagram represent ions in solid NaOH. **b** In a water solution, the ions in NaOH separate. Because they can move freely through water, they can carry electric current.

Note that the hydroxide bases listed in *Figure 12-4* are ionic compounds and are solids. Each contains positive ions (metal ions and NH_4^+) combined with negative hydroxide ions. As solids, these ionic compounds do not conduct electricity because the ions in a solid cannot move past each other.

Figure 12-11 shows a model of the ions in NaOH. Although ions are not actually touching as they are in the model, strong attractions (ionic bonds) hold the ions tightly in place.

However, ionic compounds are good conductors of electricity when they are in solution or are melted. All ions are separated, as shown in *Figure 12-10*, and electric current can move through them.

The equation below shows the separation of sodium hydroxide ions in water. Recall that (aq) indicates that the compound is in a water solution.

$$NaOH(s) \rightarrow Na^+(aq) + OH^-(aq)$$

A strong base, such as sodium hydroxide, produces many hydroxide ions in water. Strong bases are those in which group 1 or 2 metals—the most active metals—are combined with hydroxide ions. On the other hand, weak bases produce few OH^- ions in water and are poor conductors of electricity. Ammonium hydroxide is a weak base.

Ammonium hydroxide, NH_4OH, is an important industrial base. Also, many household cleaners, such as those used to clean ovens, contain NH_4OH. This base is produced when ammonia gas, NH_3, is added to water.

$$\underset{\text{ammonia}}{NH_3(g)} + H_2O(l) \rightarrow \underset{\substack{\text{ammonium} \\ \text{ion}}}{NH_4^+(aq)} + \underset{\substack{\text{hydroxide} \\ \text{ion}}}{OH^-(aq)}$$

In the reaction above, an ammonia molecule, NH_3, accepts a H^+ ion from water. The products are NH_4^+ ions and OH^- ions.

Section Review

1. What is an acid? A strong acid?
2. What is a base? A strong base?

Challenge: Hydrobromic acid, HBr, is a strong acid. What does this tell you about the relative number of molecules and ions in an HBr solution?

Recognizing Acids and Bases

Purpose

To identify acids and bases by their properties

Materials

- 8 g of washing soda
- 3 g of baking soda
- 10 mL of vinegar
- 10 mL of lemon juice
- 10 mL of dilute HCl
- 10 mL of carbonated water
- 10 mL of household ammonia
- 10 mL of liquid drain cleaner
- red and blue litmus paper
- test-tube rack
- nine 13 × 100-mm test tubes
- two 100-mL beakers
- one 25-mL graduated cylinder
- 5 cm × 5 cm aluminum foil
- fine-point marking pen
- cover goggles

Procedure and Observations

1. Copy the table shown.
2. *CAUTION: Wear cover goggles during this activity. Do not spill acids or bases on yourself.*
They can burn your skin and clothes. Measure out 10 mL of water in the graduated cylinder.
3. Put washing soda into a beaker and add the 10 mL water to dissolve the washing soda. Pour this solution into a test tube and label it *washing soda*.
4. Using a clean beaker, repeat steps 2 and 3 using the baking soda. Label the test tube *baking soda*.
5. Measure 10 mL each of the following liquids into separate test tubes: vinegar, lemon juice, HCl, carbonated water, ammonia, drain cleaner. Label the contents of each test tube.
6. Dip one piece of each color of litmus into each of the test tubes. Record any color changes in the table.
7. Drop a small piece of aluminum foil into each test tube. Record any reaction in your table.

Analysis and Conclusions

1. Use your data to classify each substance you tested as an acid or a base.
2. Which kind of substance reacts with metal?

Substance	Reaction with Litmus	Reaction with Aluminum foil

Objectives

After completing this section, you will be able to

A. Explain the usefulness of indicators.

B. Describe the pH Scale.

12-3 Indicators and the pH Scale

Indicators

Citrus fruits taste pleasantly sour because they contain citric acid, a weak acid. However, strong acids and strong bases are dangerous chemicals, and you must avoid direct contact with these compounds. Instead, you can use chemical reactions that involve color changes to test the strength of acids and bases.

An **indicator** is a substance that changes color in the presence of an acid or a base. Litmus is one of the many indicators used in a chemistry laboratory. Indicators enable chemists to distinguish between acidic and basic solutions. In addition, indicators are used to determine the strengths of acids and bases. The pictures show the colors of two indicators in acid and base solutions. As a solution becomes less acidic, the indicators change from the colors on the left to the colors in the middle to the colors on the right.

Figure 12-12 The containers show the colors of bromthymol blue and methyl orange before, during, and after a color change.

Methyl orange

Bromthymol blue

Indicators can exist in two forms. They are either an acid or a base. For example, the indicator methyl orange is red in strong acid solutions and yellow in base solutions. *Figure 12-13* shows that the red, acid form is a molecule containing a H^+ ion (a proton) at the end of the molecule. The acid form turns yellow as it donates the proton to a base. The yellow form is an ion that lacks a proton.

This proton difference causes the color changes of other indicators too. For example, the litmus molecule is red. It contains a H^+ ion. When a base is added to red litmus, the red litmus donates its proton to the base. Blue litmus ions remain.

When an acid is added to blue litmus, acid molecules donate protons to the litmus and leave the litmus red. By donating its proton to the added base, the red form of the litmus molecule acts as an acid. By accepting a proton from the acid, the blue form of the litmus molecule acts as a base. In these reactions, an indicator is both an acid *and* a base. Indicators change color as they donate or accept protons from acids or bases.

Acid Form

Base Form

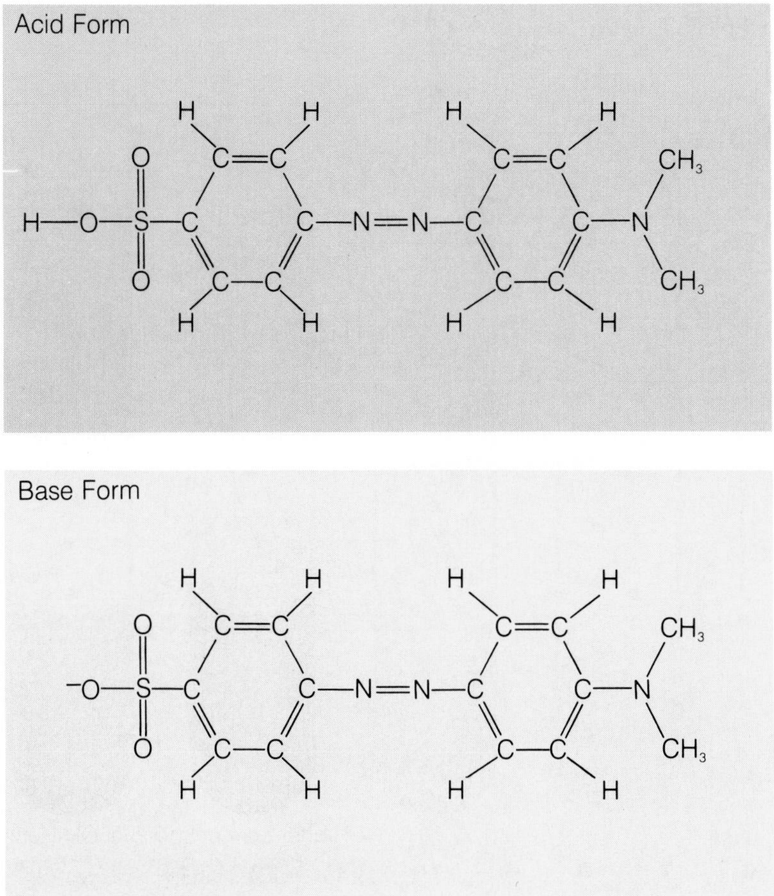

Figure 12-13 The two diagrams show the structure of a molecule of methyl orange in the acid form and the base form.

The pH Scale

Pure distilled water is a neutral solution. That is, it has as many hydrogen (or hydronium) ions as hydroxide ions. On the other hand, water that contains more H^+ ions than OH^- ions is acidic. Or, water that contains more OH^- ions than H^+ ions is basic.

The **pH scale** is a number scale used to describe the hydrogen ion concentration of a solution. The numbers on the pH scale range from 1 to 14. Although the pH scale refers to H^+ ion concentration, it can be used to describe both bases and acids. Numbers above 7 on the pH scale refer to bases, and numbers below 7 refer to acids. The middle number, 7, means neutral. Distilled water is 7 on the pH scale.

Figure 12-14 shows the relationship between H^+ ions, OH^- ions, and the pH scale. The strong acid solution with a pH of 1 (on the left) has many H^+ ions and few OH^- ions. The strong base solution with a pH of 14 (on the right) has many OH^- ions and few H^+ ions. Going from left to right, the number of H^+ ions goes down as the number of OH^- ions increases. When the concentration of the two ions is equal, the solution is neutral with a pH of 7.

Figure 12-14 An acidic solution with a pH of 1 has many H^+ ions and few OH^- ions. A neutral solution has about the same number of both ions. A basic solution with a pH of 14 has many OH^- ions and few H^+ ions.

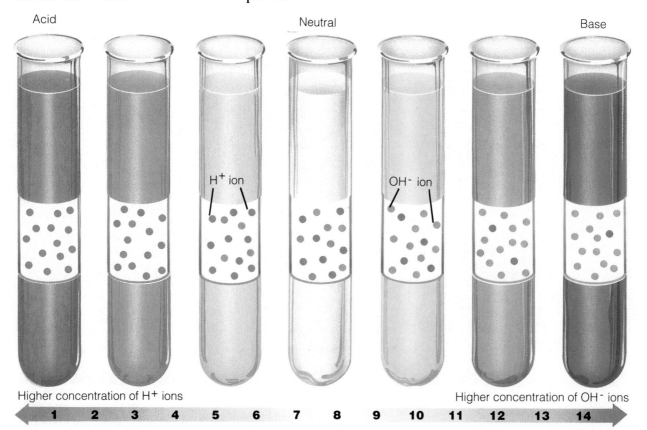

Acid   Neutral   Base

H^+ ion OH^- ion

Higher concentration of H^+ ions   Higher concentration of OH^- ions

1   2   3   4   5   6   7   8   9   10   11   12   13   14

The lower the number, the more acidic the solution. Thus, the strongest acids have the lowest pH numbers. The higher the pH number, the more basic the solution. The strongest bases have the highest pH values. *Figure 12-15* shows the average pH of some substances.

Each indicator changes color at a certain range of pH numbers. Therefore, one indicator is useful for only a a few pH values. However, chemists have combined a number of indicators to produce one indicator that operates over the whole pH scale. The mixture of indicators is called **universal indicator**. The small photograph on page 269 shows *pH paper*, which is coated with universal indicator. The pH paper changes colors at a pH of 1, 3, 5, 7, 9, and 11. Universal indicator paper can be used to test the pH of many acids and bases.

Section Review

1. What is an indicator?
2. What does a solution's pH number tell you?

Challenge: In a solution, methyl orange is bright yellow and bromthymol blue is bright blue. What do you know about this solution?

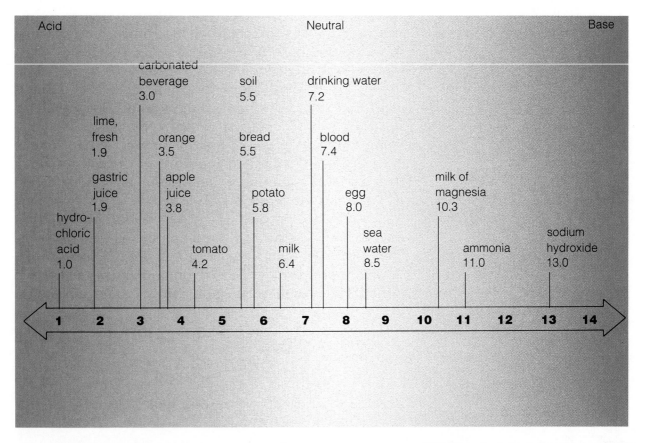

Figure 12-15 The average pH for some common substances

Pharmacist

The Greek word *pharmakon* means "drug." Our word *pharmacist* describes people who work with drugs.

You can find pharmacists in laboratories or stores where prescriptions are filled. They distribute the medicinal drugs that doctors recommend for their patients. Because pharmacists understand the chemical composition of medicines, they can safely mix, measure, and dispense them. Pharmacists also know how different drug doses and combinations affect the human body.

People's health depends on pharmacists doing their jobs well. So pharmacists need a license to practice. Students graduate from pharmacy college after five years and then take their licensing exam.

Objectives

After completing this section, you will be able to

A. Describe a neutralization reaction.

B. Identify the end-point of neutralization for a strong acid and strong base.

Have You Heard?

Vegetables and other plants grow best in soil with a pH of about 6.5. The soil in a conifer forest, which may have a pH of less than 4.2, generally is poor farming soil.

12-4 Neutralization Reactions

Products of Neutralization Reactions

Reactions between acids and bases are so common that most people are not aware of them. For example, you may have seen a gardener sprinkle lime, a white powder, on the soil around growing vegetables. Gardeners know that lime makes vegetables less sour. Similarly, farmers use lime to "sweeten" acidic soil. Lime is calcium oxide, CaO. This compound dissolves in water forming a basic solution, which contains positive calcium ions and negative hydroxide ions. When lime is applied to soil, rain and moisture in the soil trigger a reaction that neutralizes the acids in soil. This process is known as a *neutralization reaction*.

Water is one product of a neutralization reaction. Examine both forms of the equation below. When hydrogen ions from an acid meet with hydroxide ions from a base, the positive and negative ions are attracted to each other. They combine, forming neutral water molecules.

$$H_3O^+ + OH^- \rightarrow 2H_2O$$
OR
$$H^+ + OH^- \rightarrow H_2O$$

Energy is given off when water molecules form, so it is an exothermic reaction.

Look at the equations for two neutralization reactions. Note that the chemical formula for water sometimes is written HOH, instead of H_2O. Based on the equations, what type reaction is a neutralization?

Neutralization Reactions						
Strong Base	+	Strong Acid	→	Salt	+	Water
NaOH	+	HCl	→	NaCl	+	H_2O
2KOH	+	H_2SO_4	→	K_2SO_4	+	2HOH

The products are water and a second compound. However, the reaction takes place in solution, and both NaCl and K_2SO_4 are soluble in water. Therefore, positive metal ions from the base and negative ions from the acid remain in solution. *Figure 12-17* shows models of the ions that take part in the NaCl reaction.

Figure 12-16 When an acid reacts with a base, the products are a salt and water.

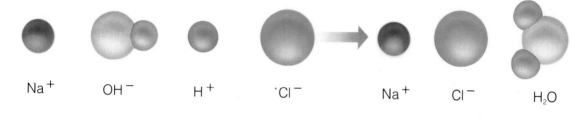

Na$^+$ OH$^-$ H$^+$ $\cdot$Cl$^-$ Na$^+$ Cl$^-$ H_2O

Figure 12-17 The spheres represent the ions taking part in a neutralization reaction. The salt formed—NaCl—is in a water solution.

If the water is removed or allowed to evaporate, these ions will combine, forming the solids, NaCl and K_2SO_4.

A compound in which positive ions from a base join with negative ions from an acid, is a *salt*. NaCl and K_2SO_4 are salts. The positive ion in a salt usually is a metal, such as potassium and sodium.

A **neutralization reaction**, then, is a process in which an acid and a base react, producing a salt and water. Many different salts form in neutralization reactions.

Note that both neutralization reactions above take place between strong acids and strong bases. The reaction between a strong acid and a strong base produces a neutral salt solution. Therefore, the solution that forms when K_2SO_4 or NaCl dissolve in water is neither acidic nor basic. The pH of the solution is about 7.

However, neutralization reactions do not always produce a "neutral" solution. A weak acid and a strong base produce a slightly basic solution. A strong acid and a weak base produce a slightly acidic solution.

Figure 12-18 Phenolphthalein was added to the two solutions. The acidic solution did not change color. The basic solution turned pink.

Figure 12-19 The student is adding a basic solution (pink) to an acidic solution.

The End-Point of Neutralization

Suppose a paper manufacturer must know exactly how much sodium hydroxide, NaOH, is required to neutralize a huge vat of sulfuric acid solution. The manufacturer wants to add just enough base to completely neutralize the acid. At the *end-point* of the neutralization, the acid and base have reacted completely and the reaction is, for all practical purposes, done. At the end-point of the reaction between NaOH and H_2SO_4, the solution has a pH of about 7, because a strong acid and strong base produce a neutral solution.

The industrial process used to neutralize the acid can be done on a small scale in a school laboratory. *Figure 12-18* shows beakers containing an acid and a base. A few drops of phenolphthalein were added to the solutions before the picture was taken. Phenolphthalein, an indicator, is colorless in an acid solution. When the pH of a solution rises above 8, however, the indicator changes from colorless to bright pink. Since the pH of the basic solution is greater than 8, the solution is pink.

In *Figure 12-19*, the student is adding the base to the acid drop by drop. He is carefully measuring how much base he adds. He will stop adding drops of base at the first sign of any pink in the acid. When the acid begins to look pink, the neutralization is at the end-point, and the solution has a pH of about 8. The amount of base the student must add in order to start the color change in acid tells him how much base is required to neutralize the acid.

A neutralization reaction called a *titration* is used to determine the concentration—or strength—of an acid or a base. Suppose chemists need to know the concentration of an acidic solution. By measuring how much base of known strength is needed to neutralize the acid, they can calculate the strength of the acid. Similarly, they can use an acid of known strength to find the concentration of a base.

Section Review

1. What are the products of a neutralization reaction between an acid and a base?
2. What is the end-point of a neutralization reaction?

Challenge: Predict the approximate pH of a solution formed when a weak acid reacts with a weak base.

A Neutralization Reaction

Purpose

To observe the process of neutralization

Materials

- 25 mL HCl solution
- 25 mL NaOH solution
- 1 mL phenolphthalein
- distilled water
- 50-mL flask or beaker
- 10-mL graduated cylinder
- large medicine dropper
- small medicine dropper
- hot plate
- stirring rod
- porcelain cup
- cover goggles

Procedure and Observations

1. Copy the table.
2. *CAUTION: Wear your cover goggles during this activity. Do not spill acids or bases on yourself.* Measure 10 mL of HCl into the graduated cylinder.
3. Add the HCl to 3 drops of phenolphthalein in the beaker.
4. Rinse the graduated cylinder with distilled water and dry it.

5. Carefully measure 20 mL of NaOH into the graduated cylinder. Use the large medicine dropper, if necessary.
6. Use the medicine dropper to add 8 mL of NaOH from the graduated cylinder to the HCl sample. Stir well.
7. Drop by drop, continue adding NaOH from the graduated cylinder to the HCl sample. Count and record the number of drops used. Stir with the stirring rod after adding each drop.
8. Stop adding NaOH when a slight pink color remains in the acid solution.
9. Record the total volume of NaOH added. In a large dropper, 20 drops equal about 1 mL.
10. Rinse the beaker, graduated cylinder, and large medicine dropper with distilled water.
11. Repeat steps 2-10.
12. Average the total volume of NaOH from the two trials.

Analysis and Conclusions

1. Why is phenolphthalein used in this experiment?
2. What has happened when the pink color remains even after stirring?

	No. ml NaOH added	No. drops NaOH added	Total No. ml NaOH added	Average No. ml NaOH
Trial 1				
Trial 2				

Science Skills

Selecting Suitable Indicators

The table shows the pH scale and the names of some common indicators. Each arrow shows the range of pH numbers at which an indicator changes color. Aniline blue changes color from about pH 10 to pH 12.5. The letters tell the colors of the indicator. Analine blue is blue (*B*) at any pH less than 10 and orange (*O*) at any pH greater than 12.5. From pH 10 to pH 12.5, the color of aniline blue is a blend of blue and orange (*M*).

1. Use the table to choose the best indicator/s for each substance below (a–l). The best indicator is the one that changes color at about the same pH as the average pH value given for the substance. Thus, you should match each substance's pH with an arrow in the table.

For example, ammonia's pH is 11. Find pH 11 at the top of the table. Place a ruler down the column at 11. The ruler cuts through the arrows for analine blue and nitramine. So, both indicators work for ammonia. For chemists, the best indicator is the one with the shortest arrow. The smaller the arrow, the smaller the pH range for the color change and the closer the chemist can come to an accurate pH value.

2. Is phenolphthalein a good indicator for a strong acid? Explain.
3. Select four or five indicators that could be used in a universal indicator.
4. Is litmus or alizarin red the best indicator for a pH of 5.2? Explain.

Some Average pH Values

a. Antifreeze, 7.2
b. Blood, 7.4
c. Lime, fresh, 1.9
d. Milk, 6.4

e. Orange, 3.5
f. Potato, 5.8
g. Salmon stream, 6.0
h. Sea water, 8.5

i. Carbonated beverage, 3.0
j. Soil, 5.5
k. Tomato, 4.2
l. Milk of magnesia, 10.3

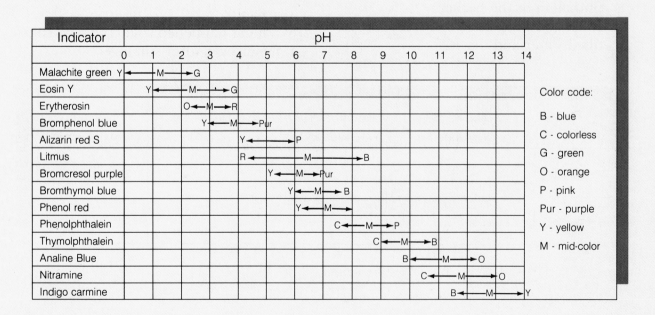

Indicator	pH	Color code:
	0 1 2 3 4 5 6 7 8 9 10 11 12 13 14	
Malachite green	Y ← M → G	
Eosin Y	Y ← M → G	B - blue
Erytherosin	O ← M → R	
Bromphenol blue	Y ← M → Pur	C - colorless
Alizarin red S	Y ← → P	
Litmus	R ← M → B	G - green
Bromcresol purple	Y ← M → Pur	O - orange
Bromthymol blue	Y ← M → B	
Phenol red	Y ← M →	P - pink
Phenolphthalein	C ← M → P	Pur - purple
Thymolphthalein	C ← M → B	Y - yellow
Analine Blue	B ← M → O	M - mid-color
Nitramine	C ← M → O	
Indigo carmine	B ← M → Y	

286

Summary

12-1 Properties of Acids and Bases

A. Acids are compounds that have a sour taste, release hydrogen gas from active metals, and turn blue litmus paper red.

B. Bases are compounds that have a bitter taste, a slippery feel, and turn red litmus paper blue.

C. The balance of acids and bases in your body has a direct effect on your health. In addition, these compounds are required for nearly all industrial and manufacturing processes.

12-2 Acids and Bases Solution

A. An acid is a substance that produces hydrogen ions in solution. The chemical behavior of the hydrogen ion is responsible for acidic properties. The strength of an acid is determined by the ratio of hydrogen ions and acid molecules in solution. A strong acid has more ions than molecules. A weak acid has more molecules than ions.

B. A base is a substance that produces hydroxide ions in solution. The chemical behavior of the hydroxide ion is responsible for basic properties.

12-3 Indicators and the pH Scale

A. An indicator is a compound that can exist in an acid form or a base form. It gives up or accepts hydrogen ions, and changes color in the process.

B. The pH scale is a number scale used to describe the hydrogen ion concentration of a solution. A pH of less than 7 is acidic; a pH of 7 is neutral; a pH greater than 7 is basic. Strong acids have low pH numbers, and strong bases have high pH numbers.

12-4 Neutralization Reactions

A. Neutralization occurs when an acid and a base react, producing a salt and water. The pH of the resulting salt solution depends on the strengths of the acid and base. A strong acid and strong base produce a neutral solution with a pH of about 7.

B. When an acid and base in solution have reacted completely, the neutralization has reached its end-point. Using an indicator, you can determine how much of one reactant is needed to neutralize the other.

Vocabulary

For each of the following terms, write a sentence that uses the term correctly.

acid	hydronium ion	neutralization reaction
base	hydroxide ion	pH scale
hydrogen ion	indicator	universal indicator

Check Your Knowledge

Part I: Matching Match the definition in Column I with the correct term in Column II.

Column I
1. substance that turns red litmus blue
2. substance produced when an acid and base react
3. substance that turns blue litmus red
4. substance that changes color in acids and bases
5. reaction between an acid and a base
6. indicates the hydrogen ion concentration
7. used to find pH of an unknown solution
8. ion produced by a base in water
9. ion produced by an acid in water
10. neither acidic nor basic

Column II
a. acid
b. base
c. helium ion
d. hydrogen ion
e. hydroxide ion
f. indicator
g. neutral
h. neutralization
i. pH scale
j. salt
k. universal indicator

Part II: Multiple Choice Choose the letter of the best answer.
11. Which is a salt? (a) $Al(OH)_3$ (b) NH_4OH (c) $MgSO_4$ (d) HNO_3
12. Neutral solution pH is (a) 1. (b) 5. (c) 7. (d) 11.
13. Use the chemical formulas to decide which of the following is an acid. (a) NaOH (b) KOH (c) HCl (d) HOH
14. Which has many H_3O^+ ions and few molecules in solution? (a) H_2SO_4 (b) acetic acid (c) NaOH (d) NH_4OH
15. Which has a pH of about 5? (a) lye (b) lemon juice (c) stomach acid (d) milk of magnesia
16. Which produces OH^- ions in solution? (a) lemon juice (b) vinegar (c) ammonia (d) battery acid
17. Which might be used for an upset stomach? (a) saltwater (b) carbonated water (c) baking soda in water (d) water
18. Which is the best conductor of electricity? (a) NaOH in water (b) solid NaCl (c) NH_4OH (d) $HC_2H_3O_2$
19. Indicators are (a) acids. (b) bases. (c) both acids and bases. (d) neither acids nor bases.
20. Which is a proton? (a) hydronium ion (b) hydrogen ion (c) hydroxide ion (d) ammonium ion
21. A process used to determine the concentration of an acid or a base is (a) oxidation. (b) reduction. (c) titration. (d) polymerization.
22. Which of the following chemical equations is a hydronium ion? (a) HOH (b) H_3O^+ (c) OH^- (d) H^+

Part III: Completion Write the word or words that complete the sentence correctly.
23. As a solution becomes more acidic, its pH _____.
24. An active metal releases _____ from an acid.
25. A pH of 1 refers to a _____.
26. A pH of 13 refers to a _____.
27. A pH of 7 refers to a _____.

Check Your Understanding

1. What safe test can you use to find out whether a liquid is an acid or a base?
2. Why does the weak acid produce the dim light on page 275?
3. Solutions *A*, *B*, *C*, and *D* have pH values of 6, 8, 1, and 13, respectively. Identify the strongest and weakest acids in this group. Explain your answer.
4. What causes an indicator to change from an acid to a base? A base to an acid?
5. What product forms when hydroxide ions and hydrogen ions react?

6. a) Describe the reaction below in words.

$$Mg(s) + 2HBr(aq) \rightarrow MgBr_2(aq) + H_2(g)$$

b) Which substance in the reaction is a salt? An acid?
c) Is magnesium bromide soluble or insoluble in water? Explain.
d) What other type reaction could be used to produce $MgBr_2$?
e) Is magnesium a reactive or a nonreactive metal? Explain.

 Apply Your Knowledge

1. List three everyday uses for acids or bases.
2. Explain how the term *neutralization* might be misleading.
3. Do reactions between these compounds produce basic, acidic, or neutral solutions? a) weak acid/strong base b) strong acid/weak base c) stong acid/strong base
4. Explain why drinking carbonated bev-erages can cause an upset stomach.
5. In 1983, a train derailed in Denver. One tankcar overturned, spilling thousands of gallons of nitric acid, HNO_3. Fire-fighters used snowblowers to blow so-dium carbonate, Na_2CO_3, over the spill. Because of the firefighters' efforts, no one was seriously injured. Explain what they did.

 Extend Your Knowledge

Research/Projects
1. Visit or phone your local water quality agency. Ask about the pH values of rain and local tap water. Test rain and tap water with pH paper. Compare your values with the official values.
2. Test samples of different shampoos and record the results in a table. Indicate in the table which shampoos are adver-tised as "pH-balanced."

Readings
Mohnen, Volker A. "The Challenge of Acid Rain." *Scientific American.* August, 1988, pp. 30–38. Discusses advance-ments that provide solutions to the acid rain problem.
Pimentel, George C. and Coonrod, Janice A. *Opportunities in Chemistry, Today and Tomorrow.* National Academy Press. 1987. Describes ways that the chemical sciences can help meet society's needs.

What is the Best Way to Reduce Acid Rain?

Picture a crystal clear lake nestled high in the mountains. Unfortunately, such a beautiful mountain lake may be completely devoid of life due to acid rain. Acid rain forms when certain pollutants in the air, including sulfur dioxide and nitrogen oxides, react with water vapor forming sulfuric and nitric acids. This water vapor collects in clouds and travels hundreds of kilometers from the source of the pollution. When it rains, the resulting precipitation is as acidic as lemon juice, having a pH of about 3.

Over the years acid rain can turn lakes into caustic baths that cannot support life. The acid seeps into the ground and leaches minerals from the soil. This robs the trees of necessary nutrients, stunts their growth, and makes them more vulnerable to disease.

The pollutants that cause precipitation to become acidic are released by coal-burning factories and electric plants and by automobile and truck exhaust. Reducing acid rain entails cutting down pollution from these sources.

Driving less is one way individuals can help reduce acid rain. Several new technologies are being developed to help factories reduce their release of the oxides that cause acid rain. One way to reduce pollutants spewed out by factories is to clean the fuel

the factories use before it is burned. High-sulfur coal can be cleaned by grinding it into small pieces and washing out the sulfur. When the cleaned coal is burned, less sulfur dioxide is released. However, coal cleaning removes less than 30% of the sulfur from the coal. Therefore, even with cleaned coal, significant amounts of pollutants are released.

Decreasing the amount of pollution produced during burning is another way to cut down the oxides that lead to acid rain. By mixing less oxygen with the fuel and burning the fuel at a lower temperature nitrogen oxide emissions can be reduced by up to 60%. This technology, however, does little to cut the emission of sulfur dioxide.

Another technology for reducing pollution is to clean smoke before it leaves the

smokestack. When the smoke is mixed with ammonia, a chemical reaction occurs. The products of this reaction—nitrogen gas and water—are harmless and cause no pollution. Mixing smoke with ammonia can reduce nitrogen oxide emissions by 90%. However, this technology may actually increase the production of sulfur dioxide when high sulfur coal is burned.

Reducing pollution from sulfur dioxide can be achieved by spraying smoke with limestone. The limestone reacts with the sulfur dioxide, forming a precipitate that can reused. Although this technique is quite effective in reducing sulfur dioxide emissions, it does nothing to reduce nitrogen oxides and it is expensive.

Each of the technologies discussed above can reduce the pollutants that cause acid rain. However, each method has serious drawbacks. Scientists will continue to do research to improve the anti-pollution technologies and to make them more affordable.

For Discussion

1. What is acid rain and how is it caused?

2. What are the pros and cons of the four technologies coal-burning factories can use to help reduce acid rain.

3. If you were a factory owner which anti-pollution method or methods would you employ?

Swimming Pool Chemistry

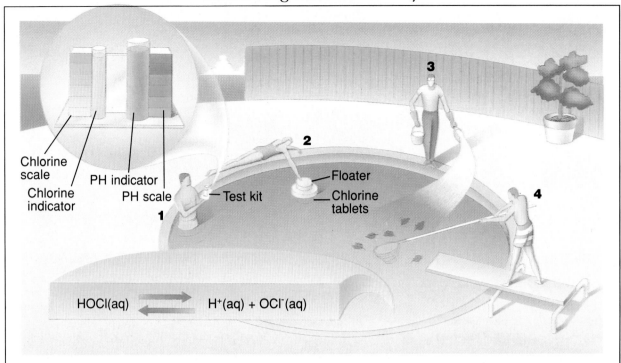

Chlorine scale

Chlorine indicator

PH indicator

PH scale

Test kit

Floater

Chlorine tablets

$$HOCl(aq) \rightleftharpoons H^+(aq) + OCl^-(aq)$$

If you go swimming, you expect the water in the swimming pool to be clear and sparkling. Even with the leaves and other debris removed, a pool may not be clean. The water may be green or murky due to the growth of algae. Harmful bacteria may also multiply in an untreated swimming pool. Keeping pool water safe for swimmers requires some chemistry.

Swimming pool chemistry involves killing bacteria by regularly adding a chlorine compound to the water and by maintaining the water's pH at about 7.5. The chlorine compound hypochlorous acid (HOCl) is the active ingredient in most swimming-pool disinfectants. This acid participates in oxidation reactions that destroy the bacteria's essential proteins.

The equation above shows the reaction that occurs when HOCl dissolves in water. If the water is too acidic, the reaction rate changes and too much HOCl builds up in the pool. High levels of HOCl cause eye irritations and promote the growth of algae. If the water is too basic, high levels of OCl$^-$ build up in the pool. This increases the rate that the disinfectant breaks down in sunlight. The diagram shows how to disinfect a swimming pool and maintain its chemical balance.

1. At least once a week, use a water testing kit to check the concentration of chlorine and the pH of the water.

2. Check to be sure that the chlorine container that feeds into the pumping system or the floaters in the pool contain the right amount of the chlorine compound. If the test indicates the chlorine concentration is too low, double check to make sure that the pump or the floaters are distributing the chlorine properly. If the test indicates that the chlorine concentration is too high, reduce the amount of chlorine being added to the pool.

3. If the test indicates that the pH is below 7.4, add sodium carbonate (Na_2CO_3) to raise the pH of the water. If test indicates that the pH is above 7.6, add sodium bisulfate ($NaHSO_4$) to lower the pH.

4. Remove any leaves or floating debris from the pool and scrub the sides of the pool with a brush to remove algae.

Manipulating matter to get wanted energy for work has been a mark of progress in all civilizations. Harnessed and directed energy drives machines. Over the years, ways of using different kinds of energy have varied, and they will continue to do so in the future.

3000 B.C.

Precisely when the wheel was invented is not known, but its influence on progress is unquestioned. With the wheel, people could transport heavier loads for longer distances over land. Over the years, wheels were greatly improved, too—made more precisely circular and also spoked rather than solid so that they were faster and also more maneuverable. Wheels served in more ways than just for transportation, too. Their first use, in fact, may have been in making pottery. Very soon, too, they were employed in pulleys for lifting heavy loads.

1000 B.C.

People continued to find new ways to use the wheel to do work. One was the water wheel. At first buckets were attached to a wheel. They filled when the wheel was at its lowest level in a body of water and then emptied as the wheel was lifted out of the water. The wheel had to be turned by people or by animals, of course, but this was nevertheless a faster, more efficient way of lifting water. Eventually wheels were put into streams where the force of the flowing water did the turning. The next step was the use of water-powered wheels to turn millstones for grinding grain and to turn other wheels for operating saws or doing work demanding constant power.

Chapter 13 Work and Machines
Chapter 14 Energy and Power
Chapter 15 Heat and Temperature
Chapter 16 Energy Resources

18th Century

Early scientists recognized the power of steam but were unable to put it to practical use. Metals first had to be improved and ways of making steam-tight joints developed. This was first accomplished in laboratories and soon inventors were experimenting with steam. Thomas Newcomen invented a steam engine, but it was noisy and inefficient, useful only in pumping water. The steam engine invented by James Watt set the stage for a whole new era in human history. Steam engines soon operated the machinery in factories and supplied the power for both trains and ships.

20th Century

Water and wind are natural sources of energy. Both were used, as were fossil fuels, as basic sources of energy and to generate electricity. Electricity became a major form of energy in the late 19th century and continues to be so to this day. A newer source of energy was tapped shortly after World War II. This was the tremendous amount of energy released by splitting atoms. In nuclear power plants, this energy is used to produce steam which can then be used to generate electricity. Technologists have not stopped their quest for energy sources. They have turned their attention to an even greater energy source—nuclear fusion. Others are looking further at the ultimate source of energy—the sun.

CHAPTER 13
Work and Machines

The Egyptian pyramids and other ancient monuments are a tribute to the skill and intelligence of engineers, artisans, and workers of the past. However, in ancient times, workers could not have built a skyscraper such as the one in the picture. The machines needed to construct such a building had not yet been invented. In this chapter you will read about machines and how they can do work for us.

Organizing Your Study Skills The outline below will help you see how the chapter is organized and what you should learn as you read.

I. Section 13-1: Machines Make Work Easier
  A. What is the scientific definition of work?
  B. How is the amount of work calculated?
  C. How do machines help people?

II. Section 13-2: Forms of Levers
  A. How do levers work?
  B. How is a lever's mechanical advantage calculated?
  C. What are two types of pulleys?
  D. How does a wheel and axle work?

III. Section 13-3: Forms of Inclined Planes
  A. Why are inclined planes used?
  B. How are wedges useful?
  C. How is a screw a type of inclined plane?

IV. Section 13-4: Compound Machines and Efficiency
  A. What are compound machines?
  B. How is the mechanical advantage of a compound machine calculated?
  C. How is the efficiency of a machine determined?

13-1 Machines Make Work Easier

Work

What do you think of when your hear the word work? This word may suggest activities that you must do but do not necessarily enjoy. In science, however, "work" has a special meaning. For example, the girl in the picture is pushing a large rock. She has been pushing it for a long time, but the rock has not moved. The girl looks as though she has worked hard. Yet, scientifically, the girl has not done any work!

According to the scientific definition, **work** is done when a force applied to an object actually moves the object. Thus, you do work on an object when you lift a chair, push a lawn mover, drive a nail into wood, throw a ball, pedal a bicycle, and so on.

Work depends on two things: force and displacement. Recall the meaning of force and of displacement. Force is any action that causes a change in motion. Displacement is a measure of the distance and direction that an object moves. For work, only the part of the force parallel to the direction of the displacement is important.

Calculating the Amount of Work

The equation below shows how to calculate the amount of work done when force and displacement are completely parallel:

$$\text{work} = \text{force} \times \text{distance}.$$

Figure 13-1 Work is done if the rock moves

296

Suppose the girl in the picture pushes with a force of 200 newtons, and moves the rock 1 meter to the left. The force and the displacement are in the same direction. The work done is:

$$\text{work} = 200 \text{ newtons} \times 1 \text{ meter}$$
$$= 200 \text{ newton-meters.}$$

If force is in newtons and displacement in meters, work is expressed in newton-meters (symbol: N-m). She did 200 newton-meters of work on the rock.

In *Figure 13-2,* the man is picking up the baby. He must exert a force of 120 newtons to overcome the force of gravity and lift the child 0.5 meters above the floor. The force required to overcome the force of gravity is the same as the child's weight. Therefore, the work done is the weight of the child times the height that the child is lifted.

$$\text{work} = 120 \text{ newtons} \times 0.5 \text{ meters}$$
$$= 60 \text{ newton-meters}$$

In the picture on the right, the man is carrying the baby across the room. The displacement is in the horizontal direction. But the force, gravity, acts in the vertical direction. According to the scientific definition, no work is done in carrying the child because no part of the force is parallel to the displacement.

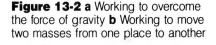

Figure 13-2 a Working to overcome the force of gravity **b** Working to move two masses from one place to another

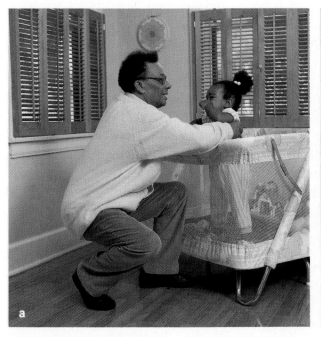

Figure 13-3 A car jack, shown here, is a useful machine for lifting a car off the ground.

Machines

Machines make our work easier. They also enable people to do tasks that otherwise are extremely difficult or impossible. Machines range from simple tools, such as pliers and brooms, to complicated machines, such as automobiles and cranes. Even a simple tool can reduce the amount of force a person needs to exert to do a particular task. Adding a motor or engine to a machine makes people's work even easier.

Machines can make work easier in three ways. First, a machine can multiply—or increase—the force a person puts into a task. Second, a machine can change the direction in which the force is exerted. Third, a machine can change the speed at which the force acts.

A car jack, shown in the pictures, is a machine that increases the amount of force a person puts into it. People use a jack to lift a car off the ground, so they can change a flat tire. Few people can lift a car using "muscle power" alone. Nevertheless, each time a person pumps the handle of a jack, a car is lifted a little. The force applied by the person is small compared to the force that lifts the car. Screwdrivers, wrenches, pliers, and many other tools are machines that increase the amount of an applied force.

Many machines make work easier by changing the direction in which a force acts. A force is applied to the machine in a direction that is convenient for the user. Then, the machine exerts a force in another direction. The pulley at the top of the flagpole in *Figure 13-4* is a machine in which the direction of the force changes. Because of the pulley, the boy can pull down on one end of the rope to raise the flag attached to the other end of the rope.

The bottle opener in the picture is another machine that changes the direction of the applied force. Pulling up on one end of the bottle opener causes the other end of the opener to go down, lifting the cap from the bottle in the process.

Many useful machines speed up the applied force, which enables people to do work faster. You can increase the speed of a bicycle a great deal by pushing slightly harder on the bicycle pedals. Baseball bats, tennis rackets, and fly swatters also are machines that increase the speed of a force.

Remember that a machine can increase the force available to do work and can speed up the rate at which the work gets done. However, a machine cannot increase the amount of work done or the energy involved. A broom makes it easier for you to sweep the floor, but the broom does not give your arms more energy.

Section Review

1. What is the scientific definition of work?
2. How much work is done when a 20 N force lifts an object 3 m off the ground?
3. List three ways that machines make work easier.

Challenge: Explain how the direction of displacement and the direction of force are related for the flag-raising in the picture.

Figure 13-4 Using a machine to raise a flag

Figure 13-5 The bottle opener is a simple machine.

After completing this section you will be able to

A. Explain how a lever works.
B. Explain how the mechanical advantage of a lever is calculated.
C. Describe several types of pulleys.
D. Tell how a wheel and axle works.

13-2 Forms of Levers

Levers

Tools with one or two parts are called **simple machines.** Six simple machines are introduced in this chapter. These machines can be separated into two general groups. One group, which includes levers, pulleys, and the wheel and axle, is discussed in this section. The second group, which includes inclined planes, wedges, and screws, is presented in the next section.

A lever can help you move an object by increasing the force you exert. A **lever** is a long, rigid bar with a support that allows the bar to pivot. The point at which the bar pivots is the **fulcrum.**

A crowbar is one kind of lever. The man in the picture is using a crowbar to help him uproot a tree stump. He pushes down on one side of the bar. The opposite end of the bar pushes up on the tree stump and lifts it. The fulcrum is the part of the bar resting on the rock.

The fulcrum of the crowbar is located between "two arms," as shown in *Figure 13-6a.* From the fulcrum to where the man pushes down is the **effort arm**—or effort. From the fulcrum to the end of the bar pushing up on the tree stump is the **resistance arm**—or resistance.

Figure 13-6 a Three parts of a lever. **b** A crowbar is a machine that changes the direction of the force and increases it.

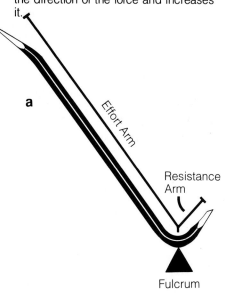

a

Effort Arm

Resistance Arm

Fulcrum

b

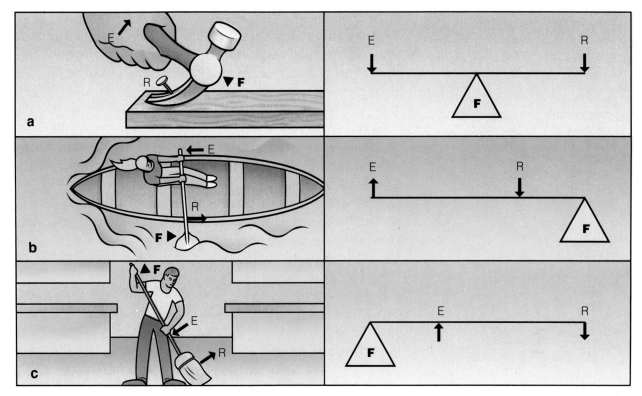

The two arms move in opposite directions. As one end of the lever goes down, the other goes up. This type of lever always changes the direction of a force and increases the amount of force.

Figure 13-7 shows three kinds of levers. The crowbar resembles the lever in *a*. The fulcrum is between the effort arm and the resistance arm.

In *b*, the resistance arm is between the fulcrum and the effort arm. Wheelbarrows and nutcrackers are levers of this kind. The drawing shows that the effort arm is longer than the resistance arm. This lever increases the force, but does not change the direction of the force. For example, you apply force to the handles of a wheelbarrow loaded with dirt. The handles are the effort arm. The dirt is the resistance. The wheel of the wheelbarrow is the fulcrum. You push the wheelbarrow in the direction that you want to move the dirt. Using the wheelbarrow helps you move heavier loads of dirt than you could carry.

In the third kind of lever, the effort arm is between the fulcrum and the resistance arm. Brooms, baseball bats, pitchforks, tweezers, and fishing poles are levers of this type. In this case, the resistance arm is longer than the effort arm.

Figure 13-7 The relative positions of the fulcrum, effort, and resistance vary in the three types of levers.

Explore!

Your forearm acts as a lever when you pick up a brick or other heavy object. Identify the fulcrum, effort, and resistance of your forearm acting as a lever. Make a diagram, showing the three parts of this "lever."

The Mechanical Advantage of a Lever

Mechanical advantage (symbol: M.A.) is a value that tells the number of times a machine increases the applied force. For example, the mechanical advantage of the crowbar used to remove the tree stump is 4. Thus, the crowbar multiplied the man's force times 4.

You can verify that the force produced by the machine is greater than the force applied by the man. Consider how much work the man does with the crowbar and how far both arms of the crowbar move.

Suppose the man pushes the end of the bar down 1 meter by exerting a 400-newton force. The work done by the lever equals the force (400 newtons) times the distance (1 meter), which is 400 newton-meters.

$$\text{work} = 400 \text{ N} \times 1 \text{ m}$$
$$= 400 \text{ N-m}$$

Although the effort arm has moved down 1 meter, the resistance arm has moved up only 0.25 meter. Yet, the amount of work done is still 400 newton-meters.

To find the force that lifted the stump, substitute the smaller distance, 0.25 meters, into the equation above.

$$400 \text{ N-m} = \text{force} \times 0.25 \text{ m}$$

$$\text{force} = \frac{400 \text{ N-m}}{0.25 \text{ m}}$$

$$\text{force} = 1600 \text{ N}$$

The force produced by the machine (1600 newtons) is four times greater than the force that the man applied to the crowbar (400 newtons).

An easy way to calculate the mechanical advantage of a lever is to compare the lengths of the two arms. Divide the length of the effort arm by the length of the resistance arm. *Figure 13-8* shows that the length of the effort arm is 80 centimeters and the length of the resistance arm is 20 centimeters.

$$\text{M.A.} = \frac{80 \text{ cm}}{20 \text{ cm}}$$

$$= 4$$

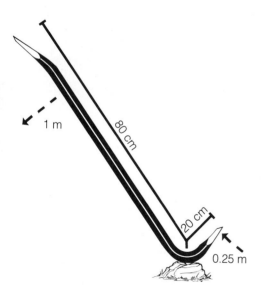

Figure 13-8 The dimensions of the crowbar and the distance each arm moves

Pulleys

A **pulley** is a simple machine consisting of a rope that passes over a grooved wheel. *Figure 13-9* shows a fixed pulley, which is the kind of simple machine used to raise and lower a flag. A fixed pulley changes the direction of the force. If you pull down on the rope, the paint can goes up. A fixed pulley can turn, but it cannot move up or down.

Figure 13-10 shows that a force of 200 newtons is required to lift the 200-newton object (the resistance), using the fixed pulley. Thus, this pulley has a mechanical advantage of only 1. A fixed pulley does not increase the force needed to do a job. Nevertheless, fixed pulleys make certain tasks easier. Using a fixed pulley to lift a heavy object enables you to pull downward, rather than upward, to lift the object. Pulling down allows you to use your own weight to help raise the object.

In *Figure 13-10*, the movable pulley moves along the rope with the object. Thus, the direction of force is not changed by this machine. The movable pulley in the picture has a mechanical advantage of 2, because a 100-newton force raises a 200-newton object.

Although it requires half as much force to raise the object using the movable pulley, the object moves only half as far. As a result, raising the object 2 meters requires the same amount of force—200 newtons—with either kind of pulley.

Using several pulleys together increases mechanical advantage. A block and tackle is a pulley system that combines both fixed and movable pulleys. The mechanical advantage of the block and tackle shown here is 4. A block and tackle enables one person to lift very heavy objects. People use this kind of pulley system for jobs such as lifting engines from cars.

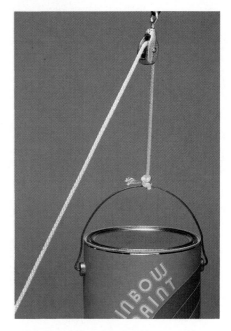

Figure 13-9 A fixed pulley

Explore!

Suppose you can exert a force of 450 N. Ignoring the effects of friction, how much weight could you lift with one fixed pulley? With one movable pulley? Explain your answers.

Figure 13-10 Types of pulleys

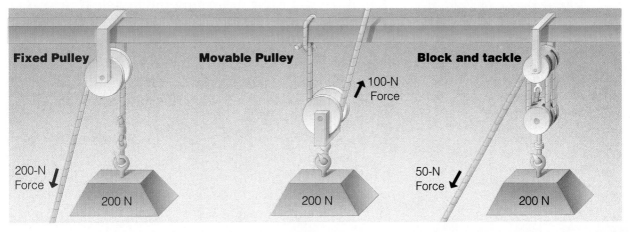

Fixed Pulley — 200-N Force — 200 N

Movable Pulley — 100-N Force — 200 N

Block and tackle — 50-N Force — 200 N

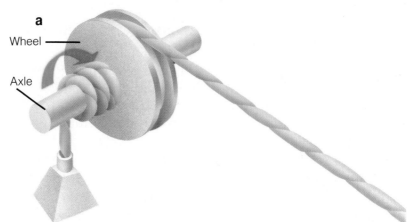

a

Wheel

Axle

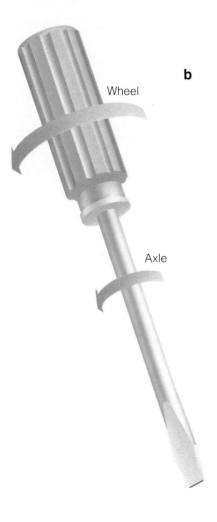

b

Wheel

Axle

The Wheel and Axle

Figure 13-11a shows the simple machine called a **wheel and axle,** which consists of a wheel and a shaft that work together. If you spin the wheel, the axle also turns. If you rotate the axle, the wheel turns too. Doorknobs, eggbeaters, pencil sharpeners, and screwdrivers are examples of this kind of machine.

You can think of the wheel and axle as a special kind of lever. The distance around the wheel is equal to the length of the effort arm. The distance around the axle is equal to the length of the resistance arm. Thus, the diameter of the wheel divided by the diameter of the axle gives the mechanical advantage of a wheel and axle. If the diameter of the wheel is 10 centimeters and that of the axle is 2 centimeters, the mechanical advantage of the machine is 5. The bigger the wheel, compared to the axle, the larger the mechanical advantage of this machine.

Figure 13-11b shows how a screwdriver acts as a wheel and axle. The handle is the wheel and the blade is the axle. When you turn the handle, the blade turns too. The force you exert in turning the handle is increased. The blade exerts this increased force to tighten a screw.

Section Review

1. Name three parts of a lever.
2. How do you find a lever's mechanical advantage?
3. What is a block and tackle?
4. How do you find the mechanical advantage of a wheel and axle?

Challenge: The axle between two wagon wheels does not turn as the wagon moves. Are the wagon wheels and axle a simple machine? Explain.

Have You Heard?

Not every wheel and axle machine has a complete wheel attached to an axle. For example, a pencil sharpener has a crank instead of a wheel. The crank, which is like one spoke of a wheel, acts as a lever. This simple machine might just as well be called a crank and axle or a lever and axle. However, because it works like other wheel and axle machines, it is called a wheel and axle too.

Examining Simple Machines

Purpose

To experiment with levers and pulleys

Materials

- 100-g, 200-g, and 500-g masses
- meter stick
- spring scale
- pulley
- pencil
- tape
- string
- scissors

Procedure and Observations

1. Copy the table to the right.
2. Tape a pencil (fulcrum) parallel to the edge of a desk or table. To make a lever, set up the meter stick and 500-g mass, as shown.
3. Hang the spring scale by its hook from the 90-cm mark on the stick. Gently pull the spring scale down until the mass end of the meter stick is lifted about 0.5 cm above the table. Record the spring scale reading.

4. Fill in the table for the 90-cm measurement. Use the markings on the meter stick to find the lengths of the effort and resistance arms. For the distance from mass to fulcrum, estimate which cm mark is under the middle of the mass.
5. Repeat steps 3 and 4 with the spring scale at the marks for 80, 70, 60, and 50 cm. Complete the table as you go.
6. Place the 200-g and 100-g masses on opposite sides of the fulcrum. Move the two masses until the meter stick comes closest to balancing. Record the distance of each mass from the fulcrum.

Steps 1–5	Length of E arm	Length of R arm	Applied Force
90 cm			
80 cm			
70 cm			
60 cm			
50 cm			
Step 6	200-g mass to fulcrum:	100-g mass to fulcrum:	

Analysis and Conclusions

1. How does the length of the effort arm affect the amount of force required to lift the masses?
2. Where is it best to place the fulcrum when the resistance is a large mass?
3. What items in everyday life work according to the same principle as the lever in step 6?
4. Compare the lengths of the two arms in step 6.

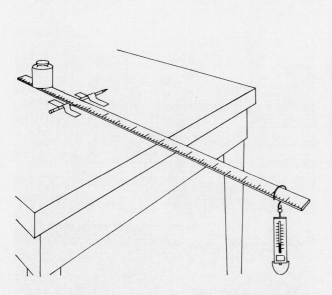

Inclined Planes

The worker in the picture is using a plank to help him load the heavy box into the truck. The plank is an inclined plane, which is a simple machine. An **inclined plane** is a flat surface with one end higher than the other. The sloping floor in a theater, a road over a mountain, and a ramp into a building also are inclined planes.

The man in the picture does the same total amount of work whether he lifts the box or pushes it up the plank. However, the inclined plane decreases the amount of force required to get the box into the truck, which makes his work easier. On the other hand, he must move the box a longer distance if he uses the plank. If he lifts the crate, it moves 1 meter from the ground to the truck. If he pushes it up the plank, it moves 2 meters.

Similarly, you can move an object, or just yourself, up a long, gentle slope more easily than up a short, steep slope of the same height. You do the same amount of work on both slopes. But you exert less force at any one time on the gentle slope than on the steep slope.

Figure 13-12 Two uses for an inclined plane

The longer an inclined plane is in relation to its height, the larger its mechanical advantage is. To find the mechanical advantage of an inclined plane, divide the length of the plane by its height. The mechanical advantage of the plank used to load the box is:

$$\text{M.A.} = \frac{\text{length}}{\text{height}}$$

$$= \frac{2 \text{ m}}{1 \text{ m}}$$

$$= 2.$$

For Practice

Solve these problems using the equation for an inclined plane's M.A.
1. A steep ramp is 20 m long. What is its M.A. if the upper end of the ramp is 5 m higher than its lower end?
2. In one 100-m stretch, the upper end of a highway is 2 m higher than the lower end. What is the highway's M.A.?

Wedge, an Inclined Plane

A **wedge** is an inclined plane with either one or two sloping sides. Each sloping side is an inclined plane. The pictured items—knife, ax, saw, and needle—contain wedges.

The point of a needle is a wedge. The force produced at the sharp point of a needle easily cuts through material. Notice how hard it is to push a needle through fabric if the point of the needle is broken or blunt.

Similarly, each tooth in a saw is a wedge. The cutting edge of a wood chisel is a wedge with only one sloping side. A knife blade is a wedge with two sloping sides. The two sloping sides of an ax produce enough force to split a log.

Figure 13-13 Tools that act as wedges

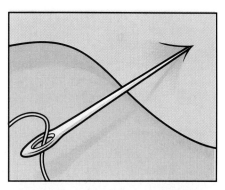

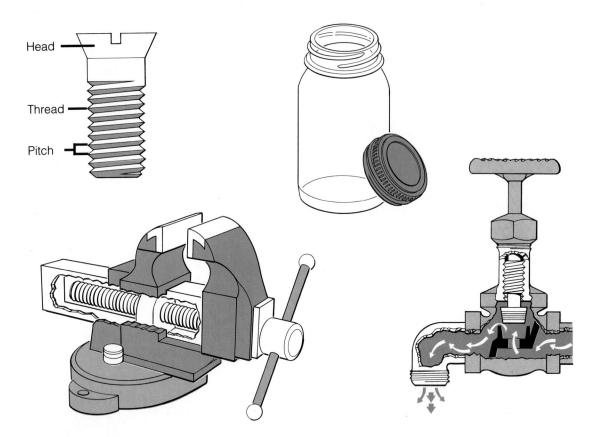

Head

Thread

Pitch

Figure 13-14 A screw and some ways it is used

A Screw Is an Inclined Plane

The pictures show some uses of screws. A **screw** is an inclined plane in a spiral form. The ridge that spirals around a screw is called its **thread,** as shown in *Figure 13-14*. The thread of a screw marks the path of the inclined plane. The longer the inclined plane, the closer together the threads. The **pitch** of a screw is the number of threads in a given length.

When you turn a screw, the direction of your force is changed and multiplied. The force you need to apply decreases as the threads get closer together.

The mechanical advantage of a screw depends on the size of the screw and its pitch. If a screw has a large circumference and threads close together, it will increase an applied force many times.

Section Review

1. How is the mechanical advantage of an inclined plane determined?
2. What are three examples of wedges?
3. How is a screw like an inclined plane?

Challenge: How does the length of an inclined plane affect the amount of force needed to do a job?

Explore!

You can prove that the thread of a screw is an inclined plane. First, cut a piece of paper in the shape of a triangle. The sloping side of the triangle is an inclined plane. Then, wrap the triangle around a pencil. Describe the path that forms as the sloping side wraps around the pencil. Use inclined planes of different lengths to vary the pitch of the threads. How does the length of the inclined plane affect the pitch of a screw?

Experimenting with Inclined Planes

Purpose

To learn how an inclined plane increases force

Materials

- empty shoe box
- board, 1 m long
- bricks or books
- meter stick
- spring scale
- string, about 20 cm long
- scissors

Procedure and Observations

PART A

1. Use a brick to support the board so that one end is 10 cm higher than the other end.
2. Carefully put 2 small holes in one of the smaller sides of the box, as in **a**.
3. Thread the string through the holes, and knot it to make a loop.
4. Place the box as in **a**.

a

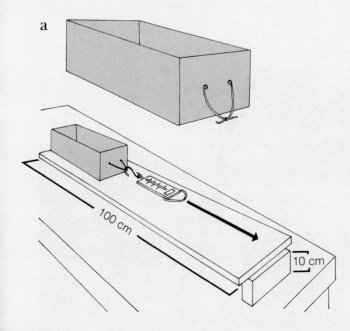

5. Attach a spring scale to the string and slowly pull the box up the ramp. Record the force needed to move the box.
6. Repeat step 5 with the height of the ramp at 20, 30, and 40 cm. Record the force required for each height.

b

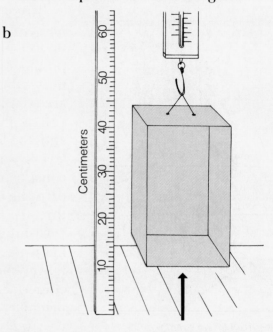

PART B

1. Place the box on the floor. Use the spring scale to lift the box 10 cm off the floor, as in **b**.
2. Record the amount of force needed to lift the box.
3. Repeat steps 1 and 2, raising the box 20, 30, and 40 cm. Record the force needed in each trial.

Analysis and Conclusions

1. In Part A, did you exert the most force when the board's slope was more or less steep?
2. How did the force needed to pull the box up the board compare to the force needed to lift it straight up?

Objectives

After completing this section you will be able to

A. Define and give examples of compound machines.

B. Explain how to calculate the mechanical advantage of a compound machine.

C. Explain how to calculate the efficiency of a machine.

13-4 Compound Machines and Efficiency

Using Compound Machines

Machines do not cut down on the amount of work to be done, but they do make work easier. Similarly, using more than one simple machine at a time can make work even easier.

Two or more simple machines often are combined to make one machine. A **compound machine** is a combination of simple machines. Hoes and axes are compound machines. Shovels, scissors, and pencil sharpeners, which are shown in the pictures on this page, also are compound machines.

In a shovel, hoe, or ax, the handle serves as a lever, and the blade is a wedge. A pair of scissors has two levers with wedge-shaped blades. A pencil sharpener consists of a wheel and axle and two screws. When you turn the crank of a pencil sharpener, the wedge-shaped threads of the two screws also turn.

Compound machines that have many parts are known as complex machines. Automobiles, tractors, and power shovels are just a few of the many complex machines. Each is made of many simple and compound machines.

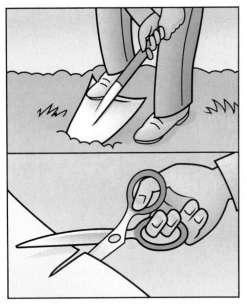

Figure 13-15 Two examples of compound machines.

Figure 13-16 A pencil sharpener is a wheel and axle and two screws.

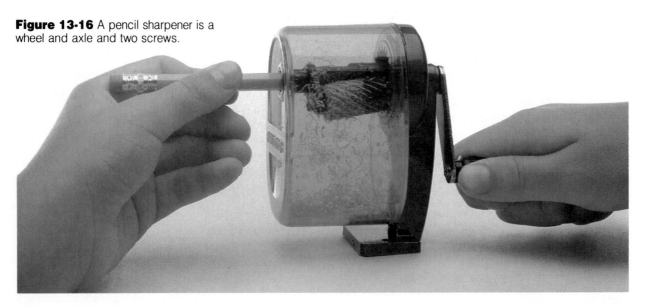

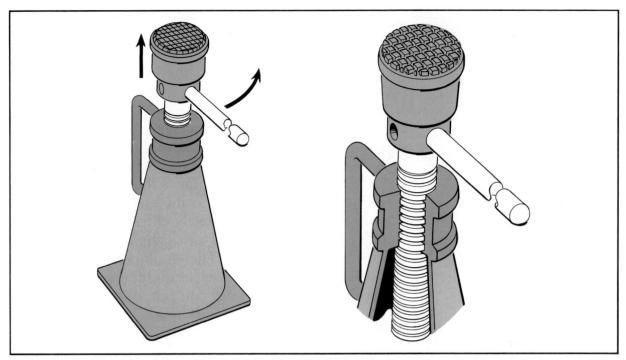

The Mechanical Advantage of Compound Machines

Compound machines may have very high mechanical advantages. The jackscrew, called a jack, is a compound machine that combines a screw with a wheel and axle that turns it. Look at the pictures of the jackscrew. Force (effort) is exerted on a rod that forms one spoke of the wheel. The resistance is overcome on the threads of the screw. Each time the effort moves around the circumference of the circle made by the rod, the resistance moves a distance equal to the pitch of the screw. The longer the rod and the smaller the pitch of the screw, the higher the mechanical advantage of the jackscrew.

Each simple machine in a compound machine contributes to the total mechanical advantage of the compound machine. To calculate the mechanical advantage of a compound machine, multiply the mechanical advantages of all its simple machines.

Suppose a compound machine is made up of an inclined plane and a movable pulley. The inclined plane is 15 meters long and 3 meters high. Calculate the mechanical advantage of the inclined plane by dividing its length, 15 meters, by its height, 3 meters. The mechanical advantage of the inclined plane is 5. The movable pulley has a mechanical advantage of 2. Therefore, the mechanical advantage of this compound machine is 2 times 5, or 10.

Figure 13-17 The jackscrew is a compound machine containing a screw and a wheel and axle.

Figure 13-18 A jackscrew has a high enough mechanical advantage to lift houses.

Machines and Efficiency

The girl below is using an eggbeater, which is a machine. She gets the same amount of work out of the machine as she puts into it. However, not all the work the machine does is useful work. Some effort is always wasted in useless work, such as overcoming friction.

Complex machines have many parts. All the movable parts produce friction. Because of this friction, less useful work is obtained from large, complex machines.

The **efficiency** of a machine is the amount of useful work obtained compared to the amount of work put into it. No machine is perfectly efficient.

To find the efficiency of a machine, divide the useful work by the work put in. Then multiply this number by 100% to find the percentage of useful work done by the machine. For example, if you put 100 newton-meters of work into a machine, and the machine does 15 newton-meters of useful work, its efficiency is:

$$\text{Efficiency} = \frac{\text{useful work}}{\text{work put in}} \times 100\%$$

$$= \frac{15 \text{ newton-meters}}{100 \text{ newton-meters}} \times 100\%$$

$$= 15\%.$$

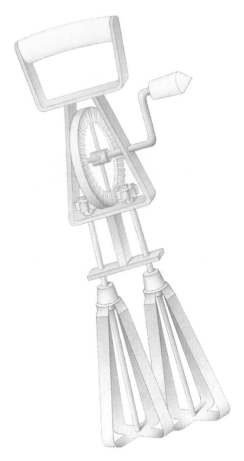

Figure 13-19 The girl gets the same amount of work out of the egg beater as she puts into it.

An efficiency of 15% means that 85% of the work put into the machine was wasted, probably in overcoming friction.

Many large machines have a very low efficiency. But if it were not for these complex machines, the jobs they perform probably would be impossible. Automobiles are usually less than 10% efficient, but they help us travel great distances on the ground quickly. Increasing the efficiency of machines is an important step in conserving natural resources.

Figure 13-20 Automobiles are usually less than 10% efficient.

Section Review

1. What is a compound machine?
2. How is the mechanical advantage of a compound machine calculated?
3. Give one reason machines are not 100% efficient.

Challenge: Do you think this statement is correct? "Increasing the efficiency of a machine also increases its mechanical advantage?" Explain.

Careers in Physical Science

Automobile Mechanic

When you look under the hood of a car, how many parts can you identify? An automobile mechanic could tell you the name and function of almost every part.

Auto mechanics work in gas stations or garages. They repair and tune hundreds of different vehicles. They also replace mechanical parts, adjust wires, and even rebuild entire engines. Mechanics also add oil or grease where it is needed to lubricate moving parts of the engine. Lubricating cuts down on friction in an engine and increases its efficiency. Mechanics should be able to understand all machines and devices in motorized vehicles.

Most auto mechanics learn their trade while working as gas station attendants or mechanics' assistants. Many take technical classes in colleges or trade schools to learn special skills. Such skills might include using computers to diagnose engine problems and repairing computerized parts of automobiles.

Science Skills

Solving Word Problems

Solving word problems is an important part of science. In this activity, you will practice using a systematic method for solving word problems. You will summarize the information given in each problem and enter this information in a table before you do any calculations.

You can use such a table to help you organize your thoughts before you try to solve a problem. Read problem 1 below. Then notice how the information is shown in the table. Often, drawing a picture that shows the given information is helpful. The last line in the table shows the solution for problem 1.

Table for Problem 1	
Information given in problem	F = 100 N D = 1.5 m
Unknown Quantity	Amount of work
Sketch of given information	 100 N → 1.5 m
Equation Used	Work = Force × Distance
Calculation	Work = 100 N × 1.5 m = 150 N-m

1. A student moved a chair 1.5 m by pushing on it with a 100-N force. How much work did the student do?

Make a similar table for each of the remaining word problems. Then solve the word problems.

2. A crane, exerting a force of 5000 N, lifted a crate 10 m into the air. How much work was done on the crate?

3. A power shovel did 24 000 N-m of work, exerting a force of 4000 N to lift a shovel full of broken concrete. How high did the power shovel lift this load?

4. A person used a crowbar to pry open a wooden crate, pushing down on the effort arm of the crowbar so that it moved 1.25 m. Opening the crate required 325 N-m of work. How much force did the person exert?

5. To open the crate in question 3, the resistance arm moved 0.2 m. How much force was exerted by the resistance arm of the crowbar?

6. A student used a pole 200 cm long as a lever to pry up a stone. The pole pivoted on a tree stump that was 150 cm from the student's hand and 50 cm from the stone. What is the mechanical advantage of the lever?

7. To unload barrels, workers use a 5-m ramp running from the ground to a dock that is 1 meter above the ground. What is the mechanical advantage of the ramp?

8. A force of 140 N is required to roll each barrel up the 5-m ramp described in problem 4. What is the weight of a barrel in newtons?

9. A compound machine gives 40 N-m of useful work for every 200 N-m of work put into it. What is the efficiency of this compound machine. (NOTE: No sketch is required for this problem.)

☑ Summary

13-1 Machines Make Work Easier

A. Scientifically, work occurs when a force acts on an object, displacing the object in a direction parallel to the direction in which the force is acting.

B. The amount of work done on an object is calculated using the equation: work = force × distance.

C. Machines can change the amount, direction, and speed of a force.

13-2 Forms of Levers

A. A simple machine has one or two parts. The lever, pulley, wheel and axle, inclined plane, wedge, and screw are six types of simple machines.

B. The mechanical advantage of a lever is found by dividing the length of the effort arm by the length of the resistance arm.

C. Pulleys consist of a grooved wheel over which a rope passes. Pulleys are fixed or movable. A block and tackle is a combination of pulleys that work together to lift heavy objects.

D. A wheel and axle consists of two wheels of different sizes that rotate together. A force exerted on the larger wheel is increased at the smaller wheel, which is the axle.

13-3 Forms of Inclined Planes

A. Inclined planes are useful because they decrease the required amount of applied force needed to do work, and they change the direction in which the force is exerted.

B. The sloping sides of a wedge are useful for cutting tools.

C. A screw is an inclined plane wrapped around a cylinder. The thread of a screw marks the path of the inclined plane.

13-4 Compound Machines and Efficiency

A. A compound machine is a combination of simple machines.

B. The mechanical advantage of a compound machine is found by multiplying the mechanical advantages of all its simple machines.

C. To find the efficiency of a machine, divide the value for useful work by the value for total work, and multiply the ratio times 100%.

Vocabulary

For each of the following terms, write a sentence that uses the term correctly.

compound machine	inclined plane	pulley	thread
efficiency	lever	resistance arm	wedge
effort arm	mechanical advantage	screw	wheel and axle
fulcrum	pitch	simple machine	work

Check Your Knowledge

Part I: Matching   Match the definition in Column I with the correct term in Column II.

Column I
1. rope over a grooved wheel
2. number of threads in a given length
3. force times displacement
4. compares useful work to total work
5. support for a lever
6. number of times a machine increases force
7. a unit used to describe work
8. combinations of simple machines
9. flat surface that makes an angle with ground
10. pulley combination

Column II
a. block and tackle
b. compound machines
c. efficiency
d. fulcrum
e. inclined plane
f. lever
g. mechanical advantage
h. newton-meter
i. pitch
j. pulley
k. work

Part II: Multiple Choice   Choose the letter of the best answer.

11. A loading ramp is a(n) (a) lever. (b) inclined plane. (c) wheel and axle. (d) wedge.
12. For a crowbar, the distance between applied force and the support is the (a) resistance. (b) effort. (c) lever. (d) fulcrum.
13. Which word can refer to the wheel part of a wheel and axle? (a) crank (b) screw (c) pitch (d) complex machine
14. A power shovel is a (a) simple machine. (b) compound machine. (c) complex machine. (d) jackscrew.
15. The inclined plane on a screw is its (a) circumference. (b) pitch. (c) thread. (d) slot.
16. What is the efficiency for 11 N-m of useful work out of 44 N-m work? (a) 25% (b) 4% (c) 40% (d) 20%
17. How much work is done when a 5-N force moves an object 1 m? (a) 1 N-m (b) 5 N-m (c) 10 N-m (d) 0 N-m

18. Which does *not* contain a wedge? (a) knife (b) broom (c) scissors (d) wood plane (e) needle
19. In which is the direction of effort *opposite* to direction of resistance? (a) inclined plane (b) wedge (c) fixed pulley (d) movable pulley
20. The blade of a screwdriver acts as a(n) (a) wheel. (b) axle. (c) wheel and axle. (d) screw.

Part III: Completion   Write the word or words that complete the sentence correctly.

21. Two or more compound machines combine to make a _____ machine.
22. _____ reduces the efficiency of a machine.
23. A 20-m ramp with a 4-m height has a mechanical advantage of _____.
24. The larger the wheel compared to the axle, the _____ the mechanical advantage of a wheel and axle.
25. The mechanical advantage of a compound machine is found by multiplying the _____ of its simple machines.

Check Your Understanding

1. Describe the crank and shaft of a pencil sharpener in terms of a simple machine.
2. Can a machine produce more force than is put into it? Can it produce more work than is put into it? Explain both answers.
3. Explain why a mountain road usually winds back and forth rather than going straight up the side of the mountain.
4. What factors cause a jackscrew to have a very large mechanical advantage?
5. Would you rather use a thin or a thick wedge to split a log? Explain.
6. Why is the efficiency of a complex machine usually very low?
7. A particular compound machine contains three simple machines, which have mechanical advantages (M.A.) of 4, 2, and 10. What is the M.A. of the compound machine? How did you get your answer?
8. What factor or factors affect the mechanical advantage of a screw?

 Apply Your Knowledge

1. When Pam and Dan made a snowman, they lifted a 200-N block of snow 1.8 m off the ground. How much work did they do?
2. Draw simple diagrams showing three possible positions of effort, resistance, and fulcrum in a lever. Give two examples of each kind of lever.
3. Should the load in a wheelbarrow be placed nearer the wheels or the handle? Explain your answer.
4. Explain why shears for cutting metal have long handles and short blades, and shears for cutting paper have short handles and long blades.
5. A factory uses two steel ramps as inclined planes. One is 10 m long and the other is 15 m long. Which ramp has the greater mechanical advantage? Explain.
6. Jim used the head of a hammer as a lever to remove a nail. Identify the effort, resistance, and fulcrum.

 Extend Your Knowledge

Research/Projects

1. Collect pictures of these simple machines: a broom, a shovel, a wheelchair ramp, an elevator cable, and a saw. Label the important parts of each.
2. Choose a compound or complex machine that you can examine carefully. List all the simple machines you can find in it. Some machines you might consider are a typewriter, an alarm clock, a nutcracker, and a corkscrew.

Readings

Weiss, Harvey. *Machines and How They Work.* Crowell/Harper, 1983. Describes six simple machines—the lever, inclined plane, screw, wedge, wheel and axle, and pulley.

Zubrowski, Bernie. *Wheels At Work: Building and Experimenting With Models of Machines.* Morrow, 1986. Shows how to make a model of a pulley, a gear, a water wheel, and other machines.

CHAPTER 14
Energy and Power

Lights, moving cars and trucks, and people are part of your daily life. Lights cannot shine, cars and trucks cannot move, and people cannot function without a source of energy. The energy for lights comes from electricity. Most cars and trucks get energy from gasoline or diesel fuel. People get energy from food. Energy can take many forms, and power is related to energy.

Organizing Your Study Skills The outline below will help you see how the chapter is organized and what you should learn as you read.

I. Section 14-1: Defining Energy
   A. How are energy and work related?
   B. How is energy measured?

II. Section 14-2: Kinetic Energy
   A. What is kinetic energy?
   B. How is kinetic energy calculated?

III. Section 14-3: Energy Is Conserved
   A. What is potential energy?
   B. What is the law of conservation of energy?
   C. How does friction affect changes in energy?

IV. Section 14-4: Forms of Energy
   A. What are some different forms of energy?
   B. How are the forms of energy related?

V. Section 14-5: Measuring Power
   A. What is power?
   B. How are energy and power related?

14-1 Defining Energy

Energy and Work Are Related

Sometimes you might feel as though you do not have enough "energy" to get up in the morning. Just as work has a slightly different meaning in science from its meaning in everyday life, so does the word energy. Scientists define **energy** as the ability to do work.

The tennis player in the picture hits the ball with her racquet. Because she moves the ball through some distance, she does work on the ball. When the archer does work by drawing the bow, the bow has the ability to do work on the arrow. When you do work by winding the spring on a clock, the spring has the ability to do work on the clock's gears to run the clock. To do work, energy is required. The tennis player and archer get their energy from the food they eat. They use some of the energy to breathe and move around. They give some of their energy to the tennis ball and the arrow.

Energy and work are closely related. You transfer energy to an object by doing work on it. For example, the tennis player did work on the ball. This work transferred energy to the ball and moved it. Thus, work is the transfer of energy. The archer did work on the bow, which then did work on the arrow. Thus energy was transferred from the archer to the arrow.

Figure 14-1 The tennis player transfers energy to the ball, and the archer transfers energy to the arrow.

Measuring Energy

The engineer in *Figure 14-2* is designing a new car. He needs to know how much energy the engine must supply to move the car at different speeds.

Because work is the transfer of energy, you can measure energy by measuring the work done. Remember that when work is done, you must have both a force and the movement (distance) of an object by that force. The unit of measurement for work combines the unit of force—the newton (N)—with the unit of distance—the meter (m). Thus, the unit is the newton-meter (N-m). The newton-meter is also called a **joule** (joul or jül).

The same units are used for measuring work and energy. For example, if a car engine does 1000 newton-meters of work, the engine puts out 1000 newton-meters of energy. You can also say that the car puts out 1000 joules (symbol: *J*) of energy.

When you ride your bicycle one block, you use about 90 000 joules, or 90 kilojoules, of energy. One kilojoule is 1000 joules.

Section Review

1. Define energy in terms of work.
2. What unit is used to measure energy?

Challenge: How much energy do you transfer to a 5-N rock if you lift it 2 meters?

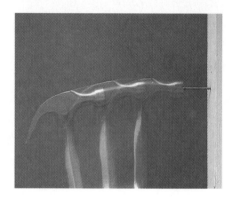

Objectives

After completing this section you will be able to

A. Tell what kinetic energy is.
B. Explain how to calculate an object's kinetic energy.

Figure 14-4 Swinging the hammer faster increases its kinetic energy.

14-2 Kinetic Energy

Moving Objects Have Kinetic Energy

A speeding car has a lot of energy. If the car hits an object and stops, the car releases that energy and causes a great deal of damage. Wind, running water, a flying airplane, and a roller skater all have energy. An object can have energy because of its motion. **Kinetic** (ki net′ik) **energy** is the energy of motion. If you try to stop a moving object, you will feel its kinetic energy. All the objects shown in *Figure 14-3* have kinetic energy.

Calculating Kinetic Energy

Kinetic energy depends on both the mass and the speed of an object. Look at the picture of the hammer about to hit the nail. The hammer does work when it drives the nail into the wood. Swinging the hammer faster or using a heavier hammer at the same speed would push the nail farther and do more work. Increasing either the speed or the mass of the hammer increases its kinetic energy.

You can calculate an object's kinetic energy by multiplying one half times the object's mass times its velocity squared.

$$\text{kinetic energy} = 1/2 \times \text{mass} \times \text{velocity} \times \text{velocity}$$
$$\text{K.E.} = 1/2 \ mv^2$$

Figure 14-3 Moving objects have kinetic energy.

This equation shows that doubling an object's mass doubles its kinetic energy. On the other hand, since v is squared, doubling the object's velocity makes its kinetic energy four times as great.

Suppose you pedal a 20-kilogram bicycle at 2 meters per second. The bicycle's kinetic energy is:

$$\begin{aligned}
\text{K.E.} &= 1/2mv^2 \\
&= 1/2 \times 20 \text{ kilograms} \times (2 \text{ meters/second})^2 \\
&= 40 \text{ kilogram-meter}^2/\text{second}^2 \\
&= 40 \text{ joules.}
\end{aligned}$$

You can see that pedaling at 1 meter per second (half as fast) would produce a kinetic energy of only 10 joules (one-fourth as much). Notice also that the unit from the kinetic energy equation is the same as the joule.

$$\begin{aligned}
1 \text{ joule} &= 1 \text{ newton-meter} \\
&= (1 \text{ kilogram-meter/second/second}) \times 1 \text{ meter} \\
&= 1 \text{ kilogram-meter}^2/\text{second}^2
\end{aligned}$$

Section Review

1. When does an object have kinetic energy? Give an example.
2. How much does the kinetic energy of a bicycle increase if you triple its velocity?

Challenge: If you wanted to hit a home run when playing baseball, should you use a heavier bat or just swing faster? Explain your answer.

Applying Science

Accident investigators know that a car traveling at 100 km/h has 4 times as much kinetic energy as a car traveling at 50 km/h. This means that the car traveling at 100 km/h would skid 4 times as far with its brakes locked as would the car traveling at 50 km/h.

For Practice

Use the equation for kinetic energy to solve the following problems.
1. A girl whose mass is 40 kg skates around a rink at a speed of 12 m/s. How much kinetic energy does she have?
2. A baseball with a mass of 0.08 kg is thrown at a speed of 20 m/s. How much kinetic energy does the ball have?

14-3 Energy Is Conserved

Potential Energy Is Stored Energy

A rock sitting at the top of a hill has stored energy. If the rock slips, it can roll down the hill and crush plants and trees. Any object can store energy because of its position.

The skier in the picture hiked up a hill. She gained energy because she did work against the force of gravity. The skier stopped at the top of the hill. Because she was not moving, she had no kinetic energy. But she still had the energy she gained from walking up the hill. This energy, called **potential** (pə ten′shəl) **energy**, is the energy an object has because of its position. It is called potential energy because in this stored state it has the potential for doing work.

Just as the skier has more potential energy at the top of the hill than at the bottom of the hill, so does a rock sitting at the top of a hill. Water stored behind a dam has more potential energy than water below the dam because of its position. Energy in fuels such as coal or gasoline is also potential energy. These fuels have the potential to do work when a chemical change releases energy stored in the chemical bonds of the fuels.

The Law of Conservation of Energy

When the skier in the picture moves down the hill, her potential energy changes to kinetic energy. Energy might change its form, but it does not disappear. You can add energy to an object or take energy away from it, but the total amount of energy does not change. If you consider all the objects in a group of objects that are giving off or taking in energy, you find that the total amount of energy stays the same. This fact has been observed so often that it is called the **law of conservation of energy**.

In *Figure 14-6*, the energy the skier gains is the work she does to reach the top of the hill. So the work is equal to her potential energy at the top of the hill. The force she acts against is gravity—her weight. The *X* marks the place where the skier pushes off. The distance she moves is the *height* of the hill—10 meters. If her mass is 50 kilograms, you can calculate how much potential energy she gains using the next equation.

Figure 14-5 The skier's potential energy changes to kinetic energy when she pushes off at the top of the hill.

P.E. = work done
= F × d
= (m × g) × h
= 50 kilograms × $\dfrac{10 \text{ meters/second}}{\text{second}}$ × 10 meters
= 5000 joules

At the top of the hill, she has 5000 joules more potential energy than at the bottom. As she skis down the hill, some of her potential energy is changed to kinetic energy.

Since energy is conserved, the skier has 5000 joules of energy at any place down the hill. We usually say she has no potential energy at the bottom of the hill.

Because energy is conserved, the energy she gained in climbing the hill must now be kinetic energy. At the bottom of the hill, where she has no potential energy, she will travel at whatever speed is needed to give her 5000 joules of kinetic energy.

For Practice

Use the potential energy equation to answer these questions.
1. Ron carries a bowling ball weighing 70 N up a flight of stairs 20 m high. How much potential energy has the bowling ball gained?
2. A table tennis ball that weighs 0.25 N is resting on the window ledge of a building 600 m above the street. How much more potential energy does the ball have here than it would have if it were on the street?

Figure 14-6 The skier illustrates the law of conservation of energy.

P.E. = mgh
m = 50kg

h = 10m

P.E. at top = K.E. at bottom of hill

Friction Wastes Energy

The example of the skier and the hill shows that all the skier's potential energy is changed into kinetic energy. This change would be true only if no friction were present. However, friction wastes some of the potential energy. Friction turns some of the potential energy into heat before it can become kinetic energy. The law of conservation of energy still applies, but you must remember that the total amount of energy can appear in several ways.

The lower the force of friction, the less energy is wasted and the more potential energy becomes kinetic energy. The more kinetic energy an object has, the faster it goes. So the less friction that is present, the faster an object goes. The roller skate in *Figure 14-7* has plastic wheels. It can go faster than a roller skate with metal wheels because plastic wheels lose less energy through friction than metal wheels do.

Section Review

1. Suggest two objects that are good examples of potential energy.
2. What is true about the total amount of energy for all objects in a group that are taking in or giving off energy?
3. Does friction affect the law of conservation of energy? Explain.

Challenge: A rock is raised above the ground so that its potential energy is 300 *J* and then it is dropped. What is its kinetic energy just before it hits the ground?

Figure 14-7 Plastic wheels help reduce friction.

Investigating Kinetic and Potential Energy

Purpose

To observe how potential and kinetic energy can do work

Materials

- tennis ball or baseball
- board to be used as a ramp (at least 1 meter long)
- meter stick
- books or pieces of wood to elevate the ramp
- empty liter or half-liter milk carton
- chalk
- balance

Procedure and Observations

1. Cut the top and one side off the milk carton, as shown in **a.**

a

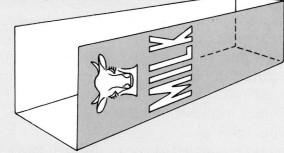

2. Support one end of the board so that it is 10 cm above the floor, as in **b.**
3. Place the milk carton 10 cm from the end of the ramp with the open side down and the open end facing the ramp. Draw a chalk line along the closed end of the carton.

b

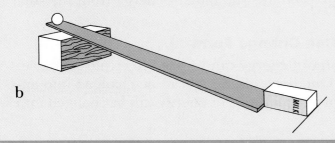

4. Hold the ball at the top of the ramp. Release the ball and let it roll down the ramp and into the carton, as in **b.**
5. Measure the distance the carton moves along the floor, as in **c.** Record the measurement in a data table like the one shown below.

c

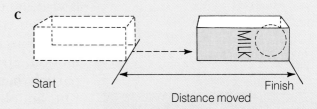

Start   Finish

Distance moved

6. Repeat steps 3–5, with one end of the ramp elevated 20 cm, 30 cm, and 40 cm above the floor.
7. Use the balance to find the mass of the ball. Then find the mass of the milk carton. Record both masses.
8. Calculate the potential energy of the ball when it is 10 cm, 20 cm, 30 cm, and 40 cm above the floor. Record the data in your table.

Height of ramp	Distance milk carton moves	Potential energy of the ball
10 cm		
20 cm		
30 cm		
40 cm		

Analysis and Conclusions

1. As the ball's potential energy increases, what happens to the amount of work done on the milk carton? How do you know?
2. Explain how the ball's potential energy and kinetic energy changed as it rolled down the ramp.

14-4 Forms of Energy

Energy Comes in Several Forms

A moving person or automobile has kinetic energy. When you climb or ride up a hill, you increase your potential energy. Both kinetic energy and potential energy are kinds of **mechanical energy**, which is energy an object has from its motion and the forces acting on it. The boxer's fist and the moving punching bag in *Figure 14-8* have mechanical energy. Mechanical energy is also the energy of machines.

If you could see the tiny atoms and molecules that form objects, you could see that these particles are in motion. So each particle has kinetic energy. Since each particle has very little mass, its kinetic energy is small. But an object has so many particles that the total amount of this energy can be measured. The total amount of energy of all the particles of an object is its **internal energy**.

Electricity is a flow of certain tiny particles of matter. Electricity carries **electrical energy**. This form of energy is very convenient to use.

Energy can also be stored in matter as **chemical energy**, which depends on how the particles of matter are arranged. Because chemical energy depends on the position of particles in objects, it is a form of potential energy. Fuels such as coal and oil contain chemical energy that becomes available when a chemical change, such as burning, takes place.

Energy can also be carried as waves through space in the form of **radiant** (rā'dē ənt) **energy**. Light, X rays, and radio waves are examples of radiant energy.

Nuclear energy is released when very small particles of matter split or combine. After the split or combination, the resulting small particles have a little less mass than the original particles. The rest of the mass is changed into energy. This process of changing mass into energy produces the radiant energy from the sun.

Figure 14-8 Both the boxer's fist and the punching bag have mechanical energy.

Energy Can Change Form

Each form of energy can be used to create a force to do work. One form of energy can be changed into another form and all forms of energy can be changed into heat.

Chemical energy in a battery can be changed into electrical energy to run a motor. In the motor, electrical energy is changed into mechanical energy.

Nuclear energy is produced when mass changes into energy. Energy can also change into mass and into other forms of energy. For example, the solar oven shown in the picture is cooking food. The energy came from mass changing into energy in the sun's center. The sun's energy causes chemical processes to happen in the food. When you eat the food, your body changes the chemical energy stored in the food into the mechanical energy of your motion.

Plants use the sun's radiant energy to grow. Some of the energy is stored in the plants. Plants that died millions of years ago formed the oil, gas, and coal people use every day. The chemical energy from these fuels is another form of the sun's energy that was trapped inside plants. Driving a car or heating a house releases this energy.

Burning oil, gas, and coal can be used to boil water. Moving steam from the water can produce mechanical energy. This energy is then used to produce electricity.

Figure 14-9 The solar oven changes radiant energy into heat energy.

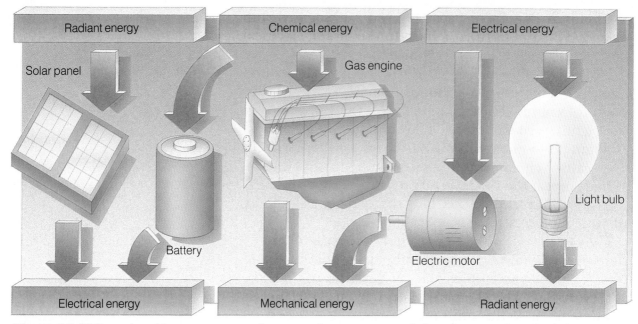

| Radiant energy | Chemical energy | Electrical energy |

Solar panel

Gas engine

Light bulb

Battery

Electric motor

| Electrical energy | Mechanical energy | Radiant energy |

Figure 14-10 Examples of how one form of energy can be changed into another

In your home you might change the electricity into light. Notice in *Figure 14-10* how people can change energy from one form to another during the day. The arrows show the direction of change.

Section Review

1. What are six forms of energy?
2. Describe how energy can change form.

Challenge: Describe three energy changes that occur in an automobile.

Careers in Physical Science

Mechanical Engineer

Mechanical engineers make a lot of power. They are the people who design machines that generate power.

Engines that run trains, planes, cars, and even rockets are developed by mechanical engineers. They concentrate on making efficient machines. The best engines use the least fuel to put out the most power. Mechanical engineers may redesign machines that consume power to use less energy.

In order to do their job properly, mechanical engineers must understand blueprints, machine-building tools, and energy efficiency. They study engineering for at least four years in college.

14-5 Measuring Power

Power Involves Work or Energy and Time

In the picture, Scott and Dean are taking care of their lawn. One week, Scott mows the lawn in one hour. The next week, Dean mows the lawn in 45 minutes. Because both boys pushed the lawn mower the same distance, each did the same amount of work. Scott and Dean differed only in how quickly they worked.

In science, **power** describes the rate at which work is done. To calculate power, you use:

$$\text{power} = \text{work/time.}$$

Because work is the transfer of energy, power also equals energy divided by time. So power is also the rate at which energy is used. If the work done by Scott or Dean is 6000 joules, the power each boy used is:

Scott's power = 6000 joules/3600 seconds
          = 1.7 joules/second.

Dean's power = 6000 joules/2700 seconds
          = 2.2 joules/second.

One joule per second is called a **watt** (symbol: W). Power is measured in watts.

Objectives

After completing this section you will be able to

A. Describe what power is.
B. State how energy and power are related.

Figure 14-11 The rate at which Scott mows the lawn determines his power.

Figure 14-12 An electric meter measures electrical power use. The meter reads 97 495 kilowatt-hours.

Explore!

Another unit for power is the horsepower. Although it is not an SI unit, it is often used in measuring the power of engines. Use an encyclopedia to find out where the name *horsepower* comes from.

For Practice

Use the equation for power to solve these problems.
1. A small wind-up truck supplies 5 W of power. If the truck travels for 30 seconds, how much work has it done? How much energy has it used?
2. A light bulb uses 60 000 W-s of energy as it burns for 12 hours. How much power does the light bulb use?

Calculating Energy from Power

Scott and Dean's parents bought a power lawn mower that supplies an average of 10 watts of power. Now each boy mows the lawn in 10 minutes (600 seconds). You can determine how much work the lawn mower does by multiplying the power, 10 watts, times the time, 600 seconds.

work = power × time
= 10 watts × 600 seconds
= 6000 watt-seconds

You can also say that the lawn mower uses 6000 watt-seconds of energy.

In this example, the watt-second indicated that a certain amount of power (watts) is used for a certain length of time (seconds). The watt-second and the kilowatt-hour measure energy used, just as joules do. The kilowatt (symbol: kW) and the megawatt (symbol: MW) are units used to measure large amounts of electrical power.

Figure 14-12 shows an electric meter, such as the ones found in most homes, and a close-up shows the dials on the meter. The meter shows how many kilowatt-hours the people in the house have used. From right to left, the five dials indicate: ones, tens, hundreds, thousands, and ten-thousands of kilowatt-hours.

Section Review

1. How can you calculate power?
2. How is a watt different from a watt-second?

Challenge: How do you know that a watt-second is the same as a joule?

Measuring Human Power

Purpose

To measure human power developed during common activities

Materials

- watch or clock with a second hand
- meter stick
- kilogram bathroom scale
- small stool
- wastebasket
- spring scale
- masking tape

Procedure and Observations

PART A

1. Copy the data table shown here. Measure a 2-m distance on the floor with the meter stick.
2. Mark the length with a piece of tape at each end. Put a few pieces of tape along the length to make a straight-line guide.
3. Put the wastebasket at one end of your taped length and next to the guide line.
4. Pull the wastebasket with the spring scale so that you can read the amount of force you are exerting. You must keep the scale horizontal and move the basket in a straight line.
5. Practice step 4 until you can keep the scale pointer fairly steady as you pull.
6. Repeat step 4, keeping the pointer steady while your partner times how long you need to pull the basket through the 2-m length.
7. Record the scale reading and the time from step 6 in your data table.
8. Repeat steps 6–7 twice. Average your force reading and your time readings, and record them.

9. Switch places with your partner and repeat steps 3–8.

PART B

1. Find your mass by using a bathroom scale.
2. Measure and record the distance from the top of the stool to the floor.
3. Ask your partner to hold the stool steady so you can step on it.
4. While your partner times you for 10 seconds, count how many times you step on and off the stool. Record this number. *CAUTION: Do not perform this part of the activity if you have a respiratory disorder, circulatory disorder, or other medical condition that could be aggravated by this step.*
5. Switch places with your partner, and repeat steps 1–4.

	Trial 1	Trial 2	Trial 3	Average
Scale reading				
Time				

Analysis and Conclusions

1. Use work = force × distance to calculate the average work you did in Part A.
2. With the answer to question 1 and your average time spent, calculate your power using power = work/time.
3. Calculate the work you did in Part B using work = m × g × h (g = 10 m/s/s).
4. Calculate the power that you exert in Part B while you are stepping up onto the stool. Your time spent is 5 seconds, because you spent the other 5 seconds stepping down from the stool.

Calculating Energy Use

You have read about how the electric company measures the amount of electrical energy you use in your home. In this activity you will learn how to use readings from an electric meter to calculate energy use.

The upper set of dials shows a meter reading for November 1st. The lower set of dials shows the meter reading exactly one month later. To calculate the amount of energy used, read both meters. Then subtract the earlier reading from the later reading. The result is the amount of electrical energy used for that month, measured in kilowatt-hours. Figure out the amount of electric energy used during the month of November and then answer the following questions.

1. Assume that the electric company charges twelve cents for every kilowatt-hour of energy used. Calculate the November electric bill based on the two meter readings.

2. What is the average amount of energy used per day between November 1st and December 1st?

3. Appliances are often rated by how much energy they use in a given time—or by their power. Remember that power is measured in watts. The table below shows the average wattage for various household appliances. Using the rate given in question 1, calculate how much it would cost to run each of the appliances for an hour. Start by converting watts to kilowatts (1000 watts = 1 kilowatt).

Appliance	Watts
Large microwave oven	700
Refrigerator/freezer	500
Toaster	1200
Television	150
Lightbulb	75
Personal computer	240

4. Imagine that on January 1st, the electric meter reads 27 907. Draw the dials shown here on a separate piece of paper, omitting the pointers. Then add the pointers to show the January 1st reading on your copy of the dials.

5. Some electric companies lower their rates in the winter and raise them in the summer. Assume that the electric company lowered its rates on December 1st. To figure out the electric bills for the winter months, use the following information: the electric company charges twelve cents for the first 400 kilowatt-hours used each month; it charges five cents for the remaining kilowatt-hours. Using the meter reading from question 4, calculate the December electric bill.

November 1

ten-
thousands thousands hundreds   tens   ones

December 1

ten-
thousands thousands hundreds   tens   ones

Summary

14-1 Defining Energy

A. Energy is the ability to do work. Work is the transfer of energy.

B. The unit of measurement for work is the newton-meter, which is also called a joule. The same units are used for measuring energy and work.

14-2 Kinetic Energy

A. Kinetic energy is an object's energy due to its motion.

B. Kinetic energy is calculated by using the formula:

$$\text{K.E.} = 1/2 \ mv^2.$$

If a moving object's mass doubles, the object's kinetic energy also doubles. If the object's velocity doubles, its kinetic energy increases times four.

14-3 Energy Is Conserved

A. Potential energy is an object's energy due to its position.

B. The law of conservation of energy states that energy can change form, but the total amount of energy remains the same.

C. Friction turns some potential energy into heat before it can become kinetic energy. The higher the friction, the greater the amount of potential energy that is wasted.

14-4 Forms of Energy

A. Some forms of energy are electrical, chemical, nuclear, internal, mechanical, and radiant.

B. Energy in one form can change into other forms of energy. Chemical energy in a battery can change into electrical energy. All forms of energy can be changed into heat.

14-5 Measuring Power

A. Power is the rate at which work is done or energy is used. Power can be calculated by using the formula:

Power = (work or energy)/time.

One joule per second is called a watt. Power is measured in watts.

B. Energy used or work done can be calculated by using the formula:

work = power × time.

Vocabulary

For each of the following terms, write a sentence that uses the term correctly.

chemical energy	kinetic energy	potential energy
electrical energy	law of conservation of energy	power
energy	mechanical energy	radiant energy
internal energy	nuclear energy	watt
joule		

Check Your Knowledge

Part I: Matching Match the definition in Column I with the correct term in Column II.

Column I
1. energy from machines
2. rate of using energy or doing work
3. ability to do work
4. energy from the sun and stars
5. the total amount of energy remains the same
6. unit of power
7. energy due to an object's motion
8. energy due to an object's position
9. unit of energy and work
10. energy from the splitting or combining of some small particles

Column II
a. chemical energy
b. energy
c. joule
d. kinetic energy
e. law of conservation of energy
f. mechanical energy
g. nuclear energy
h. potential energy
i. power
j. radiant energy
k. watt

Part II: Multiple Choice Choose the letter of the best answer.
11. A 400-N girl climbs a 2-m high staircase. At the top, the amount of potential energy she has gained is (a) 20 *J*. (b) 160 *J*. (c) 120 *J*. (d) 800 *J*.
12. The kinetic energy of a 2-kg object moving at 5 m/s is (a) 25 *J*. (b) 50 *J*. (c) 10 *J*. (d) 20 *J*.
13. Which kind of energy does a light bulb use? (a) radiant (b) electrical (c) nuclear (d) chemical
14. One newton-meter is also one (a) watt. (b) joule-second. (c) joule. (d) kilowatt-hour.
15. Burning coal is an example of (a) electrical energy. (b) nuclear energy. (c) chemical energy. (d) mechanical energy.
16. During an energy change, energy is (a) increased. (b) created. (c) conserved. (d) destroyed.

17. How much work can an electric pencil sharpener do if it uses 25 W for 5 minutes? (a) 750 W (b) 7500 *J* (c) 125 *J* (d) 1250 W
18. What is the power of a record player if it uses 60 000 W-s for 50 minutes? (a) 1200 W (b) 1200 W-s (c) 20 W-s (d) 20 W

Part III: Completion Write the word or words that complete the sentence correctly.
19. The total amount of energy of all the particles of an object is its _____.
20. Wind, running water, and a moving car all have _____ energy.
21. When Leslie carries a bucket of paint up a step ladder, she gives the bucket _____ energy.
22. Potential energy is equal to the work done against the force of _____.
23. Some potential energy is turned into heat because of _____.

Check Your Understanding

1. What kind of energy exists in each of the following: a) package on a closet shelf; b) rock rolling down a hill; c) baseball hit with a bat; d) mousetrap with its spring set.
2. A machine uses 100 000 *J* of energy. How much work can the machine do? If the machine operates with 25% efficiency, how much useful work can it do? How much energy is useless work?
3. A student throws a ball into the air with a kinetic energy of 100 *J*. Determine the amount of kinetic energy and potential energy the ball has when it is at 25, 50, and 75 percent of its maximum height.
4. A light bulb uses 1 800 000 *J* of energy in 10 hours. What is its power?
5. How does an object get potential energy?

 Apply Your Knowledge

1. An airplane takes off, flies, and lands. Describe any changes in energy during this process. Begin with the use of gasoline in the plane's engine and end with the plane coming to rest.
2. You read under a 100-W bulb for 2 hours. How many kilowatt-hours of electricity do you use?
3. A friend tells you that a glass of orange juice has potential energy. Is your friend right or wrong? Explain.
4. A 40-N package and a 60-N package are on a shelf 3 meters from the floor. If both packages were pushed off the shelf, which package would have the most potential energy at the start of the fall? Explain your answer.
5. Suppose your drop a 5-N rock from a height of 1.5 meters. Then you drop a 10-N rock from a height of 1 meter. Which would hurt more if it accidentally fell on your foot? Explain your answer in terms of potential energy.

 Extend Your Knowledge

Research/Projects
1. Keep a list of the forms of energy that you use at school and home. After several weeks, determine which form of energy is used most.
2. Record the number of kilowatt-hours registered on the electric meter at your house at the same time each day for seven days. How much energy was used at the end of the week? What is the average amount of energy used in a day?

Readings
"Blowin' Down the House: The Tricky Art of Building Demolition." *Scholastic Science World*, May 4, 1987, pages 6–9. Describes how potential energy in skyscrapers and gravity can be used to demolish a building.
McGrath, Susan. *Fun with Physics.* National Geographic Society, 1986. Explains how physics is involved in all aspects of our lives. Includes activities to demonstrate physics principles.

CHAPTER 15
Heat and Temperature

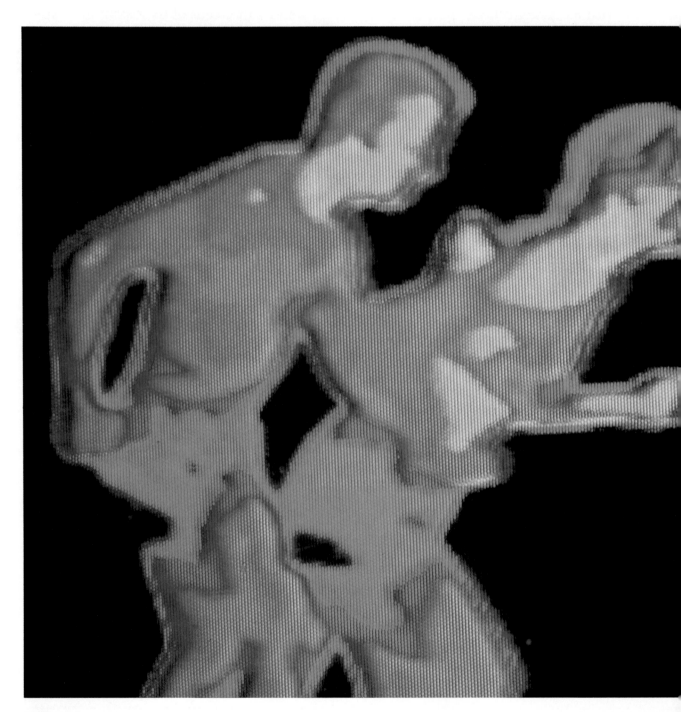

You usually think of hot and cold as something you feel rather than see. But this photograph was taken with special film that is sensitive to heat. The film records different temperatures as different colors. High temperatures appear blue or purple. Medium temperatures appear green or yellow, and cool temperatures are red or orange.

Organizing Your Study Skills The outline below will help you see how the chapter is organized and what you should learn as you read.

I. **Section 15-1: Defining Heat and Temperature**
   A. What is the kinetic theory of matter?
   B. How are heat and temperature defined?

II. **Section 15-2: Detecting Heat and Temperature**
   A. How is temperature measured?
   B. How is heat measured?

III. **Section 15-3: Producing Heat**
   A. What is a heat source?
   B. How do the forms of energy produce heat?

IV. **Section 15-4: Energy Transfer**
   A. How does energy travel by conduction?
   B. What is convection?
   C. How is energy transferred by radiation?

V. **Section 15-5: Expansion and Contraction**
   A. How are materials affected by heating and cooling?
   B. How do people allow for expansion and contraction?
   C. How do people use expansion and contraction?

15-1 Defining Heat and Temperature

Moving Particles Make Up Matter

Heat is important in your life. On cold winter days, the heating system warms your home and school. In the summer, everyone talks about the hot weather and asks what the temperature is.

The photograph shows students playing basketball on a hot summer day. After an hour or so of brisk exercise, they stopped playing and went into an air-conditioned room to cool off. Because they were so hot, the difference between the outside and inside temperatures was very noticeable.

After a winter afternoon of ice skating, a warm bathtub of water will heat you better than a spoonful of very hot water. The hot water has a higher temperature, but the large amount of warm water will heat you faster. So heat and temperature are related, but they are not the same. To understand heat and temperature, you need to review what you know about matter.

All matter is made of tiny particles called atoms and molecules. These particles are constantly in motion. Both these ideas are part of the **kinetic theory of matter.** The particles do not all move at the same speed. Water particles move faster than gold particles at the same temperature, and air particles move faster than water particles at the same temperature. Also, the air particles move at a wide range of speeds.

Heat Differs from Temperature

Because the particles of matter are in motion, they have kinetic energy. These differences are shown in *Figure 15-2.* In any object, all the particles do not have exactly the same kinetic energy. **Temperature** is a measure of the average kinetic energy of all the particles in an object or material. Particles at a high temperature have more average kinetic energy. Particles at a low temperature have less average kinetic energy. Heating a drop of water makes its particles move faster and increases their kinetic energy and temperature. Putting water in a freezer makes the particles move more slowly and reduces their kinetic energy and temperature.

Figure 15-1 On a hot, summer day, these basketball players feel hot.

Figure 15-2 Temperature is a measure of average kinetic energy. The arrows represent kinetic energy. The longer the arrow the greater the kinetic energy.

Suppose you hold an ice cube in your hand. The particles in your warm hand move faster than the particles in the cold ice cube. Fast-moving skin particles bump into slow-moving ice particles and give them energy. The ice particles move faster and become "warmer." Your skin particles move more slowly and become "cooler."

Heat is the amount of energy transferred from one place or object to another. One object at the same temperature as another object has more energy if it has more particles. More heat can be transferred from a larger object than from a smaller one at the same temperature.

Section Review

1. What does the kinetic theory say about matter?
2. What is the difference between heat and temperature?

Challenge: Which contains more heat—a cup of boiling water or a large lake whose water temperature is 18°C?

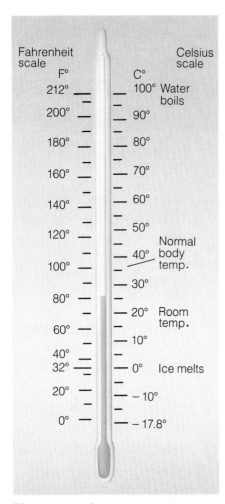

Figure 15-3 Comparing the Celsius and Fahrenheit temperature scales

15-2 Detecting Heat and Temperature Changes

Measuring Temperature

How can you tell how hot an object is? You could touch it, but touching very hot or very cold objects is not safe. You need some kind of measuring instrument. **Thermometers** are instruments that measure temperature. Thermometers contain a column of liquid, often mercury or colored alcohol, in a narrow glass tube. The liquid expands when heated and moves higher in the tube.

All temperature scales use two reference points, one hot and one cold. The temperatures at which pure water boils and freezes at sea level are usually chosen as reference points. A certain number of equal steps, called degrees, occurs between the reference points. On the Celsius temperature scale shown in *Figure 15-3*, ice melts at 0° and water boils at 100°.

Sometimes the range of temperatures on a common thermometer is too small to measure an object's temperature. For example, a steel worker might need to measure the temperature of very hot steel rods. The photograph shows a worker using an **optical pyrometer** (op′tə kəl pī rom′ə tər) to measure very high temperatures without touching the hot object.

An optical pyrometer operates on the principle that the color of light given off by a glowing object depends on its temperature. Warm objects appear reddish, hotter objects are yellow, and even hotter objects give off blue light.

Figure 15-4 A steelworker using an optical pyrometer

An optical pyrometer measures one kind of radiant energy—light. Hot objects also give off infrared rays, which are not visible. Measuring how much infrared energy an object gives off also measures the object's temperature. Even though you cannot see infrared rays, detectors which do can show a different color to represent each range of temperatures measured. A picture made with such colors is called a **thermogram.**

Some industries use thermograms to find weak spots in metal and plastic objects. Thermograms also show where heat escapes from homes and other buildings. In the thermogram in *Figure 15-5,* hot temperatures appear white. Warm temperatures look orange or red. Cold temperatures look dark blue or black.

Doctors also use thermograms of people to help detect some kinds of diseases. A higher than normal skin temperature might indicate cancer in the tissue below that area of the skin. A lower than normal temperature might indicate poor blood flow in that area.

Measuring Heat

Thermometers measure the temperature of a material. But they do not measure how much heat a substance contains. You need a different instrument and unit for measuring heat.

Heat is related to energy. Adding energy to a mass raises the kinetic energy of its particles and heats the mass. For example, about 4.2 joules are needed to raise the temperature of 1 gram of water by 1°C.

Figure 15-5 The colors in the thermogram indicate where heat is escaping from the buildings.

Figure 15-6 Water's high specific heat prevents the lake from changing temperature as quickly as the air.

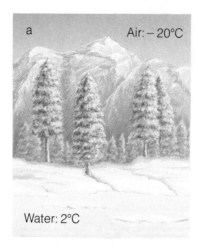

Scientists use a device for measuring heat called a **calorimeter** (kal′ə rim′ə tər). This device is a closed container. Its outer shell keeps the surroundings from affecting the material or process scientists want to measure. A substance whose heat is being measured is allowed to transfer its energy to a known mass at a lower temperature. By measuring the differences in temperatures, the original heat content can be measured.

An important use of the calorimeter is to determine a material's ability to take in or give off heat as its temperature changes. This property is called the **specific heat** of a material. Water has a high specific heat. It can take in or give off a large amount of heat without a large change in temperature. The drawings in *Figure 15-6* point out that a lake is much warmer than the air in winter and much cooler than the air in summer. The lake's large mass and the water's high specific heat prevent the lake's temperature from changing quickly or by a large number of degrees.

Iron and aluminum have low specific heats. Their temperature can be increased by the addition of a relatively small amount of heat. This property of iron and aluminum explains why these metals are used to make cooking utensils.

Have You Heard?

The calorie is an older unit for measuring heat. You have probably heard this term in connection with dieting—meaning the number of calories a certain food contains. Actually the diet calorie, called a Calorie, is a kilocalorie (1000 calories). One calorie is equal to 4.18 joules. A candy bar might supply you with about 250 Calories (250 000 calories). You have to use up that much energy so as not to gain weight. Think about that the next time you have a sweet tooth!

Section Review

1. Describe two instruments used for measuring temperature.
2. What is a material's specific heat?

Challenge: How might the specific heat of water affect the climate of cities on the shoreline of a large lake or the ocean?

Investigating Temperature Changes

Purpose

To observe and predict how objects with different temperatures affect each other

Materials

- balance
- water at room temperature
- hot and cold water
- small metal washers
- 2 plastic-foam cups
- thermometer
- 100-mL graduated cylinder

Procedure and Observations

1. Copy the data table below on a separate piece of paper.
2. Measure 100 g of water that is at room temperature. (NOTE: 100 g of water occupies 100 mL.) Pour the water into one of the plastic-foam cups. Measure the temperature of the water and record it in your data table.
3. Repeat step 2 with hot water.
4. Predict the temperature you will get if you mix the two samples of water. Record your prediction in the data table.
5. Mix the hot water with the room temperature water. After one minute, meas-ure the temperature of the mixture and record it. Empty the cup.
6. Measure 100 g of hot water and pour it into one of the cups. Measure and record the temperature of the water.
7. Measure 100 g of small metal washers and place them in the second plastic-foam cup. The washers should feel neither warm nor cool, and thus will be about room temperature. Infer the temperature of the washers by measuring the temperature of the air. Record this measurement in your data table.
8. Predict the temperature you will get if you mix the hot water and the metal washers. Record you prediction.
9. Add the hot water to the cup containing the washers. After one minute, measure the temperature of the water-washer mixture and record it in your data table.

Analysis and Conclusions

1. How did your predictions compare with the measured temperatures?
2. Which addition caused a larger temperature change in the hot water, the room temperature water or the room-temperature washers? Explain.

Substance	Original Temperature	Final Temperature
Water (room temperature)		Prediction:
Hot water		
Washers (room temperature)		Prediction:
Hot water		

After completing this section you will be able to

A. Describe what a heat source is.
B. List examples of how the forms of energy produce heat.

15-3 Producing Heat

Heat Sources

Rubbing your hands together produces heat and warms your fingers. You are using mechanical energy to produce heat.

A **heat source** is anything that gives off energy that can be absorbed. Most forms of energy produce heat. Directly or indirectly, the sun is the source of most energy. Therefore, the sun is also an important heat source. Any object or place of high temperature is a heat source. Heat moves from regions of higher temperature toward regions of lower temperature.

The Forms of Energy Produce Heat

Electrical energy is an important source of heat. Toasters, electric irons, hot plates, hair dryers, and electric blankets use electrical energy to produce heat. Appliances, such as those in the pictures, contain devices that heat up when electricity passes through them.

Figure 15-7 The stove and toaster use electrical energy to produce heat.

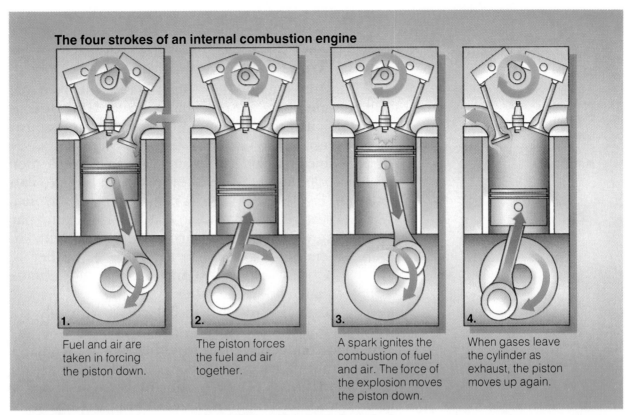

The four strokes of an internal combustion engine

1. Fuel and air are taken in forcing the piston down.

2. The piston forces the fuel and air together.

3. A spark ignites the combustion of fuel and air. The force of the explosion moves the piston down.

4. When gases leave the cylinder as exhaust, the piston moves up again.

Chemical energy can produce heat. During chemical processes, substances can release heat as they react with each other. Combustion is the chemical process of burning. The combustion of fuels such as coal, wood, fuel oil, gasoline, and natural gas produces heat and often light.

Combustion in a car's engine moves the pistons, as shown in *Figure 15-8*. This motion eventually moves the car. But combustion produces a great deal of heat. So a car's cooling system removes unwanted heat from places in the engine.

Mechanical energy also provides heat, usually from friction. Often friction causes harmful effects. For example, oil-well drills produce large quantities of heat as they drill through solid rock. Cooling the drill with water keeps the drill from melting.

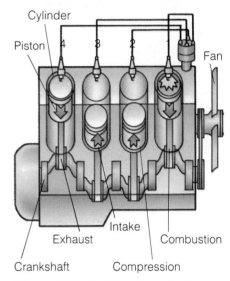

Figure 15-8 An internal combustion engine and the piston cycle

Section Review

1. How does a heat source's temperature compare with the temperature of its surroundings?
2. What are three ways of providing heat?

Challenge: You hold an ice cube in one hand and a glass of hot water in the other hand. Describe how heat moves and name the heat sources.

Explore!

Spontaneous combustion causes millions of dollars in fire damage every year. Use reference books to find out how spontaneous combustion happens.

After completing this section you will be able to

A. Explain how energy travels by conduction.
B. Explain the process of convection.
C. Explain how energy is transferred by radiation.

15-4   Energy Transfer

Energy Travels by Conduction

If you put your feet on something warm, your feet will become warm. Heat is reaching your body directly. **Conduction** is the movement of energy from a source to an object by direct contact between them.

The kinetic theory of matter explains conduction. The particles in any material move and bump into each other. In *Figure 15-9*, particles near the end of the metal bar are heated by the candle. The heat causes the particles to move faster. These particles then bump into and transfer energy—or heat—to the particles farther up the bar. In this way, energy travels through the metal bar from one end to the other.

Any material through which heat passes easily is a **conductor.** Most metals, such as aluminum and copper, are good conductors of heat. Other materials, such as wool, straw, paper, cork, and wood, are not good conductors of heat. A poor conductor is an **insulator.** It delays or inhibits the movement of heat. Because wood and plastic are good insulators, they are used to cover the handles of cooking utensils. Because wool is a good insulator, it simply prevents the transfer of your body heat to your surroundings.

People use insulators in their homes to keep heat inside during the winter and outside during the summer. In *Figure 15-10*, the middle house has good insulation. Since little heat escapes through the roof, a layer of snow coats the roof. Storm windows also keep heat in the house because they have a layer of air, which is a better insulator than glass. A wool blanket on your bed does not provide you with any heat.

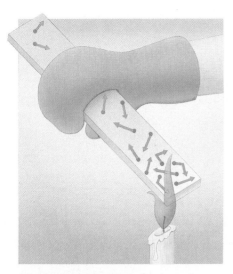

Figure 15-9 Heat moves through metal by conduction

Figure 15-10 Snow remains on the roof of the middle house because this house is insulated better than the other two houses.

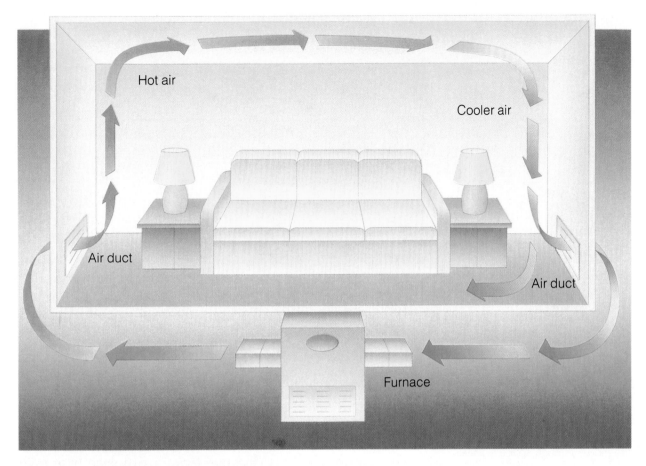

Hot air

Cooler air

Air duct

Air duct

Furnace

Figure 15-11 Convection currents in a home heating system

Energy Transfer by Convection

Placing your hands above a stove warms them. Air moving up from the stove heats your hands by convection. **Convection** is the transfer of energy when a large mass of liquid or gas moves from one place to another. The moving material flows in a **convection current.** Many air and water currents are convection currents. A temperature difference between two masses of a gas or liquid causes convection currents.

Figure 15-11 shows convection currents in one kind of home heating system. In the furnace, heated air particles begin to move faster, bump into each other, and move farther apart. So the hot air is less dense and rises above the cooler air. The hot air is forced through air ducts into a room. The hot air continues to rise above the cooler air already in the room, as the red arrows show. As the air mixes, the hot air becomes cooler and denser and sinks. Notice the blue area that shows this air. The cooler air returns through other air ducts to the furnace to be reheated. The process of convection then begins again.

Applying Science

An invention can save the lives of firefighters trapped while fighting forest fires. Carried as a pack on their belts, it quickly opens to form a meter-high tent. Inside the tent, the firefighters are insulated from the flames by layers of fiberglass and aluminum foil, and by a cushion of air.

Figure 15-12 Radiant energy from the fire moves through space in waves.

Energy Transfer by Radiation

If you sit a short distance from a fireplace, you take in heat and feel warm. But you did not touch the fireplace, and convection currents did not pass you. Energy reached you in the form of radiant energy, as in the drawing. The heat you feel results from another way of transferring energy. Radiant energy from the fire moves through space in waves. Like sunlight, the waves of radiant energy stream out from a source in all directions—they radiate. All objects radiate some energy. An object radiates more energy when it gets hotter. **Radiation** (rā′dē ā′shən) is the transfer of energy in this special kind of wave.

More energy usually reaches you through radiation than through conduction or convection. When radiant energy strikes the particles of a material, it increases the particles' energy. The particles move faster, and the substance heats up. All objects can take in some radiant energy.

Materials with dark, dull surfaces take in—or absorb—a lot of radiation. The dark-colored solar collectors on the houses in *Figure 15-13* are good for absorbing the sun's radiation and changing it into heat.

Some materials reflect or allow radiation to pass through them easily. Air, glass, and other clear materials allow radiant energy to pass through them. These materials absorb very little radiant energy. Bright, shiny surface materials reflect radiant energy.

The sun is our major source of radiant energy. On a cold winter day, the sun shines through a window and warms you. The outside air and the window panes remain cold, because radiant energy from the sun passes through the air and glass without warming them very much. But when radiant energy strikes your clothes and body, it is absorbed. The particles in your clothes and body move faster and faster, and you begin to feel warm. Thus, radiation that passes through space, the atmosphere, and window glass provides you with warmth.

Figure 15-13 The houses' solar collectors absorb the sun's radiation and change it to heat.

Applying Science

Light-colored objects are poor absorbers of radiant energy. Because of this fact, wearing light-colored clothing in summer will actually keep you cooler.

Section Review

1. Explain how conduction transfers energy.
2. How does convection differ from conduction?
3. Explain how radiation transfers energy.

Challenge: Explain why a closed car becomes extremely hot inside when left sitting in the sun.

Activity 15-2

A Material's Effect on Radiant Energy

Purpose

To observe and predict how an object's surface affects the amount of radiant energy an object absorbs or radiates

Materials

- 3 aluminum cans, one white, one black, and one shiny silver
- 3 thermometers
- hot water
- 100-watt light source
- white construction paper
- black construction paper
- metric ruler
- stapler
- colored pencils or markers
- graduated cylinder

Procedure and Observations

PART A

1. Fold the bottom edge of each sheet of paper up to within 4 cm of the top.
2. Staple the sides of the paper to form a pouch and insert a thermometer into the pouch.
3. Record the starting temperature for the white pouch at time zero in a data table like the one shown.
4. Place the pouch flat on a table. Place the light source 10 cm above the pouch, as shown. Be sure to center the light source over the pouch.

5. Turn the light on. Measure the temperature of the pouch each minute for 6 minutes. Record your measurements.
6. Repeat steps 3-5, using the black pouch.

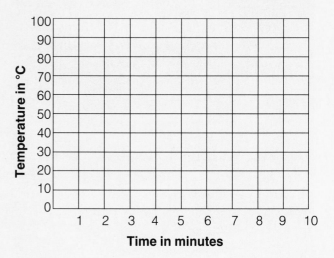

PART B

1. Fill each aluminum can three-fourths full with equal amounts of hot water.
2. Place a thermometer in each can and record the temperatures in your data table.
3. Predict which can will cool the fastest. Record your prediction.
4. Measure the water temperature in each can every minute for 10 minutes. Record your measurements in your data table.
5. Plot your data on a grid like the one shown here. Connect the points using a different color for each can.

Analysis and Conclusions

1. How do you explain the temperature differences you observed in Part A?
2. On what information did you base your prediction in Part B?
3. Explain the differences in the graphs you made in Part B.

15-5 Expansion and Contraction

Objectives

After completing this section you will be able to

A. Describe how heating and cooling affect materials.
B. Explain how people allow for expansion and contraction.
C. Explain how people make use of thermal expansion.

Materials Expand When Heated

Almost all materials take up more space when heated and less space when cooled. **Expansion** is an increase in the size of a material. **Contraction** is a decrease in size. Sometimes expansion and contraction are quite noticeable. For example, the Golden Gate Bridge in San Francisco is about 1.5 meters longer during the summer than it is during the winter.

The kinetic theory of matter explains how thermal expansion and contraction occur. When a steel rod is heated, its particles move around and bump into each other more often. Because the particles knock each other farther apart, the space between the particles increases. The rod then expands. When the rod cools, the particles move closer together and the rod contracts.

Rubber and water are exceptions and do not behave as the rod does. If you heat a stretched rubber band gently, the rubber contracts. As the rubber band cools, it expands. Cooled water contracts until it reaches 4°C. Below this temperature, water expands until it freezes at 0°C. This expansion makes ice less dense than water, so ice floats in water.

Allowing for Expansion and Contraction

Sometimes expansion and contraction cause problems in structures such as buildings, highways, and sidewalks. If concrete highways and sidewalks were made in long continuous stretches, they would crack because of the expansion and contraction caused by seasonal temperature changes. To avoid this problem, concrete is poured in sections. Each section is separated from the next by a small space. The spaces are usually filled with a substance such as tar. In summer when the concrete expands, tar is often squeezed out of the spaces.

The next time you are outdoors, notice the telephone and electric wires. In summer, the wires expand and sag. In winter, the wires are tighter and straighter. Sometimes, in extremely cold weather, the wires contract so much that they snap. The worker in *Figure 15-14* is repairing damages caused by seasonal changes.

Figure 15-14 Electric wires contract and sometimes snap in cold weather.

Figure 15-15 An expansion joint in a bridge

Figure 15-16 The bimetallic strip bends up at cold temperatures, because the brass contracts more than the iron. The strip bends down at warmer temperatures, because the brass expands more than the iron.

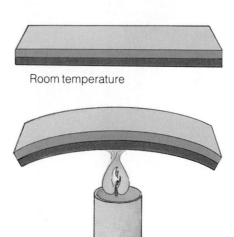

Ice

Brass

Iron

Room temperature

Long steel bridges often have only one end attached, while the other end rests on devices called rockers. This arrangement of rockers allows the bridge to expand in hot weather without danger of buckling.

Engineers design bridges with toothlike seams, called expansion joints. In the summer, the teeth move together as the bridge expands. In winter, the teeth separate as the bridge contracts. Notice the expansion joint shown in *Figure 15-14*.

Using Expansion and Contraction

If you have ever had difficulty opening a tight jar lid, you probably know that you can hold the lid under a stream of hot water. The heat from the water will cause the lid to expand. If the lid expands enough, it will loosen enough to unscrew.

Thermometers also make use of expansion and contraction. The alcohol or mercury in the column of a thermometer expands and rises with increasing temperature. When the temperature decreases, the liquid contracts and drops to a lower level.

All materials do not expand and contract the same amount, as shown in *Figure 15-16*. A **thermostat** is a device that has two different metal strips welded together—a "bimetallic" strip. Each metal expands and contracts by a different amount. *Figure 15-17* shows the bimetallic strip (copper and steel) in a thermostat. When the bimetallic strip is heated, the copper part expands more than the steel part. Thus, the strip bends, causing it to open up a bit. This moving pulls the strip away from a switch or contact that controls an appliance, such as a furnace. The furnace shuts off. When the room cools, each metal contracts by a different amount. The strip bends in the other direction and switches the furnace on. This process occurs over and over to control the room's temperature.

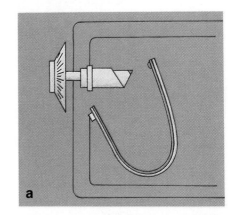

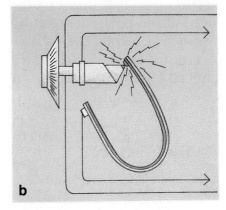

Figure 15-17 A thermostat controls a furnace. The furnace turns off in **a** and turns on in **b**.

Section Review

1. Explain how expansion and contraction happen.
2. How are bridges built to allow for expansion and contraction?
3. How does a thermostat work?

Challenge: What problems could occur if a dentist used a material for fillings that did not expand at the same rate as your teeth?

Careers in Physical Science

Heating and Air Conditioning System Installer

Who makes it cold in summer and hot in winter? A heating and air conditioning system installer lets you change the temperature inside, no matter what the weather is outside.

These installers equip new buildings with heating and cooling systems. The installer learns the path of air flow in a building, then designs a heating or cooling system to match. Installers use their knowledge of convection currents and ventilation requirements in doing their job.

Installers learn their trade in technical school, by apprenticing, or through experience at work.

Graphs of Temperature Changes

Graphs are useful to show relationships between temperature and other variables. In this activity, you will make and interpret graphs that show how temperature varies both with altitude in the atmosphere and with depth in a body of water.

PART A

When you ride in a jet airplane flying at high altitudes, the temperature of the air outside the airplane is not the same as it is at ground level. To see how air temperature changes with altitude, plot the data below on a graph.

Altitude in km	Air temperature in °C
0	10
1	5
2	−1
3	−5
4	−11
5	−16
6	−22
7	−29
8	−36
9	−42
10	−50

After you have drawn your graph, use it to answer the following questions.
1. What is the range of altitudes you plotted?
2. What is the range of temperatures you plotted?
3. What is the temperature at 6.5 km?
4. How are temperature and altitude related?
5. About how many degrees does the temperature change per meter?

Changes in Temperature vs. Depth in a Northern Lake

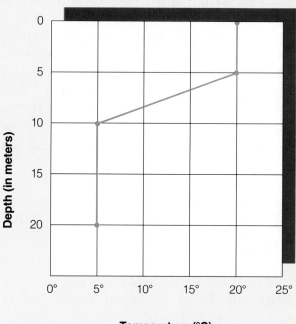

Temperature (°C)

PART B

Look at the graph shown above. Use it to answer the following questions.

Note that the vertical scale shows depth of a lake in meters. The surface of the lake (0 meters) is represented at the top of the scale.
1. What relationship does the graph show?
2. What is the temperature of the water from the surface to 5 meters in depth?
3. How does the water temperature change between 5 and 10 meters below the surface?
4. Describe the temperature of the lake below 10 meters in depth.
5. Why do you think the graph was made with 0 meters at the top of the graph?

Summary

15-1 Defining Heat and Temperature

A. The kinetic theory of matter states that tiny particles make up matter, and they are constantly in motion.

B. Temperature is a measure of the average kinetic energy of the particles of matter. Heat is the amount of energy transferred from one material or substance to another.

15-2 Detecting Heat and Temperature

A. Temperature can be measured with a thermometer or optical pyrometer. On the Celsius scale, water boils at 100° and ice melts at 0°.

B. Heat can be measured with a calorimeter. Heat is measured in joules. Heat capacity is a material's ability to take in and give off heat.

15-3 Producing Heat

A. A heat source is anything that gives off heat. Heat moves from regions of higher temperature toward regions of lower temperature.

B. Chemical energy, electrical energy, and mechanical energy are important sources of heat.

15-4 Energy Transfer

A. Conduction is heating by contact between a source and an object.

B. Convection is heating by movement of large masses of liquid or gas.

C. Radiation is heating by energy traveling through space in a special kind of wave.

15-5 Expansion and Contraction

A. Changes in speed of a material's particles cause expansion and contraction. Most substances expand when heated and contract when cooled.

B. Roads, buildings, and bridges must be built to allow for thermal expansion and contraction. Power and telephone lines must be strung to allow for expansion and contraction.

C. Thermometers use the thermal expansion and contraction of a liquid to register temperature. Thermostats use expansion and contraction to control temperature on appliances.

Vocabulary

For each of the following terms, write a sentence that uses the term correctly.

calorimeter	expansion	radiation
conduction	heat	specific heat
conductor	heat source	temperature
contraction	insulator	thermogram
convection	kinetic theory of matter	thermometer
convection current	optical pyrometer	thermostat

Check Your Knowledge

Part I: Matching Match the definition in Column I with the correct term in Column II.

Column I
1. used to measure temperature
2. measure of the average kinetic energy of particles of matter
3. amount of energy transferred from one object or place to another
4. transfer of energy as waves
5. a material's ability to take in or give off heat
6. an increase in the size of an object
7. energy transfer by contact between particles
8. energy transfer by the movement of a large mass of liquid or gas
9. object or material that prevents conduction
10. the particles of all matter are in constant motion

Column II
a. calorimeter
b. conduction
c. convection
d. expansion
e. heat
f. insulator
g. kinetic theory
h. radiation
i. specific heat
j. temperature
k. thermometer

Part II: Multiple Choice Choose the letter of the best answer.
11. Most of our heat comes from (a) electricity. (b) chemical energy. (c) the sun. (d) mechanical energy.
12. A thermostat uses the property of (a) radiation. (b) contraction. (c) color. (d) potential energy.
13. An optical pyrometer is most likely to be used with (a) very hot objects. (b) very cold objects. (c) objects at room temperature. (d) objects that are absorbing radiant energy.
14. As an object's temperature decreases, its particles (a) stop moving. (b) gain kinetic energy. (c) slow down. (d) hit other particles harder.
15. Which color indicates the coolest temperature on a thermogram? (a) blue (b) yellow (c) orange (d) red
16. Energy from the sun reaches us through (a) radiation. (b) convection. (c) conduction. (d) contraction.
17. Heat always moves from places of high temperature to places (a) of higher temperature. (b) of lower temperature. (c) with the same temperature. (d) with more internal energy.
18. The unit used to measure heat is the (a) newton. (b) watt. (c) meter. (d) joule.
19. On the Celsius temperature scale, the freezing point of water is (a) 32°. (b) 0°. (c) 100°. (d) −273.15°.

Part III: Completion Write the word or words that complete the sentence correctly.
20. The device used for measuring heat is the ＿＿＿.
21. A picture of an object made by measuring the amount of infrared energy it gives off is a ＿＿＿.
22. Wool is a good insulator and a poor ＿＿＿.
23. Anything that gives off heat is a ＿＿＿ ＿＿＿.
24. During the winter, telephone wires become shorter because they ＿＿＿.

Check Your Understanding

1. How does heating affect the molecules in a substance?
2. When you find the temperature of a material, what are you measuring?
3. What happens when two substances at different temperatures are combined?
4. Does a hot object always have more heat than a cold object? Explain.
5. Does the temperature of an object depend on its mass? Explain.
6. Why are concrete roads made in short sections?
7. Is an electric light bulb a source of heat, light, or both? Explain your answer.
8. Why does a bimetallic strip bend when it is heated?
9. How is a thermostat used to regulate the temperature of the oven on a kitchen stove?
10. Why does ice float in water?

 Apply Your Knowledge

1. To ventilate a room properly, you should open its windows at both the top and bottom. Explain why.
2. Use the kinetic theory to explain how the end of a spoon you are holding becomes hot when the other end is in a pot of boiling water.
3. In grocery stores, frozen foods are often kept in freezers with open tops. Why are the frozen foods not thawed quickly by the warm air of the store?
4. Why would automobile tires appear slightly deflated the morning after a cool night, even though the tires were fully inflated the previous warm afternoon?
5. Use the kinetic theory to explain why a thin, helium-filled, rubber balloon might explode if left in the hot sun.
6. Describe a situation in which an ice cube could be a heat source.

 Extend Your Knowledge

Research/Projects
1. Conduct an experiment on the effects of insulation. Fill a large metal can with hot water and find the best way to keep the water hot without adding more heat.
2. Experiment to discover whether equal volumes of hot and cold water have the same weight.

Readings
Santrey, Laurence. *Heat.* Troll, 1985. An introduction to thermodynamics that includes thermometers, heat, absolute zero, and heat transfer.
Whyman, Kathryn. *Heat and Energy.* Gloucester, 1986. Presents a basic introduction to heat and energy.

CHAPTER 16
Energy Resources

People need energy to keep them warm and to give them light. Much of this energy comes from the sun every day. Some of this energy came from the sun long ago. Some is released in power plants from atoms. All energy sources have advantages and disadvantages. In this chapter you will learn how you can use energy wisely.

Organizing Your Study Skills The outline below will help you see how the chapter is organized and what you should learn as you read.

I. **Section 16-1: Energy in Your Life**
   A. How do you use energy in your daily life?
   B. How is electrical energy produced?

II. **Section 16-2: Fossil Fuels**
   A. Why are fossil fuels important?
   B. What problems are caused by using fossil fuels?
   C. What problems are caused by using synthetic fossil fuels?

III. **Section 16-3: More Energy Sources**
   A. How is energy released from the atomic nucleus?
   B. What are some problems caused by using nuclear energy?
   C. What is a renewable energy source?
   D. What are some disadvantages of renewable energy sources?

IV. **Section 16-4: Making Decisions About Energy Sources**
   A. How can people choose an energy source?
   B. How can people use energy more wisely?

After completing this section you will be able to

A. Explain how you use energy in your daily life.

B. Describe how electrical energy is produced.

Explore!

An average person needs about 2000 kilocalories of food energy each day to survive. Find out how much food energy each American took in on an average day last year. Figure out how many times more that number is than the 2000 kilocalories needed to survive.

Figure 16-1 The 1965 New York City blackout

16-1 Energy in Your Life

Energy Has Many Uses

Think of all the ways you use energy. Energy warms your home in winter or cools it in summer. Energy supplies heat for warm showers and washing machines. Stoves, refrigerators, and freezers use energy.

Office buildings and factories depend on energy too. Like your home, these buildings need heating, cooling, and lighting. Office machines, such as typewriters, calculators, and computers, use energy. Factories need energy to make new products for your use.

Without realizing it, people use large amounts of energy each day. Fuels supply the energy needed by buses, trains, trucks, and airplanes. People also use energy to grow and ship food.

Electricity is a familiar form of energy. Every time you turn on a radio or flip a light switch, you use electrical energy. Appliances, such as irons, toasters, televisions, and hair dryers, use electrical energy.

If you multiply the amount of energy you use by the number of people in your neighborhood, you can imagine how much energy people use. For example, in 1986, 240 million Americans used more energy for air conditioning than over 1 billion Chinese used to supply all their energy needs.

Just think what would happen if we ever ran out of energy! A city without electrical energy might look like the picture. The photograph shows New York City during a blackout in 1965.

The electricity people use is not a source of energy. Electricity is, rather, a convenient way to move energy around. Electricity does not come from mines, as coal and uranium do, or from wells, as oil and natural gas do. People must use energy sources to make electricity.

Making Electrical Energy

Coal, oil, uranium, heat from inside the earth, and falling water are energy sources that can be used to make electricity. *Figure 16-2* shows how electricity is carried to your home. Often energy from a source in the power plant heats water. The hot water or steam turns fanlike blades in a turbine. The spinning blades turn a generator that produces electric current.

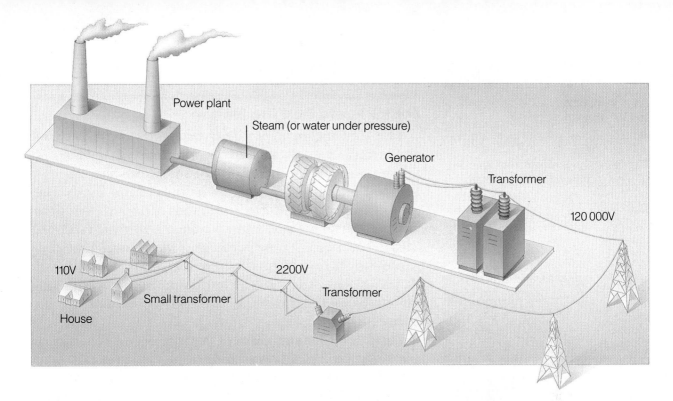

Figure 16-2 How electrical energy is transmitted from the electric-generating plant to your home

Electrical power sometimes must be transmitted many hundreds or even thousands of kilometers from generating stations to homes and businesses. Electric energy travels over power lines at high voltage in order to lose as little energy as possible. A device called a transformer boosts the voltage at the generating station. These high voltages would ruin the appliances you use at home. Therefore, large transformers near every big city reduce the high voltage. The electricity still must travel to houses, offices, and factories, so the voltage is not lowered all the way to the 110 volts you use at home. Another transformer placed near your house lowers the voltage to 110 volts.

Electrical energy has many advantages over other forms of energy. At the flip of a switch, electricity is ready to work. Using electricity, however, has some problems. In the process of making electricity, energy is lost. Only one-third or less of the energy stored in coal, oil, or uranium is changed into electricity. At least two-thirds is lost as "waste energy" in the generating plant.

Applying Science

Near a high-voltage power line you can hear humming noises. Engineers test copper and aluminum wire to find ways to make high-voltage power lines quieter.

Section Review

1. List eight ways that you use electricity.
2. Explain why electricity is not an energy source.

Challenge: Explain how your life would be affected if you had to live for a week without electricity.

After completing this section you will be able to

A. Explain why fossil fuels are important.
B. Describe the problems caused by using conventional fossil fuels.
C. Explain what problems are caused by using synthetic fossil fuels.

16-2 Fossil Fuels

Fossil Fuels Run the Nation

The drawing in *Figure 16-3* resembles the habitat of plants and animals that lived hundreds of millions of years ago. When these organisms were alive, they trapped energy from the sun as they made food. The organisms died and their remains decayed. As time passed, the plant and animal remains formed coal, oil, and natural gas. These fuels are called **fossil fuels** because they formed from the remains of fossil organisms. Burning fossil fuels releases the energy organisms obtained from the sun long ago. So fossil fuels are an indirect form of energy from the sun.

Fossil fuels take millions of years to form. When people use these resources to heat homes, to run cars, and to make fibers, plastics, and electricity, they are reducing the supply of fossil fuels. Most fossil fuels starting to form now will not be ready to use for hundreds of millions of years.

The graph shows energy sources used in the United States in 1986. About 66% of energy needs in the United States were supplied by fossil fuels.

Coal supplied 17% of the energy, natural gas supplied 17%, and oil supplied 32%. In that year, fossil fuels also provided the energy needed to produce 73% of the electricity generated in the United States.

Figure 16-3 A forest in ancient times

Disadvantages of Using Conventional Fossil Fuels

Coal, oil, and natural gas are conventional fossil fuels. Using conventional fossil fuels has both advantages and disadvantages. All other sources of energy also have both advantages and disadvantages.

A major drawback to relying heavily on fossil fuels for all our energy needs is that the world's supply of fossil fuels is steadily dwindling. Fossil fuels are called **nonrenewable energy resources,** because they cannot be replaced quickly once they are used up.

No one knows for sure when we will run out of fossil fuels. Some experts say 80% of the world's known oil reserves will be gone by the year 2013. If people continue to use natural gas at today's rates, the world's known reserves could be gone by 2033. The world has more coal than any other fossil fuel.

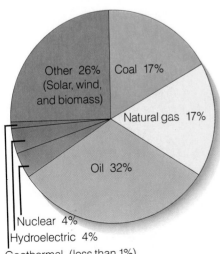

Figure 16-4 U.S. energy use for 1986 (to the nearest whole %)

If people continue to use coal at the same rate as today, the world's known coal reserves should last only until 2259. If people use energy at increasing rates, as they always have over a long term, the reserves of fossil fuels will be exhausted even faster.

Other problems occur with the use of fossil fuels. When they burn, fossil fuels release harmful waste products—or **pollutants**—into the air. These pollutants include compounds of oxygen joined with nitrogen and sulfur, carbon monoxide, and small particles. The smog in *Figure 16-5* was caused by sulfur oxides and particles. In addition, air pollutants can damage buildings. Air pollutants also can harm plant and animal life. Pollutants, for instance, can trigger health problems such as pneumonia, emphysema, and other lung illnesses. Burning fossil fuels also releases carbon dioxide, which might change the earth's climate.

Each type of fossil fuel has its own advantages and disadvantages. For example, since the first oil well was drilled in 1869, oil has been a popular fuel. It can be easily transported from one nation to another or within one nation. The energy released by burning oil can be used to move vehicles or to heat water and buildings. But burning oil causes air pollution.

Explore!

Count the number of cars in a parking lot near you. Suppose each car uses an average of 4 liters of gasoline every day for one year. How much gasoline will all these cars use in one year? Find out how many barrels of oil were needed to produce this much gasoline.

Figure 16-5 Chemical reactions between sulfur oxides and particles in the air produce smog. Sunlight acts as a catalyst in this reaction.

In addition, using oil can cause water pollution. Occasionally, a blowout takes place at oil wells drilled offshore. Millions of liters of oil can end up in the ocean. Tankers carrying oil at sea sometimes have accidents, which also can cause millions of liters of oil to pollute the ocean. Many sea birds die when the oil coats their bodies. Fish take in chemicals in the oil and become unfit for eating. It can take many years for an area to recover from the effects of an oil spill.

Natural gas burns more cleanly than other fossil fuels. It does, however, release carbon dioxide and so can help change the earth's climate. While natural gas is easy to transport in pipelines within one nation, it is not easy to transport over water. Often it is changed into liquid form as liquefied natural gas (LNG). However, LNG is dangerous to transport because it is very explosive.

Coal cannot be burned to power cars and trucks. But burning coal is the cheapest way to produce electricity in the United States. More than one-third of the coal in the United States contains large amounts of sulfur.

Figure 16-6 The effects of strip mining

Burning coal with a high sulfur content produces the most air pollution of any fossil fuel. The sulfurous gases produced by burning coal dissolve in rain or snow, forming sulfuric acid, which falls as acid rain. Acid rain can harm plants and animals and damage buildings and statues. Since 1982, coal-burning power plants in the United States have been required to control sulfur dioxide pollution. All ways of doing this are expensive.

Mining coal also creates serious problems. When coal is near the surface, it can be strip-mined. But, as the picture shows, strip-mining disrupts large amounts of land. Wastes from strip mines often wash into streams and pollute them. As coal deposits near the surface are exhausted, deeper mines must be dug. They cost more to operate than shallower mines. Shaft mining is also more dangerous. Consumers of coal-generated electricity will eventually have to pay for the additional costs.

Problems with Synthetic Fossil Fuels

Synthetic oil and gas can be made by processing coal and certain types of rock and sand. These unconventional fossil fuels are called **synfuels**. Many disadvantages must be overcome before synfuels can become a major energy source.

A type of rock called oil shale can be processed to yield a heavy oil. The world's largest deposits of oil shale are in the United States, in Colorado, Utah, and Wyoming. Canada's Alberta province has the world's largest deposit of tar sands. The sands can also be processed to yield a heavy oil.

Processing oil shale and tar sands requires a great deal of water. But water is a scarce resource in many places, particularly in the states rich in oil shale. After the oil is removed from oil shale, huge piles of waste shale are left as litter on the land. Processing tar sands has an additional problem. The sand quickly wears out machines used in the process, such as the ones in the picture. Producing oil from oil shale and tar sands has proven so expensive that many synfuel projects that were begun in the late 1970s were abandoned by the mid-1980s.

Synfuels produced from coal include synthetic natural gas, gasoline, and fuel oil. In the process of making synfuels from coal, about 30 to 40 percent of the energy content of the coal is lost. Thus, producing coal-based synfuels will cause the supply of coal to run out faster.

Applying Science

One way of reducing the sulfur content of coal is through the process of fluidized-bed combustion. This process involves burning crushed coal in a bed of limestone. Since the limestone traps sulfur from the coal, less sulfur dioxide forms. Water is circulated through the limestone bed in metal coils. The heat from the burning coal boils water to produce steam. The steam can then be used to generate electricity.

Figure 16-7 Equipment used to process tar sands

Processing coal to produce these synfuels also creates unwanted solid wastes, including harmful metal compounds. The processing requires not only large quantities of water, but also a lot of hydrogen, which is expensive to produce. Fuels made from coal contain a lot of sulfur and ash. These fuels must be purified to reduce the pollution they cause. Purifying the fuels is an expensive process.

Even if the expense of making synfuels can be reduced, two major problems remain. First, processing these synfuels releases air pollutants. Second, burning them produces carbon dioxide, which could change the earth's climate. Burning synfuels extracted from coal actually produces more carbon dioxide per ton than burning the coal itself does.

Section Review

1. How are fossil fuels important in your life?
2. List three problems involved in using conventional fossil fuels.
3. List three problems of using synthetic fossil fuels.

Challenge: How could acid rain damage forests and lakes that are hundreds of kilometers from the nearest coal-burning power plant?

Careers in Physical Science

Petroleum Engineer

When drillers strike oil, it does not come gushing out of the ground. In fact, very little oil comes up on its own. Petroleum engineers design ways to bring the sluggish oil up from below.

Petroleum engineers work to increase oil recovery. They design equipment that forces petroleum out of the earth. The engineers might inject water or chemicals into a well to move the oil, or they might use suction to vacuum up the oil. Engineers test their plans in the oil field. If the machines work, more fuel is available for everyone.

Petroleum engineers spend four years in college, where they learn about geology, chemistry, oil rigs, and machines.

16-3 More Energy Sources

After completing this section you will be able to
A. Describe how energy can be obtained from the atomic nucleus.
B. List some problems involved with the use of nuclear energy.
C. Explain what a renewable energy source is.
D. Describe some disadvantages of renewable energy sources.

Energy from the Atomic Nucleus

The nucleus of an atom contains a large amount of energy. One way of obtaining this energy is through nuclear fission. During fission, the nucleus of a heavy atom, such as uranium or plutonium, is split apart. The splitting releases a large amount of energy. In 1986, 17% of the electricity used in the United States came from fission power plants. Other countries rely more heavily on fission for their supplies of electricity.

Figure 16-8 shows the main parts of a **nuclear reactor**. The core holds the uranium that will create heat by undergoing fission. The control rods control the chain reaction that can take place once nuclear fission begins. The control rods are made of elements like boron or cadmium that can absorb some of the free neutrons that fission produces. Once these neutrons are captured, they cannot cause other nuclei to undergo fission. In this way, the chain reaction in a nuclear reactor is kept steady. The reactor vessel holds the water that is heated to make steam. The vessel also holds all other reactor parts.

In the future, power plants might be able to obtain energy from the nucleus by means of another method. During nuclear fusion, the nuclei of light atoms, such as hydrogen and helium, combine and, in the process, release large amounts of energy.

Figure 16-8 Heat generated by the fission reaction in a nuclear reactor is used to change water to steam. The steam then turns the turbine blades in a generator, producing electricity.

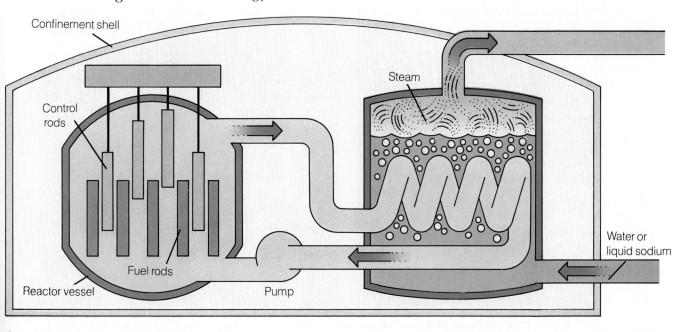

Confinement shell

Control rods

Steam

Fuel rods

Reactor vessel

Pump

Water or liquid sodium

Fusion uses a cheap raw material—water—from which deuterium is removed. However, fusion energy cannot yet be produced practically. No container can hold a gas at the high temperatures required for fusion to occur. Some scientists are using magnetism to hold the hot gas in place. One model of a nuclear fusion reactor that uses magnetism to hold the hot gas is a doughnut-shaped machine. Another method used by scientists to produce fusion reactions involves shooting intense laser and particle beams at hydrogen pellets.

Disadvantages of Nuclear Energy

Fission power plants produce no carbon dioxide to threaten the earth's climate and they produce little air pollution. But like all other energy sources, nuclear fission has disadvantages.

First, the uranium used as fuel is a nonrenewable resource. The world's supply of usable uranium should last for at least 100 years. By then, scientists hope to have fusion energy sources. Some scientists believe that breeder reactors can help overcome the problem of dwindling supplies of fuel. Breeder reactors actually produce more nuclear fuel than they use. They do this by changing a form of uranium that is not suitable for fission into a form of plutonium that is suitable for fission. Other scientists and citizens oppose breeder reactors. They fear the plutonium they produce might be used illegally to make explosive devices.

Figure 16-9 The satellite pictures show the cooling pond at the Chernobyl Nuclear Power Plant before (**a**) and after (**b**) an accident in April, 1986.

Second, fission power plants cause **thermal pollution** by releasing heated water into rivers. All electric power plants require a lot of water for cooling, regardless of the kind of energy used to run the plant. When the heated water is returned to rivers or lakes, the heat can harm the fish and other life in the water.

A third problem with the use of fission is the storage of radioactive wastes. The wastes are a hazard not only to living things today but also to future generations. Scientists are trying to devise safe methods for storing these wastes. Even if we stopped using fission as an energy source, safe storage of nuclear wastes would continue to be a problem.

A fourth problem with fission is the threat of major nuclear accidents. A major accident took place in 1986, at a fission reactor in Chernobyl in the Soviet Union. Many people were killed or injured. The pictures in *Figure 16-9* were taken with a special camera that shows cooler regions as dark patches. The pictures compare the area around the Chernobyl nuclear power plant both before and after an accident. Scientists and engineers are trying to make fission plants safer based on what they learned at Chernobyl.

If fusion reactors are ever built, they would use an energy source that does not run out—the deuterium in water. But certain metals needed for the walls of fusion reactors are nonrenewable. Fusion reactors would produce no carbon dioxide and should not pollute air or water. Although they produce smaller amounts of radioactive wastes than fission plants, those wastes would still require safe storage for thousands of years.

Renewable Energy Sources

Renewable energy resources are those that either do not run out or can be replaced in a few years. The energy sources described below are all renewable.

For centuries, people have used the energy of falling water to do work. The water turns a turbine that runs a generator. Producing electricity by water power is called **hydroelectric power**. In Washington, Oregon, and California, hydroelectric plants produce one-third of the electricity. A large hydroelectric plant is at the base of Hoover Dam, shown in *Figure 16-10*. Hydroelectric power has long been a major way of getting energy.

Have You Heard?

Some scientists think that hydrogen gas will prove to be a useful fuel when oil and natural gas run out. Since hydrogen gas does not occur naturally in useful amounts, methods will have to be developed to produce it inexpensively, without using too much energy, and without harming the environment.

Figure 16-10 Hoover Dam at Lake Mead, near Las Vegas, Nevada

Figure 16-11 This house has solar collectors built into the roof.

The sun is responsible for the energy in falling water. Energy from the sun drives the water cycle. In the water cycle, water evaporates from the earth's surface and falls again as rain. Rivers carry excess water from land to oceans. Most hydroelectric-power plants, which generally include dams, are built along river banks.

Today, people also can use solar energy more directly, though these uses are still less important than hydroelectric power. Solar energy will be available long after other energy sources have been used up. The **solar collectors** on the roof of the house in *Figure 16-11* heat water that circulates through them. The hot water can be used for cooking, washing, and heating the house. In addition, satellites use **solar cells**, which are devices that change sunlight into electricity.

The sun also supplies energy through living materials and wind. **Biomass** is any living material that can be burned as fuel. Wood is probably the best known and most widely used form of biomass. Wood-burning stoves heat many homes in the Northeast. Other forms of biomass include some forms of garbage, farm wastes, sugar cane, and other plants.

Wind power is an old energy source. The first windmills were built in Persia in the sixth century. *Figure 16-12* shows modern windmills. In regions where the wind blows regularly, windmills can be an important energy source.

The oceans are also a possible energy source. In a few bays, very high tides produce hydroelectric power. The dam across the Rance River in France has produced energy in this way since 1968. Even the motion of waves can produce energy. The temperatue differences between layers of sea water might one day produce energy. These methods, too, depend on the sun as the basic source of energy.

The earth itself is another promising energy source. Radioactive elements inside the earth produce heat as they decay. This energy from radioactive elements is known as **geothermal energy**. At The Geysers, California, hot water from geysers has been used to produce electricity for over fifteen years. Because Iceland is a volcanic island, its people use geothermal energy to produce heat and electricity. Drilling deeply enough might make it possible to use geothermal energy anywhere, not just in places where hot springs and geysers are found.

Disadvantages of Renewable Energy

Even renewable energy sources have some disadvantages. For instance, in our country, most river sites that are suitable for hydroelectric power already have been developed. Water falling over a dam eventually drops enough silt to fill the dam's reservoirs. Thus, hydroelectric-power dams have useful lifetimes of from 30 to 300 years. Damming rivers to create hydroelectric power limits recreation, such as fishing, and takes rivers out of their wild state.

A major disadvantage of solar energy is the expense involved in converting sunlight to electricity. Another problem with solar energy is storage. Even if solar cells become affordable, people will still need ways to store the electricity they generate for use at night and on cloudy days.

Using biomass produces pollutants similar to those produced by burning fossil fuels. In addition, cutting down trees for fuel can speed the erosion of land.

Wind power can be used only in places with sufficient winds. Even in those places, wind-produced electricity must be stored for use when the wind dies down. Also, the spinning blades on today's large windmills are noisy and disrupt television reception.

Few places are suitable for tidal, wave, or ocean-temperature power plants. Problems at existing plants include the corrosion of metal machinery by seawater and damage caused by severe storms. Furthermore, many people are concerned about the effect of the power plants on sea life.

The technology for deep drilling to tap geothermal energy is not yet fully developed. Some possible disadvantages of geothermal plants are the contamination of ground water and the escape of radioactive materials or harmful odors.

Explore!

Find out three advantages and three disadvantages of using hydrogen gas as a fuel.

Figure 16-12 Wind-powered turbines near Mohave, California

Section Review

1. List two advantages of using nuclear energy.
2. List two disadvantages of using nuclear energy.
3. Describe four renewable energy sources.
4. What are disadvantages of using solar energy?

Challenge: Should we consider energy problems today even if fossil fuels will last another 10 000 years? Explain your answer.

Activity 16-1

Light Energy Collector

Purpose

To observe how solar energy can be collected

Materials

- thermometer
- white paper
- black construction paper
- desk lamp with incandescent bulb
- light gray or brown, thin cardboard, 23 cm × 14 cm
- stiff, clear plastic, 20 cm × 12 cm
- watch or timer with second hand
- tape
- scissors
- book
- metric ruler

Procedure and Observations

PART A

1. Cut and fold the cardboard and tape one corner, as in **a.**

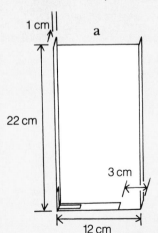

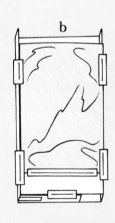

2. Cut a piece of white paper 12 cm × 3 cm. Tape the paper to one end of the plastic. Tape the plastic to the cardboard, as in **b.** You now have a heat collector.

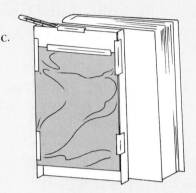

c.

3. Stand a book on edge. Lean the collector against the book with the cardboard side to the book.
4. Place the lamp 20 cm in front of the plastic. Aim the lamp directly at the plastic. Turn on the lamp.
5. To measure the temperature of the air entering the collector, place the thermometer at the bottom of the collector's opening.
6. Wait three minutes. Record the temperature.
7. Cut a piece of white paper 20 cm × 11 cm. Slide the sheet into the collector.
8. Place the thermometer in the top of the collector, as in **c.**
9. Repeat step 6.
10. Repeat steps 7-9, but use the black paper.

PART B

1. Turn the collector until the light hits it at an angle.
2. Repeat Part A, step 6.

Analysis and Conclusions

1. Compare the results from the two colors of paper and the two angles. Explain any difference in temperature.
2. How would you redesign your collector to gather the most light energy?

16-4 Making Decisions About Energy Sources

Objectives

After completing this section you will be able to

A. Describe some ways to choose an energy source.
B. List ways people can use energy sources more wisely.

Choosing Among Energy Sources

Each energy source has advantages and disadvantages. Deciding which energy source to use has been a problem for Americans only for the last fifteen years or so. For a century, people thought they had all the coal, oil, and natural gas they needed. Now they know that the fossil fuel supply eventually will be exhausted. The table in *Figure 16-13* predicts how people might be using energy supplies by the year 2000.

Making decisions about energy sources is not easy. Many things must be considered, including expense and the effect on the environment. Even the matter of expense is not simple. Sometimes a homeowner might pay what seems like a lot of money to start with, but might end up saving money in the end. For example, installing solar collectors on the roof is not cheap. But doing so may save the homeowner money in hot water bills. After a period of a few years, the savings may be more than the cost of installing the solar collectors.

For several years beginning in the mid-1970s, the price of oil was very high. As oil prices went up, people began to use energy sources that once seemed too expensive or inconvenient. Many homeowners in the Northeast bought wood-burning stoves. Several companies began to develop synfuels, even though the cost of making them is very high. When the price of oil went down again, however, many companies abandoned their synfuel projects. Some people feel that decision was unwise. They compare it to not fixing the roof of your house because it has stopped raining.

On the other hand, the decision of homeowners who continue burning wood is not necessarily a wise decision either. Wood smoke has polluted the air in many towns and cities. Wood stoves have also caused fires and other accidents. Some have contributed to indoor air pollution. Some places, including the city of Denver, now restrict or limit the use of wood stoves.

When people consider the effect of an energy source on the environment, it sometimes seems like most fuels cause problems.

Source	% in 1983	% in 2000
Coal	21	28
Oil	42	20
Natural gas	25	19
Nuclear	3.5	8
Hydro	5	5
Solar, wind, geothermal	—	9
Biomass (wood & crop wastes)	3.5	11

Figure 16-13 Projected energy use for the year 2000, based on energy use data from 1983

Figure 16-14 Oil spills have severe effects on the environment. As the oil drifted into shallow water, workers swept it up onto the beach where it could be removed. Many birds, such as the cormorant, died when their feathers became coated with oil.

Nuclear power plants have wastes that must be stored in ways to keep them from harming people now and in the future. Power plants that burn coal release harmful pollutants into the air. The carbon dioxide they give off may change the earth's climate so drastically that life will be affected for centuries. If people use oil, spills can harm the environment. The pictures show some effects of the Cadiz oil spill off the coast of Brittany in March, 1978. Even ten years later, sea life in the area still had not returned to normal.

People also need to consider location when deciding which energy source to use. For example, because the Northwest has many rivers, hydroelectric power is a good energy source there. Wind might be a better energy source in Oklahoma, which has strong winds. The Southwest could use solar energy because the sun's rays are most directly overhead and the sky is clear most of the year there.

People must consider, too, how they want to use energy. For example, solar energy can provide heat and hot water for private homes. But it is generally too expensive to generate electricity with solar energy for a whole community.

People do not have to depend on just one source of energy. They can use a combination of energy sources to meet their energy needs. The combination of energy sources should provide the most energy with the fewest disadvantages.

Saving Energy

Conservation means saving or preserving. When people talk about energy conservation, they mean ways of saving energy. For a long time, Americans used energy carelessly. But since the mid-1970s, more and more Americans have tried to conserve energy.

When people build new homes, many of them use design features that help save energy. *Figure 16-15* shows a home that has many such energy-saving features.

Figure 16-15 Today, building a home is a challenge, because we must build with energy in mind. The picture shows how to build a house that saves energy.

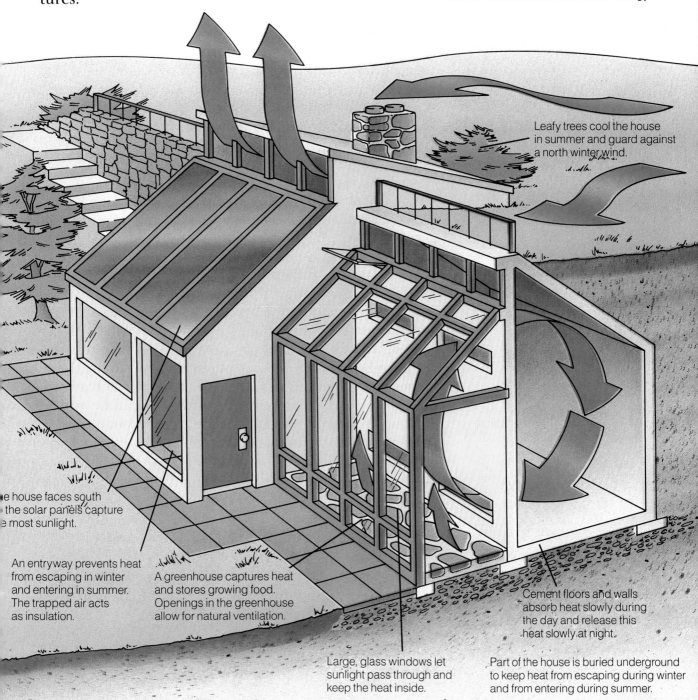

Leafy trees cool the house in summer and guard against a north winter wind.

The house faces south so the solar panels capture the most sunlight.

An entryway prevents heat from escaping in winter and entering in summer. The trapped air acts as insulation.

A greenhouse captures heat and stores growing food. Openings in the greenhouse allow for natural ventilation.

Cement floors and walls absorb heat slowly during the day and release this heat slowly at night.

Large, glass windows let sunlight pass through and keep the heat inside.

Part of the house is buried underground to keep heat from escaping during winter and from entering during summer.

Figure 16-16 Closing the blinds conserves the energy needed to run either furnaces or air conditioners.

When people remodel older homes, they often try to make better use of solar energy. Even without remodeling, homeowners can make their homes more energy efficient. Putting up storm doors and storm windows, using weather stripping, and adding insulation in the attic all help.

Businesses also conserve energy. Some factories use "waste heat" to warm buildings. Some new office buildings also use heat given off by lights and people. Computers control room temperatures by adjusting fans and vents to move warm and cool air where it is needed.

You can help conserve energy in many ways. Just closing the curtains on winter nights, as in the picture, helps keep heat in. Opening the curtains on winter days lets sunlight in. Using a 100-watt bulb for twenty hours requires a coal-powered generating plant to burn a kilogram of coal. If you remember to turn off lights, televisions, and stereos when you are not using them, you save energy and money. If you walk or ride a bicycle instead of using a car, you also save energy. When you use a car, carpooling with friends saves energy.

Conservation has its own disadvantages, just as each energy source has. When homeowners plug up all the possible air leaks in their homes to save on heating costs, they also trap different pollutants inside. In some places, the rocks on which homes are built release small amounts of radon, a radioactive gas. Household cleaners contain chemicals that give off vapors. Attached garages, wood stoves, and gas stoves are possible sources of harmful gases. When outside air does not sweep these gases and chemicals out, they can build up to harmful levels inside the home. Homeowners should be aware of this problem as they plan ways to conserve energy.

If people use energy sources wisely, the energy supplies will last longer. Then we will have more time to develop new energy sources for the future.

Section Review

1. What four factors should people consider when choosing energy sources?
2. How can conservation reduce our energy problem?

Challenge: Suppose it costs $1500 to install solar collectors on the roof of a house, and the homeowner's heating bills go down an average of $30 a month after installing them. How long does it take for the savings to equal the cost of installation?

Insulation

Purpose

To observe how insulating materials and weather stripping work

Materials

- small drinking glass
- pitcher of water at room temperature
- "fish tank" thermometer
- large ice chest
- corrugated cardboard box, just large enough to hold the water glass
- several sealed plastic bags full of ice
- bag of cotton balls
- scissors
- heavy tape
- clock or watch

Procedure and Observations

PART A

1. Fill the glass with water from the pitcher. Measure and record the water's temperature.
2. Leave the thermometer in the glass. Place the glass in the ice chest. Pack plastic bags containing ice around the glass. Check and record water temperature after 5 minutes and 10 minutes.
3. Empty the glass and let it stand at room temperature.
4. Cover the bottom of the cardboard box with a layer of cotton balls.
5. Refill the glass with water from the pitcher. Place the glass on top of the layer of cotton balls. Then use cotton balls to fill in the empty space between the glass and the sides of the box.
6. Place the thermometer in the glass and record the water temperature.
7. Repeat steps 2 and 3.

PART B

1. Remove the cotton balls from the box. Fill the glass with water from the pitcher. Place the glass in the box.
2. Put some tape over the top of the box, leaving an opening just large enough for the thermometer, as shown.
3. Place the thermometer in the glass. Place the box in the ice chest and pack the plastic bags of ice around the box. Check the water temperature every 3 minutes for 9 minutes. Record the temperatures.
4. Carefully remove the tape from the top of the box and remove the glass. Empty the glass and refill it with water from the pitcher.
5. In the middle of each of the box's four sides, cut a slot about 0.3 cm wide.
6. Repeat steps 2 and 3.

Analysis and Conclusions

1. Compare how quickly the water temperature fell in Part A before you put it in the box with cotton balls and after.
2. What do your results tell you about insulation?
3. Compare how quickly the water temperature fell before and after you removed the cotton balls from the box.
4. What do these results tell you about insulation?
5. Compare how quickly the water temperature fell in Part B before and after cutting the slots in the box.
6. What do your results tell you about the problems of leaving cracks unfilled with weather stripping or caulking?

Distinguishing Fact from Opinion

Issues concerning energy resources make the news every day. If you read about these issues, you will probably come across conflicting information. How can you figure out if the information is correct or incorrect? One skill that can help you evaluate what you read is distinguishing fact from opinion.

Solar Power: A New Star Rises

From the bright lights of Austin, Texas, to a remote well on the dry plains of Bolivia, solar power has been making an impact. Austin's new electricity-generating solar panels and Bolivia's advanced water-pumping system both rely on thin films of silicon to convert light energy into electric current. The costs of manufacturing this sun-sensitive material has dropped dramatically in the last few years. This has brought down the cost of generating electricity from solar power. Costs are further reduced because solar energy does not require complex machinery that is difficult to maintain. Most important, however, solar power takes advantage of an energy source that is virtually limitless, the sun.

Nevertheless, generating electricity from solar power does have some slight disadvantages. For example, in the United States and other developed regions of the world, solar-generated electricity is currently at least three times as expensive as electricity generated from conventional power plants. Even if new manufacturing techniques further reduce the cost of making solar panels, the panels must be set up on large tracts of flat, open land, which may be very expensive to lease or buy. In less developed regions of the world, however, solar energy is comparatively cost effective. Energy experts expect that in time, the sun will be the main source of power for all electricity needs.

PART A

Read the magazine article below. Then answer the following questions.

1. Use a dictionary to define the term <u>fact.</u> List two facts stated in the article.
2. Define the term <u>opinion.</u> List two opinions the article presents.
3. Define the term <u>bias.</u> Do you think this article is biased? Why or why not?

PART B

Based on information in the article, tell whether each statement is fact or opinion.

1. The use of solar panels to generate electricity has made a huge impact on industries in Texas and Bolivia.
2. The cost of producing thin silicon films for solar panels has dropped recently.
3. Solar panels require little maintenance.
4. In the next few years, the costs of solar panels are likely to come down.
5. Buying or leasing large tracts of flat, open land is one of the costs of producing solar-generated electricity.
6. Solar energy will be the only practical source of electricity for the future.

PART C

After evaluating the information in this article, do you think the advantages of solar-generated electricity outweigh the disadvantages? Support your opinion with facts from the article or from other sources.

✓ Summary

16-1 Energy in Your Life
A. Energy is used daily in so many ways that people frequently overlook it.
B. Electricity is a form of energy produced from many different energy sources.

16-2 Fossil Fuels
A. Most of the energy needs in the United States are supplied by fossil fuels.
B. Fossil fuels are nonrenewable and the supply is dwindling. Fossil fuels release harmful pollutants into the air and release carbon dioxide, which might change the earth's climate. Oil spills cause water pollution.
C. Synfuels are expensive to produce, require large quantities of water, and add to air pollution.

16-3 More Energy Sources
A. Energy can be obtained from the atomic nucleus through fission, which is the splitting of an atomic nucleus into two parts. In the future, energy might be obtained through nuclear fusion, which is the combining of two atomic nuclei to produce a nucleus of greater mass.
B. Fission power plants use a nonrenewable energy source, create thermal pollution, produce dangerous radioactives wastes, and pose the threat of nuclear accidents.
C. Solar energy, hydroelectric power, geothermal energy, wind power, and biomass are renewable resources.
D. Hydroelectric dams have limited lifetimes. Changing solar energy to electricity is expensive.
Biomass use produces air pollution. Wind power and geothermal energy are useful only in certain areas.

16-4 Making Decisions About Energy Sources
A. Location, effect on the environment, and use must be considered when choosing energy sources.
B. Conservation promotes wise energy use and provides time to develop new energy sources.

Vocabulary

For each of the following terms, write a sentence using the term correctly.

biomass	nonrenewable energy	solar cells
conservation	resources	solar collectors
fossil fuels	nuclear reactor	synfuels
geothermal energy	pollutants	thermal pollution
hydroelectric power	renewable energy resources	

✔ Check Your Knowledge

Part I: Matching Match the definition in Column I with the term it defines in Column II.

Column I
1. changes sunlight into electricity
2. unwanted gases and particles that harm the environment
3. energy sources produced by the remains of ancient, buried organisms
4. produced by running or falling water
5. produced from heat within the earth
6. energy source that can be used up
7. made artificially from coal, oil shale, and tar sands
8. living material that is used as a fuel
9. saving energy or using less energy
10. energy source that cannot be used up

Column II
a. biomass
b. conservation
c. fossil fuels
d. geothermal energy
e. hydroelectric power
f. nonrenewable resources
g. pollutants
h. renewable resources
i. solar cells
j. solar collectors
k. synfuels

Part II: Multiple Choice Choose the letter of the best answer.
11. Which of the following is not an energy source? (a) geothemal energy (b) coal (c) electricity (d) nuclear power
12. About how much energy is lost when electricity is made from coal, oil, or uranium? (a) 5% (b) 33% (c) 67% (d) 99%
13. Which of the following is not a fossil fuel? (a) coal (b) oil (c) natural gas (d) uranium
14. The supplies of oil and gas will probably last about (a) a year or two. (b) 25 years. (c) 500 years. (d) 3000 years.
15. Which of the following is a nonrenewable resource? (a) hydroelectric power (b) uranium (c) biomass (d) geothermal energy
16. Which of the following is not a source of nuclear energy? (a) uranium (b) oil (c) hydrogen (d) plutonium
17. In which location are solar panels most effective? (a) Northwest (b) Northeast (c) Southwest (d) Midwest

Part III: Completion Write the word or words that complete the sentence correctly.
18. A good renewable energy source to use in Oklahoma would be _____.
19. When heated water from power plants is returned to rivers or lakes, it causes _____.
20. Because Iceland is a volcanic island, its people can use _____ to produce heat and electricity.
21. Conventional fossil fuels are coal, natural gas, and _____.
22. Coal, oil, uranium, falling water, and geothermal energy are energy sources that can be used to produce _____.

Check Your Understanding

1. Explain how coal-operated power plants, nuclear power plants, and hydroelectric power plants make electricity.
2. What are three major disadvantages to using fossil fuels?
3. Describe two ways that coal can be used as fuel in addition to being burned directly.
4. What are breeder reactors and why are some people opposed to their use?
5. Why would closing down all fission power plants not eliminate the problems of thermal pollution and radioactive waste storage?
6. If hydroelectric power is renewable, why do all hydroelectric power stations have limited lifetimes?
7. Why is it important to consider location before deciding on an energy source?
8. What problem can energy conservation cause?

Apply Your Knowledge

1. What is the difference between electricity and an energy source?
2. Solar energy is easy to get. Why do people use this energy source so little, compared to fossil fuels?
3. You live on a volcanic island in the South Pacific. The island is poor in fossil fuels. Winds blow steadily over the island. Sugar cane is a major crop. Describe at least four options for producing energy for the island.
4. If an energy-efficient air conditioner costs $120 more than another model, but is $30 a year cheaper to run, how many years would it take before your savings equaled the additional cost?

Extend Your Knowledge

Research/Projects

1. Make a list of all the ways your family uses energy. Find out which energy source is used for each one.
2. Visit the plant that makes electricity for your community. Find out some safety procedures used at the plant.
3. Collect newspaper articles about energy questions in your community. Which topics are mentioned most often?
4. Find out if solar energy or wind power is being used anywhere in your community.

Readings

Weart, Spencer. *Nuclear Fear.* Harvard University Press, 1988. Describes people's perceptions of nuclear energy and compares their perceptions with actual situations.

Wilson, Richard. "A Visit to Chernobyl." *Science,* June 26, 1987, pp. 1636–1640. Discusses how the accident happened, consequences of the accident, and whether it could happen elsewhere.

How Will the Greenhouse Effect Change World Climates?

By the middle of the next century the earth's climate may be warmer than it has been for the past 125 000 years. New York City could have a climate like that of Daytona Beach, Florida.

The reason for this global warming trend is an increase in the amount of carbon dioxide in the atmosphere. Carbon dioxide traps heat radiating from the earth in a way similar to glass trapping heat in a greenhouse. The increase in atmospheric carbon dioxide means less heat can escape from the earth's surface. This "greenhouse effect" is causing warmer climates around the world.

The burning of fossil fuels has greatly increased the amount of carbon dioxide in our atmosphere in the past 150 years. The massive clearing of forests throughout the world has also contributed to the global buildup of carbon dioxide. Trees use carbon dioxide to make food; with fewer trees around, more carbon dioxide accumulates in the atmosphere.

Can anything be done to stop the greenhouse effect? Conserving fossil fuels and switching to alternative energy sources may slow the accumulation of carbon dioxide in the air. Reforesting large tracts of treeless land will also effectively reduce the atmospheric carbon dioxide. However, neither of these measures will totally stop the global warming trend.

Because of the greenhouse effect, the earth's average temperature has increased by several degrees in the last century. This has caused the polar ice caps to begin to melt. Some scientists predict that the world's warming trend will cause the oceans to rise enough to flood coastal cities and disrupt aquatic life that now flourishes near the mouths of rivers. They think that the earth's higher temperatures will cause freshwater lakes to evaporate quickly, reducing our supplies of drinking water.

Changing weather patterns due to substantial warming trends will affect agriculture throughout the world. Most scientists agree that agricultural belts will shift northward because of the warmer temperatures. Some predict years of drought for the farm belts of the American plains. Others think that the higher temperatures will give us a longer growing season and that increased carbon dioxide in the atmosphere will make plants more productive.

Although scientists disagree on how the greenhouse effect will change world climates, they do agree that changes will occur. The extent of the changes and if they will be helpful or harmful is a matter of scientific debate.

For Discussion

1. What is the greenhouse effect and what caused it?

2. Name some positive and negative results that could occur from the greenhouse effect.

3. If you were a scientist, what kind of studies would you do to try to predict possible changes due to the greenhouse effect?

Five-speed Bicycle

Riding a bicycle seems easy and natural once you know how to do it. However, a bicycle is really a complex machine made up of wheels and axles and levers.

When you push down on the pedals, the work you do is transferred via the bicycle's interconnecting parts to the rear wheel, which propels the bicycle forward. A five-speed bicycle employs five gears to help you pedal efficiently. Use the diagram below to find out how the pedaling motion causes a bicycle to move and how the gears on a bicycle allow you to adjust the force you exert when you pedal.

1. The pedals are levers that turn an axle, which connects to a wheel called the pedal sprocket. Every time you pedal one turn, alternately pushing one pedal and then the other, the pedal sprocket goes around one time.

2. The chain transfers the motion of the pedal sprocket to one of the five separate gears at the rear wheel.

3. Every time the pedal sprocket makes one revolution, the rear-wheel gear to which it is connected turns several times. This occurs because the gears are all smaller than the pedal sprocket. The number of times a particular gear turns is equal to the ratio of the pedal sprocket's radius and the gear's radius.

4. The gear turns the rear axle. The rear wheel also turns on this axle. Therefore, every time the gear makes one revolution, the rear wheel makes one revolution. For every revolution, the bicycle travels forward the circumference of the rear wheel.

5. Having different gears on a bicycle allows you to make adjustments in the number of revolutions the rear wheel makes for every turn of the pedal sprocket. A bicycle is in high gear when the chain rides on the smallest of the gears. High gear is used for riding fast on level ground or for riding downhill. In high gear, the rear wheel makes as many as revolutions for every turn of the pedal sprocket. However, pedaling in high gear requires the largest force. It is difficult to ride a bicycle in high gear up a hill.

6. When you change gears, you press the gear lever and the chain slides from one gear onto another. A bicycle is in low gear when the chain rides on the largest of the gears. Low gear is used for riding uphill. In low gear, the rear wheel makes as few as 1½ revolutions every time you pedal. However, you do not have to exert much force to pedal a bicycle in low gear. Using low gear, you can pedal up a hill without getting tired.

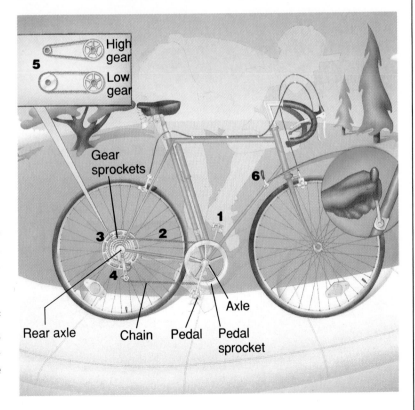

UNIT 5
Wave Motion

Technology *in Perspective*

We live in a world of waves. Waves are responsible for light and for sound as well as for giving the seas their character. Some kinds of waves are silent and invisible, detectable only with special equipment. Understanding waves and their movements has opened up frontiers in technology.

1200 B.C.

In ancient times people enjoyed music just as they do today. They made instruments of metal, wood, and leather. By experimenting, they learned how to produce various sounds and tones, using different types of wood or metal and varying the hollow that served as the instrument's resonator and amplifier. Drums also became an early means of sending communications for long distances.

17th Century

Whether Hans Lippershey, a Dutch spectacle maker, invented the telescope or whether he was one of several who produced similar instruments at about the same time early in the 1600s is still debated. However, it is unquestioned that it was Galileo who improved the telescope and then put it to practical use. He used it to study the heavens and reported sights never before seen, such as the moons of Jupiter and the craters of our moon.

Chapter 17 Waves
Chapter 18 Light
Chapter 19 Optics
Chapter 20 Lasers
Chapter 21 Sound

19th Century

In the mid 1870s, a new device extended the range of the human voice. People began talking to each other using Alexander Graham Bell's invention—the telephone. The telephone had great impact on people's lives, and it changed the way business was conducted.

20th Century

Ranked as probably the most important instrument of technology in this century, the laser can be either powerful or gentle. It affects all of our lives in some manner daily. Used in stores to read prices, in telecommunications to transmit voices by fiber optics, in medicine to perform operations and to scan internal organs, in music and entertainment—every phase of our lives has been touched by lasers. New uses for this technological advance of the 20th century are added to its credit almost daily.

CHAPTER 17
Waves

The water waves in this picture are a visible type of wave. Other waves are in the picture, too. You see everything in the picture because of light waves. When a body of water is calm, the light waves reflect smoothly and you see a mirror image of the surrounding shoreline. Water waves and light waves are only two of many kinds of waves you will study in this chapter.

Organizing Your Study Skills The outline below will help you see how the chapter is organized and what you should learn as you read.

I. Section 17-1: Properties of Waves
  A. How do waves carry energy?
  B. What are the characteristics of waves?
  C. How are a wave's wavelength, frequency, and speed related?

II. Section 17-2: Wave Motions
  A. What are transverse waves?
  B. What are compressional waves?

III. Section 17-3: Behavior of Waves
  A. How are waves reflected?
  B. How are waves refracted?
  C. Which kind of waves can be polarized?
  D. What is interference?

IV. Section 17-4: Electromagnetic Waves
  A. What is the electromagnetic spectrum?
  B. How do high-energy waves affect people?
  C. How are low-energy waves used?

17·1 Properties of Waves

Waves Carry Energy

Have you ever had a hard-thrown ball hurt your hand when you caught it? A moving ball carries energy to you from the person who threw it. Waves also carry energy from place to place, but matter does not move with the wave as it moves with a ball.

To better understand this idea, imagine that you tie one end of a rope to a doorknob, as shown in *Figure 17-1*. You then hold the other end of the rope and quickly flick it up and down. The wave passing along the rope carries the energy you give the rope when you flick it. Notice, however, that the rope itself does not move forward. Each part of the rope moves only up and down as the wave passes by.

Think about waves in a pool. Did you notice that a ball floating in the water seemed to stay in about the same place as a wave passed by? Neither the ball nor the water under it moved very much as the wave passed. In the same way, boats on a lake bob up and down as waves pass under them. Although the boats move up and down, they are not pushed toward the shore by the waves. Imagine how difficult it would be to steer a boat if it moved along with every wave that passed.

Waves in lakes and oceans are energy traveling through water. Other waves, such as sound waves, also require a material to travel through. Waves might travel through all kinds of materials, such as air or glass. People used to put their ears to railroad tracks to listen for the sound waves moving along the rails from an approaching train. Some waves, such as light and radio waves, can travel through a **vacuum**—space that is empty of matter.

Figure 17-1 Waves carry energy, but not matter.

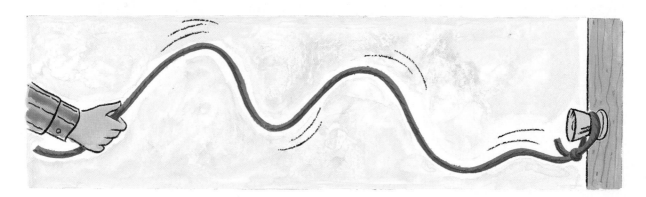

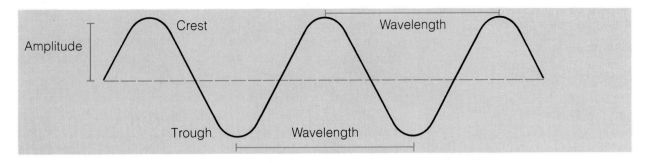

Figure 17-2 Describing a wave

Describing a Wave

All waves can be described by the same set of properties. Notice in *Figure 17-2* that the waves look like hills and valleys. The **crest** is the highest point of the waves. The **trough** is the lowest point of the wave. The dashed line marks the rope's rest position before a wave passes along it. The wave's **amplitude** is the distance from the dashed line to a crest or to a trough. The amplitude squared is proportional to the amount of energy the wave carries. For example, a wave with twice the amplitude of the one in *Figure 17-2* carries four times the energy.

On a calm day, the amplitude of ocean waves is small. During a storm, the wind gives a lot of energy to the waves. A wave's amplitude increases significantly. The wave in *Figure 17-3* has a large amplitude and carries a lot of energy.

The distance from one crest to the next, from one trough to the next, or from any point on a wave to the next similar point is the wave's **wavelength.** Find the wavelengths marked on *Figure 17-2*.

The number of crests (or troughs) that pass a place in a certain time is the wave's **frequency.** Frequency is measured in **hertz** (Hz), the number of waves that pass a given point in one second. One wave per second equals one hertz. If four water waves pass the edge of a pier in 20 seconds, the frequency is four waves divided by 20 seconds, or 0.2 hertz.

Speed is another important property of a wave. A wave's speed depends on the kind of wave. For example, light waves travel faster than sound waves. Therefore, you see lightning before you hear thunder, even though they start at the same place at the same time. Wave speed also depends on the material the wave travels through. For example, a sound wave travels faster through steel than it does through air.

Figure 17-3 A large amplitude wave

Figure 17-4 Doubling the wavelength halves the wave's frequency.

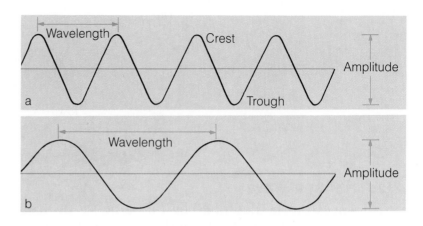

For Practice

Use what you have learned about waves to solve these problems.

1. One wave has five times the amplitude of another wave. How much more energy does it carry?
2. One wave carries 81 times more energy than another wave. Compare their amplitudes.
3. What is the speed of a sound wave whose wavelength is 17 m and whose frequency is 20 hz?
4. Calculate the speed of a wave whose wavelength is 1 m and whose frequency is 0.5 hz.

Explore!

Find out who is honored by the name of the unit of frequency, the hertz.

Speed, Wavelength, and Frequency Are Related

Wavelength and frequency are different measures of how close together a wave's crests are. However, wavelength and frequency are also related to each other. Suppose a wave's speed and amplitude remain the same, but the wavelength doubles. It then takes twice as long for the wave to pass a given place. The frequency would be halved, as *Figure 17-4* shows. What happens to the frequency if the wavelength is halved? How fast is a wave moving if its wavelength is 10 meters and its frequency is 110 hertz? This equation shows how wavelength, frequency, and speed are related:

$$\text{wavelength} \times \text{frequency} = \text{speed}$$
$$10 \text{ meters} \times 110 \text{ hertz} =$$
$$10 \text{ meters} \times 110 \text{ waves/second} = 1100 \text{ meters/second}$$

Note that the quantity "wave" has no unit, and so is unlike "meter" or "second." If you know values for any two properties of a wave, you can use the equation to find the value for the third property.

Section Review

1. Give an example of how waves carry energy but not matter.
2. What characteristics describe a wave?
3. How do you calculate a wave's speed?

Challenge: The speed of a train, the frequency with which boxcars pass you, and the length of the boxcars are related. Imagine that you are in a car stopped at a railroad crossing. The train has boxcars 13 meters long, and 40 boxcars pass you in 0.5 minute. Calculate the speed of the train.

Properties of Waves

Purpose

To observe basic wave properties

Materials

- large, shallow pan
- water
- medicine dropper
- watch or clock with a second hand
- small cork
- coiled spring, at least 30 cm long

Procedure and Observations

PART A

1. Fill the pan with water to a depth of about 3 cm.
2. Fill the medicine dropper with water. Hold it about 30 cm above the pan. Allow one drop of water to fall from the medicine dropper each second.
3. Count the number of waves that hit the side of the pan in 10 seconds.
4. Repeat steps 2-3, allowing one drop to strike the water every two seconds. Compare the frequencies of the waves made.

PART B

1. Place the cork in the water.
2. Make waves in the water by repeating Part A, step 2.
3. Observe and record how the cork moves on the water.

PART C

1. Repeat Part A, step 2.
2. Notice the distance between ripples.
3. When the water is calm again, use the medicine dropper to drop water into the pan twice each second.
4. Compare the distance between ripples and record your observations.

PART D

1. Place the coiled spring on your desk. Ask your partner to hold one end steady.
2. Stretch the spring slightly. Jerk your end of the spring quickly about 5 cm to one side and then back again to the center, as in **a**. Practice making a wave travel down the spring.
3. Flick the spring as above once each second.
4. Estimate and record the distance between 2 similar points in a row on the wave, as in **b**.
5. Repeat step 3 about twice as often.
6. Repeat step 4.
7. Compare the distances. Record this observation.

Analysis and Conclusions

1. In what ways can you change the properties of a wave?
2. What properties do waves in any material have in common?

a

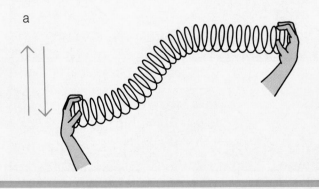

b

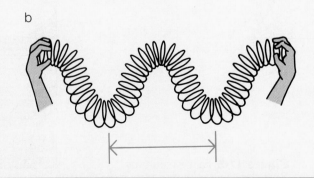

Objectives

After completing this section you will be able to

A. Describe transverse waves.
B. Describe compressional waves.

17·2 Wave Motions

Transverse Waves

Waves in water and light waves in air are traveling waves. Any moving wave is a traveling wave. You already know that a wave does not carry matter forward with it as it moves. However, matter does move a little as the wave passes through it. Compare how the buoy moves with how the wave moves past it *Figure 17-5*. The wave passes under the buoy from left to right. However, the buoy moves up on the crest, down into the trough, and back to its original position.

Notice that the wave moves the buoy up and down, but only temporarily away from its original position. Any wave that moves matter in a direction perpendicular to the direction of the wave's motion is a **transverse wave.** The crests and troughs of transverse waves can move in any direction perpendicular to the wave's direction—up and down, side to side, and so on. Waves on a rope and light waves are transverse waves.

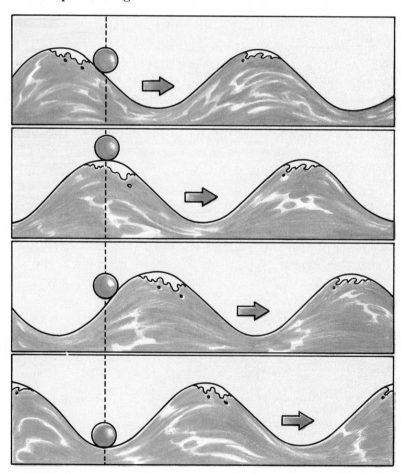

Figure 17-5 Transverse waves

In water waves, a bit of water moves in a tiny circle as a wave passes by, but that water returns to the same place it began. The larger the amplitude of the wave, the larger the circle. When the amplitude of the wave gets too large compared with the depth of the water, the wave stops being smooth. The waves "break." Matter in breaking waves does not go back to the same place, therefore breaking waves are no longer transverse waves. When waves are discussed in this book, they are smooth waves that are not breaking. These waves differ from the breakers you might see at a beach.

Compressional Waves

A second kind of traveling wave moves molecules of a material just as the coils of a spring move after a section is compressed and released. In *Figure 17-6,* the ribbon is a marker like the buoy was in the transverse wave. Compare the motions of the wave and the ribbon. The wave passes from left to right. The ribbon moves a little to the right as the wave packs, or compresses, the coils closer together. This is an area of **compression.** Then the ribbon moves a little to the left as the wave spreads the coils apart. This is an area of **rarefaction.** Finally the ribbon returns to its original position.

Note that the wave moved the ribbon back and forth; the ribbon did not move away from its original position on the spring. This kind of wave is a **compressional wave**. It compresses the material's molecules. These waves move matter in a direction parallel to the direction of the wave's motion. Sound waves are compressional waves. The molecules in steel are linked together by stronger forces than the molecules in air, allowing the sound waves to pass more quickly through steel.

Figure 17-7 compares transverse and compressional waves. Crests are like compressions, and troughs are like rarefactions. A wavelength of a compressional wave is the distance from one compression to the next, from one rarefaction to the next, or from any one point on the wave to the next similar point.

Section Review

1. How do transverse waves pass through material?
2. How do compressional waves move?

Challenge: How do transverse waves and compressional waves differ? How are they alike?

Applying Science

Ocean waves get energy from the wind. The waves then carry the energy long distances without giving up their energy to the water they pass. But once waves break, they give up their energy at the shore. Waves of high amplitude can do a lot of damage in a storm. When a storm is forecast, small boats often go out to sea so that they can bob harmlessly up and down as waves pass under them. If they stayed in the harbor, they would be in danger from the energy of breaking waves.

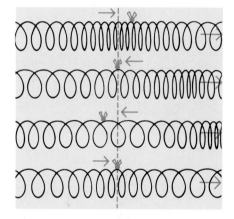

Figure 17-6 Compressional waves

Figure 17-7 Comparing transverse and compressional waves

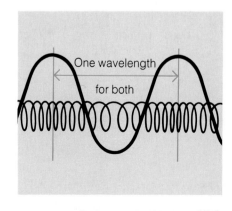

One wavelength for both

After completing this section you will be able to

A. Describe how waves are reflected.
B. Describe how waves are refracted.
C. Tell which kind of wave can be polarized.
D. Describe what interference is.

17-3 Behavior of Waves

Waves Reflect

Hockey players study one aspect of physical science. They study how objects bounce off a surface. When a hockey player slams the puck straight at the side of the rink, the puck comes right back to him. However, notice in *Figure 17-8* what happens when he hits the puck toward the side of the rink at an angle. The puck bounces away from him at the same angle. Objects bounce off surfaces at the same angle at which they hit them.

Waves behave in the same way. When a wave bounces off the surface of a material, reflection occurs. You can see yourself in a mirror because light waves reflect off the mirror. You can hear echoes because sound waves reflect off walls and other large objects.

Notice in *Figure 17-9* how the wave reflects from the surface of the sea wall. The angles at which a wave hits and leaves the surface are marked. If you measure these angles from a line drawn at a right angle to the surface, you find that both angles are the same. The arrows pointing toward the sea wall show the movement of incoming waves. The arrows pointing away from the wall show the movement of reflected waves.

Figure 17-8 The hockey puck bounces off the side of the rink at the same angle at which it hit the side.

Figure 17-10 shows a beam of light from a flashlight reflected off a mirror. Notice that the light hits the mirror and reflects off at the same angle. When any wave reflects off any smooth surface, the angle at which it leaves the surface always equals the angle at which it hits the surface.

Waves Refract

Sometimes a wave can pass from one material into another material. For example, a light wave can pass from air into a glass plate, as shown in *Figure 17-11a*. The light wave continues straight through into the second material, the glass plate. The wave continues moving in a straight line, but its speed changes. Because the wave must keep moving up and down at the same frequency, its wavelength also changes when it moves into the second material.

Waves can also enter a new material at other angles. Again, the speed changes as the wave continues moving. Notice in *Figure 17-11b* how the wave also changes direction. **Refraction** is the bending of a wave as it enters a new material.

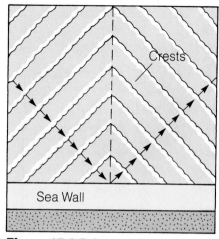

Figure 17-9 Reflection of water waves

Figure 17-10 Waves reflect off a surface at the same angle at which they hit the surface.

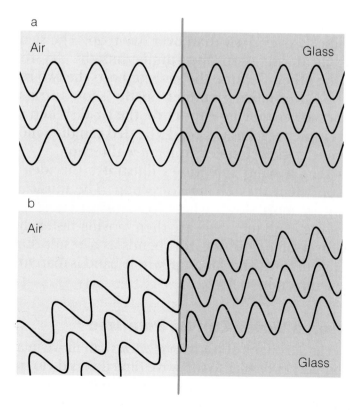

Figure 17-11a No refraction takes place when the wave moves from air to glass at a 90° angle. **b** Refraction takes place when the wave strikes the glass at an angle other than 90°.

Figure 17-12 The sled turns suddenly in the same way that waves refract.

Explore!

Find out about P, S, and L waves in earthquakes. Which kind of traveling wave is each? Where in the earth is each reflected, refracted, or absorbed?

Waves refract for the same reason that the sled in *Figure 17-12* suddenly turns. The sled's runners travel more quickly over snow than over dry road. The sled is moving at an angle, so one runner hits the dry road before the other. Because the sled connects the two runners, the faster-moving runner on the snow turns toward the slower-moving runner on the road. When the second runner reaches the road, the sled can then move forward at its slower speed in its new direction.

A marching band sometimes illustrates the idea of refraction when they change direction. The musicians start moving more slowly when they cross a slanted line. Some of the band members are then moving faster than others for a time, and the row bends as a result. Each row bends in turn, and soon the whole band is marching in a new direction.

Transverse Waves Can Be Polarized

Crests and troughs of transverse waves can move in any direction perpendicular to the wave direction: side to side, up and down, and so on. Waves with crests and troughs moving in only one of the perpendicular directions are **polarized,** as shown in *Figure 17-13*.

Why do the waves in *Figure 17-13a* pass through the grating while the waves in *Figure 17-13b* do not? If any waves are to pass through the grating, the crests and troughs must be parallel to the grating's openings. The waves in *Figure 17-13a* are polarized parallel to the grating; they can pass through it. The waves in *Figure 17-13b* are polarized in a direction perpendicular to the grating; they cannot pass through it.

The grating each picture acts like a filter that allows only certain types of waves on a rope to pass through. In a similar way, a polarizing filter can be used to polarize light waves. The filter allows only waves that move in one direction to pass through. Light waves that move in all other directions are held back.

When a road or water reflects light, it also polarizes light in one direction. The glare from a horizontal surface is mainly polarized horizontally. Some types of sunglasses are polarized in the direction perpendicular to the direction of this reflected light. For that reason, they block this light out and reduce glare.

Photographers often use polarizing filters to reduce glare. Compare the two photographs in *Figure 17-14*. How do they differ? The left picture was taken with a polarizing filter, while the right one was taken without a polarizing filter.

Figure 17-13 A wave polarized to the grating's slats can get through (**a**), but a wave polarized perpendicular to the grating's slats (**b**) cannot get through.

Figure 17-14 Photographs taken with (**a**) and without (**b**) a polarizing filter

Figure 17-15 Interference of water waves

Interference of Waves

A stone tossed into water causes waves that move out in circles from a central source. Notice in *Figure 17-15* how the pattern becomes more complicated as waves from different sources meet.

Figure 17-16 shows what happens as waves move through each other. Notice that where two crests meet, the resulting amplitude is equal to the sum of both crests. The same is true for two troughs. If the two waves are identical, the wave that results is exactly twice as high as each of the individual waves. In other words, the resulting wave has twice the amplitude.

If a crest and trough meet, the two waves combine to produce a wave whose amplitude is less than that of the original wave. In the diagram, a crest of one wave meets a trough of an identical wave. The result of the meeting between these two waves is no wave at all.

Interference is the result of different waves moving through one another. Interference affects all waves. Light waves demonstrate interference in *Figure 17-17*. Crests meeting crests or troughs meeting troughs produce the bright bands of light. Crests and troughs that meet cancel each other and produce the dark bands.

Section Review

1. Define and give an example of wave reflection.
2. Define and give an example of wave refraction.
3. How can you polarize transverse waves?
4. How do waves show interference?

Challenge: What would you expect to happen if the lenses from two polarizing sunglasses were overlapped at right angles to one another? Explain.

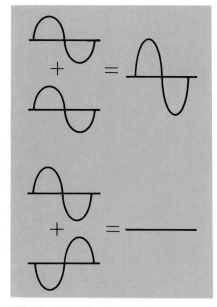

Figure 17-16 A wave with twice the amplitude results when the crests and troughs of identical waves meet. When the crest of one wave meets the trough of an identical wave, no wave results.

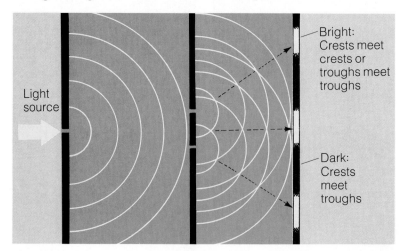

Figure 17-17 Interference of light waves

Reflection

Purpose

To observe and measure the angles of a wave during reflection

Materials

- 3 sheets of paper
- ruler or straightedge
- pencil
- small ball of clay
- protractor
- flat mirror

Procedure and Observations

1. Stand a mirror upright by attaching clay to the corners at the bottom. The mirror must be perpendicular to the table.
2. Fold the paper in half lengthwise. Crease it, open it, and draw a dashed line on the crease.
3. Place a dot labeled "X" at one end of the crease.
4. Draw a line from point X to the edge of the paper so that the angle between it and the dashed line is less than 90°. Label the line "Y."
5. Place the paper so that the dashed line is perpendicular to the bottom of the mirror at point X, as shown in **a.**
6. Position yourself so that you can look

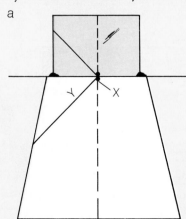

a

into the mirror from the blank half of the paper. Sight along the reflection of line Y.

7. Line up the ruler's edge with Y's reflection on the blank side of the paper.
8. Make two dots on line Y's reflection, along the ruler, as shown in **b.**
9. Remove the paper and connect the two dots and point X in a straight line. Label this line "Z."
10. Use a protractor to measure the angles formed with the dashed line, as in **c.**
11. Repeat this procedure two more times, each time using a new sheet of paper, and changing the first angle.

Analysis and Conclusions

1. How do the two angles in each set compare with each other?
2. State a general rule about the angles formed during reflection.

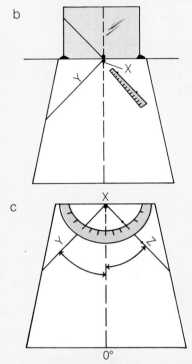

After completing this section you will be able to

A. Describe the electromagnetic spectrum.

B. List some ways high-energy waves affect people.

C. List how people use low-energy waves.

The Electromagnetic Spectrum

Did you know that you are constantly bombarded with waves you cannot feel, hear, or smell? Most of them are invisible. Because of these waves, you can see things around you, listen to a radio, watch television, or bake a potato in five minutes. These special waves—called **electromagnetic waves**—are transverse waves that carry energy in a way related to electricity and magnetism. Radio waves, infrared rays, light, ultraviolet waves, X rays, and gamma rays are all electromagnetic waves. These waves differ in the amount of energy they carry. The sun is a major source of electromagnetic waves.

All electromagnetic waves travel through a vacuum at 300 000 kilometers per second (3×10^{10} cm/s). If electromagnetic waves could bend that much, they would travel around Earth seven times in one second!

Electromagnetic waves, arranged by frequency, produce the **electromagnetic spectrum** shown in *Figure 17-18.* The waves at the left are high-energy waves. They have short wavelengths and high frequencies. The low-energy waves to the right have long wavelengths and low frequencies. Light of all colors—the colors of the rainbow—are close to the middle of the electromagnetic spectrum. These are the only electromagnetic waves people can see.

Notice that radio waves have the longest wavelengths and the lowest frequencies. Gamma rays have the shortest wavelengths and the highest frequencies. Waves with high frequencies have the greatest energy. How a wave affects people and how it is used depends on the wave's energy.

Have You Heard?

The Gamma Ray Observatory, scheduled for launch into orbit in the 1990s, will help astronomers study gamma rays. Gamma rays do not pass through the earth's atmosphere, so they can only be observed from space.

Figure 17-18 The electromagnetic spectrum

Highest energy

Gamma rays
10^{-10} cm

X rays
10^{-8} cm

Ultraviolet rays
10^{-6} cm

Visible light

10^{-4} cm

High frequency, Short wavelength

How High-Energy Waves Affect People

Exposure to large amounts of high-energy waves can be deadly to the cells of living things. People can use high-energy waves effectively, but must limit their exposure to them.

Doctors use the deadly nature of gamma rays to treat cancer and stop the growth of tumors. Machines aim beams of gamma rays directly at the diseased cells. The gamma rays kill the diseased cells, but cause less damage to healthy cells nearby. Scientists can also use gamma rays to preserve food by killing bacteria.

X rays pass right through the soft parts of your body, but are stopped by bones and teeth. X-ray pictures, therefore, can reveal broken bones, tooth decay, and medical problems within the body. In the 1970s, doctors began to use a kind of X-ray machine that gives detailed pictures of various organs that older types of X-ray machines could not give. The new machine, called a CT scanner, gives a cross-sectional view of a patient's body. The CT scanner has a source of X rays. It shoots a thin beam of the high-energy waves through the patient's body from many angles. On the opposite side of the patient's body, an X-ray detector measures the rays that pass through. A computer analyzes data from the detector and produces an image on a television screen. A CT scanner produced the detailed picture of the brain shown in *Figure 17-19*.

Ultraviolet rays from the sun can harm you. Wearing sunglasses that effectively filter ultraviolet rays helps protect your vision. Ultraviolet rays can also cause your skin to burn and is a cause skin cancer. However, ultraviolet rays are also helpful. They destroy bacteria and viruses, and therefore can be used to sterilize instruments in hospitals.

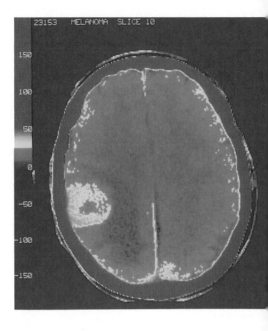

Figure 17-19 The CT scanner uses X rays to give detailed pictures of the brain.

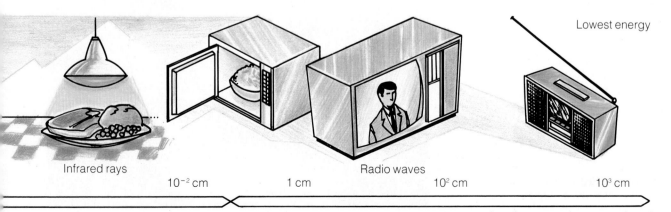

Infrared rays

Radio waves

Lowest energy

10^{-2} cm   1 cm 10^2 cm 10^3 cm

Low frequency, Long wavelength

Using Low-Energy Waves

You are able to see because your eyes are sensitive to light waves reflected from objects. Light waves are only a small part of the electromagnetic spectrum, but they are the only waves that are visible to people. The sun gives off most of its energy in this region of the electromagnetic spectrum.

The sun radiates more light waves than infrared rays. Objects that are not as hot as the sun, such as a heat lamp, give off mainly infrared rays. Even cooler objects, such as a table, a book, or the human body, give off some infrared rays. With special equipment, scientists can photograph an object's infrared rays to measure temperature and to study how energy flows.

Radios and televisions work because they receive radio waves sent by radio and television stations. Each station must broadcast a specific wave frequency. As you switch from channel to channel, you change the frequency your radio or television receives.

Radar systems, shown in *Figure 17-20,* help pilots navigate and detect moving objects. Radar uses radio waves with wavelengths a bit shorter than those used for radio and television. A radar device sends out radio waves. When the waves strike an object, such as an airplane, the object reflects the waves back to the device.

Figure 17-20 Air-traffic controllers use radar to help direct airplanes.

Since the wave's speed is known, the object's distance from the device is determined from the time between sending the wave and receiving the reflection. The microwaves that can cook your food in minutes are actually radio waves confined to a small oven.

Weather satellites, such as the one in *Figure 17-21*, detect low-energy waves. As a storm approaches, meteorologists interpret the satellite information about it. The storm's air mass sends out infrared rays and microwaves which indicate its temperature. The air mass also reflects light waves during the day, infrared rays, and radio waves. Certain radio wavelengths detect fine particles in clouds. Still other radio wavelengths can detect raindrops. All this information contributes to the weather report you see on television and into the weather maps used in newspapers.

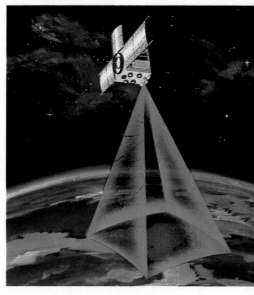

Figure 17-21 This weather satellite hovers over one area of Earth, measuring low-energy electromagnetic waves.

Section Review

1. What characteristics of waves allows them to be arranged in the electromagnetic spectrum?
2. Name three high-energy waves and describe how each is used.
3. Name three low-energy waves and describe how each is used.

Challenge: Cancer cells are warmer than healthy cells. Explain how a doctor could use electromagnetic waves to detect cancer cells.

Careers in Physical Science

X-ray Technician

Without an X ray, injuries inside your body might not be found. Technicians take the pictures that uncover such things as tiny, hair-thin cracks in bones.

Hospitals and clinics hire special technicians to take X-ray pictures for both routine checkups and emergency cases. Technicians help patients pose for their X rays. They shield areas that are not being examined, and then take the picture. Finally, technicians develop X rays so that doctors can use them to diagnose broken bones, tumors, and lung diseases.

X-ray technicians train for 1-2 years in hospitals or at technical schools. There, they learn about anatomy and how to take and develop X rays.

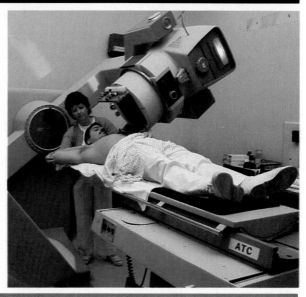

Science Skills

Graphing Waves

You can learn about interference in waves by graphing waves and combining the graphs.

First, hold a piece of graph paper sideways. Draw three horizontal lines, each separated by one centimeter, across its width. Then mark intervals of 0.5 centimeters along the length of each line.

Take a piece of string about 40 centimeters long and lay the string on the graph paper. Shape the string into a wave with a wavelength of six centimeters and an amplitude of one centimeter. Make three full cycles of crests and troughs. Use a pencil to trace the wave onto the graph paper. Mark this graph *A*. Trace the wave onto another piece of graph paper and mark this graph *B*.

At intervals of 0.5 centimeters across the middle horizontal line of each graph, measure the heights of the waves. When the wave height is above the line, the height is a positive number. When the wave height is below the line, the height is a negative number. Mark each wave height along the curve.

Place graph B directly underneath graph A so that the crests and troughs are aligned. Label a third piece of graph paper *C*. On this graph, construct a new wave so that the value of the wave at any horizontal point is the sum of the values of A and B at that point.

Move A to the right 0.5 centimeters and move B to the left 0.5 centimeters. Construct a new wave, labeled *D,* so that the value of the wave at any horizontal point is the sum of the values of A and B at that point. Note that the sum of a positive number and a negative number is the difference between the digits with the sign of the larger number.

Continue to move the graphs farther apart by the same distances and construct new waves until the waves have moved apart by one full wavelength. Lay out the resulting graphs in order. Then use your series of graphs to answer these questions.

1. How do the wavelengths and amplitudes of each of the resulting waves compare with those of the original waves?

2. What would you find if you kept sliding the curves to the sides by the same distances?

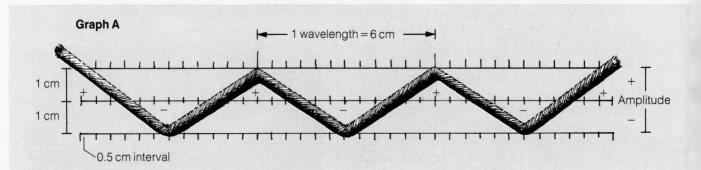

Graph A

1 wavelength = 6 cm

1 cm

1 cm

Amplitude

0.5 cm interval

✓ Summary

17-1 Properties of Waves

A. Waves carry energy, but they do not carry matter.

B. Wavelength, frequency, amplitude, and speed are four properties of waves.

C. A wave's speed can be determined by using this formula:

speed = wavelength × frequency.

17-2 Wave Motions

A. Any wave that moves matter in a direction perpendicular to the direction of the wave's motion is a transverse wave.

B. Compressional waves move matter in a direction parallel to the direction of the wave's motion.

17-3 The Behavior of Waves

A. When a wave is reflected, it bounces off the surface of a material. The angles at which a wave hits and leaves the surface are equal.

B. When a wave moves into a new material, its speed changes. If it enters at an angle other than 90°, it is refracted.

C. The crests and troughs of polarized waves move only in one direction perpendicular to the wave's direction. Transverse waves can be polarized.

D. Interference occurs as crest and troughs of one wave move through those of another and either add together or cancel each other.

17-4 Electromagnetic Waves

A. The electromagnetic spectrum arranges electromagnetic waves in order of their wavelengths or frequencies.

B. Gamma rays, X rays, and ultraviolet rays are high-energy waves. High-energy waves can be deadly to the cells of living things.

C. Light waves, infrared rays, and radio waves are low-energy waves. Radar and microwave ovens use radio waves.

Vocabulary

For each of the following terms, write a sentence that uses the term correctly.

amplitude	frequency	refraction
compression	hertz	transverse wave
compressional wave	interference	trough
crest	polarized	vacuum
electromagnetic spectrum	rarefaction	wavelength
electromagnetic wave	reflection	

Check Your Knowledge

Part I: Matching   Match the definition in Column I with the correct term in Column II.

Column I
1. the high point of a transverse wave
2. half the perpendicular distance from the top of a crest to the bottom of a trough
3. transverse waves that include X rays and visible light
4. unit for measuring frequency
5. a traveling wave that causes matter to move perpendicularly to the direction of a wave's motion
6. the distance from one crest to the next
7. the number of waves that pass a certain point in one second
8. a traveling wave that causes matter to move back and forth parallel to the direction of the wave's motion
9. the bouncing of a wave from a surface
10. the result of waves moving through each other

Column II
a. amplitude
b. compressional wave
c. crest
d. electromagnetic waves
e. frequency
f. hertz
g. interference
h. reflection
i. refraction
j. transverse wave
k. wavelength

Part II: Multiple Choice   Choose the letter of the best answer.
11. A wave transfers (a) matter. (b) speed. (c) energy. (d) frequency.
12. Which of the following are compressional waves? (a) radio waves (b) ultraviolet waves (c) water waves (d) sound waves
13. Refraction occurs because the new material changes the wave's (a) speed. (b) frequency. (c) amplitude. (d) hertz.
14. The waves with the greatest energy are (a) light waves. (b) gamma rays. (c) microwaves. (d) ultraviolet rays.
15. Which of the following is not an electromagnetic wave? (a) light (b) sound (c) X rays (d) radio waves
16. A wave on rope approaches two gratings in a row. The wave is polarized perpendicular to Grating 1 and parallel to Grating 2. The wave passes through (a) only Grating 1. (b) only Grating 2. (c) both gratings. (d) neither grating.
17. As a wave passes through a coiled spring, the area where the coils spread apart is the (a) compression. (b) trough. (c) crest. (d) rarefaction.

Part III: Completion   Write the word or words that complete the sentence correctly.
18. Microwaves, visible light, and infrared rays are some of the waves that make up the _____.
19. The angles at which a wave hits and reflects from a surface are _____.
20. In a transverse wave, the distance from one trough to the next is the _____.
21. Space that is empty of matter is a(n) _____.
22. The electromagnetic waves with the shortest wavelengths are those that have the _____ energy.

Check Your Understanding

1. Describe four properties of a wave.
2. Describe two different kinds of traveling waves.
3. At what angle is a wave reflected from a surface?
4. When does a wave refract?
5. Is there such a thing as polarized sound? Explain.
6. Name the parts of the electromagnetic spectrum.
7. How are all electromagnetic waves alike? How are they different from one another?
8. How could you send both transverse and compressional waves along a spring at the same time?

Apply Your Knowledge

1. Suppose you make waves in a pond by dipping your hand in the water with a frequency of 1 hertz. How could you make waves of a longer wavelength? How could you increase the amplitude of the waves?
2. Use speed = frequency × wavelength to find the wavelength, in meters, of a radio wave traveling at 300 000 000 m/s with a frequency of 540 000 hertz.
3. Draw a series of five transverse waves with a wavelength of 4 cm and an amplitude of 2 cm.
4. You stand in the back right corner of a racquetball court and hit the ball to the middle of the front wall. Where should the other player stand to return the ball? Assume the ball is not spinning.
5. Two sound waves interfere. The sum of their crests and troughs is 0 cm. What do you hear? Explain your answer.
6. If light traveled at the same speed through all materials, would it still reflect and refract? Why or why not?

Extend Your Knowledge

Research/Projects

1. Tie two coiled springs of different masses end to end with a string. Ask a friend to hold one end. Make transverse or compressional waves at the other end. What happens to the waves at the boundary (connection) between the waves? What happens to your friend's spring?
2. Use reference books to discover two uses that are not mentioned in this chapter for each of the different parts of the electromagnetic spectrum.

Readings

Proujan, C. "Looking Through 'Walls'." *Scholastic Science World,* October 5, 1984, page 11. A brief look at X rays.

Schlanger, S. R. "Imaging the Body with CAT Scans." *Scholastic Science World,* October 5, 1984, pages 24-25. Learn about how CAT scans aid doctors.

"The Way It Works: Microwave Oven." *Scholastic Science World,* April 30, 1982. Explains how the household appliance works to cook food in short periods of time.

CHAPTER 18
Light

The photograph shows a drop of water resting on the needle of a cedar tree. The photographer used a special filter to get the effect you see. Light, which makes pictures such as this one possible, is your main link with the world around you. Light helps you identify objects both near and far.

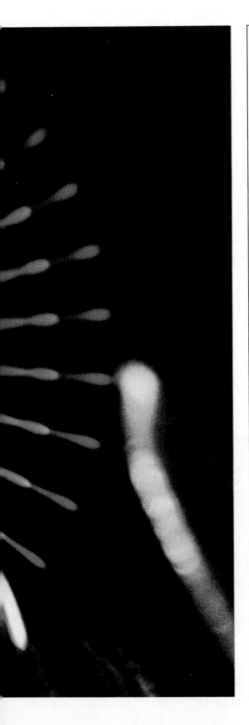

Organizing Your Study Skills The outline below will help you see how the chapter is organized and what you should learn as you read.

I. Section 18-1: The Nature of Light
    A. How does light travel?
    B. How does a source produce light?
    C. How does light behave?

II. Section 18-2: The Visible Spectrum
    A. What colors make up white light?
    B. How does a rainbow form?
    C. Why is the sky blue?

III. Section 18-3: How Objects Appear Colored
    A. What causes an object to appear colored?
    B. What does the color of a transparent object depend on?
    C. How does the mixing of primary colors in light differ from the mixing of primary colors in paint?

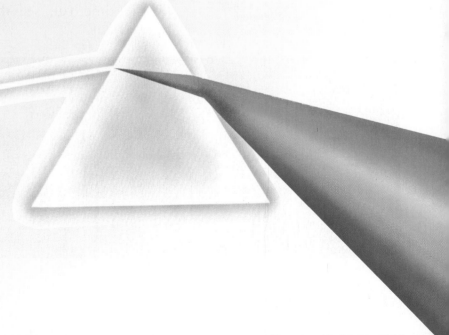

After completing this section you will be able to

A. Explain how light travels.
B. State how a source produces light.
C. Describe how light behaves.

The light-year is the unit used to measure the huge distances in space. One light year is 9.6 trillion kilometers, the distance light travels in a year. Light from the star closest to our solar system travels 4.3 light-years, which is about 41 trillion kilometers, to reach the earth.

Figure 18-1 The size of the lighted area shown in both drawings is the same. However, the intensity of light is only one-fourth as great when the distance of the light bulb is doubled.

18-1 The Nature of Light

How Light Travels

Light waves spread out from their source in straight lines called *rays*. Light rays move in straight lines away from the light bulbs in *Figure 18-1*. When an object blocks light rays, a **shadow** forms.

The rate at which light falls upon, or illuminates, a given surface area is its **intensity.** This intensity of illumination becomes less when the distance between the source and the surface increases. If the source is small, the intensity is related to the square of the distance from the source. If you move a source twice as far from a surface, the same amount of light will fall upon four times the original area. As a result, the intensity of light on the original area will be only one-fourth as great, as shown in *Figure 18-1*. If you move a source three times as far away, the intensity will only be one-ninth as great. If you move a source four times closer, the intensity will be sixteen times greater.

Because light travels so quickly, you see nearby events almost at the instant they occur. For example, when you turn on a lamp in a dark room, the room is lit up in a fraction of a second. If a light source is very far away, however, the light's travel time becomes significant. For example, sunlight takes more than eight minutes to reach the earth. Other stars are so far away that their light travels for years before it reaches the earth. In fact, by the time you see their light, some stars may be burned out.

How Light Is Produced

Atoms are tiny particles that make up all matter. Each atom has a certain amount of energy. An atom can gain energy in different ways. Heating or passing electricity through atoms provides extra energy. An atom can also gain energy from light that is passing by. When an atom gains energy, it becomes excited. The atom will give off this extra energy as it returns to its original state. Often, this energy is released as light.

Atoms gain and lose energy in steps. To understand this idea, think of a marble resting on a step of a staircase. The marble can rest on one step or the next, but cannot hover between steps. When the marble drops from a higher to a lower step, it gives off energy. Once the marble reaches the bottom of the staircase, it cannot give off any more energy on that staircase unless it is first raised back to a higher step.

Small particles within an atom—electrons—are like the marble on the stairs. Electrons in an atom exist only on certain "steps," called energy levels, shown in *Figure 18-2a*. They cannot exist between levels, just as a marble cannot hover between steps. Electrons can change their energies only by the exact amounts needed to change from one energy level to another, as in *Figure 18-2b*, or by the amount necessary to be released from an atom.

When an electron drops to a lower energy level, its atom gives off a bundle of energy—a **photon**, as in *c*. Streams of photons make up light. When an electron is at its lowest energy, the atom cannot release photons unless it absorbs at least the energy needed to raise one of its electrons to a higher energy level.

When electricity is passed through neon gas in a tube, electrons in neon atoms absorb energy and are raised to higher energy levels. When the electrons return to lower levels, the neon atoms release photons, giving off red light. For this reason, neon signs are red. The atoms of other gases release photons that produce different colors of light, as shown in *Figure 18-3*.

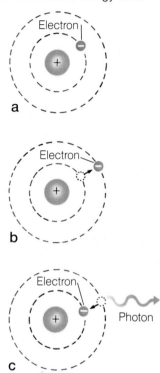

Figure 18-2 a The electron is in the lowest energy level. **b** The electron has absorbed energy and moved to the next higher energy level. **c** After some time, the electron gives off a photon and drops back to the lower energy level.

Figure 18-3 The noble gases are used to make "neon lights."

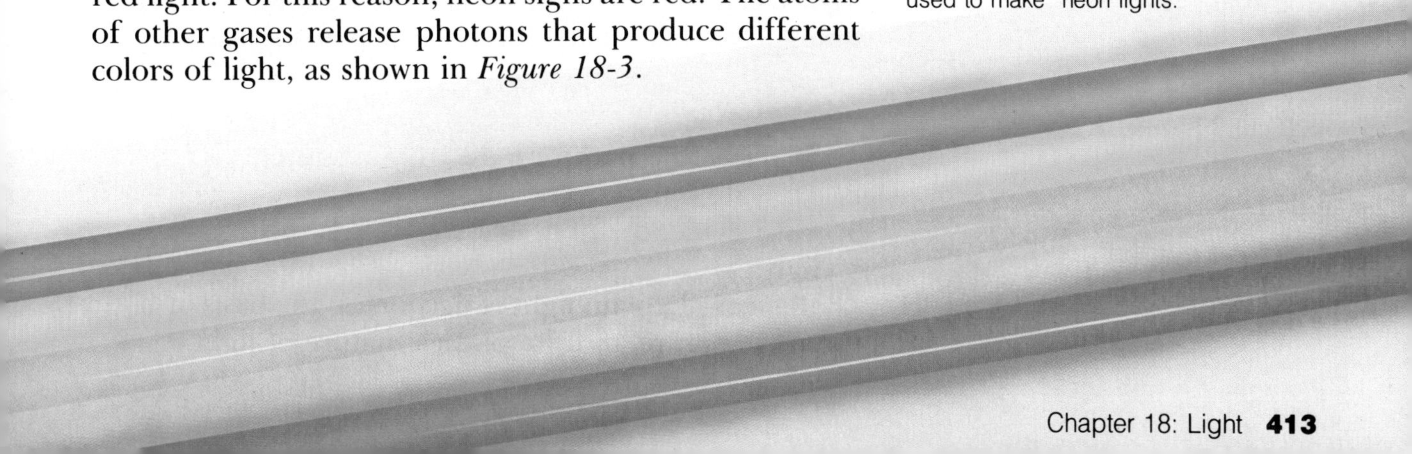

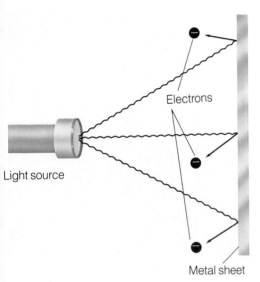

Figure 18-4 When light shines on certain metals, electrons jump out of the metals.

No matter where extra energy comes from, an object that gives off its own light is **luminous**. All sources of light, such as the sun and light bulbs, are luminous. The moon, however, is not luminous, since it merely reflects the light of the sun.

How Light Acts

For centuries, people disagreed about the nature of light. Some thought that light is made up of particles that travel through space in straight lines. Others believed that light is made up of waves. It seemed reasonable that light could consist of either particles or waves, but not both.

When scientists discovered the interference of light, they thought they had proved that light consists of waves. Particles, they felt, did not act this way. Yet, at that time, scientists believed that waves must travel through something. They could not explain how waves of sunlight traveled to the earth through the vacuum of space. Later, it was found that an electromagnetic wave, such as light, can travel through a vacuum.

Still later, scientists found evidence to prove that light does consist of particles. They discovered that light shining on certain metals can make electrons jump out of the metal, as the picture shows. Brighter light can make more electrons jump, but they jump out at the same speed. Different colors of light, though, make electrons jump out at different speeds. Scientists could explain these observations if light is made of particles of energy—photons. Each photon knocks one electron out of place in an atom just as one billiard ball knocks another out of place in a game of pool. Different colors of light have photons of different energy. Photons of higher energy produce electrons with higher speeds.

As a result of these findings, scientists concluded that light has properties of both particles and waves—sometimes acting like a particle, sometimes acting like a wave.

Section Review

1. Describe the path of light from a source.
2. How do luminous objects shine?
3. Give evidence for the wave and particle nature of light.

Challenge: Explain light reflection on the basis of both the wave nature and the particle nature of light.

The Path of Light Rays

Purpose

To observe how light travels

Materials

- flashlight
- meter stick
- shoe box
- scissors
- 4-6 flat mirrors

Procedure and Observations

PART A

1. Cut the box into three sections, as shown in **a.**

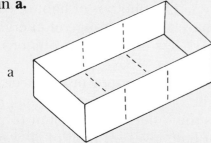

a

2. Stand the sections of the box, as shown in **b.**
3. Put a small hole in each section, also shown in **b.** The hole must be in the same place in each section. (Use the meter stick to make sure the holes are in the same place.)

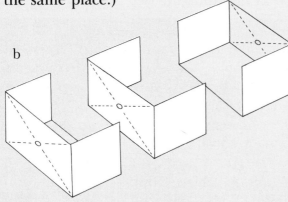

b

4. Ask your partner to shine the flashlight through one hole.

5. Line up the other sections so that you can still see the light through all the holes.
6. Hold the meter stick over the boxes to check whether or not the holes are properly aligned with the edge of the meter stick. Record your results.
7. Move one of the sections to the side. Record whether you can still see the light.

PART B

1. If the day is sunny, have someone near a window on the sunny side reflect the sun into the room with one mirror. *CAUTION: Do not look straight at the sun or its reflection. Do not shine the light into anyone else's eyes.*
2. Hand out the other mirrors to people in your group. Ask each person in turn to hold up a mirror so as to reflect the sunbeam toward the next person's mirror.
3. After the sunbeam is reflected from the last mirror, ask another person to hold up the flat surface of a notebook as though it were a screen. Have the person holding the last mirror project the sunbeam onto the notebook.
4. Diagram your setup. Using arrows, trace up path of light between the mirrors.

Analysis and Conclusions

1. Explain why you can see the light only when the cardboard sections are lined up.
2. What can you say about the path of light between one mirror and the next?
3. Use your results to explain how a shadow forms.

After completing this section, you will be able to

A. List the colors that make up white light.
B. Tell how a rainbow forms.
C. Explain why the sky is blue.

Have You Heard?

The hotter a shining object, the more blue light it emits. The sun is hotter than a light bulb, so the light bulb appears redder. But the sun is not as hot as many other stars which appear bluer. Even with just your eyes, you can see reddish stars as you look around the sky at night. The colors tell you the relative temperatures of the stars.

Figure 18-5 A prism spreads white light into the visible spectrum.

18-2 The Visible Spectrum

Colors of Light

Light is the **visible spectrum**—the small range of electromagnetic wavelengths that humans can see. White light, such as sunlight, is a mixture of all the colors of the visible spectrum. You can prove this with a **prism**—a wedge-shaped piece of glass or plastic, such as the one shown in the photograph.

When white light is refracted, it splits into a continuous band of colors in the following order: red, orange, yellow, green, blue, indigo (blue-violet), and violet. This order results because each of the wavelengths in the white light is refracted by a different amount. Each color consists of a narrow range of wavelengths. Red light has the longest wavelengths humans can see. Violet has the shortest ones. The photons of light of each color of the spectrum have a certain range of energies. Photons of red light have less energy than photons of violet light.

Luminous objects give off light of one or more colors. The sun gives off light of all wavelengths, and the amount of blue light is the same as the amount of red light. An ordinary light bulb gives off light of all wavelengths, but its red light is stronger than its blue light. If you take a color photograph indoors using ordinary light bulbs and one outdoors in the presence of sunlight, the film will show the difference between the two sources of light. Because the light bulbs give off more red light, the photograph taken inside is redder than the one taken in the sunlight.

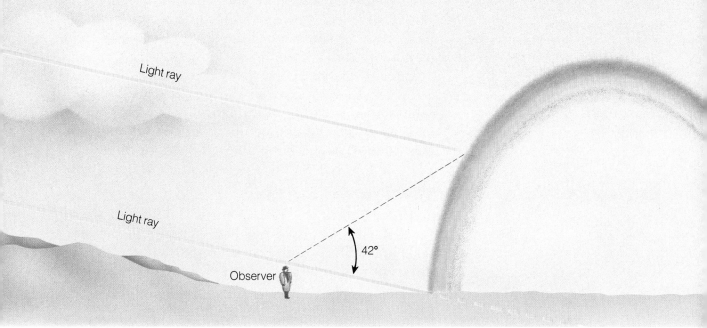

Light ray

Light ray

Observer

42°

How Rainbows Form

Rainbows, such as the one shown, are additional proof that the visible spectrum is actually a band of colors. Sometimes during or after a rain shower, drops of water in the sky act like prisms. As a ray of sunlight enters a rain droplet, the ray is refracted, as shown in *Figure 18-6*. The droplet separates the light into bands of different colors. As the ray hits the inner surface of the back of the raindrop, it is reflected. As the ray leaves the drop, it is refracted again. The raindrop thus acts as a tiny prism making it possible for the components of the visible spectrum to be seen.

Every raindrop breaks the sunlight that enters it into many colors. But you see only one color from each raindrop. The color you see depends on the angle between the raindrop and the line formed by the sun's rays. Each band of color in the rainbow occurs at a specific angle. If you measure the angle between the red band and the line formed by the sun's rays, you would see that it is about 42°, as *Figure 18-7* shows. The color in each of the other bands of the rainbow is formed by rays that reach your eye at a specific angle. Each of these other colored bands occurs at an angle slightly less than 42° from the sun's rays. Even though all the colors of the visible spectrum are present in the rainbow, they blend into one another.

Figure 18-7 Each color band in the rainbow forms by rays that reach your eye at a specific angle.

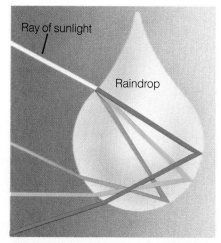

Ray of sunlight

Raindrop

Figure 18-6 The raindrop separates sunlight into bands of different colors.

You can see a rainbow when the sun is behind you and the sky in front of you is filled with moisture. If the sun is near the horizon and you are standing on a mountaintop, you might even see a rainbow as a complete circle, not just an arc.

Rainbows form in many different places. You might see a rainbow form from the droplets in a sprinkler hose. On sunny days, you might notice a rainbow over or near a waterfall. Sometimes you can see more than one rainbow at the same time.

The Colors of the Sky

At the end of the 19th century, the English scientist Lord Rayleigh figured out how particles in the air reflect light. He found that small particles reflect light differently than large particles. Particles that are much too small to be seen reflect, or "scatter," light in many directions. This effect is known as *Rayleigh scattering*.

The air contains molecules of various gases. The molecules are very small. They scatter light of shorter wavelengths more than they scatter light of longer wavelengths, in accordance with Rayleigh's law. Because blue light has shorter wavelengths than red light, the molecules scatter blue light much more than they scatter red light. As sunlight passes through the air on its way to the earth's surface, its blue wavelengths are scattered. As a result, the sky looks blue.

At sunset, the sun is low in the sky. As the drawing shows, its light passes through more air before reaching the earth than it did during the day. The air scatters more of the blue wavelengths away.

Figure 18-8 On earth, the sky looks blue during the day and reddish at sunset because of Rayleigh scattering.

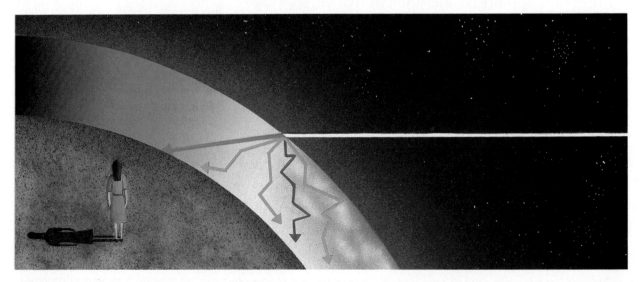

At the time of day when you see sunset, how might the sky appear to people who live in parts of the world where the sun's rays are more direct?

Water droplets often form around bits of dust in the air, making a cloud. The droplets in clouds are too large to scatter light according to Rayleigh's law. Clouds in the sky scatter all colors equally. Because white is a mixture of all the colors of light, the scattered light makes clouds look white.

Section Review

1. What determines the color of light?
2. Why do the colors of the rainbow form separate bands?
3. Why is the sky reddish at sunset and blue at noon?

Challenge: If you pass a flashlight beam through a prism, a visible spectrum is produced. Could you put the colors back together again using a prism? Explain.

People and Science

Max Planck, Father of Modern Physics

Max Planck's work ushered in modern physics, paving the way for the atomic theory and a whole new way of looking at our world.

Planck was born in Kiel, Germany in 1858. He graduated from the University of Munich in 1874 and received his Ph. D. in 1879. He taught physics at the universities in Kiel and in Berlin.

Planck's main interest was thermodynamics. Thermodynamics is the study of energy relationships, such as those involved in work, heat, and temperature. He knew that substances, or objects, absorb all frequencies of radiation then give off this energy again, sometimes at a different frequency. At that time, there was no satisfactory explanation of how the absorbed energy was given off. According

to Planck, an object gives off energy in sudden bursts.

He determined that energy exists in extremely small but distinct units. He called them quanta—from the Latin *quantum*, meaning "how much?" He

found that the amount of energy gained or lost divided by the frequency of the energy is a constant. Planck used the letter *h* to designate this constant. In the world of physicists and mathematicians, it became known as "Planck's constant."

The concept that energy is given off in quanta was simple but radical. Planck wondered whether his theory was correct or whether he had made a mathematical error. In a few years, Albert Einstein used Planck's quantum theory to explain the photoelectric effect. Since that time, the quantum theory has been a guiding force for physicists all over the world. Max Planck was awarded the Nobel Prize in 1918 for his work.

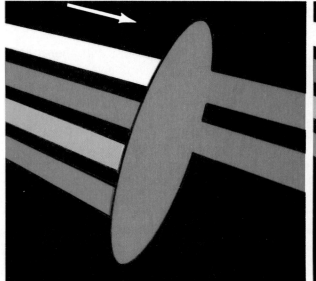

Objectives

After completing this section you will be able to

A. Explain what causes an object to appear colored.
B. Tell what the color of a transparent object depends on.
C. Compare the mixing of primary colors in light to the mixing of primary colors in paints.

18-3 How Objects Appear Colored

Color and Reflected Light

Color is an important part of our lives, though we often take it for granted. Imagine what it would be like if the whole world looked as it does on black-and-white television.

What causes the colors of objects? Most of the objects that you see around you absorb certain colors of light and reflect others. The color an object appears to be is really the color of light the object reflects—the color your eyes see. For example, a green leaf appears greenish because it reflects mainly green light. It absorbs most of the other colors. A tomato looks red when sunlight or other white light is shining on it because it reflects mainly the red wavelengths of white light while absorbing the others.

As *Figure 18-9* shows, a color filter allows only light of the same color as the filter to pass through. If light without green wavelengths strikes a green leaf, the leaf absorbs most of the light. The leaf then appears black, since it reflects almost no light. In the same way, if you look at a tomato through a filter that keeps all red wavelengths from passing, the tomato absorbs nearly all the light that hits it. It appears to be not red, but black. Black is the absence of light. When no light reaches you from an object, the object looks black.

Figure 18-9 A color filter allows only light of the same color to pass through. Only red light passes through a red filter and only blue light through a blue filter.

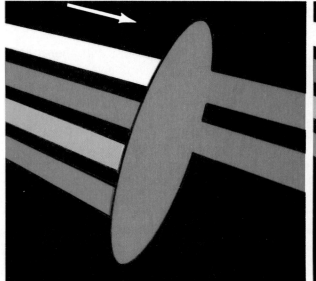
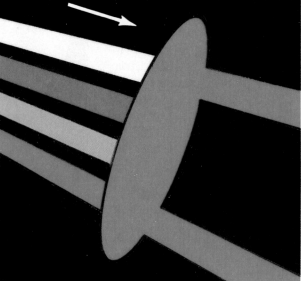

The color of an object can seem to change depending on the kind of light source that shines on it. A regular light bulb gives off light that is strong in red wavelengths. Light from some types of fluorescent lamps, on the other hand, is stronger in blue wavelengths. Compare the photographs of the gym shoes. Why do both shoes look black in the photograph taken with a blue filter?

Color and Transmitted Light

A tomato and a leaf are **opaque** objects—light does not pass through them. As you know, the color of an opaque object depends on the color of light that it reflects. But what about glass, which is **transparent?** Light passes right through a transparent object so that you can see what is behind it. Transparent objects **transmit** light, or let light through.

The color of a transparent object depends on the color of the light that it transmits. Some blue glass absorbs all the colors of white light except for blue. This blue glass transmits only blue wavelengths. Consider how a red tomato and a green leaf appear when viewed through a filter of this blue glass. The glass transmits no red or green light, so both the tomato and the leaf appear black.

The glass in ordinary windows transmits all the colors of white light equally well. For that reason, this type of windowpane is colorless. When viewed through a colorless glass, a tomato looks red and a leaf looks green.

Figure 18-10 Colors of opaque objects change when viewed through filters that transmit certain wavelengths.

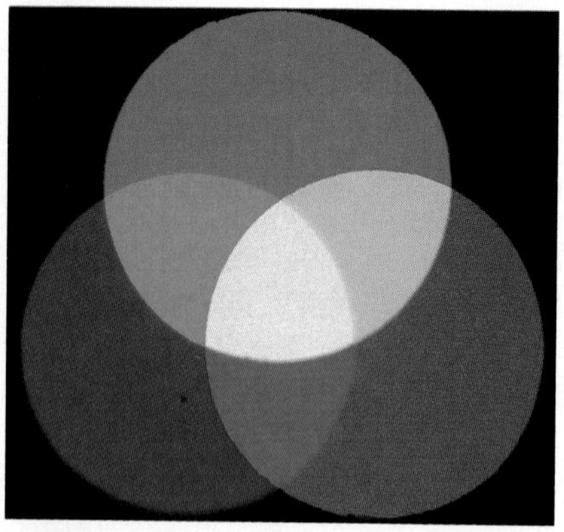

Figure 18-11 A photograph of the three primary colors in light and of the colors they make when they overlap.

The Primary Colors in Light and in Paint

You already know that white light can be broken down into all the colors of the spectrum. Yet white light can actually be formed by just three of these colors, as shown in *Figure 18-11*. These three colors—red, blue, and green—are the **primary colors in light**. Notice also that where the blue light and the green light overlap, you see a color called cyan. Where the blue light and the red light overlap you see magenta.

Color televisions work by combining the three primary colors. A close look at the screen shows that its picture is made of clusters of only red, blue, and green dots. From far enough away, your eye blends the dots together to produce a wide range of colors. When only red and green dots are glowing, you see yellow. The close-up of a white design on a television screen in *Figure 18-12* shows glowing dots of all three colors.

The **primary colors in paint** are magenta, yellow, and cyan. They are sometimes referred to simply as red, yellow, and blue, but this is not accurate. Using only the three primary colors, an artist can make a wide range of other colors.

Mixing colors of paint has different results from mixing the same colors of light. In *Figure 18-11*, cyan light and yellow light mix to make white light.

Figure 18-12 A close-up of a television screen shows glowing red, blue, and green dots.

However, mixing cyan and yellow paint makes green. Mixing the three primary colors in light makes white. Mixing the three primary color in paint makes black.

The different results are due to the different properties of light and paint. The nature of light allows one color to be *added* to another. The solid particles in paint act as filters and, as a result, the colors are *subtracted* from one another. For example, when you mix cyan paint and yellow paint, the cyan-colored paint particles absorb wavelengths of blue and violet light. Only the wavelengths of green and yellow light are reflected by the mixture. The mixture of cyan paint and yellow paint looks bright green.

Similarly, a mixture of cyan paint and magenta paint looks blue because the mixture filters out all of the wavelengths in white light except that giving a blue color. A mixture of yellow paint and magenta paint looks red because the mixture filters out all the wavelengths except those giving a red color.

What enables you to see colors? Certain cells in your eyes are sensitive to color. The back of the human eye contains small cells called *rods* and *cones*. Rods enable you to see in black and white in dim light. When light is bright, cones provide you with color vision.

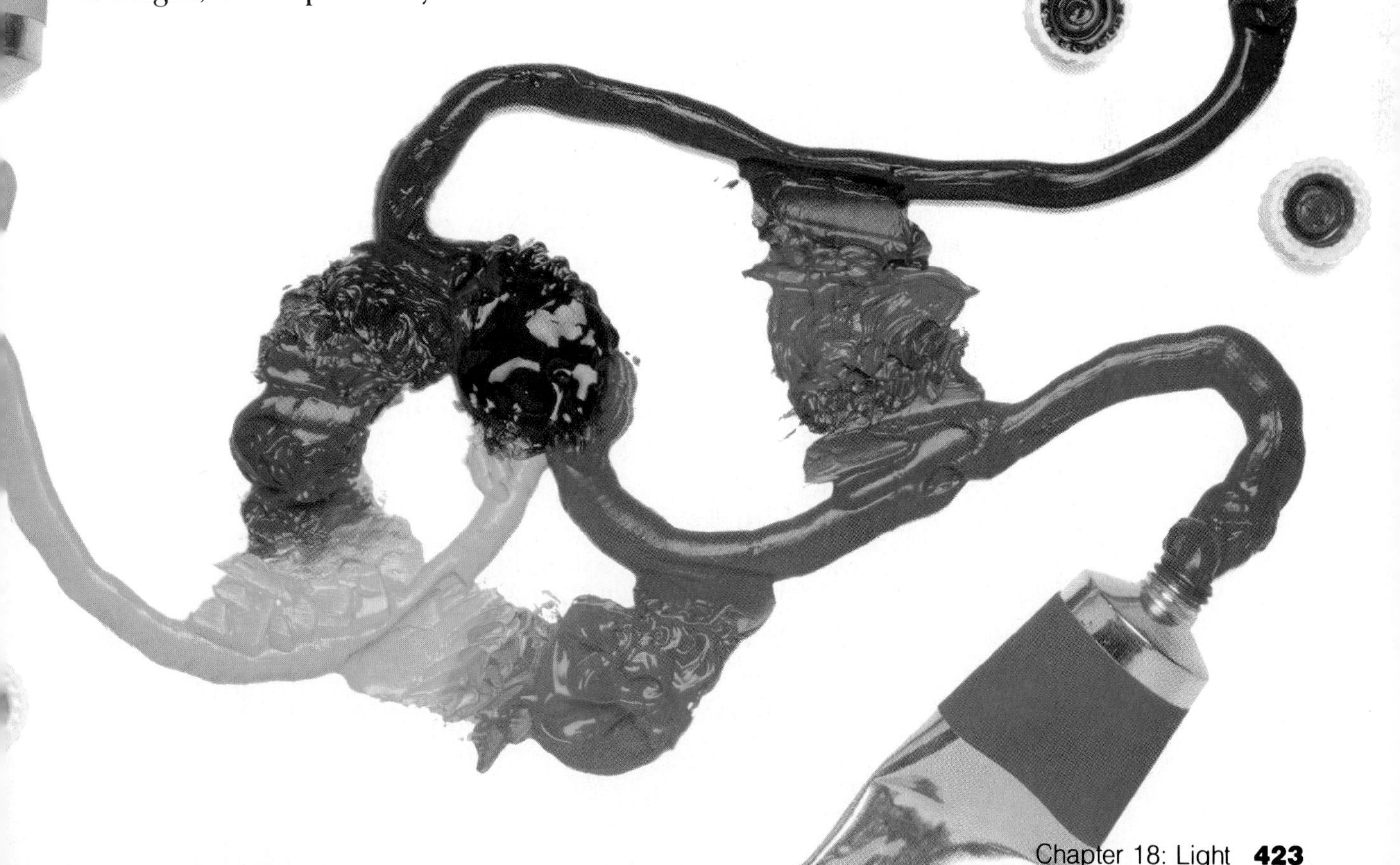

Figure 18-13 Mixing colors of paint has different results from mixing colors of light.

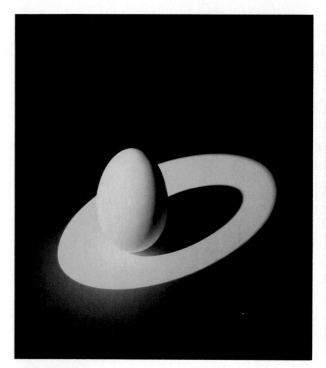
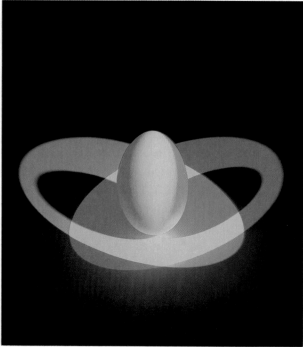

Figure 18-14 A white object looks yellow in a yellow light. It also looks yellow in a mixture of red light and green light.

Cones are of three types: those most sensitive to blue light, those most sensitive to green light, and those most sensitive to red light. The colors you perceive depend on how much the three types of cones are stimulated by the light entering your eyes.

Consider a lamp that puts out a range of wavelengths that center around yellow in the visible spectrum. Yellow is between green and red, so its wavelengths are a combination of both. Because they give roughly equal signals to the green-sensitive cones and to the red-sensitive cones, you see yellow. Now consider a lamp that puts out only some green and some red, but no yellow. The green-sensitive cones and the red-sensitive cones still receive yellow, even though there was no yellow in the original light. Similarly, the white egg in *Figure 18-14* looks yellow either in yellow light or in a mixture of red and green light.

Section Review

1. What parts of sunlight does a red apple absorb?
2. What colors of light does a red glass absorb?
3. What do you get on mixing the primary colors in light?

Challenge: What color of light can you mix with magenta light to produce white light?

Colors in White Light

Purpose

To investigate how the colors of light make up white light

Materials

- 2 cardboard disks, each 5 cm in diameter
- 2 buttons at least 3 cm in diameter
- red, orange, yellow, green, blue, and violet colored papers, felt pens, or paints
- glue or double-sided tape
- 1-meter-long piece of string or thread
- pencil
- straightedge
- scissors

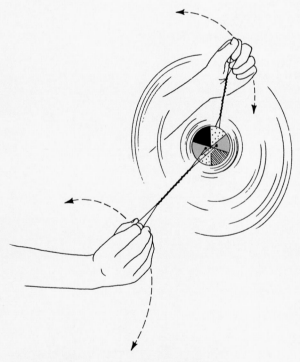

Procedure and Observations

PART A

1. Use the straightedge to mark off six nearly equal pie-shaped sections on one side of one disk.

2. Put a different color on each section of the disk. Do this by cutting and pasting the colored paper sections or using markers or paints on the disks.
3. Paste one flat button in the center of the disk on the blank side.
4. Punch two holes in the center of the disk by pushing a pencil point through two button holes.
5. Thread the string or thread through the two holes. Tie the open ends together with a knot.
6. Slip one index finger through each end of the string. With the disk in the middle of the string, twist the string at least 20 times.
7. Pull on the string in opposite directions, as shown. Loosen your pull as the string twists in one direction and then the other.
8. Watch the disk when it twirls the fastest. Record the color you see.
9. Repeat steps 7-8 several times.

PART B
1. Draw some black lines in patterns on the disk.
2. Repeat steps 6-9.

PART C
1. Repeat Part A, except divide the disk into halves, colored red and blue.
2. Record the color you see.

Analysis and Conclusions

1. Explain why you saw different colors in Part A and Part C.
2. What effect did the black markings have on the color you saw in Part B?

Reading a Graph of Illumination vs. Distance

In an experiment, a small bulb was used as a source of light. A light meter with a special scale was used to measure the intensity of the light given off by the bulb. The scale showed each intensity measurement in relative units. That is, 5 is 5 times greater than 1, 10 is 10 times greater than 1, and so on.

The intensity of the light was measured at a number of distances from the bulb. The results were plotted to produce the graph below. The value for each intensity measurement is given in parentheses.

1. How does the intensity change as the distance between the light source and the light meter increases?

2. When the distance increases from 200 cm to 400 cm, what is the change in intensity? (Give the difference in their intensities and the direction of change.)

3. When the distance increases from 200 cm to 800 cm, what is the change in intensity?

4. On the basis of your answers to questions 2 and 3, what change in intensity would you expect if the distance were increased from 200 cm to 1000 cm? Is this about what you would expect to find if the graph line were extended?

5. Write one or two general statements relating distance and intensity of light.

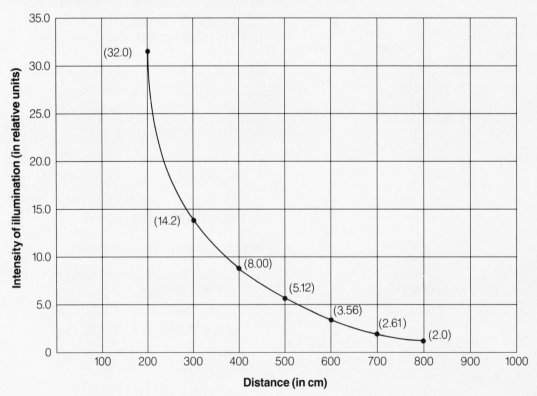

Intensity of Illumination vs. Distance from light source

✔ Summary

18-1 The Nature of Light

A. Light travels in straight lines called rays as it spreads out from its source. The rate at which light falls upon, or illuminates, a given surface area is its intensity.

B. When an atom of a substance releases energy, it gives off photons of light. Energy is released as electrons within the atom move from a higher energy level to a lower one.

C. Light has properties of both particles and waves and can behave in a manner consistent with either property.

18-2 The Visible Spectrum

A. White light is composed of the colors red, orange, yellow, green, blue, indigo, and violet. A prism will reflect each wavelength of light by a different amount, allowing each color to be seen separately.

B. Rainbows form as rays of sunlight pass through raindrops. Each raindrop, acting like a tiny prism, refracts a sunbeam, separating it into bands of different colored light.

C. As sunlight passes through the atmosphere before reaching the earth, its blue wavelengths are scattered, thus producing what is observed as a blue sky. This effect, in which molecules in the air scatter light in many directions, is known as Rayleigh scattering.

18-3 How Objects Appear Colored

A. The color an opaque object appears to be is the color of light the object reflects. The color of an object can seem to change depending on the kind of light that shines on it.

B. The color a transparent object appears to be is the color of light the object transmits.

C. The primary colors in light are red, green, and blue. When these colors are combined, the result is white. The primary colors in paint are red, blue, and yellow. When the primary colors in paint are combined, the result is black.

Vocabulary

For each of the following terms, write a sentence that uses the term correctly.

intensity	primary colors in light	transmit
luminous	primary colors in paint	transparent
opaque	prism	visible spectrum
photon	shadow	

✔ Check Your Knowledge

Part I: Matching Match the definition in Column I with the correct term in Column II.

Column I
1. a bundle of light energy
2. the colors red, blue, and green
3. a wedge-shaped piece of glass or plastic capable of refracting light
4. the small range of electromagnetic wavelengths that humans can see
5. what an object through which light can pass is called
6. the rate at which light falls upon a surface area
7. what an object that gives off its own light is called
8. the result of blocked light rays
9. what an object through which light does not pass is called
10. the colors yellow, blue, and red

Column II
a. intensity
b. luminous
c. opaque
d. photon
e. primary colors in light
f. primary colors in paint
g. prism
h. shadow
i. transmit
j. transparent
k. visible spectrum

Part II: Multiple Choice Choose the letter of the best answer.

11. Which of the following most accurately describes how light behaves? (a) as a particle (b) as a wave (c) as both a particle and a wave (d) as neither a particle nor a wave
12. If light passes through an object, the object is said to be (a) opaque. (b) luminous. (c) transparent. (d) in shadow.
13. When skies look blue, the wavelengths of light being scattered most are (a) blue. (b) green. (c) yellow. (d) red.
14. Which of the following colors has the shortest wavelength and gives off photons of the highest energy? (a) green (b) red (c) yellow (d) violet
15. Combining equal intensities of the primary colors in light results in (a) black. (b) white. (c) cyan. (d) magenta.
16. Combining equal intensities of the primary colors in paint results in (a) black. (b) white. (c) cyan. (d) magenta.

Part III: Completion Write the word or words that complete the sentence correctly.
17. Streams of photons make up _____.
18. Prisms and droplets of water can both refract white light into a band of colors called the _____.
19. The fact that molecules in the air are responsible for reflecting white light in a way such that the sky appears blue and sunsets red is due to an effect known as _____.
20. An object, such as a tomato or a leaf, through which light does not pass, is said to be _____.
21. The cells at the back of the human eye that are sensitive to different light intensities are the _____ and _____.

Check Your Understanding

1. Why do shadows form?
2. Explain how a neon light works.
3. Why is it not entirely right to say that light behaves like waves?
4. Compare the wavelengths and energies of red and blue light.
5. Why does this page look white and the print black?
6. What would this page look like under a red light?
7. In what way do raindrops act like prisms to form a rainbow?
8. Why are clouds white?
9. What is the difference between a transparent object and an opaque object?
10. How does the color of a blue coat change when you look at it in a dark room under a neon light?

 Apply Your Knowledge

1. The astronauts on the moon saw "earthlight" much as we see moonlight. Explain why.
2. When the upper atmosphere contains ice crystals, a halo often appears around the moon. How is the halo similar to a rainbow in the sky?
3. If you let red light from a prism pass through a hole that blocks the other colors and lets that red light pass through a second prism, what happens at the second prism? What color or colors emerge?
4. If you want to carry a rock up a hill but lack the strength to do the job at once, your can roll the rock uphill in gradual stages. If an electron receives some additional energy but not quite enough to raise it to a higher energy level, can it move to the higher energy level in stages? Explain.
5. Is a red rose petal a better reflector of long-wavelength or short-wavelength light?

 Extend Your Knowledge

Research/Projects

1. Find out which gases give off the different colors used in "neon signs."
2. Contact the staff at a local greenhouse or florist shop. Ask whether they use special lights to grow plants.
3. Partially fill a baking pan with water. Lean a flat mirror inside the pan from the bottom to an upper edge. Shine light from the sun or a flashlight directly on the mirror. Look at a nearby wall and explain what you see.

Readings

Asimov, Isaac. *How Did We Find Out About the Speed of Light?* Walker, 1986. Discusses the vastness of space by using examples of the travel times of light from various stars.

Fritz, Sandy. "Sailing on Sunbeams." *Scholastic Science World*, September 22, 1986, pages 35-36. Explains how sunbeams may be used to push spaceships through space.

CHAPTER 19
Optics

The photograph shows a lacy pattern produced in a kaleidoscope. This device contains two flat mirrors and bits of colored paper. An image is reflected over and over again to make the colorful pattern. Mirrors, such as those used in toys and in fun houses, provide people with amusement. However, mirrors also have many practical uses.

Organizing Your Study Skills The outline below will help you see how the chapter is organized and what you should learn as you read.

I. Section 19-1: Plane Mirrors
  A. How does a plane mirror reflect light?
  B. How are plane mirrors useful?

II. Section 19-2: Curved Mirrors
  A. What is a focal point?
  B. How does a concave mirror affect light rays?
  C. How does a convex mirror affect light rays?
  D. How are curved mirrors useful?

III. Section 19-3: Lenses
  A. How do convex lenses affect light rays?
  B. How do concave lenses affect light rays?

IV. Section 19-4: Eyes, Lenses, and Optical Illusions
  A. How do the cornea and lens in your eye focus light?
  B. How can vision be corrected?
  C. How do other animals see?
  D. What is a mirage?

V. Section 19-5: Using Lenses and Mirrors
  A. How does a camera form an image?
  B. How do telescopes use lenses and mirrors?
  C. How do microscopes use lenses and mirrors?

Explore!

Use your understanding of reflection to explain why a plane mirror must be at least half your height if you want to see yourself full length in it. Use diagrams to explain.

Figure 19-1 How an image forms in a plane mirror

19-1 Plane Mirrors

Plane Mirrors Reflect Light

Folk tales tell you that mirrors have fascinated people for ages. The witch in *Snow White* had a magic mirror. Narcissus in the Greek legend fell in love with his own image. What you see in a mirror might fascinate you, but it is not magic. You see reflected light.

Any smooth surface that reflects light acts as a mirror. **Plane mirrors** are flat surfaces that reflect light. Usually they are smooth pieces of glass backed by silvering and a dark surface.

The rules of reflection apply for light reflected from a plane mirror. The angle at which a light ray hits the surface of a plane mirror equals the angle at which the reflected ray leaves the mirror's surface, as shown in *Figure 19-1*.

The scene or object you see in a mirror is the image of that object. The image seems to be behind the mirror, as indicated by the dotted lines in the picture. In fact, the image appears to be as far behind the mirror as the object is in front of the mirror. Yet you know that neither the object nor the image is really behind the mirror. This image is a **virtual image**, which means the image seems to be in one place, but it is not really there. If you put a sheet of paper where the image seems to be, no image will appear on the paper.

When you look at your reflection in a plane mirror, the image is right side up and the same size as you are. But if you raise your right hand, the image looking back at you from the mirror seems to have raised his or her left hand. The "mirror image" *seems* to be flipped from left to right.

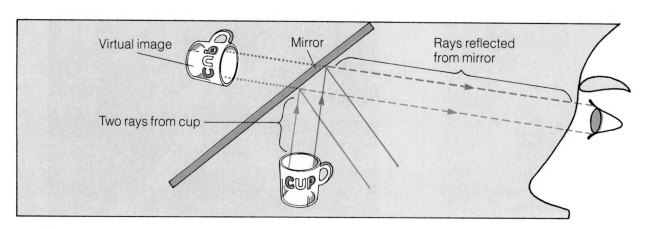

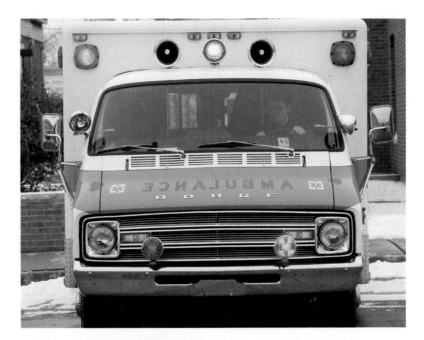

Figure 19-2 Plane mirrors flip the image from left to right

Uses of Plane Mirrors

Most mirrors in your home are plane mirrors. Bedroom doors and medicine cabinets often have plane mirrors attached to them. People use plane mirrors because the images they produce have the same proportions as the object.

Rearview mirrors inside automobiles and outside the driver's window are usually plane mirrors. The images you see in them show the true size and distance of an object. If you see the image of a car in a plane rearview mirror, you can judge how far away the car is.

On the other hand, the image in a rearview mirror is flipped. Compare the photographs in *Figure 19-2*. Notice that the letters in the word *AMBULANCE* are flipped. However, the driver using a rearview mirror sees *AMBULANCE* written as it should be.

In *Figure 19-3*, several plane mirrors used together make a periscope. Periscopes help people see around corners. Sometimes a periscope is used to see over a crowd. Submarines have long used periscopes to see what is above the ocean while remaining under the surface.

Section Review

1. What kind of image does a plane mirror form?
2. State two uses of plane mirrors.

Challenge: Explain why you cannot shake hands with yourself in a plane mirror.

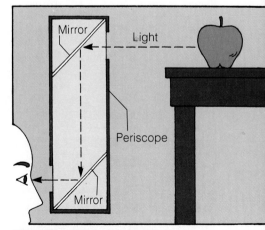

Figure 19-3 Plane mirrors in a periscope allow you to see around a corner.

Objectives

After completing this section you will be able to

A. Explain what a focal point is.

B. Describe how a concave mirror affects light rays.

C. Describe how a convex mirror affects light rays.

D. Explain how curved mirrors are used.

19-2   Curved Mirrors

Focal Point

The story is told that around 220 B.C., the Greek scientist Archimedes used shiny metal shields as plane mirrors. He used the shields to focus the sun's light on an enemy ship. The sunlight was so intense that it started a fire that destroyed the ship.

In *Figure 19-4a,* several plane mirrors are arranged on a curve. The light rays that hit the mirrors at an angle bounce off at the same angle. You can arrange the mirrors so that all the parallel light rays are reflected to one spot, as Archimedes did with the metal shields. Bringing light rays together at one point is called focusing the rays.

Now consider one curved mirror that follows the curve in which the plane mirrors are arranged. In *Figure 19-4b,* light rays are coming toward the mirror from the left. The rays are parallel to each other and to a line through the center of the mirror. This curved mirror focuses the parallel rays to a point, which is called the **focal point**. The distance from the center of the mirror to the focal point is called the **focal length**.

Concave Mirrors Focus Light Rays

One kind of curved mirror—a **concave mirror**—curves like the surface of a ball as seen from the inside. The inside of the spoon shown in *Figure 19-5* is a concave mirror.

Figure 19-4 Each of the three plane mirrors reflects one of the rays of light toward the same point as the others. The curved mirror focuses the light rays to the focal point.

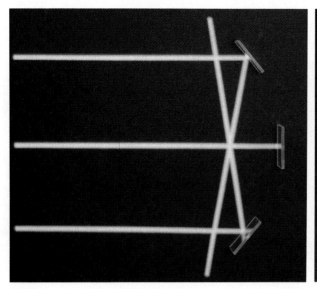
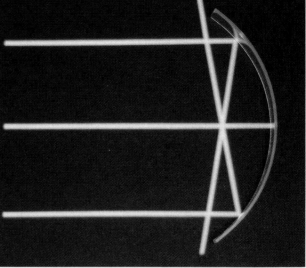

The image that a concave mirror forms depends on how far the object is from the mirror. Follow the four light rays from the distant object, shown in *Figure 19-6*. Each ray hits the mirror at an angle and bounces off that spot at the same angle. You can imagine that a tiny flat mirror is there.

To find out where the image of the top of the pencil is focused, follow the two blue rays. Look at the blue ray from the top of the pencil parallel to the center line. All rays parallel to the center line pass through the focal point after they are reflected. Next, look at the blue ray that passes directly through the focal point. Rays passing through the focal point bounce off the mirror parallel to the center line. The image of the top of the pencil appears where the two dashed blue lines meet.

Tracing the two red rays shows where the image of the bottom of the pencil appears. Notice that the image of the pencil is in front of the mirror, upside down, and smaller than the pencil itself. This image is called a real image. A **real image** is one that would appear on a piece of paper or a screen placed there.

Note that an object farther from the mirror than the focal point always has an upside-down, real image. In addition, when the image is more than two focal lengths from the mirror, as it is in *Figure 19-6a,* the image is smaller than the object.

In *Figure 19-6b,* the pencil is between one and two focal lengths from the mirror. Follow the rays to see that an upside-down, real image forms in this case, too. But now the image is larger than the object.

Applying Science

A concave mirror can be used as a solar cooker. The heat of the focused light can cook food.

Figure 19-5 The inside of a spoon is a concave mirror.

Figure 19-6 How a concave mirror forms images much further from the mirror than the focal point and between one and two focal lengths from the mirror

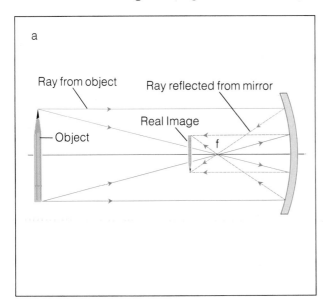

a

Ray from object   Ray reflected from mirror

Real Image

Object   f

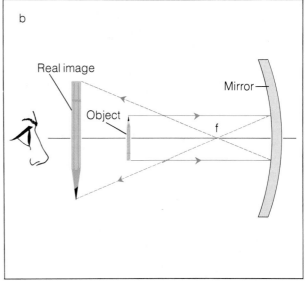

b

Real image   Mirror

Object   f

The pencil in *Figure 19-7* is closer to the mirror than the focal point. Again choose pairs of rays to follow. The reflected rays, shown again as dashed lines, would never meet, so we follow them backwards, shown as dotted lines. The image forms where the dotted lines meet. The image is right side up and larger than the pencil. Also, the image is virtual. No rays actually meet there. The image would not show up on paper.

Convex Mirrors Spread Light Rays Apart

A second kind of curved mirror—a **convex mirror**—curves like the surface of a ball as seen from the outside. The backside of the spoon in *Figure 19-8* is a convex mirror. If you look at your reflection on the backside of a spoon, you will see a small image of yourself right side up.

The drawing in *Figure 19-9* shows how a convex mirror forms an image. A convex mirror makes light rays spread out, as shown with the dashed lines. Again, dotted lines show where the dashed lines are traced backwards. The spreading rays seem to come from the point where the dotted lines meet. This point is always behind a convex mirror. The image is virtual because light rays only seem to come from this point. The image therefore will not show up on a piece of paper if you hold it there. The image formed in a convex mirror is always smaller than the object. The closer to the mirror the object is, the larger the image is.

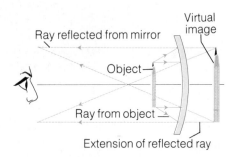

Figure 19-7 How a concave mirror forms an image of an object closer to the mirror than the focal point.

Figure 19-8 Convex mirrors are often used in store security.

Figure 19-9 The image that forms in a convex mirror is always behind the mirror, smaller than the object, and right-side up.

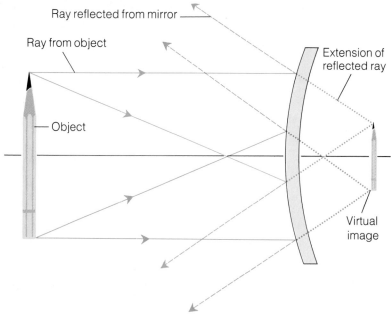

Uses of Curved Mirrors

You might have amused yourself by looking at your image in funhouse mirrors. When you look at yourself in the concave part of a mirror, you look short. In the convex part of the mirror, your image is stretched out. Curved mirrors also have more practical uses.

Flashlights, searchlights, and headlights contain concave mirrors. In these lights, the source of light is at the focal point. The mirrors are shaped so that light rays from the focal point are reflected outward in parallel rays, as in *Figure 19-10*. Directing light rays in this way is the opposite of focusing them to a point.

Concave mirrors can focus electromagnetic waves other than light. A radio antenna uses a concave mirror made of wire mesh to focus incoming parallel radio waves to a point. The giant radio telescope shown in *Figure 19-11* is the largest in the world. Its concave mirror is wider than the length of three football fields. The mirror focuses the radio waves onto the receiver suspended at the focal point. The telescope detects faint radio waves from objects in the universe.

A more familiar example of a concave mirror is the shaving or makeup mirror often found in bathrooms. If you are close to the mirror, your image is magnified and right side up. It is a virtual image. It is not useful to use these mirrors from far away, for then your image would be small and upside down.

Cars and trucks have one plane rearview mirror inside the vehicle and another plane mirror outside the driver's door. However, they sometimes have convex rearview mirrors outside the passenger door. The convex mirror lets the driver see objects that are farther off to the side than a plane mirror does. Convex mirrors are also sometimes used in banks and stores. These mirrors give clerks and store detectives a view of a wide area of the store.

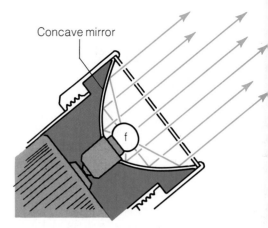

Figure 19-10 The light bulb is placed at the focal point of the concave mirror.

Figure 19-11 The radio telescope at Arecibo, Puerto Rico, has a giant concave mirror.

Section Review

1. At what point do parallel light rays reflected from a curved mirror come together?
2. How does a concave mirror focus light?
3. How does a convex mirror make light rays spread?
4. State three uses of curved mirrors.

Challenge: Explain why your image reflected from chrome bicycle handlebars is tall and thin.

Roger Angel

Traditionally, people have made telescope mirrors by grinding and polishing large pieces of glass until the glass had the correct curvature. This process requires a great deal of time, effort, and expense. For instance, workers spent seven years grinding and polishing the mirror for California's Palomar telescope.

The big mirrors are very sensitive to temperature changes and very fragile. Thus, the production and moving of large mirrors is a major problem.

Roger Angel, an astronomer at the University of Arizona, has simplified telescope-making. Dr. Angel designed the Multiple Mirror Telescope. It consists of six 1.8-meter mirrors that work together as one large mirror. The telescope has the light-gathering power of a single 4.8-meter mirror.

The multiple-mirror telescope has its flaws. Air turbulence causes more blurring when more than one mirror is used. But Dr. Angel proved that telescopes with more than one mirror are good alternatives to conventional telescopes.

Dr. Angel also designed and built a rotating oven to shape the large blocks of glass. As molten glass spins in the oven, it takes on the desired curved shape. This process eliminates—or cuts down on—the usual grinding and polishing required for mirror-making. Dr. Angel's creative ideas and designs are giving telescope makers a new approach to the old art of telescope-making.

Objectives

After completing this section you will be able to
A. Describe how convex lenses affect light rays.
B. Describe how concave lenses affect light rays.

19-3 Lenses

Convex Lenses Focus Light Rays

Refraction is the bending of light as it passes from one transparent material to another. How much the light bends depends on what the two materials are and on the angle at which light hits the surfaces.

A piece of glass or other transparent material that is shaped so that light hitting it always bends to make an image is called a **lens**. Light travels more slowly in a lens than in the surrounding air. For that reason, a light ray is refracted both where it enters the lens and where it comes out of the lens back into the air.

The surfaces of lenses usually are ground or molded into a smooth curve. As *Figure 19-12* shows, a lens can be flat, convex, or concave on one or both sides.

Convex lenses are thicker in the middle than at their edges. Convex lenses focus parallel light rays to a point, the focal point. The distance from the center of the lens to its focal point is the lens's focal length. You can assume that the lenses are so thin that all the refraction takes place at a line perpendicular to the center line. Actually, the refraction takes place only at the surfaces.

Lenses whose surfaces are curved by different amounts have different focal lengths. Look at the parallel light rays passing through the convex lenses in *a* and *b* of *Figure 19-13*. The three rays are shown in three different colors. In *a*, the lens is very thin and its surfaces are not very curved. You can see how far from the lens the focal point is. Compare this lens with the one in *b*. The lens in *b* is thicker and its surfaces are more curved. In this case, the focal point is closer to the lens.

Both drawings show that a convex lens bends light toward the center line. The upper and lower rays hit the lens parallel to the center line. The upper and lower rays bend as they pass through the lens, and meet at the focal point. However, the ray that passes through the center of each lens does not bend. The opposite sides of a convex lens are parallel near the center of the lens. So rays enter and leave the center without bending.

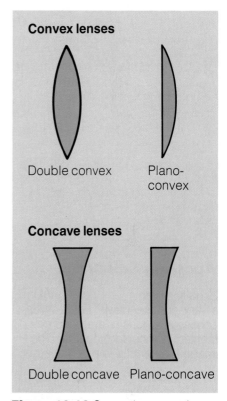

Convex lenses

Double convex   Plano-convex

Concave lenses

Double concave   Plano-concave

Figure 19-12 Convex lenses and concave lenses

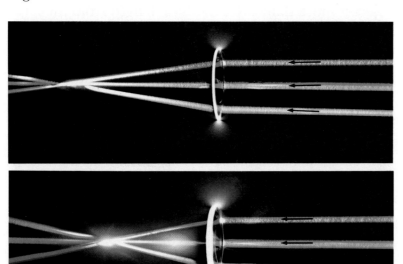

Figure 19-13 The surfaces of the lenses are curved by different amounts, so the lenses have different focal lengths.

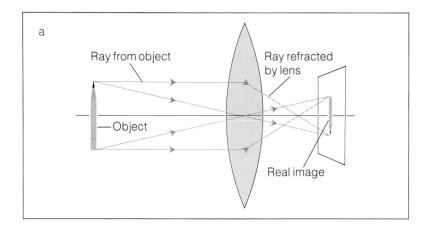

Figure 19-14 The object is more than two focal lengths from the lens in *a*. The object is less than one focal length from the lens in *b*.

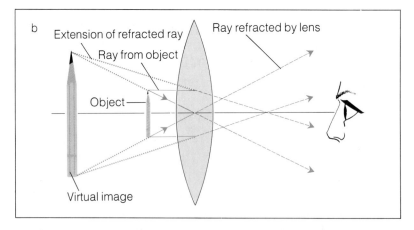

Figure 19-15 A magnifying glass contains a convex lens.

The kind of image a convex lens forms depends on the object's distance from the lens. In *Figure 19-14a*, the object is more than twice the focal length from the lens. An image appears on paper placed near the focal point, so this image is real. The image is upside down and smaller than the object.

In *Figure 19-14b*, the object is between the focal point and the lens. The rays do not come together on the far side of the lens. Again, you must trace the rays backward, as shown with the dotted lines. Where the dotted lines meet, a virtual image forms. No image shows up on paper placed where the image appears to be. The image appears right side up, larger than the object, and on the same side of the lens as the object.

In the Sherlock Holmes movies, the famous detective uses a magnifying glass to examine evidence from a crime. A magnifying glass contains a convex lens to make objects appear larger. These lenses are used to examine small objects, such as the small print on the metric ruler in *Figure 19-15*.

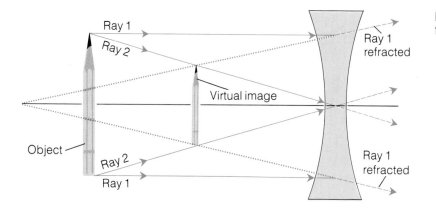

Figure 19-16 How a concave lens forms an image

Concave Lenses Spread Light Rays Apart

Another kind of lens, a **concave lens**, is thinner in its center than at its edges. A concave lens spreads light rays apart.

Figure 19-16 shows two pairs of rays reflected from the pencil. The two rays shown in red are from the top of the pencil and the two in blue from the bottom. For both pairs, ray 1 is parallel to the center line. Ray 1 bends when it passes through the lens. But since ray 1 bends outward, the focal point is on the near side of the lens. The focal point is the point at which the red dotted line and the blue dotted line intersect.

For both pairs, trace ray 1 backwards along the dotted line to the dot where ray 2 and the extension of ray 1 intersect. The top of the image appears at the red dot, and the bottom of the image appears at the blue dot. The rest of the image falls in-between.

The image appears right side up, smaller than the object, and on the same side of the lens. A paper would not show this virtual image because the light rays do not really meet at the image.

Although concave lenses are less common than convex lenses, they are useful for certain purposes. *Figure 19-17* shows a peephole containing a concave lens. Because of the lens, you have a good view of someone standing outside your door.

Section Review

1. Explain how a convex lens forms an image.
2. What happens to light rays when they pass through a concave lens?

Challenge: Why are convex mirrors used in stores for security purposes?

Figure 19-17 A peephole uses a concave lens to provide a wide view.

Activity 19-1

Lenses

Purpose

To observe how lenses affect light rays

Materials

- plastic wrap
- water
- piece of paper with printed words on it
- scissors
- paper towel
- color picture from a newspaper
- eye dropper
- ruler

Procedure and Observations

1. Cut out a piece of plastic wrap 5 cm × 5 cm .
2. Lay the plastic flat over the print on the paper. Note whether the plastic affects how the print appears.
3. Remove the plastic. Put a drop of water onto the plastic with your finger or an eye dropper, as in **a**. Make sure the drop is fairly large.

a

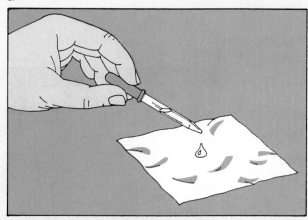

4. Blot any other water off the plastic with a paper towel.
5. Repeat step 2, but be sure that the drop is the only water on the plastic.

6. Move the plastic so that the drop is over a small letter "e." Slowly move the plastic toward you, as in **b**. Observe and record what happens to the image of the "e".
7. Hold the plastic so the "e" image is inverted. Move the plastic, first to the left, then to the right, along a line of print. Record which way the image moves each time.
8. Repeat step 7, but move the plastic toward the top and bottom of the page.
9. Use your drop to examine the newspaper picture. Record what you observe.

b

Analysis and Conclusions

1. Look at the pictures of lenses on page 440. Which lens is like your water drop lens?
2. What kind of image is formed when the water drop acts as a magnifying lens?
3. How are colors printed in the newspaper? What other objects do you know of that use this method to show color?

19-4 Eyes, Lenses, and Optical Illusions

How Your Eye Focuses Light

Your eyes are amazing organs that adapt to many conditions. For example, most people can see nearby objects as well as they can see distant objects. Refer to the drawings as you read how the eye works.

When you look at an object, the light it gives off or reflects enters the pupil, a small opening in your eye. Muscles in your eye adjust the size of the pupil to let in the right amount of light, as shown in *Figure 19-18a*.

Just as a watch is covered by a transparent crystal, the colored part of your eye has a transparent covering called the cornea. Under the cornea is the lens. Together, the cornea and lens act as a convex lens. They bend light rays from an object toward one another and focus them on the retina. The retina, which is in the back of the eye, is the part of your eye that is sensitive to light.

The lens and cornea produce an upside-down image on the retina, as shown in *Figure 19-18b*. The retina, in turn, converts the image into electrical messages and sends them to your brain. Your brain interprets the image as right side up. If the image were really right side up, your brain would perceive it as upside down.

You see best when the image on your retina is in focus. Your eye muscles help keep the image focused on your retina by changing the shape of the lens.

Notice the shapes of the lenses in *Figure 19-18b* and *c*. Light rays from nearby objects, such as the pencil in *b*, travel in all directions. Only four light rays are shown entering the eye. When this light reaches the eye, the muscles relax and the lens becomes rounder and thicker. The thicker lens has enough power to bend the light rays together and focus them.

Assume the pencil in *Figure 19-18c* is much farther from the eye. Light rays from distant objects are nearly parallel when they reach your eyes. To see a distant object clearly, the muscles tighten, making the lens thinner. The lens does not need to provide as much bending power to bring the parallel light rays together and focus them.

a
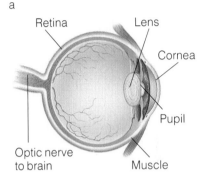

Figure 19-18a Some parts of the eye

b
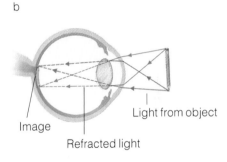

Figure 19-18b Light rays from a nearby object

c
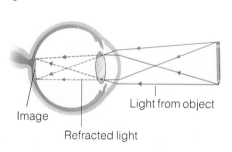

Figure 19-18c Light rays from a distant object

Correcting Vision

If the cornea and lens in your eye do not focus as they should, an extra lens usually can solve the problem. People who cannot see distant objects clearly are **nearsighted**. The retina is too far from the eye's lens. In *Figure 19-19a,* the lens focuses images of distant objects in front of the retina—not on the retina—so the images appear fuzzy. You can see how a concave lens, shown in *Figure 19-19b,* corrects the focus.

People who cannot see nearby objects clearly are **farsighted**. *Figure 19-19c* shows how a farsighted person sees. The retina is too near the lens. The images of nearby objects appear behind the retina. The images appear fuzzy because the light hits the retina before it can form a clear image. Notice in *Figure 19-19d* how a convex lens helps correct the focus.

Some people become more and more farsighted as they get older. In this case, the muscles become weaker, Thus, the lens does not thicken to see nearby objects well.

Another common visual problem is **astigmatism,** a condition in which the cornea is not shaped normally. The abnormal shape causes light rays to focus at different places. For example, some rays from an object may focus before they reach the retina. Other rays from the same object may focus on the retina. A person with an astigmatism usually sees blurred images of both distant and nearby objects. A lens with a special shape is used to help correct the problem. Such a lens is ground so that it bends light more powerfully in one direction than in others.

Figure 19-19 Corrective lenses help remedy nearsighted and farsighted vision.

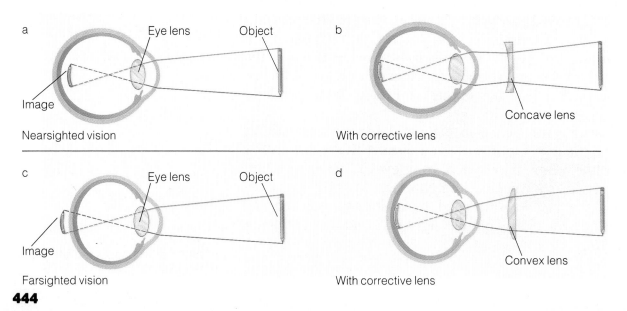

a — Nearsighted vision (Eye lens, Object, Image)

b — With corrective lens (Concave lens)

c — Farsighted vision (Eye lens, Object, Image)

d — With corrective lens (Convex lens)

The Eyes of Other Animals

Like the eyes of people, the eyes of many animals use lenses to form images. Many insects, such as the praying mantis shown in *Figure 19-20,* have two kinds of eyes. The two larges compound eyes have many tiny lenses. Each lens lets in light from a single direction. All the pieces of information combine to form an image of what the insect sees. Three small simple eyes form a triangle between the compound eyes. Each simple eye has only one lens. The simple eyes respond to light quickly, but they do not form images.

Most spiders have eight simple eyes. These eyes are arranged so that a spider can tell when something is moving. Spiders have no compound eyes. Most lobsters and crabs, on the other hand, have two compound eyes, and many have simple eyes as well.

Birds have the best vision of all animals, including humans. A vulture flying four kilometers above the earth's surface can see a dead animal lying below. Most birds have three eyelids on each eye. Two eyelids move up and down. Birds close these two eyelids when they sleep. They blink with the third eyelid, which moves from side to side.

Animals with backbones tend to have eyes that resemble human eyes. Animal habits, however, account for some differences. For example, animals that live in total darkness might have tiny eyes that can see little, if anything. But animals that hunt at night, such as owls, have huge eyes that let them see well in dim light.

The glowing eyes of the cat family have fascinated people for ages. In addition to a lens, cats have a mirror-like surface inside their eyeballs that reflects light onto the retina, making the cat's eyes appear to glow.

Figure 19-20 A praying mantis, like many other insects, has two compound eyes and three simple eyes.

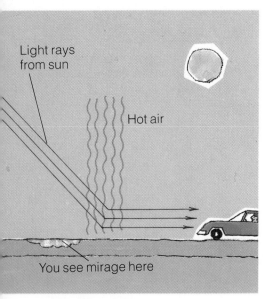

Figure 19-20a Hot air bends light rays upward.

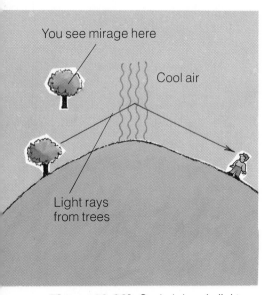

Figure 19-20b Cool air bends light rays downward.

Mirages Are Optical Illusions

Sometimes what you see is not really there. It is an optical illusion—a trick played on your eyes. A camera, which works like your eyes, can be tricked too. You can photograph some optical illusions.

Refraction of light by air can produce a **mirage**, which is a kind of optical illusion. A mirage is something you think you see that is not really there. Mirages happen because light is refracted when it passes from air of one temperature and density into air of another temperature and density. The greater the change in temperature, the greater the refraction of light. The atmosphere acts like a lens, producing the mirage.

When you ride in a car on a hot day, you might see what seems to be a puddle of water ahead of you. However, the puddle disappears as you approach it. What looks like a puddle was really light from the sky. The road heats up much more from sunlight hitting it than the air does. Heat from the road surface warms the air directly above it. Light rays speed up when they reach the hot air near the ground. Thus, the rays are refracted—or bent—upward, as shown in *Figure 19-20a*. The bending of the light rays causes the mirage.

Figure 19-20b shows a mirage caused by cold air near a surface. In this case, a distant object can appear very close and very large. A mirage once tricked the Arctic explorers, Robert E. Peary and Matthew Henson. On their way to the North Pole in 1906, they thought they saw a mountain range. But when they drew close, they realized they had seen a mirage. The mountains were real. But they were actually far from the place where the mirage made them appear to be.

Refraction made the mountains look closer and larger. As light rays from the mountains moved from air of one temperature to air at a lower temperature, they slowed down. The slowing caused the rays to bend downward, which created an optical illusion.

Section Review

1. How do eye lenses change shape to focus light?
2. Explain how lenses are used to correct poor vision.
3. Describe the eyes of insects.
4. How can air cause a mirage?

Challenge: Why do you think your eye cannot form a sharp image of a nearby object and of a distant object at the same time?

19-5 Using Lenses and Mirrors

Objectives

After completing this section you will be able to

A. Explain how a camera forms an image.

B. Describe how telescopes use lenses and mirrors.

C. Describe how microscopes use lenses and mirrors.

How a Camera Works

A camera uses a lens to photograph objects. A viewfinder allows you to look through the camera's lens to see what you want to photograph. When you press a button, called the shutter, light given off or reflected from an object enters a convex lens in the front of the camera.

A camera also has an opening to control the amount of light entering the lens. This opening can be adjusted. If you make the opening too large, too much light hits the film and the picture is light and faint. If you make the opening too small the picture is too dark.

The lens focuses light on the film, which is coated with chemicals that are sensitive to light. As *Figure 19-21* shows, a real, upside-down image forms on the film.

The eye has muscles that automatically change the shape of the lens to keep images in focus on the retina. The shape of most camera lenses cannot be changed. Several different lenses together make up the main lens of a good camera. To make the image sharp for objects at different distances, the positions of these lenses can be adjusted. The adjustment keeps the image focused on the film, no matter how far away the object is.

Different kinds of main lenses are used to produce pictures magnified by different amounts. A wide-angle lens is useful for photographing a large scene. A normal lens makes a scene appear the way it appears to the unaided eye. A telephoto lens is useful for making distant objects appear larger and closer.

Have You Heard?

The Italian painter Canaletto (1697-1768) used wide-angle and telephoto views of the city of Venice that he later painted.

Figure 19-21 How a camera's lens forms an image

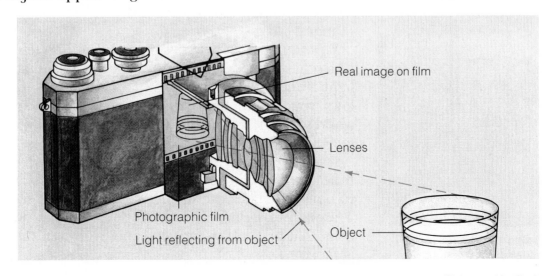

Real image on film

Lenses

Photographic film

Light reflecting from object

Object

Figure 19-22 Refracting telescope

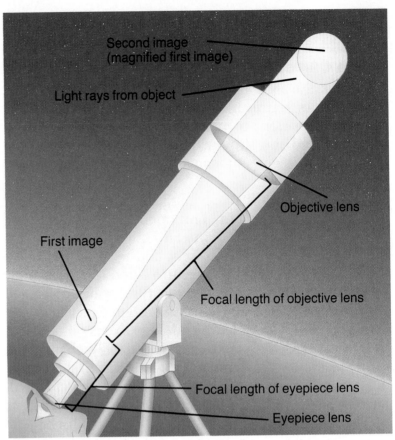

Second image (magnified first image)

Light rays from object

First image

Objective lens

Focal length of objective lens

Focal length of eyepiece lens

Eyepiece lens

Explore!

Find out what the world's largest optical telescopes are. Make a list of them in order of size, along with their names and locations.

Figure 19-23 The Yerkes telescope, the largest refractor in the world

Seeing Distant Objects

Around 1600, Dutch children playing with eyeglass lenses discovered that using two of them together could make distant objects appear closer. The Italian scientist Galileo soon used a pair of lenses to make a telescope. When he pointed the telescope at the sky, he made several important discoveries. He discovered that the moon was covered with craters, that four moons orbited Jupiter, and that a hazy patch in the sky was really made of many stars.

Figure 19-22 shows a simple **refracting telescope**, which has convex lenses. Light enters a lens that bends light from a star to make an image. The other lens allows you to see this image. *Figure 19-23* shows the world's largest refracting telescope. It has a lens one meter across.

About 70 years after Galileo, Isaac Newton used a concave mirror instead of a convex lens to make a telescope. He made one of the first reflecting telescopes. The path of light in a reflecting telescope is different from that in a refracting telescope. However, the effect is similar.

Figure 19-24 The Mauna Kea Observatory in Hawaii is the site of several of the world's largest telescopes.

Explore!

The amount of light a telescope collects increases with the area of its mirror or lens. The 10-m reflector being built by the California Association for Research in Astronomy for Mauna Kea will be the world's largest. The Yerkes refractor is 1 m in diameter. How many times larger will the area of the new telescope be?

In the **reflecting telescope**, a concave mirror reflects light to a place where you can see the image, as shown in *Figure 19-25*. Usually a second mirror reflects the light to a position where it is more convenient to record it.

Because large mirrors are easier to make than large lenses, the largest telescopes today are reflecting telescopes. *Figure 19-24* shows the site of several of the world's largest reflecting telescopes. The main mirror of the one in the largest dome is 3.8 meters across. A mirror 10 meters across is being built for this site. Giant telescopes can collect so much light that astronomers can observe objects over a million times fainter than the eye can see without a telescope. It is usually more important to collect more light than it is to make images look larger.

Astronomers usually do not look through telescopes with their eyes. Sometimes they use film to record images. Sometimes they use electronic devices something like television cameras. The devices change the light into electrical signals. Astronomers then use computers to help them study the signals.

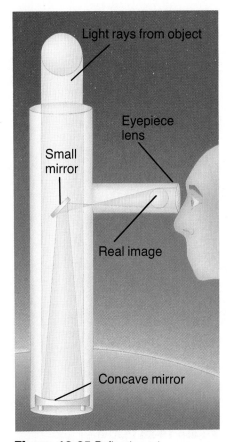

Figure 19-25 Reflecting telescope

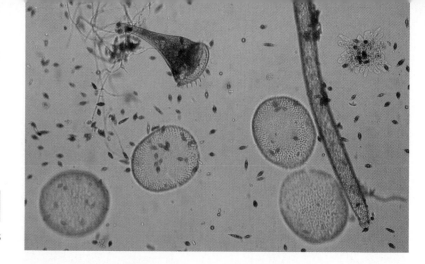

Figure 19-27 How organisms in pond water appear under a microscope

Seeing Tiny Objects

The first optical microscope was invented at the end of the 16th century by a Dutch lens-maker and his son. They placed two convex lenses so that one would magnify an enlarged image placed in the focus of the other.

Figure 19-26 shows the path of light rays in an optical microscope. Light hits the mirror at the bottom and is reflected up. It passes through a lens, which makes the rays parallel so they evenly light up the object you are viewing. After the light passes through the object, it passes through the microscope's objective lens. The convex lens makes a real image that is viewed with the convex eyepiece lens. The total effect of the three lenses is to magnify the object's appearance.

A microscope must do more than magnify an object, however. It must also produce a clear image of the object's closely spaced parts. A microscope's ability to produce such an image is called its resolving power. The best optical microscopes cannot resolve parts of an object that are closer together than 0.2 micrometer, which is 0.0002 millimeter. For that reason, an optical microscope cannot be used to study such tiny objects as atoms, molecules, or viruses.

The microscope is useful for studying organisms. *Figure 19-27* shows how tiny organisms in pond water appear when viewed with the microscope.

Section Review

1. How does a camera use a lens to produce a picture?
2. How do telescopes produce images?
3. How do microscopes produce images?

Challenge: Movie film runs upside down through a projector. Why is the real image on the screen right side up?

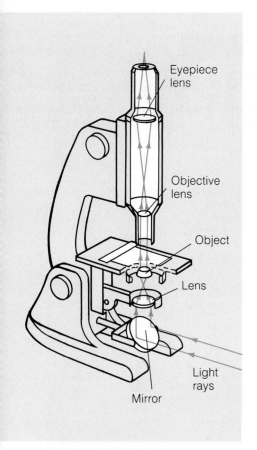

Figure 19-26 Light rays in a microscope

- Eyepiece lens
- Objective lens
- Object
- Lens
- Light rays
- Mirror

Making a Pinhole Camera

Purpose

To observe how a simple camera works

Materials

- shoe box
- straight pin
- some heavy cardboard, somewhat wider, but not higher, than the end of the box
- adhesive or masking tape
- aluminum foil
- "slow" photographic film, cut in pieces and wrapped in aluminum foil

Procedure and Observations

1. Cut a 3 cm × 3 cm square in the center bottom of one end of the box.
2. Tape some foil over the square, as shown.
3. With a pin, punch a hole near the top of the foil over the square hole. *CAUTION: Handle the pin carefully.*
4. Bend the ends of the cardboard so that it stands in the box as shown. Cover the box tightly.

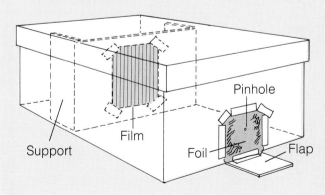

5. NOTE: Check the box to be sure that light enters only at the pinhole.
6. Tape a cardboard flap over the foil to cover the pinhole, as shown.
7. Take the box, one piece of wrapped film, tape, and scissors into a pitch-dark room. NOTE: Read step 8 before you enter the dark room.
8. Unwrap the film, but save the foil. Tape the film to the heavy cardboard so it faces the pinhole. Leave the darkroom with the foil and covered box.
9. Choose a dark object against a bright background to photograph. The distance between the film and the pinhole and the time the pinhole is open will affect your image.
10. To take a picture, uncover the pinhole for at least 10 minutes. Rest your camera on something steady while the pinhole is open.
11. Cover the hole and return to the dark room with your foil and box.
12. Open the box and remove the exposed film. Wrap it carefully in foil.
13. Repeat steps 8-11 using another piece of film. Choose a scene of different brightness and distance from your camera.
14. When you are finished, give your exposed film to your teacher to be developed.

Analysis and Conclusions

1. What could happen to your image if light rays entered your camera from places other than the pinhole?
2. How does the pinhole affect light rays?

Analyzing Images

The drawing shows how a convex lens can be set up to produce a real image. Examine the diagram. Notice that it identifies four items that you can measure.

1. distance between the lens and the object
2. distance between the lens and the image
3. size of the object
4. size of the image

A mathematical relationship exists among the four measurements. The relationship is a proportion—a term you learned in mathematics class. The proportion is:

$$\frac{\text{distance of object}}{\text{distance of image}} = \frac{\text{size of object}}{\text{size of image}}$$

Thus, the ratio of the two distances equals the ratio of the two sizes.

You can use this proportion to find the value of any one of the four measurements, if you know the other three values. For example, suppose an object 5 cm tall is placed 25 cm from a convex lens. The image formed is 15 cm from the lens. Substitute the three given values into the proportion above to find the size of the image.

$$\frac{25 \text{ cm}}{15 \text{ cm}} = \frac{5 \text{ cm}}{\text{size of image}}$$

$$\text{size of image} = \frac{15 \text{ cm} \times 5 \text{ cm}}{25 \text{ cm}}$$

$$= 3 \text{ cm}$$

Copy the table below. Use the proportion to complete the table.

Object Distance (cm)	Image Distance (cm)	Object Size (cm)	Image Size (cm)
75	25	9	
200		10	2
60	12		1.6
	25	10	2.5
150		30	3

✔ Summary

19-1 Plane Mirrors

A. Plane mirrors reflect light to produce virtual images that are as far in back of the mirror as the objects are in front of the mirror.

B. Plane mirrors are used in homes and in automobile mirrors.

19-2 Curved Mirrors

A. Focal point is where parallel light rays are brought together.

B. The image formed by a concave mirror depends on how far the object is form the mirror.

C. A convex mirror spreads light rays to produce a virtual image.

D. Concave mirrors are used in flashlights and telescopes. Convex mirrors are used on vehicles and in stores.

19-3 Lenses

A. The image formed by a convex lens depends on the object's distance from the lens.

B. A concave lens spreads light to produce a virtual image.

19-4 Eyes, Lenses, and Optical Illusions

A. The cornea and lens focus light by bending rays toward one another.

B. Concave lenses can correct nearsighted vision. Convex lenses can correct farsighted vision.

C. Many animals have lenses in their eyes to form images.

D. Mirages are optical illusions caused by the refraction of light in air of different temperatures.

19-5 Using Lenses and Mirrors

A. A camera uses a lens to photograph objects. The size of the opening helps control the amount of light that falls on the film. An actual, upside-down image forms on the film.

B. Refracting telescopes use convex lenses to form images, but reflecting telescopes use concave mirrors.

C. Microscopes use mirrors and lenses to produce magnified images.

Vocabulary

For each of the following terms, write a sentence that uses the term correctly.

astigmatism	convex mirror	lens	real image
concave lens	farsighted	mirage	reflecting telescope
concave mirror	focal length	nearsighted	refracting telescope
convex lens	focal point	plane mirror	virtual image

✔ Check Your Knowledge

Part I: Matching Match the definition in Column I with the correct term in Column II.

Column I
1. condition in which the eye does not properly focus nearby objects
2. lens whose middle part is thicker than its edges so that it bends light rays together
3. smooth, flat surface that reflects light
4. image at which the light rays appear to meet but actually do not
5. lens whose middle part is thinner than its edges so that it spreads out light rays
6. mirror shaped like the outside of a spoon
7. image formed by a lens or mirror for which the rays of light actually come together and can be focused on a screen
8. condition in which the eye does not properly focus distant objects
9. mirror shaped like the inside of a spoon
10. single location to which parallel rays of light are brought together

Column II
a. concave lens
b. concave mirror
c. convex lens
d. convex mirror
e. farsighted
f. focal length
g. focal point
h. nearsighted
i. plane mirror
j. real image
k. virtual image

Part II: Multiple Choice Choose the letter of the best answer.
11. Mirrors affect light by (a) changing its speed. (b) refracting it. (c) reflecting it. (d) changing its color.
12. Your image in a plane mirror is (a) magnified. (b) flipped left to right. (c) exactly like you. (d) refracted.
13. Cameras use (a) concave lenses. (b) convex lenses. (c) convex mirrors. (d) concave mirrors.
14. All lenses (a) spread light apart. (b) focus light. (c) are usually curved and transparent. (d) magnify objects.
15. The eye usually forms images on the (a) pupil. (b) lens. (c) cornea. (d) retina.

Part III: Completion Write the word or words that complete the sentence correctly.
16. An optical illusion caused by light refracting as it passes from air of one temperature into air of another temperature is a _____ .
17. The distance from mirror or lens to the focal point is the _____.
18. People with an _____ see blurred images of distant and nearby objects.
19. The transparent covering over the colored part of your eye is the _____ .
20. If your camera's lens opening is too large, your photograph will be too _____ .

Check Your Understanding

1. How can you determine whether an image is a real image or a virtual image?
2. Why does a concave lens not form a real image?
3. Why can a camera be called a mechanical eye?
4. Describe two different types of mirages.
5. Contrast the ways a reflecting and a refracting telescope produce images.
6. Compare the human eye with the eyes of other animals.

 Apply Your Knowledge

1. Imagine that you have written the word "reflect" on a piece of paper. Describe how the image of the word would look if you held it in the following places:
   a) in front of a convex mirror
   b) close to a concave mirror
   c) in front of a plane mirror
   d) behind a concave lens
   e) at a distance behind a convex lens
   f) behind a convex lens and close to the surface of the lens
2. After you step in a rain puddle, it no longer produces a true image. Why?
3. Explain why plate-glass windows do not focus or spread light rays apart in the same way that lenses do.
4. Compare the distance of the light in a lighthouse and the lighthouse's lens with the focal length of the lens.
5. If you sit in the middle of a reflecting telescope to record the light from a distant star and block a circle 1 meter in diameter, what fraction of the incoming light are you blocking if the telescope's mirror is 5 meters across?
6. The strength of an eyeglass lens in diopters is 1 divided by its focal length in meters. For example, a lens with 2-m focal length has a strength of 0.5 diopters. Which would be better used by someone with very bad eyesight, a lens of 1 diopter or a lens of 3 diopters?

 Extend Your Knowledge

Research/Projects
1. Hold a book up to a mirror and read the words as you watch the mirror. Explain your observations.
2. Examine print in a book with a magnifying glass. Hold the magnifying glass very close to and very far from the page. Notice when the image is upside down and right side up. Compare this lens to your water-drop lens. When is the image real? When is the image virtual?

Readings
Simon, Seymour. *Hidden Worlds: Pictures of the Invisible.* Morrow, 1983. Collection of photographs, produced with special instruments, of things that are too small, too far, or moving too fast to be seen by the human eye.

Ward, Alan. *Experimenting with Light and Illusions.* Batsford/Dyrad, 1985. Contains experiments that illustrate the nature of light and illusions.

CHAPTER 20
Lasers

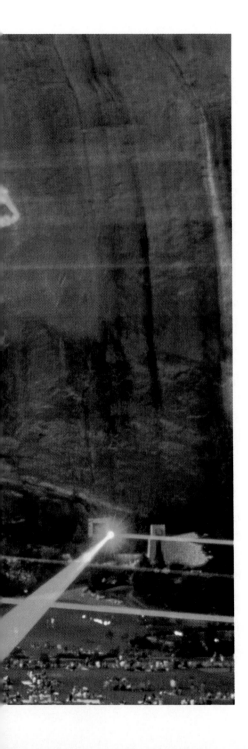

Lasers produced the beautiful effects for the light show in the photograph. Within a few years, lasers have become part of our everyday lives. They have many uses in science, medicine, industry, and business.

Organizing Your Study Skills The outline below will help you see how the chapter is organized and what you should learn as you read.

I. Section 20-1: Laser Light
 A. What is laser light?
 B. How does laser light work?

II. Section 20-2: Different Types of Lasers
 A. How do solid lasers work?
 B. What are semiconductor lasers?
 C. What are two advantages of liquid lasers?
 D. How do gas and solid lasers compare?
 E. How do free-electron lasers compare with conventional lasers?

III. Section 20-3: Using Lasers
 A. How are lasers used for communication?
 B. What are four ways lasers are used in industry?
 C. How are lasers used in medicine?
 D. What are four ways lasers are used in scientific research?

IV. Section 20-4: Holograms
 A. How are holograms made?
 B. What are three uses for holograms?

After completing this section, you will be able to

A. Define laser light.
B. Explain how a laser works.

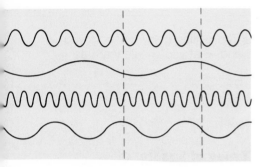

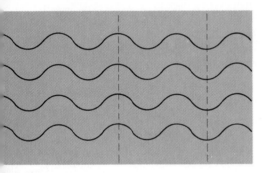

Figure 20-1 Ordinary light waves are out of step with each other. Laser light waves are in step.

20-1 Laser Light

How Laser Light Differs from Ordinary Light

One kind of light source, called a **laser**, produces a special kind of light beam. To understand the difference between laser light and ordinary light, think about the water in a crowded swimming pool. The waves move around in every direction, with no definite pattern. The sun, light bulbs, and other ordinary light sources give off light waves that also move around in all directions, with no definite pattern.

Notice in *Figure 20-1a* how the crests and troughs of ordinary light waves do not match. They are out of step with each other. Even light waves of the same wavelength traveling in the same direction can be out of step. Ordinary light waves are like a crowd of people going every which way. But the laser light waves shown in *Figure 20-1b* are like members of a band marching in step. All the crests and troughs line up. Light waves from a laser are like this and can have exactly the same wavelength.

The color of light depends on its wavelength. Ordinary red light has many wavelengths of slightly different reds. Red laser light has only one wavelength or a narrow range of wavelengths.

Ordinary light travels in all directions and spreads out. Laser light, however, travels in one direction with little spreading. Therefore, laser beams can be brighter and narrower than ordinary light beams. Laser beams are so bright that they can seriously damage your eyes. Never look directly into a laser beam or even into its reflection.

How a Laser Works

Recall how an ordinary light source gives off photons—or particles of light energy. An electron is in a higher-than-normal energy level. When the electron spontaneously drops to a lower energy level, it gives off a packet of energy, called a photon.

A laser contains a substance in which many atoms are excited to the same energy state. In *Figure 20-2a,* a photon of a certain energy is approaching an electron that is in a higher-than-normal energy level. The photon causes the electron to drop to its normal energy level, as shown in *Figure 20-2b*. Note that the electron gives off *two* photons as it moves to the lower energy level. The two photons have the same wavelength and are traveling in the same direction. The two photons, in turn, stimulate other excited atoms to give off photons. The single photon, which starts the process, leads to many more photons being given off. Thus, the light has become stronger, or amplified. "Laser" stands for **l**ight **a**mplification by **s**timulated **e**mission of **r**adiation.

The energy that pumps atoms to an excited state can come from an electric current, chemical reactions, radio waves, or a flash of light. Some lasers fire off pulses of light that last only a tiny fraction of a second. Other lasers can beam light steadily for many years. The first lasers gave off light of only one wavelength. Some lasers can now be tuned to give off light of different wavelengths.

Section Review

1. What are two ways in which laser light is different from ordinary light?
2. In a laser, after one photon strikes an atom, how many photons leave the atom?

Challenge: Does a laser make use of the wave nature or the particle nature of light or both? Explain.

Have You Heard?

A laser that occurs naturally in Mars's atmosphere steadily generates as much energy as 1000 nuclear reactors.

Explore!

Find out who made the first laser.

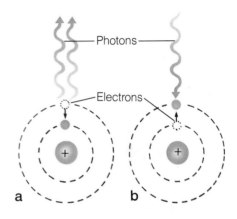

Figure 20-2 In a laser, a photon stimulates an excited atom to give off a photon with the same energy as the first photon.

Careers in Physical Science

Laser Technician

Laser beams play an important role in medicine and industry. Their use is becoming more widespread every day. A laser technician oversees the production of laser equipment and makes sure it is built exactly as planned.

Laser technicians study for two years to get a degree, and with on-the-job training learn about both the design and the mechanics of a laser. This preparation helps the technician when he or she has to explain design ideas to shop workers and mechanical problems to people who design lasers.

After completing this section, you will be able to

A. Describe how solid lasers work.
B. Describe semiconductor lasers.
C. List two advantages of liquid lasers.
D. Compare gas lasers with solid lasers.
E. Contrast free electron lasers with conventional lasers.

Explore!

Look in an encyclopedia to learn more about types of substances used to produce light, power sources, and laser light itself.

20-2 Different Types of Lasers

Solid Lasers

Every laser contains a power source and a substance whose excited atoms produce light. If that substance is a solid, the laser is known as a **solid laser.** The substance in the solid laser in *Figure 20-3* is a ruby crystal. The power source is the flash tube. Two mirrors are at opposite ends of the ruby crystal. The first laser ever made was much like the one in the drawing.

A flashing lamp in the flash tube gives extra energy to the atoms in the ruby rod. Electrons in many of these atoms are excited to a high energy level. When a photon of the proper energy hits these atoms, many of the excited electrons drop to the same lower energy level. As they drop, they give off their extra energy as photons of red light. This light bounces back and forth between the mirrors. It makes other atoms release energy as photons of the same red light. As more photons are released, the light becomes more intense.

One of the mirrors reflects all the light that hits it. The partially mirrored surface lets a small part of the light that hits it pass through.

The light that shoots out through the partially reflecting mirror is the laser beam. A ruby laser gives off bursts of light. A single burst of the most powerful ruby lasers can burn a hole through steel more than one millimeter thick!

Other solids are now used instead of ruby crystals in most solid lasers. These solid lasers also have a lamp as their power source. They can produce bursts or a steady beam of laser light. Lasers that give off bursts of light have different uses from lasers that give off steady beams. Very powerful solid lasers can be made.

Figure 20-3 A solid laser. The black arrows represent photons from the flash tube that excite atoms in the ruby rod. The colored arrows represent photons given off by atoms in the rod.

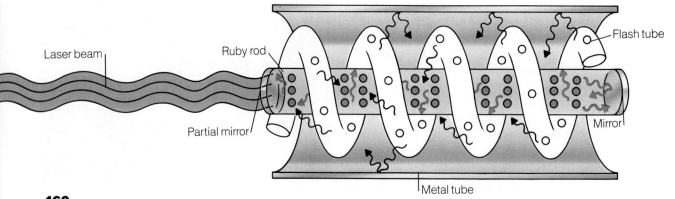

Semiconductor Lasers

Some solid lasers are semiconductors. A **semiconductor** is a material that conducts electricity better than an insulator like rubber but not as well as a conductor like copper or iron. Semiconductors are useful because scientists can control how well they conduct electricity.

In a **semiconductor laser**, the substance that provides atoms is a material that has semiconductor properties. The semiconductor laser in *Figure 20-4* is made of two layers of material with different electric charges. Current passes through the layers, producing laser light in the area that joins them. The laser light passes out as shown.

Semiconductor lasers are used in new telephone lines and in compact disk players. They are much smaller and more convenient to use than other lasers. In fact, 400 semiconductor lasers can be cut from a sheet of semiconducting crystal that is only the size of a telephone push button! They are also cheaper to make than other lasers, and they last for a long time.

Liquid Lasers

A liquid substance provides the atoms in a **liquid laser**, shown in *Figure 20-5*. These lasers usually contain dyes, such as those in the photograph, which are dissolved in wood alcohol or another liquid.

Because molecules in the dyes have so many energy levels, a wide range of wavelengths is possible. Scientists use a prism or similar device to pick out the desired wavelength. Thus, they can "tune" the laser. Another advantage of dye lasers is that they can give off especially short pulses of light. Dye lasers that produce continuous light usually are excited by solid lasers or by gas lasers.

Figure 20-4 How a semiconductor laser works

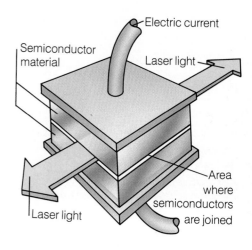

Figure 20-5 Liquid laser

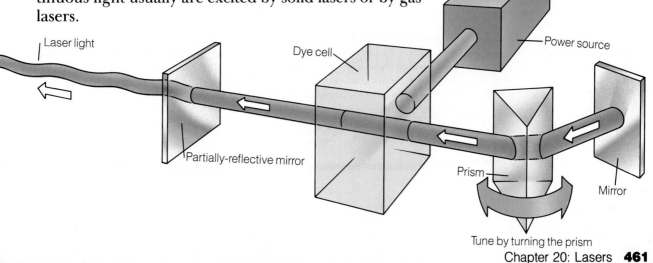

Tune by turning the prism

Gas Lasers

The substance that provides atoms in a **gas laser** is either a gas or a mixture of gases. The gas is usually held in a tube like the one in *Figure 20-7*. Some gas lasers have tubes 9 meters long, but the tube generally ranges from 15 to 100 centimeters in length.

In the gas laser shown here, the power source is an electric current. The current excites atoms of gas inside the tube. As in other lasers, the laser light passes out through the partial mirror. Gas lasers are usually used to give off steady beams of laser light in a very narrow range of colors.

One important laser uses a chemical reaction for its power source. Carbon dioxide (CO_2) can produce laser light if it is present when the elements hydrogen (H_2) and fluorine (F_2) react to produce hydrogen fluoride (HF). Only a small amount of hydrogen and fluorine are needed for a carbon dioxide laser to release a lot of energy. Because of their high power and because they give off infrared light, these lasers are very useful.

Free Electron Lasers

In all the types of lasers you have just read about, the power source excites electrons in atoms to move into higher energy levels. These conventional lasers often convert to laser light only a small fraction of the energy put into them. Not all the electrons are raised to higher energy levels, and raising them to those levels requires more energy than they later give off.

Figure 20-6 Gas laser in use

Figure 20-7 A gas laser

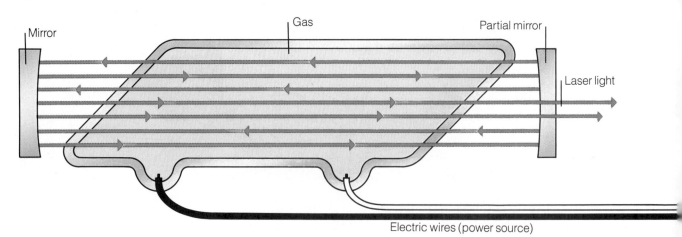

Mirror

Gas

Partial mirror

Laser light

Electric wires (power source)

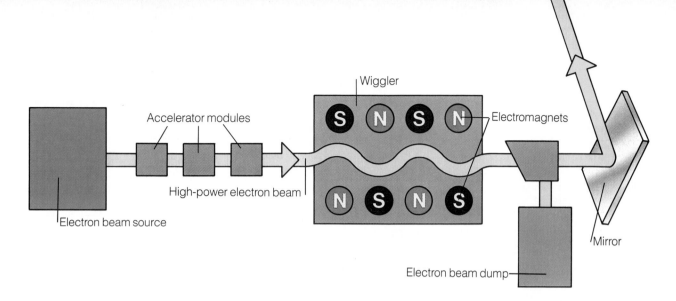

Figure 20-8 A free electron laser

A new type of laser—a **free electron laser**—uses free electrons, which are not bound to atoms, to produce laser light. *Figure 20-8* shows how this free electron laser works. High-speed electrons are sent into a "wiggler," a series of strong magnets that pull the moving electrons back and forth. An electron gives off a photon every time it makes a sharp turn.

Billions of these photons combine to make a strong laser beam, which passes out through the partial mirror. The wavelength of the laser light from a free electron laser can be controlled by controlling the speed at which the electrons are fired into the wiggler. For this reason, scientists can adjust the wavelength of free electron lasers.

By 1986, only a dozen free electron lasers were in operation, but one had already converted as much as 42 percent of the energy put into it into laser light. Scientists are hoping for 70 percent efficiency or even higher.

Applying Science

When magnetic fields of exploding stars, or supernovae, change the directions of electrons speeding through space, photons are given off. Dr. John Madey, the electrical engineer who invented the free electron laser, reasoned that lasers could be produced by using powerful magnets on the earth to alter the paths of speeding electrons.

Section Review

1. How do a laser's two mirrors differ?
2. What are two advantages of semiconductor lasers?
3. What are two advantages of liquid lasers?
4. What is the power source in a carbon dioxide laser?
5. How are free electron lasers different from other lasers?

Challenge: Each wavelength of light has a specific frequency associated with it. How does this fact help to explain why the waves in a laser beam stay "in step" over a long distance?

Activity 20-1

Laser Model

Purpose

To understand a laser

Materials

- 12 cardboard disks, 2 cm in diameter
- 2 cardboard squares, 4 cm × 4 cm
- 20 cm × 30 cm piece of aluminum foil
- pencil or pen
- scissors
- 1 die with 1 to 6 dots on each side

Procedure and Observations

PART A

1. Copy table **a** for use in Part A.
2. Number six disks 1 to 6 and lay them out in a row, as shown below, to represent atoms in their normal energy state.

3. Cover one cardboard square with foil. Place this reflecting mirror at the left end of the row.
4. Partly cover the second square with foil, as shown. Cut a 2-cm hold in the middle of this partly-reflecting mirror. Place it at the right end of the row.
5. Number the remaining disks 1 to 6. They represent extra energy that can be added to the six atom disks.
6. Roll the die 5 times. Put the energy disk labeled with the number rolled on top of the corresponding atom disk. If, however, an energy disk is already present, remove it instead. Adding a disk is exciting an atom; taking away a disk is an atom spontaneously giving off energy.
7. Record in your table the numbers of excited atoms and of normal atoms.
8. Repeat the procedure 4 more times.

PART B

1. Put an energy disk on top of each atom disk.
2. Move energy disk 6 to the left, skipping two disks. Pick up the energy disk covering the atom 3 spaces over, and move *both* to the left. When they get to the mirror, they are "reflected." Continue picking up every third energy disk. The second time you reach the partial mirror, the energy disks you are holding go out of the system.
3. Repeat step 2, but start with the energy disk closest to the right mirror.
4. Continue until all 6 disks are gone.

Table a

rolls of dice	excited atoms	atoms at normal energy
5		
10		
15		
20		

Analysis and Conclusions

1. How many photons come off at each time (each roll of the die) in Part A?
2. In Part B, how many photons pass through the partial mirror each time?
3. Which part is the laser? Why?

20-3 Using Lasers

Optical Fibers Carry Messages

When lasers were first invented, some people wondered what good they would be. Now, however, lasers are part of our daily lives. Every year we find many new uses for lasers.

Laser beams sent through narrow glass threads can carry messages. *Figure 20-9* shows these glass threads, called **optical fibers**, which are narrower than a human hair. The insides of the fibers reflect light—even around curves in the tube. *Figure 20-10* shows how the reflected beam moves along the fiber.

Telephone companies use laser beams and optical fibers to send telephone calls from city to city. A 1000-kilometer-long laser communications system runs from Washington through Philadelphia and New York City to Boston. The system can carry 80 000 telephone calls at the same time on laser beams shot through optical fibers.

Optical fibers are better than the older wiring for several reasons. First, fibers are much thinner and take up much less space under city streets. Second, messages move through optical fibers as pulses, and lasers can make very short pulses. These pulses move very quickly through an optical fiber, so a fiber can carry more messages than a copper wire.

Figure 20-10 The arrows represent light moving through two optical fibers.

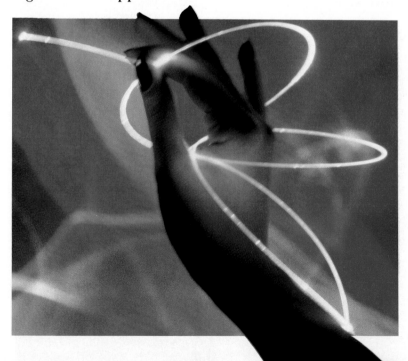

Figure 20-9 Optical fibers are extremely thin.

Figure 20-11 A Universal Product Code

A third advantage of optical fibers over copper wiring is that static, which can affect messages in copper wires, does not affect the light in optical fibers. Also, signals fade easily as they move through copper cables and need to be strengthened every few kilometers. By contrast, the signal in an optical fiber can travel for over 30 kilometers before it needs to be strengthened.

Lasers are used to carry information in ways that do not involve optical fibers. For example, movies and other information can now be recorded with a laser on a special disk. The disk is then read with a laser beam instead of with a phonograph needle. The signals can be played back through your television. The disk's plastic surface covers billions of pits so tiny that 100 of them could fit in the width of one of your eyelashes. A single side of a disk can hold over 50 000 color images or text of thousands of books. A smaller, compact disk, or CD, uses the same technology to store music without background hiss. Compact disks are also read by laser beams.

Lasers in Industry

Many stores use lasers to speed up checkout lines. Each product carries a Universal Product Code that resembles the one in *Figure 20-11*. A clerk bounces a laser beam off the bands of the code as shown in *Figure 20-12*. A computer senses the beam and identifies the code. It then figures out the bill and keeps track of what the store sells.

Figure 20-12 One of many uses for lasers in retail sales.

Figure 20-13 A laser can "read" printed words.

The laser in *Figure 20-13* "reads" printed words. Its signals are sent by satellite to another city to be printed. Newspapers and magazines also use lasers to transfer photographs and maps to printing plates. Laser systems also count newspapers accurately. This keeps newspaper companies from printing too many copies.

The heat from powerful laser beams welds sheet metal parts and joins glass or plastic parts. Lasers can be used to cut fabric for fifty suits at once or to cut through the toughest metal.

Since laser beams travel in straight lines, camera makers use them to line up lenses in cameras. Construction companies even use the straight line of laser light to show them the direction in which to dig a tunnel. Tunnels drilled by machines that are guided by lasers are straight to within a centimeter or two, which is much straighter than older tunnels.

The automobile industry has many uses for lasers. Lasers weld car parts. Lasers check how well the engine burns fuel and help manufacturers design cars that use fuel more efficiently. Researchers are hoping to use optical fibers to replace the metal wires that send signals and power to car parts. A switch to optical fibers also would reduce the weight of cars.

Industry has also found that lasers are an inexpensive way to clean all sorts of surfaces. A controlled laser beam can break the chemical bonds that hold unwanted dirt onto a surface. A laser removed all the rust from the steel supports of a Texas courthouse for 20 percent of the cost of sandblasting. Unlike sandblasting, the laser did not damage the building's structure.

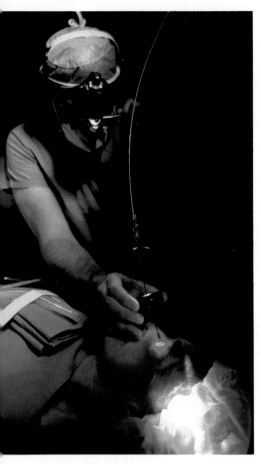

Figure 20-14 Optical fibers and lasers are used to destroy eye tumors and many other types of cancer.

Medical Uses of Lasers

Lasers and optical fibers have many medical uses. Doctors often use lasers to cut one part of the body without hurting others. The laser's heat cleans and seals the area by boiling away blood, tissue, and infectious agents.

Doctors expect to find many uses for free electron lasers as they become more common. These lasers control electrons so precisely that they can provide very short and powerful laser bursts. Such laser bursts can remove a layer of body cells without heating what lies beneath them.

The retina covers the back, inside part of the eyeball. An eye injury can cause the retina to pull away from the rest of the eye, and blindness might result. Now a laser beam can be focused onto the edge of the retina. It welds the retina back in place in a fraction of a second. Operations to do this used to take hours and did not do the job as well.

Lasers are helpful in finding and treating cancer. A doctor can inject a special dye made from cow's blood into the patient's body. All the body's cells first absorb the dye and then give it off as a waste product. Cells with cancer keep the dye longer than healthy cells, however. Optical fibers carry laser light to the cancerous cells and dissolve the membranes. The surgeon in *Figure 20-14* is using an optical fiber to direct the beam from a liquid dye laser onto an eye tumor. Lasers can also destroy brain and spinal cord tumors that could not be operated on previously.

Laser cancer treatments affect only the cells that have tumors. They do not have the same unpleasant side effects, such as nausea, headaches, hair loss, and weakness, that other cancer treatments often cause.

Lasers can also detect other medical problems. In *Figure 20-15*, a medical technician is using an instrument that contains a laser in the bandage wrapped on the patient's finger. The instrument measures the patient's pulse rate and oxygen saturation.

Figure 20-16 shows another medical use of optical fibers and lasers. Doctors use the device, called an **endoscope**, to see inside a patient's body. An endoscope does not expose a patient to radiation the way an X-ray machine does. An endoscope is a long, hollow tube. Inside the tube there are flexible optical fibers. Some of the fibers transmit light from an outside source into the body. Other fibers transmit light from the body so that the doctor can see what is inside. Some fibers can carry light from a laser machine. The doctor can direct a laser beam onto parts of the patient's body. The laser light can burn off cancerous growths.

Another medical use of optical fibers and lasers is to treat patients with blocked arteries. The arteries are the blood vessels that carry blood from the heart to all parts of the body. Millions of Americans have buildups of fatty deposits and fibers that block the flow of blood through the arteries. If arteries are so blocked that blood cannot flow through them, the patient suffers a stroke or heart attack.

Until recently, the most common way to solve the problem of blocked arteries has been bypass surgery. This type of surgery sends the blood through a new route around a section of blocked artery. Bypass surgery involves making an incision in the chest and operating directly on the heart. It is an expensive operation, and more than one patient in 100 dies from the procedure.

Explore!

Find out how lasers are used to treat glaucoma, an eye disease that often leads to blindness.

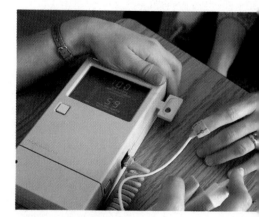

Figure 20-15 Lasers help detect various medical problems.

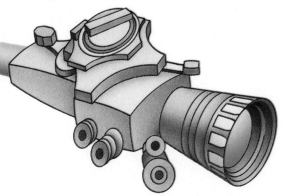

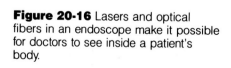

Figure 20-16 Lasers and optical fibers in an endoscope make it possible for doctors to see inside a patient's body.

The laser in *Figure 20-17* can treat blocked arteries in a much less complicated operation. A tube carrying optical fibers can unblock the coronary artery, which supplies blood to the heart muscle. The tube is threaded up the arm and over to the blocked coronary artery. As in the endoscope, there are optical fibers that carry light and laser beams into the body. Other fibers carry light to the doctor's eye. Bursts of laser light are aimed at the deposits that block the inside of the artery. The laser bursts are turned on and off. In fractions of a second, the laser light destroys the harmful deposits.

Using Lasers for Scientific Research

Lasers help scientists to do many kinds of research. Since they were invented in 1960, lasers have increased the accuracy of many measurements. For example, astronauts took mirrors to the moon to reflect laser light. A set of these mirrors is shown in *Figure 20-18*. Scientists on the earth can bounce laser beams off these mirrors and time the beam's round trip. They are finding the distance to the moon with an accuracy of a few centimeters. The speed of light has been known for years. However, the speed of light can be measured so accurately using lasers that scientists now use the speed of light to define distance.

Figure 20-17 Lasers and optical fibers make it possible to clean out arteries without major surgery.

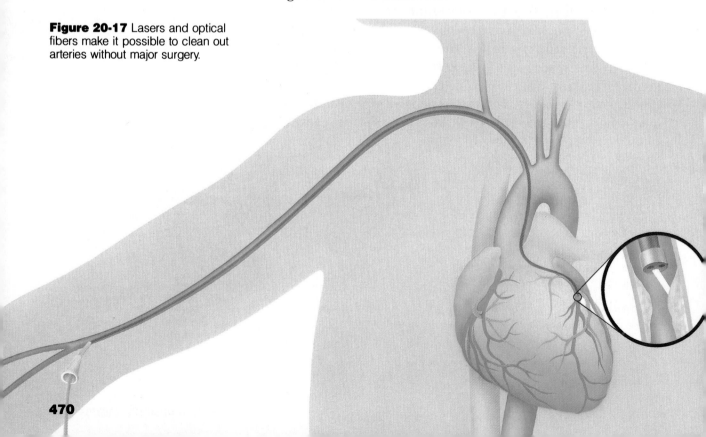

Lasers are also used to help protect our environment. Scientists bounce laser beams off atmospheric particles. The way the laser beam bounces tells what kinds of particles are in the air. From kilometers away, scientists can detect a natural gas leak or pollutants from power plants.

Lasers are helping scientists improve their understanding of atoms. By using beams of one precise wavelength, scientists can excite and study whatever energy level they are interested in.

Today, scientists even use lasers to "trap" atoms. In one such experiment, they used nine lasers to trap a few sodium atoms for close study. They directed the first laser beam onto a sodium pellet. The energy from the laser freed some atoms from the element. A second laser beam from the opposite direction slowed down the atoms to a speed of 2000 centimeters per second. Next the atoms entered what the scientists call an "optical molasses." Just as molasses is very viscous and flows slowly, an optical molasses is so densely packed with photons of light that atoms can barely move through it. The researchers prepared the optical molasses by focusing six lasers on one cubic centimeter of space. In the thick bed of photons, the atoms slowed down to a speed of 60 centimeters per second. A focused laser beam then trapped the atoms for about a second in a tiny volume. Scientists are trying to make larger traps for atoms. They also hope to be able to use the laser technique as an "optical tweezers," to handle atoms one at a time.

The use of lasers has spread very fast in chemistry research. Using a laser, a chemist can cause a particular chemical reaction to take place without also causing unwanted side reactions. Typically, chemical reactions are started with heat, but heating excites many things at once. A laser, by contrast, can excite a particular kind of electron or molecule.

Another feature of laser chemistry is the ability to separate one atomic form (isotope) of an element from another. For example, natural uranium contains mainly the isotope uranium-238 and a small amount of uranium-235. The proportion of uranium-235 must be raised in order for uranium to be used as a fuel in nuclear reactors. The laser process of separating the isotopes is less expensive than any of the alternative methods.

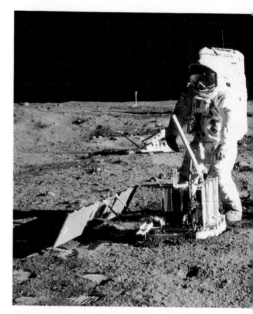

Figure 20-18 Laser beams can be made so strong and focused so well that we can bounce them off mirrors on the moon.

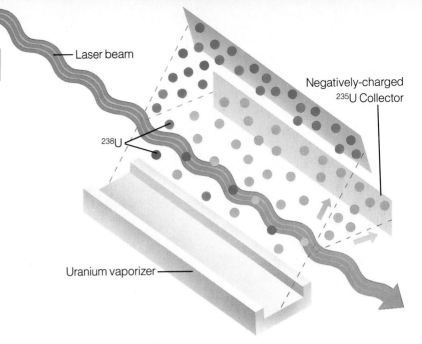

Laser beam

Negatively-charged
^{235}U Collector

^{238}U

Uranium vaporizer

Figure 20-19 A laser can be used to separate uranium-235 from uranium-238.

When a special laser beam is focused on uranium, the uranium-238 atoms are unaffected, but each of the uranium-235 atoms loses an electron, becoming a positively charged atom—or ion. In *Figure 20-19*, the red balls are uranium-235 ions. These positive ions are attracted to a plate with a negative electric charge, because opposite charges attract. Thus, the two isotopes are separated, and the uranium-235 can be collected at the plate.

A long-range hope is that lasers will help us meet our energy needs in another way. In one process for generating energy, many powerful laser beams are sent at the same instant at a tiny ball that contains hydrogen. If the lasers add enough energy to the hydrogen all at once, two hydrogen atoms will fuse—or merge—to make a heavier atom. During the fusion process, energy is released. Energy produced using lasers to fuse hydrogen atoms is called **laser fusion.**

Section Review

1. Give three reasons why telephone companies are switching to optical fibers.
2. What laser features make them useful for building tunnels?
3. Give two medical uses of optical fibers and lasers.
4. How do lasers help scientists in their study of atoms?

Challenge: The element hydrogen is present in many compounds, including water. What is one potential advantage of energy production by means of laser fusion?

Optical Fibers

Purpose

To investigate the path of light through an optical fiber

Materials

- 10 pocket mirrors
- flashlight with a narrow beam
- pencil
- index card
- masking tape
- sheet of white paper

Procedure and Observations

PART A

1. Place 5 of the pocket mirrors in a row, end to end, as in **a**. Tape the mirrors in an upright position, as shown.
2. Place the other 5 mirrors in a row facing the first row and separated by about 2 cm from the first row. Tape the mirrors in an upright position.
3. Shine the pocket flashlight into the gap at one end so that the beam reflects off one of the mirrors.

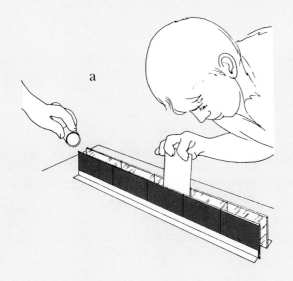

a

4. Move an index card slowly down between the rows to follow the reflection of the beam as it bounces back and forth between the mirrors.
5. Observe the light as it emerges at the end of the two rows of mirrors. On a clean sheet of paper, sketch the path the light took between the mirrors.

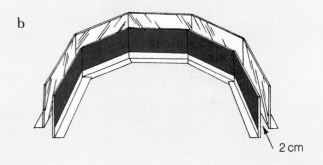

b

2 cm

PART B

1. Place the first 5 mirrors in a row, but make the row curve slightly. Tape them upright. The mirrors now lie on the circumference of a large circle, as shown in **b**.
2. Place the other 5 mirrors on a similar circle facing the first circle and separated from it by 2 cm and tape them upright.
3. Repeat steps 3, 4, and 5 of Part A.

Analysis and Conclusions

1. In Part A, does the light emerge in straight or curved lines? Explain why the light behaved this way.
2. In Part B, does the light emerge in straight or curved lines?
3. Explain how the light is able to follow the bend of the curved mirrors.

After completing this section, you will be able to

A. Explain how a hologram is made.
B. Describe three uses of holograms.

20-4 Holograms

Making a Hologram

A photograph shows you one flat view of a scene from one angle. With a laser, however, you can produce a three-dimensional image, called a **hologram**. When you look at a hologram, you can see a scene from a range of angles. Hologram comes from the Greek words meaning "whole image."

Figure 20-21 illustrates how a hologram is made. A partial mirror near the laser splits laser light into two beams. The lower beam reflects from another mirror and then from the object—a book. The beam then strikes a light-sensitive surface, usually a kind of photographic film mounted on glass. On the other hand, the upper beam strikes only the film. Because the lower beam struck an object before it reached the film, these waves are now out of step with the waves in the upper beam. The beams interfere, and the interference pattern of the waves is recorded on the film.

When you develop the film, you have a hologram. To see the image, you shine the same wavelength of laser light on the hologram. The hologram's interference pattern scatters the laser beam. The scattered light forms an image you can see as you look through the hologram. The person in *Figure 20-20* is looking through such a holographic image.

Figure 20-20 Using laser light to make a hologram.

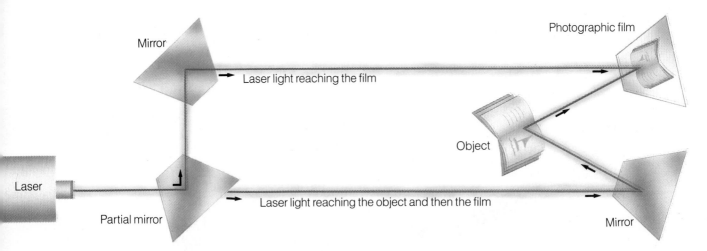

Figure 20-21 Looking through a holographic image

Ordinary light cannot make a hologram because its waves are out of step. So many different waves strike the film that no definite image appears. Laser light, with a narrow range of wavelengths, is best for making a hologram.

Using Holograms

One use of holograms is to search for flaws that are invisible to the unaided eye. Hologram-tested products include airplane and car parts, tires, computer disk drives, and tennis racket handles. Holograms have a similar medical use. Taking holograms of the skin, for example, can help detect small flaws on the surface. These flaws might indicate that a tumor is present.

Some credit card companies print holograms on their cards, as shown in *Figure 20-22*. The hologram covers several digits of the account number. The numbers cannot be changed without ruining the hologram. A merchant seeing such a card would know that someone had tampered with it. The United States is considering minting new currency with holograms on the bills. This measure would provide extra protection against counterfeiters.

The automobile industry might soon use holograms to design and manufacture new cars. Present methods for designing new cars involve the use of drawings and clay models. The use of holograms would shorten the time needed to perfect a new design. In addition, the information about the holograms could be stored in a computer. The computer data could then help engineers set up a computerized manufacturing process. Researchers hope that the use of holograms and computers will cut the time it takes to design a car from five years to eighteen months.

In the future, holograms will be used to store other sorts of information as well. All the information in a huge library could be stored on a hologram about the size of a sugar cube.

Section Review

1. How is a hologram different from a photograph?
2. What is a major industrial use for holograms?

Challenge: What other uses of holograms can you name?

Figure 20-22 Holograms are used to protect credit cards.

Figure 20-23 Holograms can be used to design new products.

Science Skills

Drawing Graphs and Measuring Angles

The steps below explain how to draw an optical fiber model on graph paper. The graph has two lines representing the optical fiber itself. In addition, a series of short, connected graph lines represent laser light passing through the optical fiber.

1. Draw an x-axis and a y-axis that intersect near the lower left corner of a piece of graph paper, as in **a.** Write (0,0) where the axes intersect. Select a scale almost large enough to fill the paper. Then label the x-axis from 1 to 20 and label the y-axis from 1 to 20.

2. For the first line in the graph, plot the following points. The first number in parentheses is the x value and the second is the y value: (0,0), (1,0), (3,1), (5,1), (7,3), (10,3), (12,4), (16,5), (18,5), (20,6), (20,13), (16,13), (12,13), (8,16), (5,18), (3,19), (0,20). Now draw a line connecting the points in the same order as they are listed above.

3. For the second line, repeat the procedure in step 2, using the following points in order: (0,2), (1,2), (3,3), (5,3), (7,5), (10,5), (12,6), (16,7), (18,7), (18,11), (16,11), (12,11), (8,14), (5,16), (3,17), (0,18).

4. To start the laser light path, plot the points (0,0.5) and (2,0.5). Connect the two points with a line. Continue drawing short, connected lines showing the path of light through the optical fiber. Use a ruler for straight lines and a protractor to measure the angle at which the beam hits and is reflected from the wall. Remember that the angle at which light hits a surface is the same as the angle at which it is reflected, as shown in **b.**

a

Optical Fiber Model

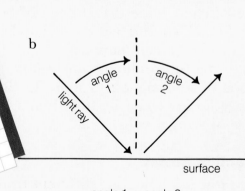

b

light ray

angle 1

angle 2

surface

angle 1 = angle 2

✔ Summary

20-1 Laser Light

A. Laser beams are brighter and narrower than ordinary light beams.

B. In a laser, excited atoms are stimulated by photons of proper energy to give off photons of the same wavelength as the stimulating photons.

20-2 Different Types of Lasers

A. In a solid laser, atoms in the solid are excited by a flashing lamp, and they give off photons as they return to their normal energy level.

B. Semiconductor lasers are much smaller than other solid lasers, and they are convenient to use.

C. Liquid lasers can give off light in short bursts or a steady beam.

D. The gas in a gas laser is generally stimulated by an electric current or, sometimes, by a chemical reaction.

E. In free-electron lasers, the electrons are not bound to atoms. They give off photons when passing through a magnetic field, or wiggler.

20-3 Using Lasers

A. Laser beams can be used to communicate information, both in traveling through optic fibers and in reading and recording on disks.

B. Industries use lasers to read UPC codes, cut, weld, establish straight lines, and the clean surfaces.

C. Lasers are used to treat patients and detect medical problems.

D. Scientists use lasers to increase their understanding of atoms, make more accurate measurements, detect air pollutants, and "trap" atoms.

20-4 Holograms

A. A hologram is made by splitting a laser beam in two and having one beam hit the object being photographed. The beams are recombined to make an interference pattern.

B. Holograms are used to detect weaknesses and flaws in objects, to make credit cards tamperproof, and to design new products.

Vocabulary

For each of the following terms, write a sentence that uses the term correctly.

endoscope	laser	semiconductor
free electron laser	laser fusion	semiconductor laser
gas laser	liquid laser	solid laser
hologram	optical fiber	

✔ Check Your Knowledge

Part I: Matching Match the definition in Column I with the correct term in Column II.

Column I
1. light amplification by the stimulated emission of radiation
2. a photograph that produces a three-dimensional image
3. travels in all directions and spreads out
4. in one type, a chemical reaction is the power source
5. travels in one direction with little spreading
6. where a burst of light leaves a laser
7. gives extra energy to atoms in some lasers
8. a very small laser that is convenient to use
9. makes use of electrons that are not bound to atoms
10. usually contains a dye

Column II
a. flashing lamp
b. free electron laser
c. gas laser
d. hologram
e. "laser"
f. laser light
g. liquid laser
h. optical fiber
i. ordinary light
j. partially reflecting mirror
k. semiconductor laser

Part II: Multiple Choice Choose the letter of the best answer.
11. Compared to beams of ordinary light, laser light (a) is dimmer. (b) spreads out more. (c) has a narrower range of wavelengths. (d) travels in more directions.
12. A laser gives off its extra energy in the form of (a) photons. (b) electrons. (c) protons. (d) sound waves.
13. A laser using electrons that are not bound to atoms is a (a) gas laser. (b) solid laser. (c) liquid laser. (d) free electron laser.
14. Which of the following processes does *not* make use of lasers? (a) reading Universal Product Codes (b) digging tunnels (c) making automobiles (d) destroying insect pests
15. Which of the following medical processes does *not* make use of lasers? (a) using an endoscope (b) repairing hu-

man eye retinas (c) setting a broken wrist (d) treating cancer
16. Which of these scientific studies does not make use of lasers? (a) detecting particles in the air (b) "trapping" atoms (c) detecting fish in the ocean (d) measuring the speed of light

Part III: Completion Write the word or words that complete the sentence correctly.
17. In _____, hydrogen atoms combine, producing energy.
18. Every laser includes a power source and a substance whose excited atoms produce _____.
19. A material that conducts electricity better than an insulator but not as well as a conductor is a _____.
20. Dye lasers that produce continuous light are usually excited by _____.
21. Narrow threads of glass through which light can travel are called _____.

Check Your Understanding

1. Why is it dangerous to look at a laser beam or at its reflection even for a fraction of a second?
2. Why is a laser designed with two mirrors?
3. Why do some lasers give off only one wavelength of light while others can be tuned?
4. How are lasers and optical fibers used together to help doctors work inside a human body?
5. Describe two ways in which a hologram is different from a photograph.
6. In a solid laser, what is the function of a flashing light? A ruby crystal?
7. Is a laser used for recording information onto a disk, for reading information recorded on a disk, or for both purposes?
8. What is one advantage liquid lasers have over other lasers?
9. Give two reasons why optical fibers are more useful than copper wiring.

 Apply Your Knowledge

1. What can you conclude about the energy levels in an atom that can give off laser light at two different wavelengths?
2. Why can free electron lasers give off more than a few special wavelengths of light?
3. Why are optical fibers made out of very transparent materials?
4. What would be an advantage of holographic television?
5. Is a particular type of substance needed to provide atoms in a free electron laser? Explain your answer.
6. In the future, do you think most appliances used in the home will contain lasers? Explain your answer.
7. Why do scientists beam laser light to the moon rather than white light?
8. How are holograms useful for fighting crime?

 Extend Your Knowledge

Research/Projects

1. Write to the Public Information Office of the Los Alamos Scientific Laboratory, Los Alamos, NM 87545, or the Lawrence Livermore Laboratory, Livermore, CA 94550, to get more information about their laser fusion projects.
2. Contact a local hospital or medical center to inquire about the medical uses of fiber optics.
3. Inquire at local science museums to find a hologram on exhibit.

Readings

Filson, Brent. *Exploring with Lasers*. Messner, 1984. Describes characteristics of lasers, tells how they operate, and how they are used.

Heckman, Philip. *The Magic of Holography*. Atheneum, 1986. Presents the history of optics from Isaac Newton to today's holograms. Describes the ways holography is used today and some of the ways it may be used in the future.

CHAPTER 21
Sound

How do elephants communicate in the jungle? People have long known about the trumpeting elephants make when they are excited. More recently, scientists discovered that elephants also make sounds too low for the human ear to hear. These low sounds travel well through the jungle.

Organizing Your Study Skills The outline below will help you see how the chapter is organized and what you should learn as you read.

I. Section 21-1: Sound as a Wave
   A. What causes sound?
   B. Why does sound move at different speeds through different materials?
   C. What is one cause of refracted sound?
   D. What are some uses of reflected sound waves?

II. Section 21-2: Characteristics of Sound
   A. What kind of sound is noise?
   B. What determines the pitch of a sound?
   C. What is the Doppler effect?

III. Section 21-3: Musical Sounds
   A. How do the three basic instrument groups produce music?
   B. What are three ways to increase vibrations?

Objectives

After completing this section you will be able to

A. Explain what causes sound.

B. Explain why sound moves at different speeds through different materials.

C. Describe one cause of refracted sound.

D. Describe some uses of reflected sound waves.

21·1 Sound as a Wave

Making Sound

A ringing bell, a thunderclap, laughter, and music are sounds that seem very different to people. However, all sounds are alike because they are waves.

If you touch your throat while you hum, you can feel your vocal cords moving. The strings on a guitar also move back and forth to make music. **Vibrations** are quick, back-and-forth motions. Often vibrations produce sounds. A vibrating object makes the matter around it vibrate. The tuning fork in *Figure 21-1* is an example. When it is struck, its vibrations cause waves through both water and air.

You will recall that sound waves travel through matter as compressional waves. They travel through matter just as other compressional waves move through a spring. Because sound is a vibration of molecules, matter must be present to provide the molecules. So sound waves can move only through matter.

You can hear because, when sound waves reach your ears, the waves make your eardrums vibrate. Nerves sense the vibrations, then send your brain messages about the vibrations. The brain interprets the messages as sound.

The astronaut in *Figure 21-2* needed a radio to talk to the astronauts aboard the space shuttle. There is no air in space to carry the sound waves of voices.

Figure 21-1 Vibrations cause sound.

Figure 21-2 In space, there is no air to carry sound.

The Speed of Sound

Sound moves at different speeds through different materials. As *Figure 21-3* shows, sound travels much faster in solids than in gases. In which of the materials listed do sound waves travel fastest?

The speed of sound depends on how easy it is to squeeze the material's molecules closer together. Sound travels fastest through materials that do not compress easily, such as solids. In solids, molecules are close together. Since sound waves travel through matter, the closer the molecules, the faster sound waves can move.

Scientists' measurements show that the speed of sound through air is 331.29 meters per second. This value applies to dry air at 0°C and at standard air pressure at sea level.

People once thought an airplane could not fly faster than the speed of sound without destroying itself. In 1947, test pilot Chuck Yeager proved that both pilot and plane can survive flights at speeds greater than the speed of sound.

As a plane flies, it compresses air in front of it, as shown in *Figure 21-4*. A wave of compression travels outward at the speed of sound. If the plane flies more slowly than the speed of sound, the plane never catches up with the wave of compression. To fly faster than the speed of sound, the plane must pass through a "wall" of compressed air—the sound barrier.

While the plane flies faster than the speed of sound, the air is compressed along a cone, as shown. This air hitting the ground causes a sonic boom, which can be louder than thunder. The boom trails behind the plane as long as the plane flies faster than sound.

Material	Speed(m/s)
Air (0°C)	331
Water (15°C)	1450
Brick	3650
Oak	3850
Aluminum	5100
Steel	5200
Granite	6000

Figure 21-3 Speed of sound in various materials

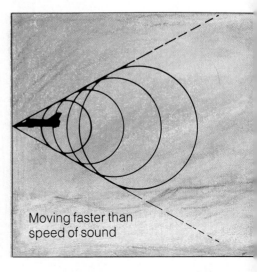

Figure 21-4 How a plane compresses air in front of it

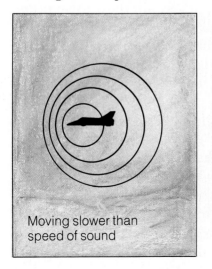

Moving slower than speed of sound

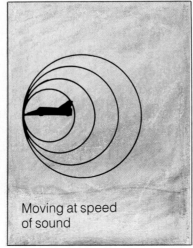

Moving at speed of sound

Moving faster than speed of sound

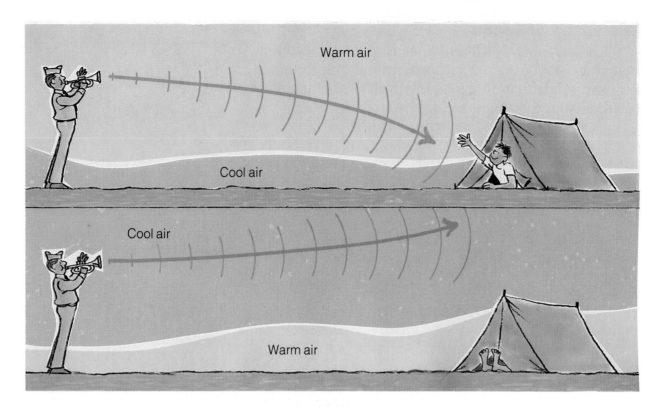

Figure 21-5 Differences in air temperature cause sound waves to refract.

Sound Waves Refract

Sound travels more quickly in warm air than in cold air. The molecules in warm air move more quickly than those in cold air, and so bump into each other more often. As a result, sound waves are refracted when they move from air of one temperature to air of another temperature.

Figure 21-5 shows how sound waves are refracted by temperature differences. At night, air near the ground is colder than the air above it, so sound travels more slowly near the ground. As the sound waves from the trumpet move up into the warmer air, they travel faster. The upper part of each wave moves ahead. The trumpet's sound waves bend toward the ground and wake up the camper. On a hot day, the air near the ground is hotter than the air above it. The waves curve upward, and the camper sleeps on.

Just as a lens can focus light waves by refracting them, refraction can focus sound waves. For example, the girl in *Figure 21-6* can hear the watch's tick quite clearly through the balloon. The balloon contains exhaled air, part of which is carbon dioxide. Sound waves move more slowly through carbon dioxide than through air. Therefore, sound waves from the watch are refracted and focused as they move in and out of the balloon.

Figure 21-6 The balloon focuses sound just as a lens can focus light.

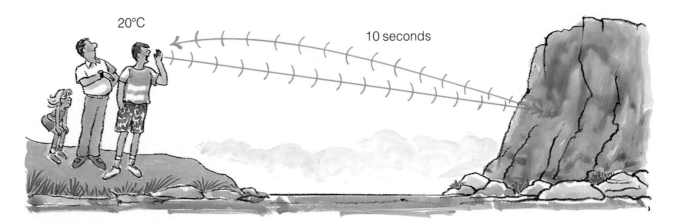

20°C

10 seconds

Sound Waves Reflect

You know that you can see your reflection, but did you know that you can hear your reflection? Like all waves, sound waves can be reflected. An echo is a reflected sound wave. If you know the speed of sound, you can use echoes to find distances to objects. The family in *Figure 21-7* is hiking on a 20°C day; the speed of sound in air is about 344 m/s. The son calls out "Hello." If an echo returns from the mountain in 10 seconds, then the sound took half that time—5 seconds—to reach the mountain and 5 seconds to return. The distance to the mountain is 344 m/s × 5 s, which is 1720 meters.

Knowing the speed of sound in the ocean (about 1500 m/s), people can use the echoes of sonar (**so**und **na**vigation and **r**anging) to chart the oceans. A ship sends out sound waves. *Figure 21-8* shows that these waves hit the ocean floor and are reflected back to the ship. The distance that the sound travels is calculated using the speed of the sound wave and the time the wave needs to travel to and from the ocean floor. This calculation tells the depth of the ocean at that place.

Bats also use sound waves for navigation. They find food and other objects in their paths by sending out bursts of sound. The time it takes for echoes to come back tells bats how far the objects are.

Section Review

1. How are all sounds produced?
2. How does a material affect the speed of sound in it?
3. How does a balloon of gas focus sound?
4. How can echoes reveal distance?

Challenge: Does sound travel more quickly at the top or at the bottom of a mountain? Why?

Figure 21-7 Using echoes to find distance

For Practice

How far above the ocean bottom is a ship if it takes 2 seconds for an echo to return to it?

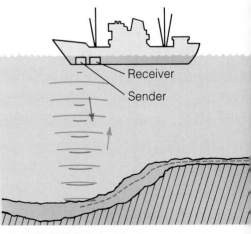

Figure 21-8 Using echoes in sonar

Properties of Sound

Purpose

To observe how matter affects sound

Materials

- Erlenmeyer or Florence flask
- stopper to fit flask
- wire
- small bell
- hot plate, or Bunsen burner, ring stand, ring, wire gauze, and matches or Flor-
- tongs or hot pad
- cover goggles

Procedure and Observations

1. *CAUTION: Wear your cover goggles during the entire activity. Use the tongs or hot pad to hold the flask. Do not touch hot glass, hot water, or any hot surface.*
2. Attach the bell to the wire and insert the wire into the stopper, as in **a**.

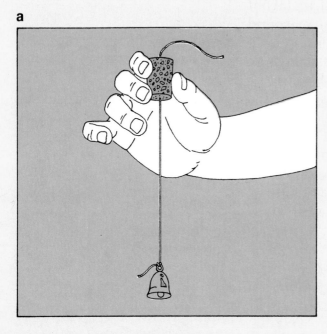

a

b

3. Stopper the flask so that the bell hangs in it, as in **b**.
4. Shake the flask and record whether you can hear the bell.
5. Unstopper the flask and put a small amount of water in it.
6. Arrange the flask on the hot plate or on the wire gauze on the ring and ring stand.
7. Boil the water in the flask until steam comes out of it.
8. Use the tongs or hot pad to remove the flask from the heat.
9. Stopper the flask and let it cool for a few minutes.
10. Repeat step 3 and record whether the sound is louder or softer than it was before.

Analysis and Conclusions

1. After you stoppered the heated flask, what happened to the gases in it?
2. What property of sound caused the result you observed in step 10?

21-2 Characteristics of Sound

Objectives

After completing this section you will be able to

A. Distinguish between sound and noise.
B. Explain what determines the pitch of a sound.
C. Describe the Doppler effect.

Sound Intensity, Loudness, and Noise

Sound waves spread out in all directions, much as light from a lamp spreads. Therefore, you can hear sounds in any direction from their source. As the waves move farther out, they spread over a greater region. As with light, sound intensity decreases if you move farther away from the source.

Intensity and loudness are not the same. The intensity of sound is measured in units called **decibels**. Every increase of ten decibels means that the intensity of a sound is ten times greater. Loudness is more difficult to measure because what seems loud to one person might not seem loud to another. However, most people agree that sounds of more than 120 decibels are painful.

A very intense sound has a lot of energy and a large amplitude. It seems loud. A less intense sound has less energy and a smaller amplitude. It seems soft. *Figure 21-9* lists some common sounds and their intensities. Which familiar sounds are the loudest? Listening too often to sounds above 85 decibels in intensity may permanently injure your inner ear and cause hearing loss.

Anyone who has been disturbed by the sound of a vacuum cleaner knows that sounds do not have to be very intense to be annoying. Any unwanted or unpleasant sound is considered noise. **Noise** is pollution because it harms people and property. High-intensity noises can break plaster and glass and harm your hearing. These noises produce enough pressure to break your eardrum or an object, such as a glass vase. All noise raises your blood pressure and can make you irritable.

To control noise, you can either reduce the noise that a source produces or you can reduce the amount of noise that your ears receive. Quieter trucks, motorcycles, and vacuum cleaners help reduce the amount of noise that our ears receive from those sources. We can also reduce noise from cars, planes, and other noisy devices by muffling them. Special ceiling materials for rooms absorb sound and lessen noise. Workers can protect themselves from noise by using ear plugs. The United States has laws to regulate noise from some construction equipment, some transportation equipment, as well as from air conditioners and lawn mowers.

Explore!

Use an encyclopedia to find out how the human ear works.

Sound	Decibels
Threshold of hearing	0
Rustle of leaves	15
Whisper	20
Library	40
Light traffic	50
Normal conversation	55
Background music	60
Vacuum cleaner	70
Dishwasher	80
Busy city street	90
Power lawn mower	100
Jackhammer	110
Rock band	115
Thunder overhead	120

Figure 21-9 Intensity of some common sounds

Frequency Determines Pitch

When sound waves travel from a vibrating object, they have the same frequency as the object's vibrations. A sound's **pitch**—how low or high a sound seems—depends on how quickly the sound source vibrates. In other words, a sound's pitch depends on frequency. A high-frequency sound has a high pitch. A low-frequency sound has a low pitch.

Human ears can detect sounds between frequencies of 20 and 20 000 hertz. **Ultrasonic** sounds are those above 20 000 hertz, which vibrate too fast for humans to detect.

On the other hand, you can call your dog with an ultrasonic whistle, because dogs hear frequencies up to 25 000 hertz. At these frequencies, they hear leaves rustle or animals moving in the grass. The echoes bats use as they fly around in the dark are about 80 000 hertz.

Dog whistles are not the only use of ultrasonic waves. One kind of self-focusing camera sends out waves of about 50 000 hertz. The object to be photographed reflects the waves back to the camera. A device in the camera times the trip back and forth and figures out the object's distance. The camera focuses for that distance and takes a picture.

A new kind of cane for blind people works in a similar way. It also sends out waves of about 50 000 hertz. The signals reflect off obstacles and return to a sensor that the blind person wears. A sounding device in the cane gives off sounds of different frequencies for different distances.

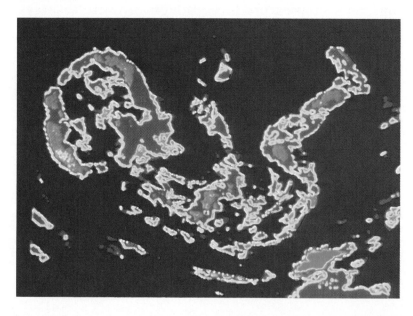

Figure 20-10 An ultrasonic image of a fetus

Industrial testing companies can use ultrasonic waves to find fine cracks and breaks in parts. Some medicines are sealed in their bottles with high-frequency waves to prevent tampering. Doctors use ultrasonic waves to examine soft tissues in the body. Images, such as the one in *Figure 21-10,* help medical workers diagnose and treat individuals.

Recently, scientists have learned that elephants communicate using low-frequency sounds. *Figure 21-11* shows a spot on the elephant's forehead that flutters at frequencies between 14 and 24 hertz. The fluttering produces sound waves that are below the range of human hearing. Sound waves with frequencies too low for people to hear are called **infrasonic**. When the animal lets out rumbles, growls, or other sounds we can hear, the spot on the elephant's forehead flutters at lower frequencies.

High-frequency sounds carry only short distances and fade quickly in heavy woods. Infrasonic waves, however, can travel much farther before losing their strength. Scientists think that elephants use infrasonic calls when they are traveling through a forest together but are not within sight of each other.

Some types of birds, including pigeons, can sense infrasonic waves. Scientists do not yet understand what role these sounds play in the birds' lives. Fin whales produce intense infrasonic calls too. The purpose of the whales' infrasonic calls is unknown.

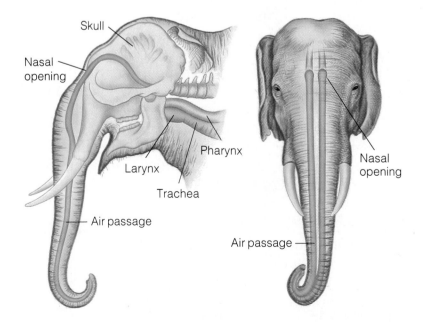

Figure 21-11 This spot on an elephant's forehead flutters to produce infrasonic waves as well as waves humans can hear.

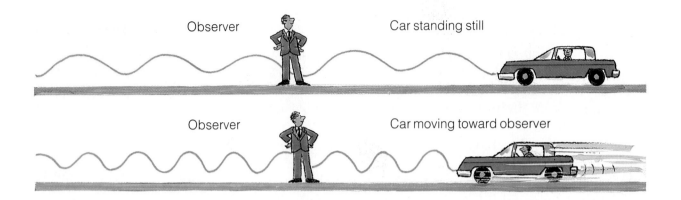

Figure 21-12 The Doppler effect takes place whether the observer or the sound source moves.

The Doppler Effect Changes Pitch

Have you ever observed how the pitch of a car's engine drops as the car passes you? Since pitch depends on frequency, something must happen to the frequency to cause this effect.

Figure 21-12 shows what happens. As the car approaches, each sound wave travels a shorter distance to reach you than earlier waves did. The car seems to chase its own waves. However, the car never catches up, because sound moves much faster than the car. Since more waves reach you every second that the car nears you, the wavelength is shortened, and the frequency and pitch are higher than normal. As the car passes, the pitch drops as the wavelength returns to its true length. When the car moves away, fewer waves reach you each second, so the pitch is lower.

A similar change happens when you move instead of the sound source moving. Any change in frequency when you or a wave source moves is named the **Doppler effect** for its 19th-century discoverer, Christian Doppler.

Figure 21-13 shows how police radar uses the Doppler effect in radio waves to detect speeders. The radar set sends out a very-high-frequency wave. When the radio wave reflects off a moving car, the reflected wave has an even higher frequency. Electronic devices in the police car convert the change in frequency into the speed of the approaching car.

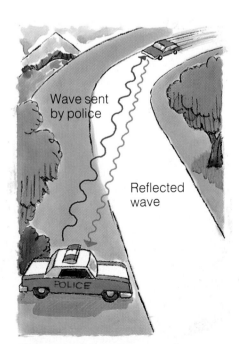

Wave sent by police

Reflected wave

Figure 21-13 The Doppler effect in police radar

Section Review

1. What unit measures the intensity of sound?
2. Which frequencies can people hear?
3. Name two waves that show the Doppler effect.

Challenge: If you were on a train, how would the train's whistle sound to you as the train moved?

Studio Engineer

When you watch a movie with an old sound track, you might see the actors' lips move before or after you hear their voices. Today, such delays would be fixed by a studio engineer.

Studio engineers work wherever sound is reproduced for movies, television, radio, and records. They study the acoustics of recording studios and decide where to place microphones or speakers. Studio engineers work to cut down echoes, reverberations, and delays. They control sound volume and quality to improve recorded sound tracks.

Studio engineers learn acoustics in college or technical school. They also study the electronics of complex audio equipment.

21-3 Musical Sounds

Music from Instruments

No one would mistake the sounds of a banjo for those of a trumpet or drum. Yet all three instruments produce the same types of sound waves. Music is pleasant sound because it has regular wave patterns. Musical instruments usually make sounds that go well together. The three basic groups of musical instruments are the string, percussion, and wind instruments.

String instruments, such as guitars, have strings stretched over a box. A player vibrates the strings with a finger, a bow, or a pick. The vibrating string, such as the one in *Figure 21-14,* vibrates air which sends sound waves to your ear so you can hear the music.

To play the correct notes, the player must adjust the pitch each string will produce. A string instrument's pitch depends on the tightness, thickness, heaviness, and length of the string. The thinner, tighter, lighter, or shorter the string, the higher the pitch. Note in *Figure 21-14* that most guitar strings, for example, are about equal in length, but not in thickness. Generally, the string that makes the highest notes is shorter than the others. A player tunes a a guitar by tightening or loosening a string. Once a string is tuned, a player can press down to shorten it, thus raising its pitch.

Objectives

After completing this section you will be able to

A. Describe how each of the three basic instrument groups produces music.
B. Compare three ways of strengthening vibrations.

Figure 21-14 The strings of a guitar differ in thickness.

Explore!

Find out what standing waves are and what they have to do with music.

Percussion instruments produce sounds when a hand or stick strikes them. For example, the flexible, stretched material on a drum vibrates when struck. A drum can be tuned by tightening its surface.

The piano is both a percussion and a string instrument. Because you strike a key, it is a percussion instrument. But when you strike a key, a padded wooden hammer hits a wire string inside the piano. The vibrating strings make the sounds. When you take your finger off the key, a pad called a damper presses against the string and stops it from vibrating. Pressing the right pedal with your foot holds the dampers for all the notes away from the strings. In this way, holding the pedal down allows the notes to sound for a long time.

A piano has 88 keys. Each makes a hammer hit several strings of the same length. The strings range in length from about 5 centimeters to about 200 centimeters. It does not matter whether the strings are run up and down, as in an upright piano, or horizontally, as in a grand piano. The strings are attached to a sounding board, as shown in *Figure 21-15*.

Figure 21-15 Parts of a piano

How hard you strike the keys affects the intensity of the sound of the piano. But no matter how hard you strike a piano key, the key will always play that same frequency. Only the loudness changes. Every object has its own frequency of vibration, which is called its **natural frequency**. The natural frequency of an object depends on the object's size, shape, and material.

A wind instrument produces sound when the air inside it vibrates. The clarinet, shown in *Figure 21-16*, is a wind instrument. The player blows air onto a reed in the clarinet. The reed vibrates and makes the air inside the instrument vibrate. To change the pitch, the player presses the keys or covers the holes. This action changes the length of the air column, which changes the pitch. As with the strings, short air columns sound high, and long ones sound low.

The trumpet and the trombone shown here work like the clarinet. However, instead of a reed, the player's lips vibrate to make the air column vibrate. Pushing down on the buttons, called valves, lengthens the trumpet's air column. Pulling or pushing the trombone's slide changes the length of its air column.

Figure 21-16 A player pushes down on a trumpet's valves to lengthen the air column. A player's breath makes the clarinet's reed and the air inside the clarinet vibrate.

Figure 21-17 The player pulls or pushes the trombone's slide to change the length of the air column.

Chapter 21: Sound **493**

Increasing Vibrations

The vibrations of a reed, a string, or a player's lips are actually very faint. Therefore, musical instruments are built to strengthen the original vibrations. For example, plucking banjo strings causes the strings to vibrate. These vibrations, in turn, start vibrations in the banjo itself and the air inside the banjo. As a result, the sound coming from the banjo is louder. The vibrating strings "forced" the banjo and the air inside to vibrate. **Forced vibrations** occur when one object causes another to vibrate at the original frequency. For the banjo, the original frequency is the natural frequency of the strings. The natural frequencies of the body of the banjo and the air inside it are not the same. As a result, the strings provide the banjo's sounds.

A similar effect strengthens a piano's sounds. When someone strikes piano keys, vibrations travel through the wires to the sounding board. Vibrations in the sounding board help strengthen piano sounds.

Another effect—called resonance—strengthens sounds from wind instruments. **Resonance** occurs when a vibration reinforces vibrations from another object that has the same natural frequency. Wind instruments are built so that each length of the air column produces only its natural frequency. When the player blows into the instrument, the air column reinforces the original vibration from the player, making the sound louder.

Figure 21-19 illustrates another effect—sympathetic vibrations. Both tuning forks have the same natural frequency. When one fork is struck and vibrates, the second fork starts vibrating without being struck. **Sympathetic vibrations** occur when waves from one vibrating object cause another object with the same natural frequency to vibrate.

Because of sympathetic vibrations, a singer can produce a note powerful enough to shatter glass. If the glass has the same natural frequency as the strong note, the glass begins to vibrate. Strong vibrations can shatter the glass.

Section Review

1. How do the three instrument groups differ?
2. What are three ways to strengthen a vibration?

Challenge: Why can you make music by blowing across bottles holding different amounts of water?

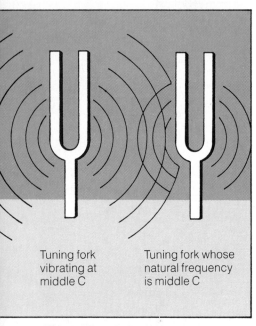

Tuning fork vibrating at middle C

Tuning fork whose natural frequency is middle C

Figure 21-18 Since the two tuning forks have the same natural frequency, only one needs to be struck. The other vibrates sympathetically.

Making Music

Purpose

To observe the factors affecting vibrations and pitch

Materials

- 4 rubber bands of different thicknesses
- ruler
- 2 pencils
- empty soft-drink bottle
- tuning fork
- water
- cover goggles

Procedure and Observations

Part A

1. Put on your cover goggles. Stretch a rubber band around the length of the ruler.
2. Note the rubber band's tightness by pulling gently on it.
3. Insert the 2 pencils under the rubber band, as in **a**.

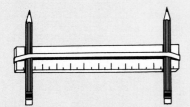

a

4. Pluck the rubber band, and note its pitch.
5. Repeat steps 1–4 for the other rubber bands.
6. Record how the band's thickness and tightness affect its pitch.

Part B

1. Using the same setup as in Part A, pluck one rubber band and note its pitch.
2. Hold down the middle of the rubber band, as in **b**.

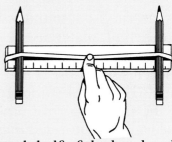

b

3. Pluck each half of the band and note the pitch.
4. Record how the pitch of the shortened rubber band compares with the pitch of the whole rubber band.

Part C

1. Put some water in a bottle.
2. Blow across the top and listen.
3. Hit a tuning fork on something soft, such as the rubber heel of your shoe.
4. Move the vibrating tuning fork up and down over the bottle's mouth, as in **c**.

c

5. Record what happens to the loudness as you move the tuning fork.
6. Repeat steps 1–5 with different amounts of water in the bottle.

Analysis and Conclusions

1. What factors affect the pitch of the rubber bands?
2. Why does the tuning fork sound louder at certain positions than at others?

Solving Word Problems About Sound

You have learned that sound waves travel through different materials at different speeds. You have also learned that sound waves reflect off solid objects and return to their source. Use this knowledge to help you solve the following word problems.

1. Imagine standing on a mountain, looking down on the town in the photograph. You are 3.5 km (3500 m) from the town. The bells in the bell tower begin to ring. How long does it take for the sound to reach you on a summer day? on a winter day? (Hint: The speed of sound through air at 20°C is about 344 m/s; the speed of sound through air at 0°C is 331 m/s.)

2. Imagine snorkeling near the coral reef in the photograph. You hear a loud banging sound from the boat from which you dove, about 1 km away. How long does it take for the sound to reach you? (Hint: Refer to page 485 to find the speed of sound through ocean water.)

3. You have learned that light waves travel much faster than sound waves do. Use this fact to help you analyze the distance of lightning in a thunderstorm. You see a flash of lightning. Nine seconds later you hear a clap of thunder. Assume the air temperature is about 20°C. How far away did the lightning strike?

4. Imagine you are on an expedition to map the deepest part of the Pacific Ocean, the Mariana Trench. A sonar device sends out sound waves that bounce back after 14 seconds. At the point where the sonar hit, how deep is the Mariana Trench?

5. Imagine standing near the top of a mountain in winter and shouting out "Hello!" You hear three echoes, one after 6 seconds, one after 8 seconds, and one after 11 seconds. How far away is each of the three objects that the sound bounced off?

6. Imagine visiting a deep canyon on a warm summer day. You say your name and hear echoes after 1 second, 2 seconds, 4 seconds, and 8 seconds. How many times did the sound bounce off the walls? How wide is the canyon?

✔ Summary

21-1 Sound as a Wave

A. Sounds are made by rapid, back-and-forth motions called vibrations. Sound waves travel through matter as compressional waves.

B. Sound moves at different speeds through different materials. Sound materials that are more difficult to compress.

C. Sound waves are refracted when they move from air of one temperature to air of another temperature.

D. Sound waves can be reflected. An echo is reflected sound. The echoes of sonar can be used to calculate the depth of the ocean.

21-2 Characteristics of Sound

A. A very intense sound has a lot of energy and a large amplitude. It seems loud. Intensity of sound is measured in decibels. Any unwanted or unpleasant sound is noise.

B. The pitch of a sound depends on how quickly the sound source vibrates. Sounds above the human hearing range are ultrasonic. Sounds below the range of human hearing are infrasonic.

C. The Doppler effect is a change in frequency caused when the sound source or the observer moves.

21-3 Musical Sounds

A. String instruments produce music from vibrating strings. Percussion instruments produce sound when air inside them vibrates. Similary, all objects vibrate. The frequency at which any object vibrates—its natural frequency—depends on its size, shape, and the material of which it is made.

B. Forced vibrations, sympathetic vibrations, and resonance transfer vibrations from one object to another.

Vocabulary

For each of the following terms, write a sentence using the term correctly.

decibels	**natural frequency**	**sympathetic vibrations**
Doppler effect	**noise**	**ultrasonic**
forced vibrations	**pitch**	**vibrations**
infrasonic	**resonance**	

Check Your Knowledge

Part I: Matching Match the definition in Column I with the correct term in Column II.

Column I
1. unit for comparing intensity of sounds
2. back-and-forth motion
3. highness or lowness of a sound
4. too high for humans to hear
5. one source makes another vibrate at the original frequency
6. unwanted or unpleasant sound
7. a vibration reinforces another of the same natural frequency
8. apparent change in pitch
9. depends on an object's size, shape, and material
10. a vibration causes another of the same natural frequency

Column II
a. decibels
b. Doppler effect
c. forced vibrations
d. infrasonic
e. natural frequency
f. noise
g. pitch
h. resonance
i. sympathetic vibrations
j. ultrasonic
k. vibrations

Part II: Multiple Choice Choose the letter of the best answer.

11. A sound's frequency determines its (a) pitch. (b) amplitude. (c) intensity. (d) energy.
12. Sounds travel fastest through (a) solids. (b) liquids. (c) gases. (d) a vacuum.
13. A very intense sound (a) has little energy. (b) has a small amplitude. (c) seems loud. (d) seems soft.
14. The Doppler effect can happen to (a) sound waves only. (b) compressional waves only. (c) water waves only. (d) all waves.
15. As a sound source moves past a stationary observer, the observer may hear (a) a rise in pitch. (b) a drop in pitch. (c) a rise in pitch, then a drop. (d) no change in pitch.
16. A sonic boom occurs when (a) a sound becomes ultrasonic. (b) an echo occurs. (c) an object moves faster than the speed of sound. (d) a noise is made.

17. Shortening a vibrating string causes the pitch of the sound produced to (a) go up, then down. (b) go up. (c) go down. (d) remain the same.
18. Wind instruments make sound you can hear with (a) forced vibrations. (b) resonance. (c) sympathetic vibrations. (d) sonar.

Part III: Completion Write the word or words that complete the sentence correctly.
19. Dog whistles are one use of _____ waves.
20. How hard you strike the keys of a piano affects the _____ of the sound produced.
21. In a wind instrument, a short air column produces sound with a _____ pitch.
22. Shortening or tightening a banjo string raises its _____ .
23. A ship can use the echoes of _____ to determine the depth of the ocean.

Check Your Understanding

1. The speed of light refers to the speed in a vacuum. Does the speed of sound also refer to the speed in a vacuum? Explain.
2. What are ultrasonic and infrasonic waves?
3. How can you hear your reflection?
4. When air temperature close to the ground is different from the temperature further up, mirages can occur. What happens to sound?
5. When does an aircraft produce a sonic boom?
6. What part of a banjo has the same function as the sounding board of a piano? What is that function?
7. Describe how the police use the Doppler effect.

Apply Your Knowledge

1. A tin-can telephone is made of two cans with a string stretched between them. Each end of the string is tied to a button that is pulled against the bottom of the can. How does the telephone work?
2. Suppose a radio playing rock music at full volume is placed in an airtight room with no air. Could the music be heard inside the room? outside the room? Explain.
3. The sound of a train reaches you more quickly through the rails than through the air. Why?
4. The cracking sound of a lion-tamer's whip is a sonic boom. What causes it?
5. You hear the pitch of a car horn become lower. Explain how you know whether the car has started moving toward or away from you.
6. What happens to the sound of a tuning fork when its handle is pressed against a table top? Explain your answer.
7. How would you adjust a single wire to produce notes of different frequencies?
8. If you hold a glass over your ear and play a few notes on a piano, some notes sound louder than others. Explain why.
9. In general, the larger a wind instrument, the lower the notes it can play. Why?

Extend Your Knowledge

Research/Projects

1. Ask a friend to stand about 25 m away from you down the length of a chain link fence. Tap a post with a hammer. Explain what you and your friend observe.
2. Make a musical instrument by filling at least eight empty soda pop bottles with different amounts of water. Use a tuning fork or pitch pipe to get started. Play a song on your instrument.

Readings

Kilgore, Jim. "Cracking Down on Speeders with Doppler Radar." *Scholastic Science World*, November 17, 1986, pages 14-15. Learn how police use a property of physics to nab speeding motorists.

Wicks, Keith. *Sound and Recording.* Warwick, 1982. Discusses the world of sound from simple vibrations to complex areas of acoustics.

Microwaves to Guide Planes to a Safe Landing

At peak hours of travel, nearly one million Americans are in flight. Landing planes safely and on schedule is a critical problem at busy airports. In a few years, a new type of landing system at many major airports will make flying safer for airplane passengers and quieter for people living near the airports.

Most airports now use an instrument landing system (ILS) to guide planes to the runway. This system beams low-frequency radiowaves from the base of the runway. Planes attempting to land tune in the correct frequency when they are about 13 km from the airport. The pilots use the beam of radiowaves to position the plane for its descent to the airport and to guide it onto the runway. The beam of the ILS makes an angle no wider than 6° and no taller than 3°. This gives planes a very narrow lane for their approach. Planes must line up one behind the other, following the same path to the runway at intervals of at least three minutes.

Because the electromagnetic waves used in the ILS have relatively long wavelengths, they are easily distorted by buildings and by radio transmissions from the ground. This limits the width of the beam that can be used to guide the planes safely to the runway. Because the planes have to approach the runway using a single narrow corridor, all the planes landing at a particular runway must follow identical flight patterns. This means that people who live under the path of approaching planes are subjected to noise repeatedly.

A microwave landing system (MLS) is set up the same way as an ILS. But because microwaves have shorter wavelengths than radiowaves, microwaves are subject to less distortion. Because microwaves are not used for broadcasting, there is little interference from the ground and the MLS can use a much wider beam than the ILS.

The MLS projects a guidance beam that is more than 80° wide and 20° tall. The wide approach afforded the planes using this guidance system means that the planes do not have to line up one behind the other. The height of the beam allows for variations, such as curved approaches, banked approaches, and steeper descents. The steepness of the descents reduces plane noise on the ground in general. The variation in flight paths helps reduce noise over particular regions.

Computer equipment on the ground and in the plane tracks the exact location of the plane in the wide funnel. Using the computer in combination with the MLS, planes virtually land themselves. Because planes using the MLS can land every 40 seconds instead of every three minutes, planes do not have to circle before landing. This reduces fuel consumption as well as traffic jams in the air.

For Discussion

1. Describe how an instrument landing system works.

2. What advantanges does the microwave landing system have over the instrument landing system?

Lasers as Sighting Devices

In putting up any kind of building, construction workers must be able to determine whether corners are perpendicular, walls are parallel, and surfaces are level. For hundreds of years, builders and surveyors have had to work in pairs to make such determinations. They traditionally have used an instrument called a transit, which is a telescope with cross-hair markings on the lens, and a rod marked with fine gradations.

Following is the standard method of determining whether a surface is level using a transit. One member of a surveying team sets up the transit some distance from the construction site and adjusts it so that it is completely level. The other member of the surveying team holds the pole at a marked spot on the construction site. The surveyor at the transit sights through the telescope and uses the cross hair to take a reading off the rod. Then the surveyor at the site moves the stick and the other surveryor takes additional readings. If all the readings are identical, the surveyors know that the ground is level.

Today, surveyors and construction workers can use lasers instead of a transit in surveying work. A laser produces a fine, straight line that can be used as a sight-

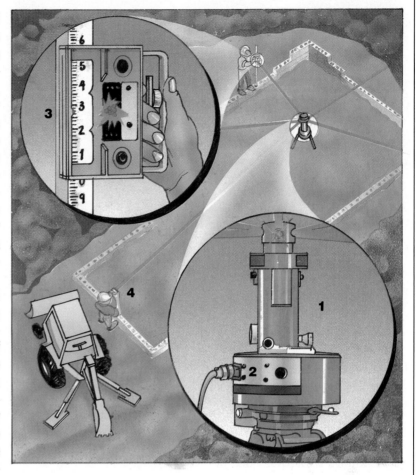

ing device. Placed at a central location at a construction site, the laser replaces the transit and the surveyor looking through the transit. Instead, the person holding the pole takes a measurment by noting where the laser light hits a detector at the pole. The laser beam rotates. Therefore, a number of people can use the laser at the same time. Follow the diagram to see how a laser can be used to determine whether a building site is level.

1. Place the laser at a central location at the construction site.

2. Set the laser's automatic leveler, so that accurate measurements can be taken from the machine.

3. Sight through the detector and take a reading off the measurement rod.

4. Take more readings at other spots on the site or correlate the readings with those taken from other locations. If they are all the same, the site is level.

Electricity and Magnetism

Electricity is so common in our lives that it is difficult to imagine how people ever lived without it. Until late in the 1800s, however, electricity was known only to experimenters. Combined with magnetism, the practical uses of flowing currents spawned our present-day revolution in electronics.

13th Century

Who invented the magnetic compass? Most historians credit the Chinese, but there are others who say it was the Arabs. Still others give credit to the Italians, and some say it was the Scandinavians. No matter who it was, the important fact is that with the compass navigators could for the first time in history chart their direction on the seas with unfailing accuracy. The compass made possible the exploration of the world, traveling uncharted waters and through wildernesses on land.

18th Century

Electricity was only a curio until the 1700s when scientists began serious studies of it. Benjamin Franklin recognized that lightning was due to electricity. His experiment with flying a kite during an electrical storm added to the fundamental knowledge about electricity. It also resulted in the use of lightning rods to protect buildings from these sometimes damaging discharges of electricity from the sky.

Chapter 22 Electricity
Chapter 23 Magnetism
Chapter 24 Electronic Revolution

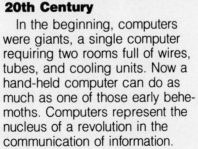

19th Century

Thomas Edison took electricity out of the laboratory and put it into our everyday lives. Electric light bulbs had already been invented, but they burned only briefly and had no practical worth. Edison perfected the electric light bulb so that it could be used for home lighting. His lights took cities out of darkness. Edison also introduced the first large-scale electric lighting system.

20th Century

In the beginning, computers were giants, a single computer requiring two rooms full of wires, tubes, and cooling units. Now a hand-held computer can do as much as one of those early behemoths. Computers represent the nucleus of a revolution in the communication of information.

They are the "banks" of information about the past and the prognosticators of events to come. They are as close to being "brains" as electronic devices can be. Their memories, in fact, are better. At present their only lack is the power of reasoning.

CHAPTER 22
Electricity

Often during a heavy thunderstorm, streaks of lightning seem to erupt between the clouds and the ground through a blackened sky. Lightning can do a great deal of damage because it is a form of electricity—a very dangerous form. Yet, "tamed" electricity is a very important part of our lives. In this chapter you will learn about electricity and the ways we use electricity.

Organizing Your Study Skills The outline below will help you see how the chapter is organized and what you should learn as you read.

I. **Section 22-1: Electric Charge**
   A. What is the electrical nature of matter?
   B. How does electric charge build up?
   C. How do sparks occur?

II. **Section 22-2: Electric Current**
   A. How do conductors and insulators differ?
   B. How does a voltage source produce electric current?
   C. In what way are voltage, current, and resistance related?
   D. What are the three basic parts of an electric circuit?

III. **Section 22-3: Circuits**
   A. What path does electric current take through a series circuit?
   B. Why are homes wired in parallel circuits?
   C. What are three ways of controlling electric circuits?

IV. **Section 22-4: Using Electricity**
   A. How do direct and alternating current differ?
   B. How are electric power, voltage, and current related to each other?

After completing this section, you will be able to:

A. Describe the electrical nature of matter.
B. Describe how charge builds up.
C. Give two examples of sparks and explain how they occur.

Matter Is Electrical

The atoms in all matter contain small particles. Many of these particles, including electrons and protons, have electric charges. Each proton has one positive charge. Each electron has one negative charge. The movement of electrons makes the electricity we use every day. A third type of particle, the neutron, is neutral. It has no electric charge.

An atom normally has the same number of electrons and protons. The electrons' negative charges balance the protons' positive charges. The sum of the negative and positive charges is zero, so the atom is neutral.

Scientists know that objects, including atoms, change their motion only if a force is applied. An **electric force** provides the attraction or repulsion between charged particles. Particles with unlike charges, such as an electron and a proton, pull on—attract—each other. Two negatively charged electrons or two positively charged protons push away from—repel—each other.

In atoms, protons and neutrons are tightly bound together by a very strong force. A much weaker force holds electrons within atoms. Often a neutral atom loses some of its electrons. It then has more protons than electrons and is said to have a postitve charge. If a neutral atom gains one or more electrons, it has more electrons than protons and is said to have a negative charge.

For example, a neutral lithium atom has 3 electrons and 3 protons. If a lithium atom becomes positively charged by losing an electron, it is left with only 2 electrons. A neutral fluorine atom has 9 electrons and 9 protons. A fluorine atom can become negatively charged by gaining an electron, giving it 10 electorns.

How Charge Builds Up

If a neutral object is rubbed against another neutral object, some of the electrons might move from object to object. Both objects become charged.

You might feel the effects of electric charge when you comb your hair. Keep in mind that your hair is usually neutral. When you pull a comb through your hair, the comb rubs against your hair and removes electrons.

Applying Science

A familiar process of making "photocopies" of pictures and printed material is possible because unlike charges attract. In this process, called "xerography," the metal drum in the copy machine is given a positive charge. An image of the page to be copied is projected onto the drum, and the areas exposed to light lose their charge. Negatively charged black powder then sticks to the remaining positively charged areas. Finally, the black powder is transferred to positively charged paper and heated—a process that affixes the black-powdered image to the paper's surface.

Now the atoms in your hair have more protons than electrons; they have a positive charge. The extra electrons give your comb a negative charge. Because unlike charges attract, your positively-charged hair sticks to your negatively-charged comb. Your hair moves toward the negatively-charged comb even before they touch.

Each strand of hair now has a positive charge. Because like charges repel, your hairs move away from each other. Charged objects do not have to touch for an electric force to exist between them.

The charge from your hair and from your comb will eventually leak out into the air. Moist air carries charge away better than dry air. For that reason, you are more likely to have "fly-away" hair on a dry day.

The girl in *Figure 22-1* is using electric charge to decorate a room with balloons before a party. Just as with a comb, when she rubs a balloon against her hair, electrons move from her hair to the balloon. The balloon now has a negative charge. The excess negative charges on the balloon repel the negative charges on the part of the wall near it. This leaves the wall near the balloon with a positive charge. The wall and the balloon now attract each other since they have unlike charges.

Figure 22-1 The girl's positively-charged hairs repel each other and are attracted to the negatively-charged balloon.

Figure 22-2 As a result of built-up charges, these balloons will stick to the walls.

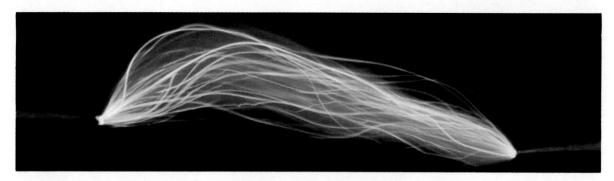

Figure 22-3 A spark results when a blast of charge jumps from one object to another.

Sparks Are Moving Charges

Sometimes a lot of charge builds up on an object. If that charge jumps from one place to another, a spark is produced. *Figure 22-3* shows sparks made by charges jumping from one object to another.

You might notice some weak sparks when you walk across a rug and touch a metal doorknob. Your shoes rub against the rug and pick up additional electrons. As the electrons repel each other, they spread out over your body. When you touch the metal doorknob, you feel a shock and might even see a spark as the electrons jump from you to the doorknob.

Lightning is a much stronger type of spark. Before and during a thunderstorm, some parts of clouds become positively charged. Other parts become negatively charged. Although the details of this process are not clear, it is known that electrons move away from each other within a cloud. Usually, the upper part of a thundercloud has a positive charge while the lower part has a negative charge. When too much negative charge builds up within a cloud, the electrons move suddenly to another part of the same cloud, to another cloud, or to the ground. We see the moving electrons as lightning. Usually a group of electrons move downward in a series of steps for about a second. After the electrons reach the ground, a stronger charge moves more rapidly back to the cloud along the same path. This returning spark is the bright, explosive flash of lightning that we see.

Section Review

1. What makes an atom neutral?
2. How does an object become charged?
3. Explain what can happen when you rub your feet on a carpet and then touch a doorknob.

Challenge: Under what circumstances might lightning jump from one cloud to another?

Electric Charge

Purpose

To produce and observe the effects of electric charge

Materials

- Erlenmeyer flask
- 1-hole cork or rubber stopper to fit flask
- 20 cm of copper wire
- two 3 cm x 1 cm aluminum foil strips
- plastic or rubber comb
- piece of wool

Procedure and Observations

1. Place the wire through the hole in the stopper.
2. Bend the wire's top end so it does not slide through the hole.
3. Bend the wire's bottom end into a hook. The wire should look like the one in **a**.
4. Hang the foil strips closely together on the hook, but loosely, as shown in **b**.

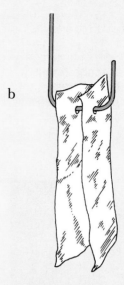

b

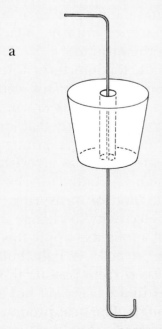

a

5. Insert the stopper into the flask. You have just made an electroscope, which you can use to detect charge.
6. Rub the comb with the wool cloth about 25 times, or comb your hair about 25 times.
7. Bring the comb near the wire sticking out of the stopper.
8. Observe and record what happens to the foil strips.
9. Move the comb away from the electroscope.
10. Repeat step 8.
11. Repeat steps 6–7.
12. Touch the wire with the comb.
13. Repeat step 8.

Analysis and Conclusions

1. Use the idea of building up charge to explain your observations.
2. What caused the foil strips to move? (What causes a change in any object's motion?)

After completing this section, you will be able to:

A. Contrast conductors and insulators.

B. Give an example of a voltage source and describe how it produces electric current.

C. Explain how current, voltage, and resistance are related.

D. List the three basic parts of an electric circuit.

Figure 22-4 Because rubber is a good insulator, the worker's rubber-soled shoes protect her.

Charges Move Through Conductors

As you already know, lightning involves moving charges. The electricity used in your home or school involves moving charges as well. But some differences exist between these examples of electricity.

When lightning flashes through the sky, charge moves from one place to another in single blasts. But the electrical appliances in your home work because charge can flow through matter in a steady stream. This flow of electric charge is **electric current.**

When you flip on your light switch, electrons start flowing through wires in your wall. Electrons hit atoms in the wire and bounce around. A single electron may take hours to reach the light source. Yet, because each electron has a repelling effect on the next electron and thus pushes it along, the end result is an electric current that moves quickly through the wire. Thus the light comes on with little delay once the switch is turned on.

A material that allows electric current to pass through it easily is a good electrical **conductor.** Atoms in a conductor have electrons that are free to move. Metals, like copper, are good conductors. In other materials, called **insulators,** the electrons are not as free to move. Thus current does not flow through them easily. Rubber is a good insulator. The worker in *Figure 22-4* is wearing rubber-soled shoes and standing on a rubber mat so that any electricity that escapes from her machine will not flow through her to the ground.

Even the best conductor interferes with the flow of electrons a little. Atoms in a conductor scatter electrons. The scattering slows the electrons down. Atoms in an insulator hold electrons so strongly that little or no current flows through the material. Anything that slows or stops the flow of electrons acts as a **resistance.** Insulators have high resistance. Conductors have low resistance. The **ohm** is the unit for measuring resistance.

Resistance causes electricity to change into light and heat. Many electrical appliances apply this fact and use poor conductors on purpose. A light bulb's thin wire glows because it resists current passing through it. The high-resistance wires in a toaster get hot as they resist current passing through. The heat produced as a result can be used to toast bread.

Voltage Sources Produce Electric Current

A current of electrons flowing through a wire can be thought of in terms of a current of water flowing through a pipe. In *Figure 22-5a,* water would not flow through the pipe unless a pump were to push it. In order for electric current to flow through the wires in *Figure 22-5b,* the charge must be pushed through the wires. Just as the pump pushes the water, the battery pushes the charge. The energy the battery gives to the electrons is the **voltage.** The **volt** is the unit used for measuring voltage.

Batteries are common sources of voltage. All batteries contain chemical fuel that makes electrical energy. One type of battery is a **dry cell,** such as the flashlight battery shown in *Figure 22-6.* Though the name suggests that the cell is free of liquid, the dry cell is really made of a carbon rod surrounded by a moist paste of manganese dioxide, ammonium chloride, and carbon powder. A zinc case encloses the rod and the paste. As the cell operates, a chemical reaction takes place between the paste and the zinc case that results in the release of electrons. When the zinc case and the carbon rod are connected, the free electrons flow in a steady stream to the carbon rod, setting up an electric current.

The lead storage battery, found in most cars, is an example of the type of battery known as a **wet cell.** Each cell of the battery contains a series of plates. Some plates contain lead only, and some contain lead dioxide. The plates are immersed in a solution of sulfuric acid.

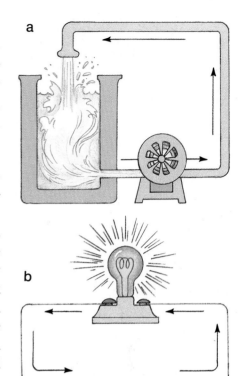

Figure 22-5 A battery acts in an electrical system as a pump does in a water system.

Zinc case

Paste

Carbon rod surrounded by manganese dioxide

Figure 22-6 A dry cell

Figure 22-7 A wet cell

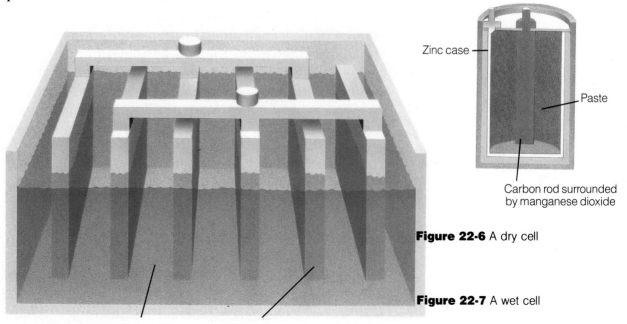

Solution of sulfuric acid   Lead plates

Explore!

Find out why you should take a dead battery out of a device as soon as the battery stops working.

As the battery operates, the plates and the sulfuric acid undergo a series of reactions. As these reactions occur, a continuous flow of electrons move from one type of plate to the other. This produces an electric current.

After batteries have been in use for a while, their ability to produce electric current decreases as the chemicals inside are used up. Though batteries can be "recharged" to provide voltage again, wet cells can be recharged more easily than ordinary carbon-zinc dry cells and hold their charge for longer periods of time. Dry cells using nickel and cadmium are rechargeable.

Current Is Related to Resistance and Voltage

Resistance and voltage determine how much current flows through a conductor. To understand this idea, consider two pipes. The only difference in these two pipes is in the diameter of their openings. A pump pushes water equally in both cases. But more water passes through the pipe with the larger opening. This pipe offers less resistance to the flow of water than the pipe with the smaller opening. In a similar way, more current flows through a conductor with less resistance than through a conductor with more resistance.

Figure 22-8a shows how the amount of resistance and voltage affect the current. Copper wires connect a bulb to a dry cell. The bulb glows brightly.

In *Figure 22-8b*, a thinner wire replaces one of the original wires. The total resistance goes up, and the amount of current going through the bulb decreases. The light produced in the bulb becomes dimmer.

What if the thick copper wire were replaced with an aluminum wire of the same thickness as in *Figure 22-8c?* Aluminum wire does not conduct electricity as efficiently as copper. The total resistance is increased again, so the bulb dims even more.

You can make up for higher resistance by applying more voltage, as shown in *Figure 22-8d*. If you add a second battery, the current increases. With increased current, the bulb glows brightly again.

In the 1800s, George Ohm discovered that certain materials had definite resistances. Current voltage, and resistance are related by **Ohm's law.** This law states that for certain materials:

$$current = voltage/resistance$$

Remember that voltage is measured in volts, and resistance is measured in ohms. Current is measured in **amperes,** the amount of charge moving past a given point in one second. Ohm's law is important for designing any electric device, from toasters to stereos.

You can use Ohm's law to calculate how much current runs through a toaster. If a wall outlet's voltage is 110 volts and a toaster's resistance is 10 ohms, then using Ohm's law:

$$current = 110 \text{ volts}/10 \text{ ohms} = 11 \text{ amperes}.$$

This equation means that to toast bread, 110 volts produce 11 amperes of current in a wire with a resistance of 10 ohms.

Current Moves in a Circuit

A current flows only when it can follow a complete path back to its starting point. Such a path is called a **circuit.** If the path has a gap, the circuit is open and current cannot flow. When the path has no gap, the circuit is closed and the current can flow.

Figure 22-8 A thinner wire has more resistance to current than a thicker wire of the same material. Aluminum wires have more resistance to current than copper wires of the same thickness. Increasing the voltage by adding a dry cell makes up for the higher resistance.

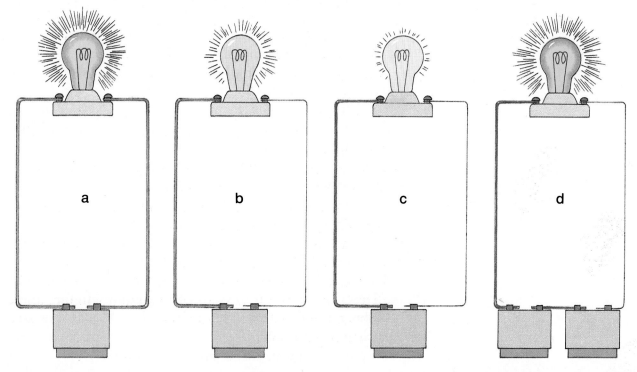

Figure 22-9 A simple circuit contains a voltage source (the dry cell), a useful object (the bulb), and a complete connection from the source of the object and back to the source (the wires). It often also contains a switch.

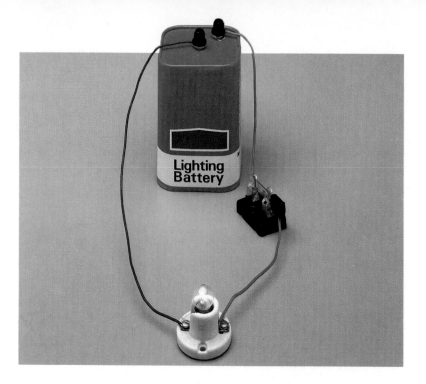

Applying Science

Lithium batteries last much longer than carbon-zinc batteries because lithium can give more electrons per unit volume.

For Practice

Use Ohm's law to solve the following problems.
1. An oven with a resistance of 10 ohms is plugged into a 220-volt electric line. How much current flows through the oven?
2. The two dry cells in a flashlight put out a total of 3 volts. The bulb's resistance is 6 ohms. How many amperes flow through the circuit?

A circuit has three basic parts, as *Figure 22-9* shows: a source of voltage, an object the current passes through, and connections between the voltage source and the object and back to the starting point.

The voltage source changes some type of nonelectric energy into electric energy. For example, batteries convert chemical energy into electricity. Electric outlets in your home supply electric energy, but the outlets are not voltage sources. The voltage source for the outlets is a generator at an electric power plant. The generator converts other types of energy into electricity. Power lines connect the generator to the outlets.

The object through which the current passes may be a lamp or a motor. A lamp provides light. A motor runs many different types of machines.

The voltage source must be connected to the object in a complete path so that current can flow from the source to the object and back to the source. Otherwise, the circuit will be incomplete and current will not flow.

Section Review

1. Explain why insulators have high resistance.
2. How is a battery like a water pump?
3. What is Ohm's law?
4. Describe the path of current through a circuit.

Challenge: What experiment could you do to prove that iron wire has higher resistance than copper wire of the same thickness and length?

22-3 Circuits

Series Circuits Have One Path

You can add lights or appliances to a circuit in one of two ways. A simple circuit is shown in *Figure 22-10a*. A dry cell, a flashlight bulb, a socket, a switch, and wires form a complete path. The switch makes it possible to open and close the circuit easily. In this kind of circuit—a **series circuit**—all the parts are connected one following another. Notice the connection between the two bulbs in *Figure 22-10b*. Both are in the same path with the other parts of the circuit.

Removing any part of a series circuit leaves a gap in the current's path. For instance, removing a bulb in *Figure 22-10c* opens the circuit. Because current cannot flow in the circuit, the second bulb does not light.

When you connect voltage sources in series, the sources provide more voltage together than any of them can supply alone. For this reason, series circuits are used in flashlights and in batteries. When voltage sources are connected in series, you can find the total voltage they provide by adding their individual voltages. For example, the two 1.5-volt dry cells in a two-battery flashlight supply 3 volts when they are connected in series. The same amount of current flows through each battery and the flashlight bulb.

In the same way, inside the case of the 9-volt battery that may power a transistor radio you would find six 1.5-volt dry cells connected in series. A car probably has six 2-volt cells connected in series to make a 12-volt total.

Objectives

After completing this section, you will be able to:

A. Descirbe the path that current takes through a series circuit.
B. Explain why homes are wired in parallel circuits.
C. List and describe three ways of controlling electric circuits.

Have You Heard?

A computer or television has hundreds or thousands of circuit parts. The circuits in these and most other devices are complex circuits, which contain both series and parallel circuits.

Figure 22-10 Current path through a series circuit

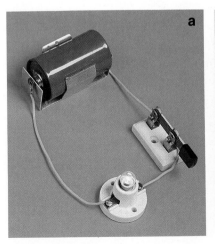

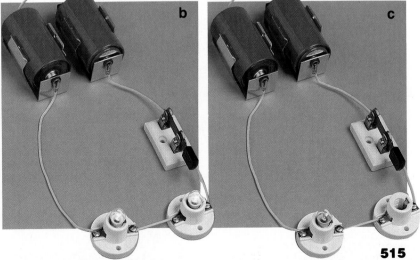

Parallel Circuits

The circuit in *Figure 22-11* shows another way in which lights or appliances can be added to a circuit. It is a **parallel circuit** because a different path connects each appliance to and from the source of voltage.

Notice that one of the bulbs is unscrewed in the second picture. However, the current can still flow along to the other bulb with no gap in its path. The path is marked with arrows. The second bulb remains lit.

If homes were wired in series, all the lights and appliances would have to be on at the same time for any of them to work. Parallel circuits, on the other hand, provide more than one path for the current. Your home is wired in parallel circuits to allow you to use only the lights and appliances you need at any given time. A parallel circuit also allows all the appliances and lights in your home to operate on the same voltage.

The voltage in a parallel circuit is set by the source of voltage. A 9-volt battery, for example, puts out 9 volts. Each object in parallel must use the full 9 volts because each of its ends is connected directly to the battery. However, since each object also has its own resistance, it draws a different amount of current:

$$\text{current} = \text{voltage/resistance.}$$

If you add an object to the circuit, the additional object draws additional current even though the voltage remains the same. As a result, the total current passing through the circuit increases.

To find the total current in a parallel circuit, add the number of amperes used by each object. If an iron and a toaster, each drawing 10 amperes of current, are connected in parallel, the total current is 20 amperes.

Figure 22-11 Current path through a parallel circuit

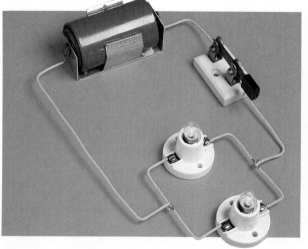
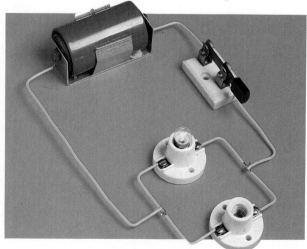

Controlling Electric Circuits

Sometimes too many appliances are running at the same time in the same circuit. **Fuses** or **circuit breakers** then act as automatic switches to open circuits. If they did not do so, the current could make the wire so hot that a fire could start.

A fuse, like the one in *Figure 22-12,* has a piece of metal in it that melts when it gets too hot. A kitchen circuit might have a 20-ampere fuse. Other circuits might have 15-ampere fuses. If you use too many appliances at the same time, too much current will flow. As the picture shows, the metal in the fuse will melt and the circuit will open, thus preventing any further electricity from flowing. You can close the circuit by replacing the fuse with a new one, but first you should turn off some of the appliances or the fuse will "blow" again.

Most houses now have circuit breakers instead of fuses. Some circuit breakers are made of a strip that consists of two metals placed one right next to the other. Each metal expands by a different amount when it is heated. As a result, when the strip is heated, it bends. When too much current flows through the strip, it bends so much that it opens the circuit. However, as the strip in the circuit breaker cools, it becomes straight again. Therefore, you do not have to replace a circuit breaker once you have corrected the problem that caused the circuit to overload. Instead, you can simply flip a switch to reclose the circuit.

Making sure wires are properly insulated can protect homes from fire. For example, the insulation on a wire can wear away. Current can then pass out of the original circuit and into something else. Instead of going through the circuit, the current takes a shorter path— a **short circuit.** The device that needs the current to work cannot do so because not enough current reaches it, and the current flowing through the short circuit can start a fire.

Section Review

1. How are the parts of a series circuit connected?
2. Why are our homes wired in parallel?
3. How do fuses and circuit breakers protect homes?

Challenge: Is a fuse or circuit breaker wired into a circuit in series or in parallel with a light or appliance? Why?

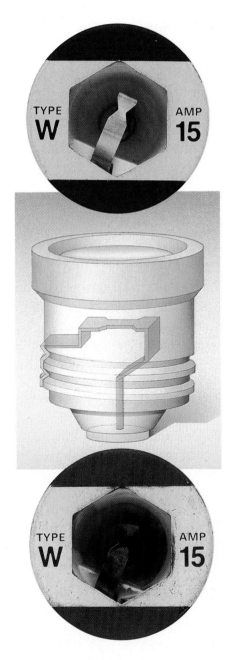

Figure 22-12 When too much current causes the metal in the fuse to melt, the circuit opens.

Switches and Fuses

Purpose

To observe the effects of a simple switch and fuse

Materials

- 1.5-volt dry cell
- flashlight bulb
- miniature socket
- block of wood
- 2 thumbtacks
- piece of aluminum foil, 10 cm x 2 cm
- three 15-cm pieces of insulated wire, with ends stripped
- scissors

Procedure and Observations

PART A

1. To make a switch, place the tacks and foil on the wood, as in **a**. Do not press the tacks all the way in.
2. Current leaves one dry cell terminal and returns to the other. Either both terminals are on the cell's top or one is on the bottom. Connect a wire from a terminal to a tack.
3. Connect another wire to a socket terminal and the other dry cell terminal.
4. Connect the third wire to the other socket terminal and the other tack, as in **b**.
5. Screw the bulb into the socket.
6. Place the loose foil end on the tack.
7. Record what happens.

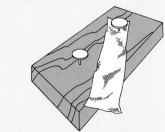
a

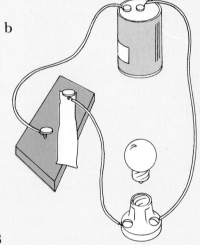
b

PART B

1. Remove the bulb.
2. Remove the foil.
3. Cut the foil, as in **c**.
4. To make a fuse, tack the foil to the wood at both ends. Do not push the tacks all the way in. Make sure the wires still touch the tacks.
5. Replace the bulb.
6. Record what happens.

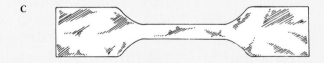
c

PART C

1. Unscrew the bulb.
2. Remove both wires from the socket.
3. Touch the stripped ends to each other.
4. Record what happens.

Analysis and Conclusions

1. How did the switch make the light go on?
2. How did the foil fuse protect the circuit?

22-4 Using Electricity

Two Kinds of Current

A battery produces current that differs from the current that is used in your home. Batteries produce **direct current** (d.c.), which always flows in one direction. Current reaching your home—**alternating current** (a.c.)—goes through 60 cycles each second. During each cycle, the current changes direction two times. If you are reading by the light of a lamp, the current flowing through the bulb is turning off and on 120 times per second! You cannot notice the effect because the change takes place too quickly. The thin wire inside the light bulb that glows as it resists the current passing through it does not have time to cool and become dimmer.

Low-voltage current loses too much energy when traveling over long distances, so power lines carry high-voltage current. Electric companies use a.c. instead of d.c. because it is easier to change a.c. voltages than d.c. voltages into high-voltage current. *Figure 22-13* shows a **transformer,** a device that changes the voltage. Many large a.c. generators produce current with voltages of about 20 000 volts. A transformer at the power station raises the voltages to as much as 765 000 volts. Such high voltages can be maintained farther before dying down as much, but they cannot be used safely in homes.

Applying Science

Superconductors are special types of substances which conduct electric current with no resistance. Power lines may be made of superconductors in a decade or two. With superconductors, the voltage is maintained indefinitely over long distances.

Figure 22-13 This large transformer handles high voltages.

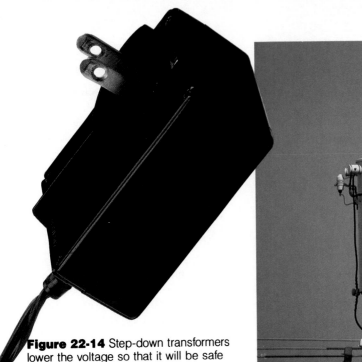

Figure 22-14 Step-down transformers lower the voltage so that it will be safe to use.

A series of transformers must lower the voltage gradually before it reaches your home's outlets. Another transformer, shown on the right of *Figure 22-14,* lowers the voltage near your home to 110 volts.

Home computers, portable tape recorders, and other electronic devices operate at about 6 volts. The small transformer on the left of *Figure 22-14* lowers the voltage to 6 volts from 110 volts.

Using Electric Power

You might have noticed that light bulbs have stamped on them the word "watt" and a number. The **watt** is the unit for electric power. Power is the energy used or produced per unit of time. A watt is one joule of energy per second. A 100-watt bulb uses four times as much energy each second as a 25-watt bulb does.

Not all devices are marked with the number of watts they use, but you can figure out how much power in watts is being supplied to an appliance by multiplying the current in amperes by the voltage in volts.

$$\text{power} = \text{current} \times \text{voltage}$$

For example, when you plug a toaster into a wall socket that supplies 110 volts, the toaster draws 11 amperes of current. To find out how much power the toaster uses, multiply 11 amperes by 110 volts.

The toaster uses 1210 watts. Since 1000 watts equals 1 kilowatt, the toaster uses 1.21 kilowatts.

You can use this equation to figure out how much current a light bulb uses. Since power = current × voltage, then current = power/voltage. To find out how much current a 250-watt bulb draws when plugged into a 110-volt outlet, divide 250 watts by 110 volts. The bulb uses about 2.3 amperes of current.

When a person gets a bill from the electric company, it represents the cost of the electrical energy supplied to the person's home in a given amount of time. Electrical energy is measured in units of kilowatt-hours. The electric company uses a device called a "watt-hour" to measure the amount of energy its customers use.

Section Review

1. Explain why a.c. is sometimes more useful than d.c.
2. How do you calculate the power supplied to an appliance?

Challenge: How can Ohm's law help you figure out the power an object uses if you know only its current in amperes and its resistance in ohms but do not know the voltage it runs on?

For Practice

Use this equation to answer the question below: power = current x voltage.
● How much power does an electric hair dryer use if it draws 10 amperes of current when plugged into a 110-volt outlet?

Careers in Physical Science

Electrical engineer

What do the inventors of television, radar, and computers have in common? These people might not have realized it then, but they did the work of electrical engineers.

Electrical engineers design many kinds of electrical and electronic systems. They develop hospital machines for medical tests and design new kinds of military missiles. Because of energy shortages, many electrical engineers work to create different types of power generators.

In order to design this complex equipment, electrical engineers must understand electricity. They learn circuitry, electronics, wiring, and other special skills during four years of college.

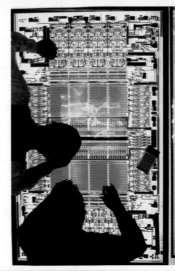
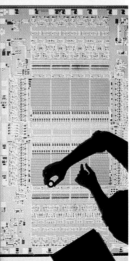

Interpreting Circuit Diagrams

You have read about circuits and how they can be set up. Scientists use circuit diagrams to illustrate different types of circuits. A circuit diagram is like a map of a circuit. Standard symbols are used to show the parts of a circuit. In this activity you will learn how to interpret circuit diagrams.

Look at this picture of a circuit.

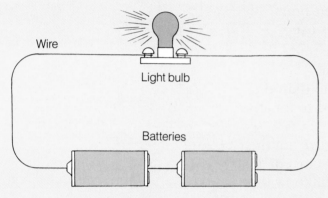

Notice the batteries, the light bulbs, and the wires connecting them. Now study this circuit diagram.

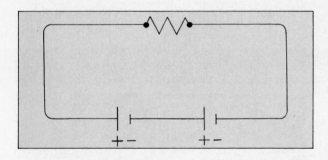

This diagram represents the circuit shown in the picture. The straight lines represent wires; the jagged lines represent sources of resistance, the light bulb in the picture of the circuit. The parallel lines with the plus signs and minus signs represent voltage sources (in this case, batteries).

The chart below shows other symbols used in circuit diagrams. Use this chart to interpret the circuit diagrams and answer the questions below.

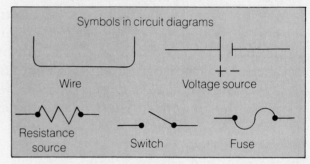

1. Which diagram represents a circuit with three batteries?
2. Which diagram represents a circuit with a fuse?
3. Which diagram shows an open switch?
4. Which diagrams show series circuits?
5. Which diagrams show parallel circuits?

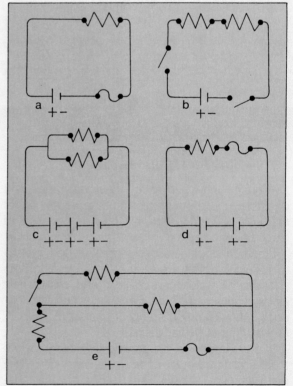

Summary

22-1 Electric Charge

A. Atoms contain protons, electrons, and neutrons.

B. If two neutral objects are rubbed together, some electrons might move from object to object. Both become electrically charged.

C. Sparks result from an excess of negative charge that moves quickly from object to object.

22-2 Electric Current

A. Conductors permit electric current to pass through them easily. Insulators do not permit the free flow of electric current.

B. A dry cell battery is one source of voltage. As the battery operates, chemical reactions occur within it that release electrons and result in a steady flow of electric charge.

C. According to Ohm's law, a relationship exists between current, voltage, and resistance such that current = voltage/resistance.

D. A simple circuit consists of a source of voltage, an object through which current passes, and connections from the voltage source to the object and back to the voltage source.

22-3 Circuits

A. In a series circuit, current flows from the source of voltage through the objects and back to the starting point. In a parallel circuit, a different path connects each object in the circuit to and from the voltage source.

B. Homes are wired in parallel circuits so that separate lights and appliances can be used as needed.

C. Fuses and circuit breakers control electric circuits by opening the circuits when they are overloaded.

22-4 Using Electricity

A. Direct current flows in one direction. Alternating current changes direction in 60 repeating cycles each second.

B. The relationship between power, current, and voltage is summarized as follows: power = current × voltage.

Vocabulary

For each of the following terms, write a sentence that uses the term correctly.

alternating current	dry cell	Ohm's law	volt
ampere	electric current	parallel circuit	voltage
circuit	electric force	resistance	watt
circuit breaker	fuse	series circuit	wet cell
conductor	insulator	short circuit	
direct current	ohm	transformer	

Check Your Knowledge

Part I: Matching   Match the definition in Column I with the correct term in Column II.

Column I
1. a type of voltage source containing a moist paste
2. the flow of electric charge through matter
3. a device that changes voltage
4. a path that may be taken by current flowing through poorly insulated wire
5. the energy given to electrons by a battery
6. the type of circuit in which each object is connected to a voltage source by a different path
7. a type of voltage source that may contain an acid solution
8. a material through which current easily flows
9. a complete current path from a voltage source through objects and back to the voltage source
10. that which provides the attraction or repulsion between charged particles

Column II
a. conductor
b. dry cell
c. electric current
d. electric force
e. insulator
f. parallel circuit
g. series circuit
h. short circuit
i. transformer
j. voltage
k. wet cell

Part II: Multiple Choice   Choose the letter of the best answer.
11. Current is measured in (a) watts. (b) ohms. (c) amperes. (d) volts.
12. A charged object may cause another charged object to (a) be attracted only. (b) be repelled only. (c) be attracted or repelled. (d) remain unchanged.
13. The push given to electrons by a battery is measured in (a) amperes. (b) watts. (c) volts. (d) ohms.
14. Resistance is measured in (a) volts. (b) ohms. (c) amperes. (d) watts.
15. A device that opens a circuit in case of overheating is a (a) conductor. (b) transformer. (c) fuse. (d) dry cell.
16. When four light bulbs are wired in series, if one goes out (a) the second bulb goes out, but the other two continue to shine. (b) all the remaining bulbs go out. (c) the three remaining bulbs continue to shine. (d) the remaining bulbs flicker on and off.
17. A unit for electric power is the (a) volt. (b) watt. (c) ohm. (d) ampere.

Part III: Completion   Write the word or words that complete the sentence correctly.
18. An atom with the same amount of negative and positive charge is said to be _____.
19. If a gap develops in the path of electric current, the circuit is _____.
20. The kind of current that a dry cell produces is called _____.
21. Homes are wired in _____ circuits.
22. Materials such as rubber, glass, and plastic that do not allow electricity to flow through them easily are examples of good _____.

Check Your Understanding

1. If you rub a balloon on your hair or sweater and touch the balloon to a wall, it will stay there for a while. Explain why.
2. What makes metals good conductors?
3. What are two differences between a car battery and a flashlight battery?
4. If you double both the resistance and the voltage of a circuit, how is the current affected?
5. If 10 amperes of current flow through your home wiring, use Ohm's law to determine the overall resistance of all the appliances and wires in your home's 110-volt circuit.
6. Explain why the flow of current needs a complete circuit.
7. Discuss why series circuits would be unacceptable for household wiring.
8. How can you prove that your home is wired in parallel?
9. Explain why damaged wiring is dangerous to use in your home.
10. Why is the current brought over power lines to your home alternating current instead of direct current?
11. What does a transformer do?
12. What is the difference between electrical power and electrical energy? What is the unit used for each?

 Apply Your Knowledge

1. You have rubbed a balloon against your hair and have stuck it against the wall. Now you touch a metal wire to the balloon at the point where it touches the wall. What do you think will happen to the balloon and why?
2. A car battery consists of six 2-volt cells connected in series. How much current does the battery provide the 1/2-ohm starter motor connected to it?
3. Use Ohm's law to explain what happens to the brightness of each lamp in a series circuit as more lamps are added to the circuit.
4. How many watts does an electric frying pan use if it has a resistance of 10 ohms and draws 11 amperes of current?

 Extend Your Knowledge

Research/Projects
1. Look on the bottoms or backs of appliances in your home. List those that use the most current.
2. Look at a bill from the power company, and find out how many kilowatt-hours of electricity your household used during the billing period. What was the average cost of electricity per kilowatt-hour?

Readings
Gutnik, Martin J. *Simple Electrical Devices.* Watts, 1986. Describes the development of electrical devices and includes a project for each device.
"High-energy Battery," *Popular Science,* March, 1987, page 60. Describes a new zinc-bromine battery that could last almost indefinitely.

CHAPTER 23
Magnetism

This beautiful scene is not a fireworks display. It is a natural light show that occurs often over the very northern and southern parts of the earth and sometimes at middle latitudes. These lights brighten the night sky with their flickering patterns and, sometimes, their colors. The earth's magnetism and the sun's magnetism both contribute to this effect.

Organizing Your Study Skills The outline below will help you see how the chapter is organized and what you should learn as you read.

I. Section 23-1: Magnetic Properties
  A. What are the properties of magnetic poles?
  B. What is a magnetic field?
  C. What do scientists know about Earth's magnetism?
  D. What do scientists know about the magnetism of other planets?

II. Section 23-2: Magnets from Magnetic Substances
  A. How do magnetic domains in magnetics substances that are unmagnetized compare with domains in those that are magnetized?
  B. What are the properties of permanent magnets?

III. Section 23-3: Changing Electricity into Magnetism
  A. How does electricity affect magnetism?
  B. How does an electromagnet work?
  C. How do electric motors use electromagnets?

IV. Section 23-4: Changing Magnetism into Electricity
  A. What demonstration proves that magnetism can produce an electric current?
  B. How does a generator make electricity?

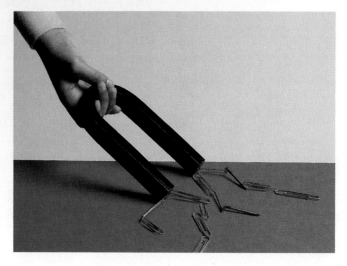

After completing this section you will be able to

A. List the properties of magnetic poles.

B. Explain what a magnetic field is.

C. Describe what scientists know about the earth's magnetism.

D. Describe what scientists know about the magnetism of other planets.

Explore!

A navigator must be able to tell the difference between geographic north and magnetic north to plot a ship's course. Look in an encyclopedia or a book about navigation to find out how this difference is found.

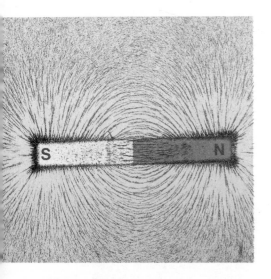

Figure 23-1 Iron filings line up in a magnetic field.

23-1 Magnetic Properties

A Magnet Has Two Poles

Magnets are objects that attract objects made of iron and a few other elements. The force that attracts these objects is called **magnetism**. Only a few elements can be made into permanent magnets. Iron does not always attract other iron, but when it does, it is considered magnetic. Nickel, cobalt, and gadolinium are other elements that can be made into permanent magnets.

A bar magnet picks up steel paper clips because steel contains iron. The paper clips do not have to be magnetic to be attracted to the magnet. The ends of a magnet—its **poles**—are the regions where magnetism is strongest.

Even though magnets come in many shapes and sizes, every magnet has at least two poles. If you cut a magnet into pieces, each piece will still have at least two poles.

If you let a magnet swing freely, it turns so that the same pole always points north. The end that points north is the magnet's **north pole.** The end that points south is its **south pole**. If you move the magnet, it will turn until its north pole again points north.

Once people discovered that a magnet always points north, they used magnets to find directions. For over 900 years, sailors have used a small, free-swinging magnet—or **compass**—to navigate. Because the magnet pointed north-south, sailors knew in which direction they were sailing.

A north pole of one magnet and a south pole of a second magnet attract each other. Two north poles push away—or repel—each other, while two south poles also repel each other. Like electric charges, like poles repel and unlike poles attract. Because magnetic poles attract and repel, you know that a force acts between them.

A Magnetic Field Surrounds Every Magnet

If you shake iron filings near a magnet, they form a pattern around the magnet as shown in *Figure 23-1*. Notice that most of the filings do not touch the magnet. The region around a magnet where its magnetism acts is the **magnetic field**. The filings trace the shape of the magnet's magnetic field.

Figure 23-2a Magnetic field between like poles of two magnets

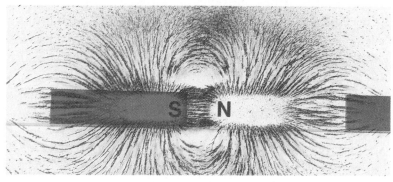

Figure 23-2b Magnetic field between unlike poles of two magnets

Notice that the lines traced by the filings are closest together at the magnet's poles, where the magnetic field is strongest. The magnetic field two centimeters away from a pole is only one-fourth as strong as it is one centimeter away.

Figure 23-2a shows how the magnetic field acts between the south poles of two magnets. The lines of magnetic field from the south pole of each magnet are bent away from the south pole of the other magnet. The pattern would be the same if the two north poles were placed near each other.

When you place unlike poles near each other, the filings line up in still another way. *Figure 23-2b* shows that the magnetic field links the two unlike poles.

The SI unit for measuring the strength of a magnetic field is the tesla (symbol: T). It is named for Nicola Tesla, a Yugoslav-American scientist. He developed transformers that make it possible to send alternating current over long distances. The field near the poles of an ordinary toy magnet is about 0.01 tesla. The special magnets in *Figure 23-3* are used to help scientists study the tiny particles inside atoms. These large magnets produce a magnetic field of about 10 tesla. The world record for the strongest steady magnetic field produced in a laboratory on earth is over 30 tesla.

Figure 23-3 These large magnets, with magnetic fields of about 10 tesla, will be used to study particles in atomic nuclei.

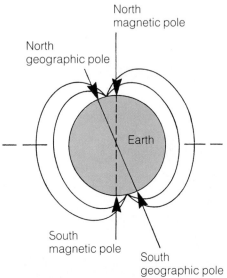

Figure 23-4 Earth's magnetic and geographic poles are not located in the same place.

Earth's Magnetism

In 1600, an English physician reported that the earth acted like a giant magnet. Scientists now know that a magnetic field surrounds Earth. It acts much like the field of a bar magnet. On the average, the magnetic field at Earth's surface is about 0.00005 tesla.

Auroras, such as the one shown on page 526, are one proof that Earth has a magnetic field. Charged particles from the sun enter Earth's magnetic field and hit molecules in the atmosphere. The molecules then radiate light. Auroras are most visible near Earth's magnetic poles, because the magnetic field guides the particles toward them. If you live close enough to the magnetic poles, you can see an aurora nearly every night.

Auroras are only one result of the magnetic storms that Earth regularly experiences. Magnetic storms are strong variations in the magnetic field. Magnetic storms can also cause power transmission lines to surge and can interfere with short-wave radio reception. Magnetic storms are caused when matter and radiation are ejected from the sun, guided by the sun's magnetic field.

Scientists think Earth's spinning and the movement of molten iron inside Earth are responsible for its magnetic field. No bar magnet exists inside Earth, but the field is almost as though there were one nearly lined up with Earth's axis of rotation.

The north geographic pole is not at the north magnetic pole. The south geographic and magnetic poles are not in the same location either. *Figure 23-4* shows the positions of the poles. A compass points to magnetic north, not geographic north. The magnetic poles are slightly under Earth's surface, so compasses point slightly downward.

Scientists have discovered that Earth's magnetic field has reversed itself several times during history. A study of rocks shows that what is now magnetic north reverses its direction about every half-million years. Scientists are not sure why the field reverses.

Magnetism of Other Planets

Spacecraft have detected magnetic fields around some planets. Studying these magnetic fields helps scientists learn more about earth's magnetic field.

Mercury is surrounded by a weak magnetic field. At the surface of Mercury, the magnetic field is only about one percent as strong as Earth's. Although Mercury rotates, scientists think it has a solid, rather than molten, interior. Many scientists think that Mercury's magnetic field might be left over from the time when the planet's interior was molten.

Scientists have suggested that the more rapid a planet's rotation, the stronger its magnetic field. Jupiter, for example, has the shortest rotation period of any of the planets and the strongest known magnetic field. This planet rotates once every 10 hours, as compared to Earth's 24-hour period of rotation. Also, Saturn rotates almost as rapidly as Jupiter. Saturn's magnetic field is 1000 times stronger than Earth's and 20 times weaker than Jupiter's. In addition, Venus rotates very slowly—once every 243 days. Any magnetic field Venus has is too weak to detect. Mars, however, does not fit into the pattern. This planet rotates only slightly more slowly than Earth does, yet it has no detectable magnetic field.

Until the *Voyager 2* spacecraft flew by Uranus in 1986, scientists had only suspected that Uranus has a magnetic field. The spacecraft reached the magnetic field about 500 000 kilometers away from the planet. Uranus's magnetic field is about 50 times stronger than Earth's.

In general, the magnetic poles of the planets are very close to their geographic poles. However, the *Voyager 2* mission revealed that Uranus is an exception. *Figure 23-5* shows that Uranus's magnetic and geographic poles are very far apart. Scientists do not know why this planet's magnetic field is so tipped. Perhaps the field is in the process of reversing direction. Perhaps an object about the size of Earth hit Uranus shortly after it formed and caused the planet to tip over on its side.

Section Review

1. Where is a magnet's force strongest?
2. Where does a magnetic field exist?
3. How do scientists know that the earth has a magnetic field?
4. What is special about Uranus's magnetic field?

Challenge: Is the magnetic pole in the earth's northern hemisphere like the north or the south pole of a bar magnet? How do you know?

Have You Heard?

Earth is surrounded by two belts of charged particles held in orbit by Earth's magnetic field. These Van Allen belts were the first scientific discovery of the space age.

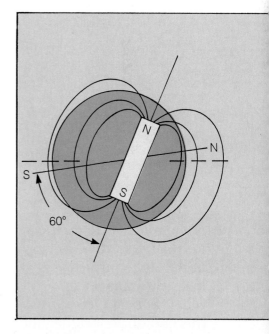

Figure 23-5 The magnetic field of Uranus is so tipped and off-center that it wobbles as Uranus spins on its axis.

Magnetic Poles

Purpose

To observe some properties of magnets

Materials

- 2 small bar magnets
- 2 wide corks
- bowl of water
- masking tape

Procedure and Observations

PART A

1. Mount one bar magnet on top of each cork with masking tape, as shown in **a**.
2. Float one of the corks with the magnet in the bowl of water. Keep the magnet out of the water, as in **b**.

a

b

3. Note which end of the magnet points north. If you do not know which way is north, ask your teacher.
4. Take the magnet and cork out of the water. Stick a piece of masking tape on this end of the magnet and mark it with an "N" for "north pole."
5. Mark a piece of masking tape on the other end with an "S" for "south pole."

6. Put the magnet and cork back in the water pointing in a different direction.
7. Allow them to come to rest and note which way they point.
8. Record whether the north-south directions in steps 4 and 8 are the same or different.
9. Repeat steps 2–5 for the second magnet and cork.

PART B

1. Remove the bar magnets from the corks. Place both magnets flat on a desk with the marked sides up.
2. Move the north pole of one magnet next to the north pole of the other, as in **c**.

c

3. Record what happens.
4. Move the south pole of one magnet next to the south pole of the other.
5. Record what happens.
6. Move the north pole of one magnet next to the south pole of the other.
7. Record what happens.

Analysis and Conclusions

1. How do the results of Part A make a compass useful?
2. How do like poles interact? Unlike poles?

23-2 Magnets from Magnetic Substances

Objectives

After completing this section you will be able to

A. Compare magnetic domains in magnetic substances that are unmagnetized with domains in those that are magnetized.

B. Describe the properties of permanent magnets.

Magnetic Domains Line Up

Why can some substances be magnetized while others cannot? Different magnetic fields exist in tiny regions of all substances. In the atoms of nonmagnetic substances, the magnetic effects of the different magnetic fields face every direction. They cancel each other. But in magnetic substances, the magnetic effects do not cancel each other. In a magnetic substance, the magnetic fields of groups containing many billions of atoms line up in a region called a magnetic **domain**.

Because atoms are tiny, the size of each domain is small. Each of these magnetic domains acts like a tiny magnet inside the substance.

The domains in an unmagnetized piece of steel are not aligned, as shown in *Figure 23-6a*. Therefore, the domain's magnetic effects cancel each other. But placing the steel in a magnetic field causes the domains to line up in the direction of the field. The steel becomes a magnet.

Any substance that a magnet can attract can be made into a magnet. When you buy a steel sewing needle, a magnet can attract it. But the needle is not a magnet itself because it does not attract other needles. The domains in an unmagnetized needle line up in many different directions.

You can make the needle into a magnet by placing the needle in a strong magnetic field. Most of the domains in the needle line up in the direction of the field, as shown in *Figure 23-6b*.

a   b

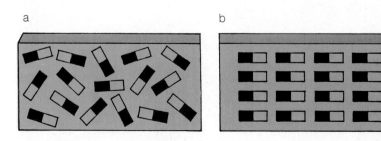

Figure 23-6 Domains in an unmagnetized steel face in different directions so their magnetism is canceled. Placing the steel in a magnetic field causes the domains to line up mainly in a single direction, thus magnetizing the steel.

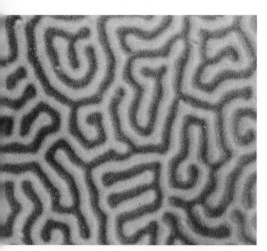

Figure 23-7 An optical micrograph of a sample containing cobalt and samarium, showing aligned domains.

The optical micrograph in *Figure 23-7* shows the domains in a material that can be made into especially strong magnets. Discovering such materials allows magnets to be made smaller. The existence of such small, but powerful, magnets allowed the development of the tiny earphones on many radios and tape players.

Permanent Magnets

Even when you remove the outside magnetic field from certain substances, some of the domains remain lined up. The object is a permanent magnet. These magnets are made of substances that keep their magnetism for a long time. Most bar magnets are permanent magnets made of steel.

Figure 23-8a shows how you can make a steel sewing needle into a permanent magnet. Rub a bar magnet many times along the needle in one direction. The magnet's field makes the steel's domains line up. You could help magnetize the needle by hammering or tapping it while it is in the bar magnet's magnetic field.

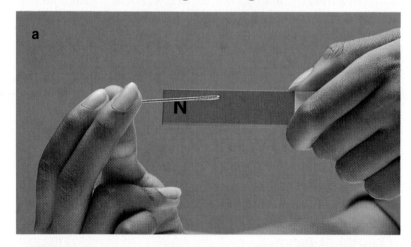

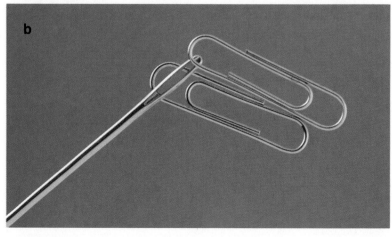

Figure 23-8a Rubbing a bar magnet in one direction along the steel needle causes the domains in the needle to line up. **b** The needle then is a permanent magnet.

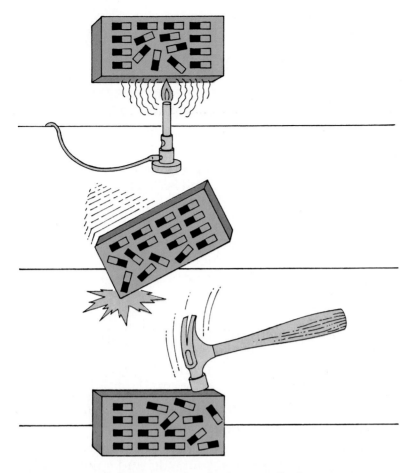

When the field is removed, the needle is a permanent magnet. The needle can be used to pick up paper clips and other small metal objects, as shown in *Figure 23-8b*.

A strong magnetic field is needed to force domains in steel to line up. Once these domains line up, they stay in place under normal circumstances. You can, however, force the domains out of line by heating, striking, or dropping the magnet. Then its atoms move enough to move the domains out of line. The substance is no longer magnetized. Even a permanent magnet does not stay magnetized forever. After many years, it loses its magnetism as the domains slip out of line.

Section Review

1. How do magnetic domains act in a magnet?
2. How are the domains of a permanent magnet special?

Challenge: Explain whether or not you can magnetize a steel paper clip by moving a bar magnet along it in both directions.

Explore!

Find out what the Curie temperature is and what it has to do with magnetism.

After completing this section you will be able to

A. Describe how electricity affects magnetism.

B. Describe how an electromagnet works.

C. Describe how electric motors use electromagnets.

23-3 Changing Electricity into Magnetism

Electric Currents Cause Magnetism

Sometimes important scientific discoveries are made accidentally. Such was the case with the discovery that electric currents produce magnetic fields. In 1820, Hans Christian Oersted, a Danish physics teacher, was lecturing about electric current to a class of students. A compass happened to be lying on his desk. When he ran current through wire that was near the compass, he noticed that the compass needle moved. His discovery led to the understanding that a magnetic field exists around every electric current.

In *Figure 23-10*, current starts to flow through a wire coil. As this happens, the needle of a nearby compass suddenly turns away from Earth's magnetic pole and points to the coil. The coil has become a magnet with a stronger field than Earth's field. The coil's poles reverse if the current flows in the opposite direction. The coil loses its magnetism when the current stops.

Scientists now know that electricity causes all magnetism. Within every atom, moving and spinning electrons produce electric currents that set up magnetic fields. These fields cancel in nonmagnetic substances; in magnetic substances they line up to make domains.

Figure 23-10 When current flows through the coil, the coil becomes a magnet. The north pole of the compass needle turns in the direction of the south pole of the coil's magnetic field. The south pole of the compass needle turns in the direction of teh north pole of the coil's magnetic field. The coil's magnetic field is stronger than Earth's field.

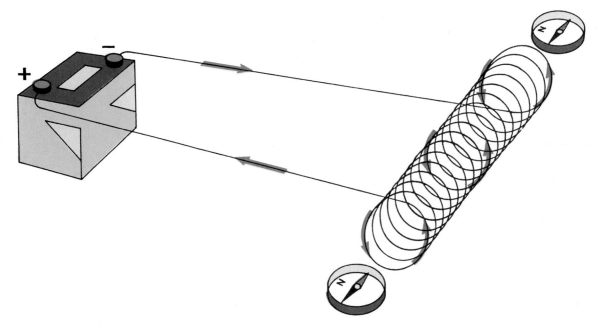

Electromagnets Use Electricity to Cause Magnetism

The discovery that electric current causes magnetism helps people every day. Every time you listen to a record or tape recording, dry your hair with an electric dryer, ring a doorbell, or talk on a telephone, you use electricity and magnetism. Each of these devices contains an **electromagnet,** a coil that is magnetized by an electric current passing through it. The first practical electromagnet was built in 1827 by Joseph Henry, an American physicist. Electromagnets are very useful because their magnetism can be switched on and off, in much the same way a light switch operates.

One example of the use of electromagnets is shown in *Figure 23-11*. The crane uses a strong electromagnet to move metal scrap. When the current is on, the electromagnet is magnetized and attracts the metal. The crane can then lift the scrap. Turning the current off makes the electromagnet lose its magnetism. As a result, the scrap falls off of the magnet.

Notice the switch by the security guard's hand in *Figure 23-12*. When the guard flips the switch, current flows to a coil in the door. The coil becomes an electromagnet. The electromagnet pulls back a latch, and the door can be opened. When the guard flips the switch back to its original position, the current is stopped. The latch loses its magnetism and resecures the door.

Electromagnets are also useful at home. For example, when you push the button of a chiming doorbell, you close the circuit and send current through the coil. The coil becomes an electromagnet. It repels a permanent magnet inside the coil. The permanent magnet bounces against a chime.

Strong electromagnets are made by putting iron or another substance that can be magnetized in the center of the coil. The coil magnetizes the iron; the fields from the coil and the iron are combined. You can also strengthen an electromagnet by increasing the number of turns of wire in the coil, the amount of voltage going through the coil, or the current in the coil. All these methods increase the coil's magnetic field. Thus, the coil attracts more or larger objects.

Figure 23-11 When the current is on, the electromagnet lifts the metal scrap. When the current is off, it drops the metal scrap.

Figure 23-12 A flip of the switch opens an electromagnetic latch in the door.

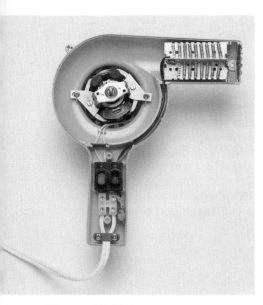

Figure 23-13 An a.c. motor

Electric Motors Use Electromagnets

An electric **motor** uses an electromagnet to change electric energy into mechanical energy. Then the mechanical energy can be used to perform work. Factories use electric motors to run machines. Commuter trains use electric motors to carry people to work. People use electric motors of many sizes around the house—in refrigerators, clocks, air conditioners, blenders, and many other appliances.

Figure 23-13 shows a simple motor in a hair dryer. Alternating current (a.c.) from the wall outlet passes through a coil, making the coil an electromagnet. The opposite poles of a nonmoving magnet are attracted to the poles of the coil.

At the moment that the opposite poles of the two magnets (the permanent magnet and the coil) line up, the current reverses. Reversing the current reverses the poles of the coil. The poles of the coil repel the poles of the permanent magnet. As a result, the permanent magnet keeps turning in the same direction. The permanent magnet is connected to a shaft that turns a miniature fan. The fan blades push out the heated air.

Figure 23-14 shows a simple motor in a toy car. Direct current (d.c.) from a battery passes through a coil, making the coil an electromagnet. The coil's poles are attracted to the opposite poles of a nonmoving magnet.

A motor made to run on direct current has a reversing switch called a commutator. The commutator reverses the current the coil receives just before the opposite poles of the two magnets line up. Reversing the current reverses the poles of the coil. Then the poles repel the poles of the other magnet. The coil keeps turning in the same direction until its two poles find the opposite poles of the magnet. The coil is connected to the axle in the car. It turns the axle to move the car.

Section Review

1. What discovery led to the development of the electromagnet?
2. What happens when you change the direction of current in an electromagnet?
3. What does an electromagnet do in a motor?

Challenge: Why does an a.c. motor not need a special device to reverse current while a d.c. motor does?

Figure 23-14 A d.c. motor

Electromagnets

Purpose

To identify the variables that affect the strength of an electromagnet

Materials

- two 1.5-volt dry cells
- insulated wire, with stripped ends
- switch
- large nail
- small metal objects, such as paper clips or tacks

Procedure and Observations

PART A

1. Wind ten turns of wire around the large nail. Do not overlap them.
2. Connect one dry cell terminal to one switch terminal with wire.
3. Connect one end of the coil's wire to the dry cell and the other end to the switch, as in **a**. *NOTE: The current in this circuit is too weak to harm you.*

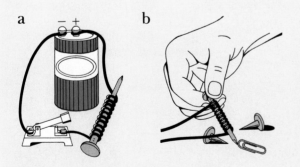

4. Close the switch and try to pick up some small metal objects with the large nail, as in **b**. Record how many you can pick up.
5. Open the switch. Observe and record what happens to the objects.

PART B

1. Repeat steps 1–5 with 25 turns of wire around the nail.
2. Record how many objects you can pick up. Then open the switch and disconnect the wires.

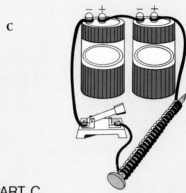

PART C

1. Connect both dry cells in series, by attaching a wire from one center terminal to the end terminal on the other cell.
2. Connect a second wire from the other terminal of a cell to the switch, as in **c**.
3. Connect one end of the electromagnet from Part B to the remaining cell terminal. NOTE: The current in this circuit is too weak to harm you.
4. Close the switch, and try to pick up paper clips or tacks.
5. Record how many objects you can pick up.
6. Open the switch, disconnect the wires, and unwind the electromagnet.

Analysis and Conclusions

1. What does the switch do to the electromagnet?
2. What factors affect the strength of the electromagnet?
3. Did you pick up the greatest number of objects in Part A, B, or C?

Objectives

After completing this section you will be able to

A. Describe a demonstration that proves that magnetism can produce an electric current.
B. Explain how a generator makes electricity.

23-4 Changing Magnetism into Electricity

Magnetism Produces Electric Current

The discovery that electricity can be changed into magnetism may have been made by accident. But that discovery made many scientists feel that it must also be possible to change magnetism into electricity. In 1831, American scientist Joseph Henry and British scientist Michael Faraday proved just that. They found that moving a magnet through a wire coil caused a current to flow in the coil. Today their discovery is used to produce electricity for homes and factories.

The pictures in *Figure 23-15* show an instrument used to measure electric current. This instrument gives a zero reading when no electric current is moving through it. The zero is in the middle of the dial. In *Figure 23-15a*, a magnet moves into the coil, and the pointer moves. Current must be flowing in the wire.

In *Figure 23-15b*, the magnet moves out of the coil. The pointer moves again, but to the opposite side of the scale. Current is flowing in the wire, but in the opposite direction.

Figure 23-15 Moving a magnet through the coil in one direction causes a current to flow and the pointer to move. Reversing the direction of the magnet's motion through the coil reverses the current's direction.

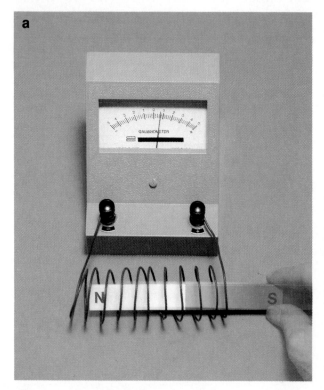

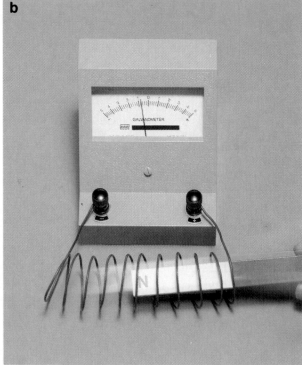

Current also flows in the wire if the coil moves instead of the magnet. Moving the magnet faster, or increasing the number of coils, increases the current. The process by which magnetism causes electric current is named **electromagnetic induction**.

Electromagnetic induction occurs when a changing magnetic field and a coil are near each other. If the magnetic field that goes through the coil changes, a current flows in the coil. The field might be changing because either the magnet causing the field or the coil is moving. If the magnet is an electromagnet, its field also might be changing because the amount of current flowing into it is changing. *Figure 23-16* shows that a magnet whose field is not changing does not cause a current.

Sometimes people use electromagnetic induction in their homes. For example, the electric toothbrush in *Figure 23-17* is charged when it rests in its base even though it is not connected by a wire. A coil of wire surrounds its handle and causes electricity to flow inside the toothbrush by electromagnetic induction. Some kitchen stoves have cooktops that work by electromagnetic induction, heating pots without first heating the surface below them.

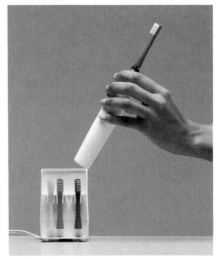

Figure 23-17 The toothbrush is charged by electromagnetic induction.

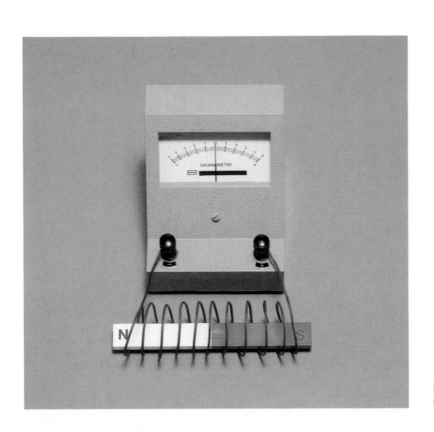

Figure 23-16 If the magnet does not move, it does not cause a current.

Have You Heard?

A magnetometer, which measures the strength of a magnetic field, works because of electromagnetic induction. A simple magnetometer has a tiny wire coil. Electric voltage is produced in the coil when it is moved through a magnetic field. The voltage tells how strong the magnetic field is.

Explore!

Find out what a magneto is and how it is used.

Because electricity can cause magnetism and magnetism can cause electricity, scientists link these two forces in a single theory. **Electromagnetism** is the study of the effects of electricity and magnetism. According to this theory, electricity and magnetism result from a single force.

In 1864, Scottish physicist James Clerk Maxwell was the first to identify light as an electromagnetic wave. He predicted that other, invisible electromagnetic waves would be found traveling through space. In 1887, German physicist Heinrich Hertz showed that a vibrating electric charge produces electromagnetic waves. These waves are much longer than light. Today they are called radio waves. They bring people not only radio, but also television programs. They also carry information from far out in space.

Electric Generators Produce Electricity

An electric **generator** uses electromagnetic induction to produce electricity when a magnet or a coil of wire moves. A generator changes the mechanical energy of a moving coil or magnet into electric energy. Therefore, a generator and a motor perform opposite tasks. A motor uses current to produce motion, while a generator uses motion to produce current.

Figure 23-18 A U-shaped magnet and a loop of wire are the main parts of a simple generator.

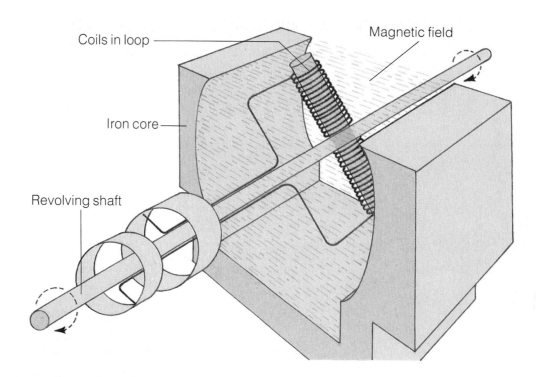

Coils in loop

Magnetic field

Iron core

Revolving shaft

The two main parts of a generator are a magnet and a loop of wire, as shown in *Figure 23-18*. A source of mechanical energy is needed to move the magnet or coil, and drive the generator. Some possible sources of mechanical energy are steam in a nuclear or conventional power plant, a water wheel, or a hand crank.

Generators produce almost all the electricity we use. *Figure 23-19* shows a generator on the back wheel of a bicycle. It furnishes electricity to operate the bicycle's headlight. As the bicycle's back wheel spins, it turns a wheel of the generator that touches the tire. The wheel turns a magnet that is near loops of wire inside the generator. The lines of the magnet's field cut through the loop, making current flow in the loop. A wire carries current to the headlight, and the current returns to the generator through the bicycle's frame.

A similar system is used to generate energy at power plants located at waterfalls along rivers. The falling water makes a magnet turn in a giant generator. A huge rotating coil turns hundreds of times each second, producing electric energy.

Figure 23-19 A generator resting on the bicycle tire produces electricity to light the headlight bulb.

Section Review

1. What is electromagnetic induction?
2. What are the two main parts of a generator?

Challenge: Why must a generator be driven by an outside energy source?

Applying Science

Automobiles are equipped with small generators called alternators. An alternator supplies the energy needed to power the car's headlights, radio, and other parts of its electrical system.

Careers in Physical Science

Service Technician

Behind every television screen and stereo system, hundreds of wires, chips, and modules are hidden. Only service technicians who understand these parts can fix appliances when they break down.

Often, these appliances stop working because a faulty circuit or antenna cannot receive currents or waves. The technician finds the damage and repairs it. Technicians might use electronic equipment to locate the faulty part.

Technicians must know each part of a device and how it works. They receive special training after high school and learn still more on the job.

Constructing Models

You have probably seen and put together scale models of various objects. A model can help a person more clearly understand objects, events, or ideas. Scientists often construct various models to more clearly explain scientific objects, events, or ideas.

You already know that the magnetic field that surrounds a magnet is not visible. You can draw a diagram to show what a magnetic field is like. However, that particular model only shows two dimensions of a magnetic field. A magnetic field is actually three dimensional.

You can construct a three-dimensional model of a magnetic field to more clearly explain the idea of magnetic fields. Follow the steps listed here.

1. Take a small, clear jar that has a lid. Fill the jar with clear vegetable oil.
2. Add one teaspoon of powdered iron (not iron filings) to the oil. Put the lid on the jar, making sure it is tightly closed. Shake the jar to mix the oil and the powdered iron.
3. Hold the jar steady over the poles of a horseshoe magnet. Notice what happens to the particles of iron in the oil. Describe what happened to them as they were affected by the field surrounding the magnet.

Try using a bar magnet in place of the horseshoe magnet. Describe the magnetic field. How does this model help explain the idea of magnetic fields?

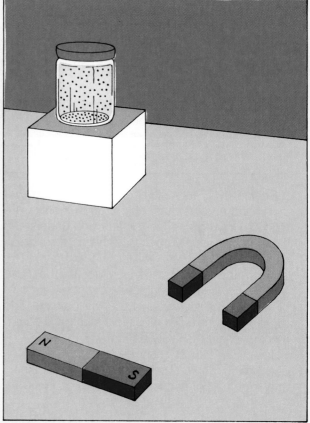

 Summary

23-1 Magnetic Properties

A. Like magnetic poles repel, and unlike poles attract.

B. The region around a magnet where its magnetism acts is the magnetic field.

C. A magnetic field surrounds Earth.

D. Mercury has a weak magnetic field. Jupiter and Saturn have strong magnetic fields. Venus and Mars have no detectable magnetic fields. The poles of Uranus's magnetic field are very far from the geographic poles.

23-2 Magnets from Magnetic Substances

A. Atoms in magnetic substances gather into domains. The domains in unmagnetized substances do not face in the same direction. In a magnetized substance, the domains line up.

B. Permanent magnets keep their magnetism for a long time. Their domains remain lined up even when they are removed from an outside magnetic field.

23-3 Changing Electricity into Magnetism

A. Moving electrons in atoms cause magnetic fields. A magnetic field exists around every electric current.

B. An electromagnet is a magnet made of current flowing through a coil of wire. When the current is on, the electromagnet is magnetized. Turning the current off makes the electromagnet lose its magnetism.

C. An electric motor uses an electromagnet to change electrical energy into mechanical energy.

23-4 Changing Magnetism into Electricity

A. Moving a magnet through a wire coil attached to a device that can measure the strength of an electric current shows that a current flows in the coil when the magnet moves.

B. A generator uses electromagnetic induction to produce electricity when a magnet or a coil of wire moves.

Vocabulary

For each of the following terms, write a sentence that uses the term correctly.

compass	electromagnetism	motor
domain	generator	north pole
electromagnet	magnetic field	poles
electromagnetic induction	magnetism	south pole

☑ Check Your Knowledge

Part I: Matching Match the definition in Column I with the correct term in Column II.

Column I
1. region around a magnet where its force acts
2. group of atoms in magnetic substances
3. device that converts electric energy into mechanical energy
4. magnet made of a coil with a current flowing in it
5. theory that explains both electricity and magnetism
6. device that converts mechanical energy into electric energy
7. force between magnetic objects
8. device used to find direction
9. process by which magnetism causes electricity
10. place on a magnet where its magnetism is strongest

Column II
a. compass
b. coil
c. domain
d. electromagnet
e. electromagnetic induction
f. electromagnetism
g. generator
h. magnetic field
i. magnetic pole
j. magnetism
k. motor

Part II: Multiple Choice Choose the letter of the best answer.
11. All magnets (a) are surrounded by a magnetic field. (b) have only two poles. (c) are shaped like a bar. (d) always retain their magnetism.
12. All electric generators (a) do not need a source of mechanical energy. (b) convert electric energy to mechanical energy. (c) convert energy as a motor does. (d) convert mechanical energy to electric energy.
13. The domains of a magnetized substance (a) line up in all directions. (b) cancel each other. (c) line up mainly in one direction. (d) can never be shifted.
14. A permanent magnet loses its magnetism (a) after a very short time. (b) when its domains line up. (c) when you heat or strike it. (d) when a current is flowing in a coil around it.

15. An electric current in a wire coil produces (a) another current. (b) a generator. (c) a source of voltage. (d) a magnetic field.
16. Electromagnetic induction can occur if a (a) current flows in a coil. (b) circuit has a battery. (c) magnet moves in a coil. (d) motor runs a device.

Part III: Completion Write the word or words that complete the sentence correctly.
17. Unlike magnetic poles _____ .
18. A free-swinging magnet used by sailors to navigate is a _____ .
19. Iron filings can be used to show the shape of a magnet's _____ .
20. Light given off as charged particles from the sun enter the earth's magnetic field is called an _____ .
21. The SI unit for measuring the strength of a magnetic field is the _____ .

Check Your Understanding

1. If you break a bar magnet in two, what magnetic properties do the halves show?
2. Compare the magnetic fields of a bar magnet and the earth.
3. How could you magnetize a steel screwdriver?
4. Why do paper clips hanging from a magnet pick up other paper clips? What would happen if you carefully removed the magnet?

5. How are electromagnets like permanent magnets? How are they different?
6. If a magnet is inside a wire coil, how can the magnet or coil cause a current in the wire?
7. Motors contain both a permanent magnet and a temporary magnet. Explain why.
8. Compare and contrast how electric motors and electric generators work and change one kind of energy into another.

 Apply Your Knowledge

1. If you have two disk-shaped magnets, with north poles on one side and south poles on the other, what happens if you put one magnet on top of the other?
2. Why does a magnet attract a nail to either of its poles, but attracts another magnet to only one of its poles?

3. How could you use the same device as both a motor and a generator?
4. What is the outside source of energy for a bicycle generator?
5. List the planets in order of decreasing strength of magnetic field.

 Extend Your Knowledge

Research/Projects

1. Visit an electric power plant to find out how electricity is generated. Then make a report to your class.
2. Use an encyclopedia to learn how electromagnetism is used to record information on tapes in tape recorders.
3. Find out about the Van Allen belts surrounding Earth and those surrounding Jupiter. Sketch what they look like.
4. Use reference books to learn about superconductivity, and how it is useful in making powerful magnets.

Readings

Hogan, Paula. *Compass*. Walker, 1982. Traces the history of the compass from its invention by the ancient Chinese to its modern uses.

Satrey, Laurence. *Magnets*. Troll, 1985. Discusses the history of discoveries about magnetism, including Oersted's and Faraday's work.

Vogt, Gregory. *Electricity and Magnetism*. Watts, 1985. How one scientist uses the discoveries of others in the understanding of electricity and magnetism.

CHAPTER 24
Electronic Revolution

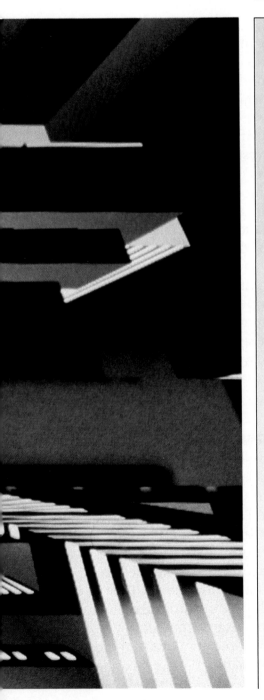

A computer produced the overhead view of buildings you see here. When computers were first developed, they were very big and very expensive. Now computers are small enough and inexpensive enough to be in many homes. Smaller computers became available only after tiny parts were developed that could do the work of large parts. These tiny parts also are used in stereos, televisions, and many other electronic devices.

Organizing Your Study Skills The outline below will help you see how the chapter is organized and what you should learn as you read.

I. Section 24-1: Electronics
  A. How do electronics and electricity compare?
  B. How do electronic devices work?
  C. What are four problems caused by the use of vacuum tubes?

II. Section 24-2: Making Electronic Devices Smaller
  A. What are some advantages of transistors over vacuum tubes?
  B. What are three advantages of chips over transistors?

III. Section 24-3: Computers
  A. What are the parts of a computer?
  B. What can computers do, and what can they not do?
  C. What are two computer languages?
  D. How do you write a simple computer program in BASIC?

IV. Section 24-4: Personal Computers and Microprocessors
  A. What is the function of a microprocessor in a personal computer?
  B. What are four other uses of microprocessors?

V. Section 24-5: Using Computers
  A. What are some uses of computers in business and industry?
  B. How are computers used in government and law enforcement?
  C. What are some uses of computers in engineering and the sciences?
  D. How are computers used in medicine?

After completing this section you will be able to

A. Contrast electronics and electricity.
B. Describe how electronic devices work.
C. Describe four problems caused by using vacuum tubes.

Applying Science

When light hits certain materials, including copper oxide and selenium, electric current flows through them. *Photoelectric devices* are electronic devices made from these materials, which convert light into electricity. Since the current from a photoelectric device is usually very weak, amplifiers strengthen the current before it can be put to work. The light meters on most cameras are run by photoelectric devices.

Figure 24-1 Headphones are one type of electronic device.

24-1 Electronics

Electronics Can Do Jobs That Electricity Alone Cannot Do

Electronics is a branch of physical science that deals with electrons in motion and their use in radio, television, computers, and other such devices. The pictures on this page show some of the ways we use electronics in daily life.

You know from studying about electricity that an electric current is made up of moving electrons. Electric current can be used as a form of energy that flows through wires or other conductors. Electric currents can be used to operate electrical equipment, such as heaters or light bulbs. In contrast, **electronic devices** use electric current in the form of signals. The signals might represent sounds, pictures, numbers, or other information. *Figure 24-1* shows one such device.

Electronic devices enable electric current to carry information by changing the current in several ways. One basic change is to allow the electric current to flow in only one direction. This change converts alternating current (a.c.) to direct current (d.c.). A second change is to convert direct current to a signal that vibrates a specific number of times per second. Perhaps the most important function of electronic devices is to strengthen weak signals and to turn signals off and on. Your television, radio, and stereo system would not be possible without electronic devices to make these changes in electric current.

How Electronic Devices Work

Electrons moving through wires or other conductors cannot be controlled quickly and accurately. Scientists long tried to discover ways to overcome this problem. The first solution followed the discovery that electrons can flow through a glass tube emptied of air—that is, in a glass tube with a vacuum inside it.

The first important **vacuum tube,** an electronic device, worked like a valve that controlled the flow of electrons. *Figure 24-2* shows how a vacuum tube looks. The positive charge on the plate attracts electrons, which have a negative charge. As a result, a beam of electrons flows from the wire to the plate.

Later, scientists improved the control of the electron beam through the gap between the wire and the plate. They put a wire grid in the gap, as *Figure 24-3* shows. The beam passes through the grid. Giving the grid an extra negative charge repels the electrons and weakens the electron beam. Giving the grid a positive charge helps the plate attract the electrons, which strengthens the beam. Feeding a weak incoming current to the grid causes a strong change in the electron beam received by the plate. A vacuum tube or other electronic device that changes a weak signal into a strong one is called an **amplifier.** *Figure 24-3* shows the first vacuum tube that could strengthen a weak signal.

The vacuum tube brought about a major advance in communications and electronics. Messages could be sent over long distances because weak currents could be strengthened. Vacuum tubes made radios and other types of electronic equipment practical.

An important type of vacuum tube is the **cathode-ray tube.** Cathode-ray tubes are still in use as television picture tubes. In a picture tube, an electron beam moves from side to side. A signal from the television station makes the beam weaker or stronger. The stronger the beam, the brighter that spot on the picture. After the beam makes a sideways line, it moves down slightly. Then it goes sideways in the reverse direction. It does this over and over until the entire screen is filled. In a color-televsion tube, the beam or beams make red, green, and blue dots. The dots glow in varying degrees to make all the colors.

To make the picture, a television camera in the studio picked up the light reflected from an object. Video equipment changed the light into electric signals. The brighter the image at a point, the stronger the signal for that point was. At the same time, a microphone changed sound into other electric signals. Electronic amplifiers made these signals stronger. Finally, the signals were changed into radio waves.

The radio waves carrying the television signal weakened as they spread out from the sender, just as light dims as it spreads out from its source. A television antenna in your home or at a cable-TV center might have picked up these weak waves. The waves were then changed into the signals that made the picture and the sound.

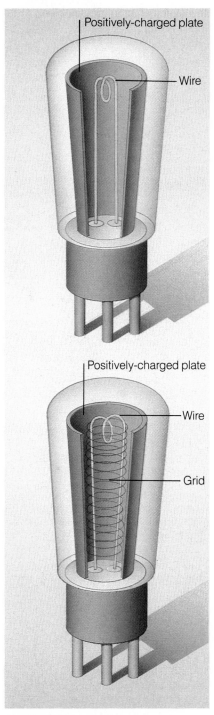

Figure 24-2 A vacuum tube

Figure 24-3 The first vacuum tube that acted as an amplifier.

Figure 24-4 Early computers were very large because they contained thousands of large vacuum tubes.

Have You Heard?

In 1946, the first large electronic computer, ENIAC (*E*lectronic *Nu*merical *I*ntegrator *a*nd *C*omputer) was built. It contained over 18 000 vacuum tubes. The air-conditioning equipment needed to cool ENIAC was enough to cool the whole Empire State Building.

Explore!

Find out the difference between standard television and digital television.

Vacuum Tubes Caused Problems

Even though vacuum tubes were a great advance in electronics, they had some problems. For one thing, they were too big. Some of the first tubes were as large as soft-drink bottles. Some electronic machines used hundreds or thousands of these big tubes. Often several people were needed to find and replace just one bad tube. *Figure 24-4* shows part of an early computer. It contained rows of vacuum tubes wired together.

Using vacuum tubes in electronic equipment caused several problems. First, their size limited their use. Complicated machines had to be very large to use either large tubes or many tubes. Second, because the tubes were so large, they used a lot of electricity. Third, tubes give off a lot of heat, and they had to be cooled to prevent them from being ruined. Fourth, the tubes tended to burn out, and had to be replaced. This made the equipment that contained the tubes unreliable, since the tubes had to be changed regularly.

Section Review

1. How is the use of electric current in electronics different from its use in electricity?
2. How does an amplifier affect current?
3. What four problems did using vacuum tubes in electronic equipment cause?

Challenge: Tube A in a television breaks every 4.5 months, tube B breaks every 5 months, and tube C breaks every 7 months. During the second year of use, how many times is the television broken because one of its tubes is broken?

Breaking Up a Picture

Purpose

To see how a television breaks up pictures into small areas that can be sent and received

Materials

- paper
- hole punch
- pencil
- marked ruler
- magnifying glass
- black-and-white magazine picture
- color picture from a magazine

Procedure and Observations

PART A

1. Punch a hold in a piece of paper as far from the edge as possible.
2. At the edge of the second sheet of paper, draw 5 boxes, each 1 cm². Label them 1 through 5. Leave Box 1 blank and shade Box 5 so that it is completely blackened. Shade Boxes 2 through 4 in increasing amounts, as shown below.

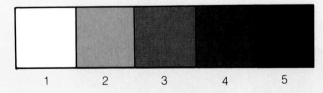

3. Pick one 4 cm² area of the black-and-white picture. Mark off this region with the ruler and pencil. Within the square, draw horizontal lines separated by the height of the hole you punched.
4. Hold the first paper over the picture so that the region at the left of the top line shows through the hole. Slide the edge of the second piece of paper around until you find which shading most closely

corresponds to the average darkness of whatever is showing through the hole. Record this number in your notebook as Line 1, Position 1.

5. Repeat this step over and over, moving the hole one of its widths to the right each time, giving the current line number and position number.
6. Your lab team should now exchange notebooks with another lab team. On another piece of paper, draw a box and horizontal lines similar to those in step 3. Using the numbers the other lab team has recorded, shade the various small areas to see what picture they recorded. Do not look at their picture.

PART B

1. On the color magazine picture, outline 3 squares of different colors, each 4 mm on a side.
2. With the magnifying glass, examine each of the squares and note which color dots appear.
3. Try to count the number of dots across one of the squares.

Analysis and Conclusions

1. What was the picture that the other lab team sent you? Now compare it with their original picture.
2. How might you improve the accuracy of the picture sent?
3. Compare the colors of the dots in the color picture with the colors that the squares you outlined appear to be without the magnifying glass.
4. How many dots are there across one of the small squares? How many of these dots would there be across the area you measured in Part A?

Explore!

Use an encyclopedia to find out what n-type and p-type semiconductors are and the different ways they are layered in transistors.

24-2 Making Electronic Devices Smaller

Transistors

In 1948, scientists found a way of controlling electrons that move through certain solids instead of a vacuum. These solids make **solid-state devices.**

An early solid-state device was the **transistor.** Like a vacuum tube, a transistor controls current. Transistors are made of materials that, when small amounts of other materials are added, can control the flow of electrons. These materials are semiconductors. The elements silicon and germanium are two important semiconductors. The added materials are known as impurities.

A transistor is a sandwich of thin layers of semiconductor material treated with different impurities. The impurities give each layer different properties. Small wires attached to the sandwich conduct current in and out. With the sandwich, electrical signals can be amplified, just as they had been with vacuum tubes.

Transistors were a great improvement over vacuum tubes because they are so much smaller, as shown below. They use less electricity, give off less heat, and last longer. Radios, record players, televisions, and toys are only a few of the many items that were "transistorized."

One problem remained. Transistors and other devices still had to be connected with wires to complete the circuits. These connections took up much space and often came apart.

Figure 24-5 Comparing the sizes of a transistor and a vacuum tube.

From Small to Smaller

In 1959, engineers took a giant step forward in electronics. They figured out how to eliminate connecting wires. On a small piece of silicon, engineers deposited materials not only to make the transistors, but also to make the connections for the whole circuit. In this arrangement—an **integrated circuit**—all the connections and components are built into one piece.

Engineers can design a single integrated circuit the size of a dime that does the work of many regular circuits. The integrated circuit held on the fingertip in *Figure 24-6* contains over 1000 transistors and other electronic devices. Under a microscope, you can see how complicated the integrated circuit actually is.

A technician prepares a large master design of an integrated circuit. A photographic process then reduces the completed design so that all the parts fit on a single silicon chip.

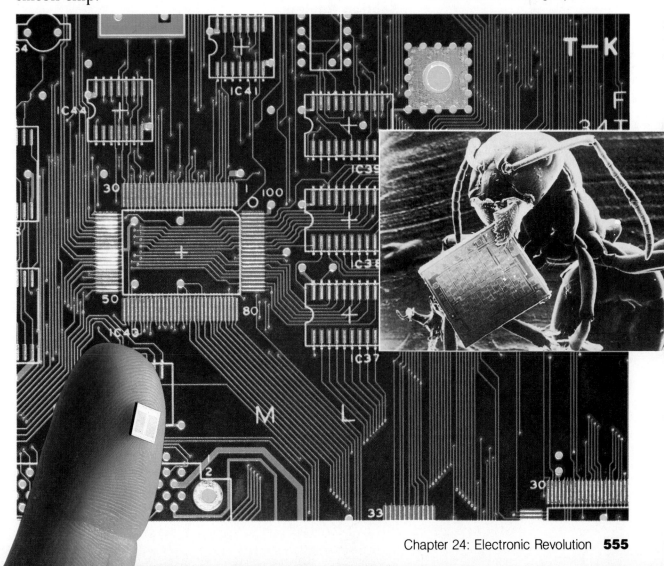

Figure 24-6 An integrated circuit containing more than 1000 electronic devices can fit on a fingertip.

The integrated circuit is now more commonly called by its nickname—the **chip.** A chip is a tiny piece of silicon that has been treated with different impurities. The way the impurities of different kinds are arranged determines what job each tiny region of the chip performs. Every chip has connections for electricity to flow from one part to another. Since the chip is so small, electrons can move quickly across it to do many different tasks.

Silicon is the earth's most abundant element after oxygen. So the raw material for chips is very inexpensive. Chips also use less power and last much longer than older components. Chips are so small and light that an ant can carry one off. As a result, you can now fit into your pocket a radio that outperforms older, bigger ones. And repairs are often as simple as replacing a single chip.

Section Review

1. State four ways that the transistor is better than the vacuum tube.
2. How is a chip made? How is it better than a transistor?

Challenge: If each full-size transistor takes up a square centimeter of space, how large a table would you need to spread out 100 000 transistors, the number of mini-transistors that might be present on a chip?

Figure 24-7 A person uses an input device to send instructions to the main memory. The control unit sends the information to be processed to the arithmetic unit. From there, the control unit sends the processed data either to an output device, an auxiliary storage unit, or back to the main memory.

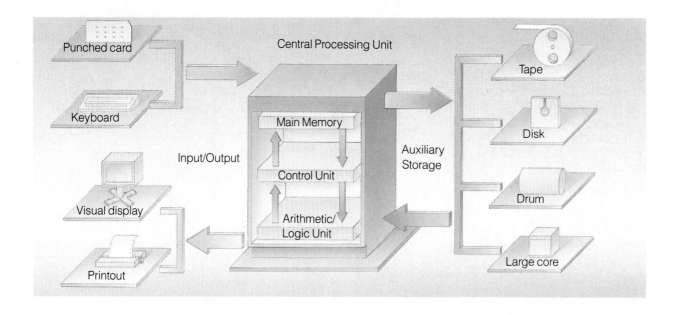

24-3 Computers

The Parts of a Computer

The electronic revolution probably has affected the computer more than any other device. As electronic devices became smaller, computers became smaller. They also became faster and were able to do more difficult tasks. While early computers used as much power as a locomotive, today's small computers use only as much power as a light bulb.

Figure 24-7 shows the main parts of a computer. The information going into a computer is called **input.** The results from a computer are its **output.** There are many different input and output devices. The most common form of input is the keyboard. Another form of input uses a special pad and pen to enter graphs and drawings into the computers. Some computers are able to use input from a human voice.

Computer output might appear on a television-like screen. It might be printed on a printer, which gives the user a "hard copy" of the results. The computer can also send output to a special pen that draws graphs or pictures on a special tablet. Some computers have output devices that can combine sounds to produce words.

The **central processing unit (CPU)** of the computer is the part that actually does the computing. It includes a control unit which tells the computer what to do, and an arithmetic unit, which carries out the instructions.

The CPU stores instructions, data, and results in the computer's memory until they are needed. The memory is a set of chips. It might have a set of permanent instructions built into it. No computer has a large enough built-in memory to contain all the information its users need. But the information can be stored in other ways. It might be stored magnetically on tape in a cassette or on plastic disks. It might be stored as a pattern of holes on cards or tapes. Or it might be stored in tiny pits on disks that a laser beam can "read."

The parts of a computer are considered **hardware**, and the data and instructions given the computer are **software.** The CPU, the memory, and the disks or tapes and their holders are hardware. The information and instructions that the computer receives from the disks, tapes, or keyboard are software.

After completing this section you will be able to

A. Describe the parts of a computer.
B. Explain what computers can and cannot do.
C. Name two computer languages.
D. Write a simple computer program in BASIC.

What Computers Can and Cannot Do

A computer works by recognizing two conditions in each of its circuits: "on" and "off." The computer must change all information into combinations of 1s and 0s, or of "on" and "off" circuits. The more circuits the computer has, the more information it can hold.

A computer's main purpose is to handle numbers and other information quickly. In one minute, a computer can do as many additions as a person could do in a lifetime. By solving many simple arithmetic problems one after the other, a computer can solve complex mathematical problems. Unlike adding machines, computers can go from one problem to the next automatically, following the instructions people give them. These detailed instructions are a **program.** Rear Admiral Grace Murray Hopper was one of the first programmers. She had the idea that computers should be able to recognize instructions in words.

A computer is much faster and more accurate than a person could ever be. Repeating the same task over and over again does not cause a computer to become bored or forgetful. However, a computer does not "think" on its own. People have to tell it what to do.

A computer does not usually make errors unless a part is broken or unless there is an error—a "bug"—in the program that tells the computer what to do. A computer can put out nonsense if it is given nonsense information. For example, if your address is Lee Terrace, you or your parents might have received a computer-printed letter addressed to Mr. Lee Terrace. The mistake might have happened because a person typed the address into the space that is supposed to contain the name. The computer will continue to send letters to Mr. Lee Terrace until someone corrects the error.

Figure 24-8 Different computer languages serve the needs of different users.

People who work with computers have a saying about programs and computers: "Garbage in, garbage out" ("GIGO"). This saying means that the information and work we get *out* of computers is only as good as the information and work we put *into* the computers.

The fact that a computer might beat you at chess or another game does not mean that it is smarter than you. When a computer is programmed to play a game, it receives a set of rules. The computer can then work out many possible moves for every point of the game. Its speed in analyzing the effect of each of many possible moves contributes to the computer's victory. No computer can play as well as the best human players—yet.

Many researchers are studying **artificial intelligence**, ways of making the computer more closely mimic human thinking. Artificial intelligence programs give computers so many choices that we might be fooled into thinking a person, instead of a computer, is responding to our requests. But it will be many years, if ever, before computers become as flexible as humans are in understanding language and figuring out alternatives.

Computer Languages

Computers, such as the one shown in *Figure 24-8*, can work with words by treating the letters as numbers. Each letter and punctuation symbol has been assigned a number in a standard code. In fact, a computer changes all numbers, words, pictures, and musical notes into a code of 1s and 0s. But it would be very hard to program a computer by changing all the instructions yourself into that number code.

For that reason, different computer "languages" have been invented for different purposes. One language is especially designed for business use and another language is for mathematical and scientific problems. There is even a language for artists who want to use a computer to help make designs.

One common language is called **BASIC,** which is short for "**B**eginner's **A**ll-Purpose **S**ymbol **I**nstruction **C**ode." Your school might offer courses in BASIC, which is based on English words. Another language taught in schools, expecially to younger children, is LOGO. LOGO makes it especially easy for students to draw graphs and pictures.

Applying Science

Researchers are trying to develop a new kind of computer that uses photons of light instead of electrons to carry signals. Computers using light might be made smaller and faster.

Explore!

Find out what an analog computer is and how it differs from the kind of computer (digital) described here.

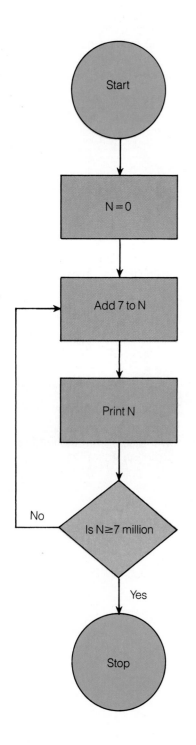

Figure 24-9 Flow chart for a program to count from 0 to 7 million by 7s

Programming a Computer

Writing a program is simply telling the computer step by step what to do. Before you can write a program for a computer, you must figure out exactly what the computer needs to know and what steps it should go through. To help you, you might draw a plan called a **flow chart.** A flow chart shows the steps in the order the computer should follow.

To program a computer to count from 0 to 7 million by 7s, you might prepare the flow chart shown in *Figure 24-9*. Notice the point where the computer has to answer a question. It must choose between a "yes" path and a "no" path. If you left out this question or made another mistake in your flow chart, your program would not work properly.

The following BASIC program adds 4 + 4 and prints the result:

```
1 A = 4 + 4
2 PRINT A
3 END
```

The computer adds 4 + 4 and puts the answer in a place in its memory called A. It then prints whatever is in A. The 1, 2, and 3 are line numbers, showing the order of the commands.

You hardly need a computer to add 4 + 4. However, for other mathematical problems, having a computer handy and knowing how to program it can save you a lot of time. For example, if you need to add 137 to all the numbers from 1 to 1500, you can use the program:

```
1 FOR B = 1 TO 1500
2 A = B + 137
3 PRINT A
4 NEXT B
5 END
```

Section Review

1. Name two input devices, two output devices, and two devices for storying memory.
2. How does a computer know what task to perform?
3. How does a computer understand words?
4. Why is a flow chart sometimes useful?

Challenge: Some shampoo bottles have the instructions: "Lather. Rinse. Repeat." If this were a program, what mistakes would have to be corrected? Draw a flow chart to show the correction.

The Computing Process

Purpose

To show how a computer stores information and understands instructions

Materials

- paper
- pencil
- scissors

Procedure and Observations

PART A
1. Draw a very simple picture of a house.
2. Write exact step-by-step instructions that explain how to draw the house.
3. Exchange instructions with your partner. Do not show each other your pictures.
4. Draw your partner's house by following the instructions word for word.
5. Check your partner's drawing and correct your instructions accordingly. Keep correcting your instructions until your partner draws the house as you did in your original picture. Record how the number and type of instructions changed.

PART B
1. Cut out 12 squares of paper, each 3 cm × 3 cm.
2. Label each square "ON" on one side and "OFF" on the other side.
3. Arrange three columns of four squares each on your desk, as in **a**.
4. Each column stands for one digit in a three-digit number. You can use different patterns of the off-on squares to represent each number, just as a computer does. Let the pattern for zero be "off-

off-off-off." Let the pattern for one be "off-off-off-on."
5. Make a list of patterns for the other digits (2-9). Each digit must have its own combination of offs and ons.

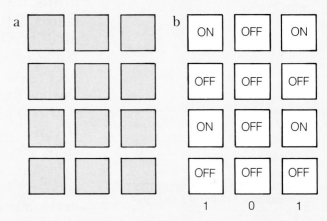

6. Use your code of patterns to represent the numbers 302, 498, and 756. The number 101 is shown in **b**.
7. Exchange codes with your partner and compare your systems.

Analysis and Conclusions

1. Compare your Part A instructions and Part B codes with how a computer follows a program.
2. What additional materials do you need to represent larger numbers in Part B?
3. What problem might occur if you did not have a standard code for all the digits?
4. How could you change Part B to represent negative numbers?

After completing this section you will be able to

A. Describe how a personal computer uses a microprocessor.
B. List four other uses of microprocessors.

Figure 24-10 A tiny microprocessor contains all a computer's problem-solving circuits.

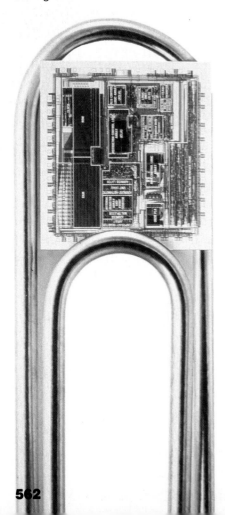

24-4 Personal Computers and Microprocessors

Microprocessors and Personal Computers

If you have ever played a computer game, you have enjoyed using what is sometimes called a "computer on a chip." Chips were already amazing when researchers in the early 1970s developed a single chip that contained all the abilities of a computer's central processing unit. This chip, called a **microprocessor,** calculates as fast as many large computers do, but it costs much less. As *Figure 24-10* shows, a microprocessor is much smaller than a paper clip.

Microprocessors have circuits to follow instructions. If you add memory circuits and input and output circuits, you have a compact computer. Computers used to be huge devices used mainly by government agencies and large businesses. Microprocessors made possible the development of **personal computers** for use at home and at work.

A personal computer might use a home television screen instead of a computer monitor to show what it is doing. You can use the same personal computer to help you review your school subjects or to play many different games. A special box can be attached to the side of some types of computers to make the computer "talk." The microprocessor directs a device inside the box to put together words out of individual sounds.

Personal computers can also be used to monitor expenses. Farmers can use personal computers to keep track of the cost of feeding each farm animal. They can then compare that figure with the animal's selling price.

Microprocessors Have Many Uses

Every day we find more microprocessors around us. A common use of microprocessors is in digital watches. A microprocessor can count many cycles of a vibrating object. The microprocessor in a watch counts enough cycles to equal one second. Then it sends signals that change one or more numbers shown on the face of the watch. By simply changing a microprocessor's program, you can direct it to do different tasks. That is why pressing a button can turn your watch into a stopwatch or an alarm.

Microprocessors are now common in many devices around the house. Videocassette recorders might have chips inside them to control their timing, turning them on automatically when you are not at home. The chip in some microwave ovens, such as the one shown in *Figure 24-11,* is programmed to time and direct the oven to prepare a roast. You can program the chip to defrost the roast at a certain time, to cook it for another time interval, and to keep it warm until you are ready to eat. Some coffeepots can be directed by built-in microprocessors when to turn on. The breakfast coffee can brew while family members are getting up.

Microprocessors in cars save a lot of energy. A microprocessor's program can compare signals from the engine and the outside temperature. The microprocessor can calculate how much gas can be used to make the engine run most economically. Then it directs a valve to release that amount of gas.

Section Review

1. How is a microprocessor different from a computer?
2. What are four uses for microprocessors?

Challenge: There is not much of a market for used personal computers. Why do you think this is so?

Explore!

Look at a digital watch to determine how many individual straight segments make up each number. How many segments does the microprocessor inside have to control to show the time?

Applying Science

An experimental device for enabling paralyzed victims to walk again involves a microprocessor programmed to send electrical signals through the skin. The signals stimulate the leg muscles. The microprocessor, which can be worn on a belt, has several different buttons. Each button stimulates a different set of muscle movements, such as those needed for walking or those for climbing stairs.

Figure 24-11 Many microwave ovens contain microprocessors.

After completing this section you will be able to

A. Describe three uses of computers in business and industry.

B. Describe three uses of computers in government and law enforcement.

C. Describe three uses of computers in engineering and in the sciences.

D. Describe three uses of computers in medicine.

Figure 24-12 The airline industry uses computers in many ways.

24-5 Using Computers

Computers in Business and Industry

You might not have a personal computer or other devices run by a microprocessor. Still, computers affect your daily life in many ways.

Computers are important in business and industry. For example, computers can operate machines and control robots to perform boring or dangerous tasks. In the fashion industry, programmers store precise instructions for cutting out suits of different sizes. The computer directs electric shears to cut out the exact size each time. In the automotive industry, computer-controlled robots on assembly lines weld joints on cars.

The airline industry also makes use of computers in several ways. Computers keep track of seat reservations and print boarding passes and tickets. Computers are also used to train pilots. *Figure 24-12* shows how computers are used to teach people to fly planes without being in an actual plane. A special room is fitted out to resemble a cockpit. A computer creates and changes the view through the window. The trainee can learn to handle problems that might arise without risking lives or using fuel.

More and more businesses are being computerized. A computer can keep track of a company's supplies and orders. It can help determine the amount of stock a business should have on hand. A computer can send bills to customers and second bills to those who are late in paying. It can also keep records of the company's employees and figure out and print paychecks and income-tax reports.

Typewriters have become a thing of the past in many offices. Computers of all sizes are used as word processors that not only print out words, but also make correcting typing errors or revising drafts easy.

The fastest, most powerful computers are called supercomputers. Some industries, including the oil industry, use supercomputers. Supercomputers analyze data gathered around the world to help oil companies locate new supplies of scarce resources. Movie studios use supercomputers to make animations—that is, motion pictures that photograph successive positions of inanimate objects.

Computers in Government and Law Enforcement

Government and law-enforcement agencies rely on computers. The National Crime Information Center links thousands of computers. This computer network stores information on wanted persons, missing persons, and stolen property. The Federal Bureau of Investigation stores more than 20 000 fingerprints each day in computers. Law enforcement agents throughout the country can check suspects' fingerprints against those in the computer records. *Figure 24-13* shows a law-enforcement official using a computer to retrieve information relating to a particular situation.

Police departments in large cities use a computer system to keep track of the locations of patrol cars. Within seconds, the computer can locate the patrol car nearest to the scene of a crime or accident and automatically send an emergency call to it.

The United States Postal Service uses computers to help speed mail to you. A computer controls machines that sort letters. The computer reads ZIP codes and groups letters according to their destinations.

One government agency keeps track of the population of the country through computers. Another agency uses computers to check tax returns for mistakes. For example, the computer can compare the amount of interest a bank reports that it paid an individual with the amount of interest listed on that individual's income-tax return.

Figure 24-13 Computers can be used in law-enforcement work.

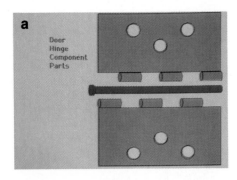

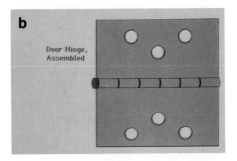

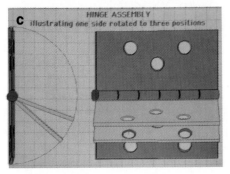

Figure 24-14 Computer generated model of a door hinge: (**a**) parts; (**b**) assembled model; (**c**) animated model

Computers in Engineering and the Sciences

Computers have revolutionized engineering. Drawings can be made much more quickly than ever before. Several alternative designs can be produced at the same time. Computers enable engineers both to focus on a small area to make changes in it and then to back off and see the entire project just as clearly. In the past, engineers had to figure out by hand such properties as weight, volume, and center of gravity. Now computers do the calculations rapidly and accurately. Speeding up the design process saves both time and money.

Figure 24-14 shows a design for a hinge drawn on a computer. First, the computer shows the designer's specifications for the individual parts of the hinge. Then it assembles the separate parts into a complete model. Finally, the computer animates the model to make sure that the parts work together properly.

Computerized engineering has made the space age possible. The engineers who design spacecraft and equipment for studying the universe rely on computers. So do the engineers who launch, control, and track spacecraft.

Computer-assisted engineering has designed a wide variety of objects, including tire treads, railroad car interiors, space stations, bridges, skyscrapers, power plants, and computer printers. A supercomputer analysis was even used in designing the American 12-meter yacht that won the America's Cup in 1987.

Scientists use computers in many ways, too. Computers and supercomputers help researchers devise models of such complicated systems as the world's weather. They use the laws of heat and motion together with weather observations from all over the world. The computer puts together the data and produces equations that show how parts of the weather system might be related. Computers also help scientists make weather forecasts. Before computers, it took so long to process the available data that the weather had changed long before the forecast was completed.

Computers are vital in space science. Orbiting satellites, rockets, and space probes are equipped with microprocessors. The chips enable the spacecraft to act as scouts for astronaut missions. Without computers we would have none of the exciting pictures of the planets and their moons that spacecraft have transmitted.

Physical scientists on the earth use computers, too. Chemists and physicists use computers to analyze their data and to keep track of readings on their laboratory equipment. Astronomers need computers to guide telescopes and to analyze data collected from objects in space.

Computers are now able to interpret photographs in ways that aid scientists. Northern California's Mount Shasta was photographed by a satellite with radar. A powerful computer analyzed the space photograph and enabled the scientists to produce a two-dimensional topographic map. The computer was then able to produce a three-dimensional view of Mount Shasta. The three-dimensional view, shown in *Figure 24-15,* is similar to what an observer would see from a plane flying around the mountain.

Scientists recently grew concerned that only industry and a few government laboratories could afford powerful supercomputers. As a result, the National Science Foundation set up several national supercomputer centers for use by teachers and researchers from universities all over the country. Special or regular telephone lines link universities all over the country with the supercomputer centers. Now more students will graduate knowing how best to use supercomputers.

Figure 24-15 Computer-produced three-dimensional topographic map

Explore!

Use an encyclopedia to find out how computerized axial tomography (CAT) scanners work and what advantages they have over other medical imaging systems.

Have You Heard?

An oceanographer in the mid-1970s developed a model of the Atlantic Ocean but was unable to solve a problem it posed with the computers then available. In the early 1980s, a supercomputer solved the problem in just over eight seconds.

Figure 24-16 Before surgery, the scientist working at this computer determined precisely what the surgeon should do.

Computers in Medicine

Computers are useful in medicine. They help both diagnose and treat patients. They also make it possible for doctors to learn quickly about changes in a patient's condition.

If a computer's memory stores the symptoms of many diseases, doctors can input a patient's symptoms and quickly learn what illness the patient might have. Doctors can also use computers to interpret special kinds of X rays. The computers use the X rays to make detailed images of internal body parts. These computer-assisted scans can help doctors find tumors or other serious disorders before they threaten the patient's life.

At the patient's bedside, computers can analyze the results of different tests. Doctors can then decide what course of action to take. Computer-controlled equipment is often used to assist or replace diseased organs, such as hearts and kidneys. The scientist in *Figure 24-16* is studying a woman's image on the computer screen. The woman will have plastic surgery performed on her face. Using a special pointer as a scalpel on the image, the scientist can figure out exactly what the surgeon should do during the operation.

Computers keep doctors up to date on changes in their patients' health. For example, a telephone or microwave signals can send up-to-the-minute information about a patient's heart activity to a computer. The computer analyzes the signals within minutes. Then, whether the patient's doctor is in the same building or kilometers away, the computer returns the results to the doctor.

Section Review

1. What are three uses of computers in the airline industry?
2. How do police departments use computers to speed patrol cars to the scene of an accident?
3. How are computers used in the space program?
4. What are two ways computers help doctors treat patients?

Challenge: Why might supercomputers be important for interpreting coded messages?

Applying Science

A computerized device might be used to treat diabetics. Surgeons implant an insulin pump under the patient's skin in a short operation. The patient can control the amount of insulin sent into the body by holding a small radio transmitter over the pump and dialing a number that corresponds to a specific computer program. Every three months, the patient returns to the doctor, who refills the insulin container without having to remove the pump. The pump's battery is expected to last from 5 to 10 years.

People and Science

Noel Runyan, Inventor

Noel Runyan grew up in Los Alamos, New Mexico. He was interested in nuclear power, and science became his life pursuit.

At age 16, he was working with unstable compounds that exploded, leaving him permanently blind. Runyan did not let the accident stop him. He graduated from the University of New Mexico at the top of his class as an electrical engineer.

Today, Runyan is more interested in computers than in nuclear power. He has developed the Talking Tablet, a personal computer for the blind. The computer does not have a video display screen. It responds with a loud, clear voice.

Runyan's computer receives commands from a panel of vertical plastic ridges that can be interpreted with the fingertips. It has a touch-type keyboard that can be used to send messages to any ordinary printer. At the tap of a key, it gives the date and time.

Using the Talking Tablet, visually-impaired people can "read" four times faster than they can with Braille. Surprisingly, more publications are available for use in this computer than are available in Braille. The Talking Tablet has a number of other useful functions, such as for shopping or paying bills. The Talking Tablet enriches the lives of the blind, which is a great source of satisfaction to Noel Runyan.

Looking at Computer Programs

Examine the computer program shown below. It is written in the computer language, BASIC:

```
1  N = 5
2  S = N * N
3  PRINT "FOR N ="; N; ", N
   SQUARED = "; S
4  IF N = 20 GO TO 7
5  N = N + 1
6  GO TO 2
7  END
```

Follow the statements in numerical order, unless you are instructed to jump to some other statement. To interpret the program, use the following rules:

a. The symbol * means "multiply."

b. Where the program says PRINT, write down the answer that you have calculated.

c. Anything between quotation marks following a PRINT statement should appear just as it is written.

d. A semicolon means to continue printing on the same line without any skipped spaces.

e. In programs, lines that look like equations really mean that you should substitute. For example, $N = N + 1$ means "take N, add 1, and take the result for your new value of N."

Use the information above to answer the following questions.

1. What does the program do?

2. Why is it useful to use quotation marks in some parts of PRINT statements and not in others? Why is it useful to use spaces inside quotation marks?

3. Study the sample flow chart shown here. Then draw a flow chart for the program shown above.

4. Write a similar program to compute the 9 times table, ranging from 1×9 up to 30×9.

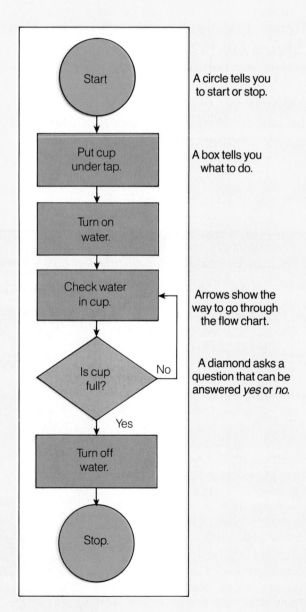

A circle tells you to start or stop.

A box tells you what to do.

Arrows show the way to go through the flow chart.

A diamond asks a question that can be answered *yes* or *no.*

✔ Summary

24-1 Electronics

A. Electronic devices use electric current to carry information.

B. Electronic devices use electric current in the form of signals that represent information.

C. Vacuum tubes were a great advance in electronics, but they are too large, use much electricity, give off much heat, and burn out fairly often.

24-2 Making Electronic Devices Smaller

A. Transistors are smaller, use less electricity, give off less heat, and last longer than vacuum tubes.

B. A single chip can contain thousands of transistors and other circuit components, all connected together to form an integrated circuit.

24-3 Computers

A. The main part of a computer is the central processing unit.

B. Computers can do only what they are told to do.

C. BASIC and LOGO are two well-known computer languages.

D. Using BASIC, even beginners can write simple computer programs.

24-4 Personal Computers and Microprocessors

A. Because of their small size and large capabilities, microprocessors make personal computers possible.

B. Microprocessors can be used in digital watches, household appliances, and automobiles.

24-5 Using Computers

A. Computers can be used to operate and control robots, to train airplane pilots, and to keep track of business expenses and income.

B. Computers can be used to keep track of criminals, to dispatch police patrol cars, and to check tax returns.

C. Computers can aid in product design and weather forecasting.

D. Computers can help doctors to diagnose illnesses, treat patients, and monitor a patient's condition.

Vocabulary

For each of the following terms, write a sentence that uses the term correctly.

amplifier	electronic device	personal computer
artificial intelligence	flow chart	program
BASIC	hardware	software
cathode-ray tube	input	solid-state device
central processing unit (CPU)	integrated circuit	transistor
chip	microprocessor	vacuum tube
electronics	output	

✓ Check Your Knowledge

Part I: Matching Match the definition in Column I with the correct term in Column II.

Column I
1. the first important electronic device
2. it changes a weak signal into a stronger one
3. vacuum tube still found in television sets
4. an early solid-state device
5. contains thousands of components on a small chip
6. information going into a computer
7. a popular computer language
8. results coming out of a computer
9. instructions given to a computer
10. computer that can be used at home

Column II
a. transistor
b. vacuum tube
c. personal computer
d. amplifier
e. hardware
f. output
g. cathode-ray tube
h. integrated circuit
i. software
j. input
k. BASIC

Part II: Multiple Choice Choose the letter of the best answer.

11. Which of the following is *not* an electronic device? (a) radio (b) television (c) computer (d) light bulb
12. A useful property of vacuum tubes is (a) their size. (b) their power requirements. (c) the heat that they give off. (d) the ability to control the flow of electrons.
13. The transistor is (a) larger than a vacuum tube. (b) a solid-state device. (c) computer software. (d) one type of computer-input device.
14. A computer chip is often made out of (a) silicon. (b) oxygen. (c) nitrogen. (d) mercury.
15. Microprocessors might be found in (a) digital watches. (b) household appliances. (c) automobiles. (d) all of these.
16. The fastest and most powerful computers are called (a) microcomputers. (b) minicomputers. (c) supercomputers. (d) personal computers.

17. Computers are *not* used to (a) design products. (b) manufacture products. (c) keep track of criminals. (d) control the weather.

Part III: Completion Write the word or words that complete the sentence correctly.

18. A branch of science that deals with the use of electrons in devices such as radios, televisions, and computers is called _____.
19. A tiny piece of silicon that has been treated with impurities is known as a _____.
20. In devising a computer program, it can be helpful to draw a plan called a _____.
21. A single chip that has all of the abilities of a computer's central processing unit is known as a _____.
22. Materials that conduct electricity better than insulators but not as well as conductors are called _____.

✔ Check Your Understanding

1. What effect did putting a grid in a vacuum tube have on the electron beam?
2. How does television bring pictures and sound from a studio into your home?
3. What main change(s) in devices did the electronic revolution cause?
4. What is a chip?
5. Draw a box for each part of a computer and show the order in which they are connected by drawing lines between them.
6. Why do we use computer languages?
7. How have computers affected your life?

✔ Apply Your Knowledge

1. A computer might need 1 000 000 components. If vacuum tubes must be 5 cm away from each other to keep the heat from building up, how large would the computer have to be?
2. If transistors must be 1 cm away from each other, how large would the computer be, still needing 1 000 000 components?
3. What do the transistors in computer chips do?
4. Write a program to print "HELLO" and your name. Use the line "INPUT NAME," which takes what you type on the keyboard as the input and stores it in a place in memory called NAME.
5. Write a program to divide 100 by 4 and to print the question and its answer.

✔ Extend Your Knowledge

Research/Projects

1. Find out if any devices in your home, aside from the cathode-ray tube in a television, still have vacuum tubes. If there are any, list the age of each device, and whether it still works.
2. List the devices at home that a microprocessor controls.
3. Find out about the computer languages Pascal and Ada. Report on why they were invented and what their advantages are.
4. Find out what a "mouse" is and how it is used to control a computer.
5. Find out how the picture is displayed on a color television.

Readings

DeWeese, Gene. *Computers in Entertainment and the Arts.* Watts, 1984. Discusses how computers are used in writing, graphic arts, music, and special effects for movies and the stage.

Math, Irwin. *Bits and Pieces: Understanding and Building Computing Devices.* Scribners, 1984. Includes experiments and projects following the problem-device-solution format.

Stevens, Lawrence. *Computer Graphics Basics: An Introduction for Young People.* Prentice Hall, 1984. An excellent introduction to computer-generated visuals.

Advances in Artificial Pacemakers

A healthy heart beats an average of 72 beats per minute, 60 minutes every hour, 24 hours a day. The steady rhythmic working of the heart is controlled by a built-in electrical system. A small node of tissue on the right side of the heart generates minute electrical impulses that travel through the heart muscle. These impulses cause the muscle to contract and relax, so that the heart beats regularly.

The node of tissue that sends electric impulses is the heart's natural pacemaker. Sometimes this node of tissue stops functioning properly due to disease or damage to the heart. When the natural pacemaker fails, the heartbeat may slow down and become irregular. To correct this life-threatening problem, physicians can implant an artificial pacemaker to reestablish the heart's regular beating.

The first artificial pacemakers, which were developed in the 1950s, were sizable units. The batteries that powered the first pacemakers were housed in a case that was strapped to the outside of the body. By 1960, however, transistors made smaller pacemakers possible. The batteries for the smaller pacemakers were about the size of a bar of soap and could be implanted under the skin. They were connected to the heart with hairlike wires that

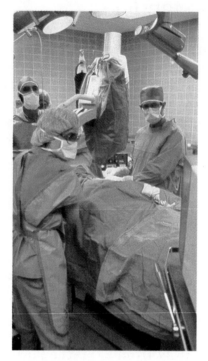

were threaded through veins. Roughly every two years, the batteries needed to be replaced to assure that the pacemaker continued working without interruption. The frequent operations required to replace these short-lived batteries posed a slight, but definite health risk to patients with pacemakers.

In the 1970s scientists developed lithium batteries that are both lighter and longer lasting than the previous batteries that powered pacemakers. Lithium is a highly reactive metal that produces hydrogen gas, which is flammable, when on contact with water. Therefore, to make a safe battery using lithium, a liquid other than water must be used to form the paste that

conducts electrical charges inside the battery. Scientists have found that crystals of lithium iodide conduct electricity. They used this information to design the lithium-iodine battery. The rod of this battery is made of lithium, the case is made of iodine, and the paste between contains lithium iodide. Lithium batteries last up to 10 years. These lightweight, safe, reliable batteries have reduced the health risks for people who have artificial pacemakers.

New generations of pacemakers will be attached to sensors in the body that monitor the wearer's activity level. The information from the sensors would be collected and analyzed by a tiny computer that would signal the pacemaker to speed up or slow down the heart. This would allow people with pacemakers to theoretically lead lives as active and vigorous as Olympic athletes.

For Discussion

1. How does a lithium battery work, and why is the lithium battery an improvement over batteries that were previously used in artificial pacemakers?

2. What are some other recent advances in artificial pacemakers?

3. What are some other ways you think artificial pacemakers could be improved? What kind of research would you do to make these improvements?

Magnetic Levitation Trains

Friction—steel wheels rolling on steel rails—is what prevents the fastest conventional trains from breaking the 300 km per hour limit. However, new kinds of trains can float 10 cm above the tracks and travel at speeds greater than 480 km per hour. Electromagnets supply the forces that lift and move these trains. Therefore, these speeding-bullet vehicles are known as magnetic levitation trains or maglev trains for short. Follow the steps in the diagram above to learn how one type of magnetic levitation train works.

1. The train starts up, rolling on rubber wheels. Until the train reaches a speed of about 80 km per hour, the forces produced by the electromagnets are not strong enough to lift the train.

2. Current is sent through metal coils in the sides of the train. These coils are cooled to −270° Celsius, which lowers the resistence and strengthens the current. The strong current induces a magnetic field in the coils, and the coils become superconducting electromagnets.

3. As the train moves, the superconducting magnets in the train obviously also move. The movement of these magnets induces an electric current in metal coils in the tracks. This electric current induces a magnetic field, which is the same polarity as that of the superconducting magnets. When the train reaches a speed of 80 km per hour, the repulsive force between the electromagnets in the train and those in the track causes

the train to rise above the track.

4. Rows of electromagnets along guideways at the sides of the train propel the train forward. The electromagnets ahead of the train are the opposite polarity as that of the superconducting magnets in the train; the attractive force between these electromagnets pulls the train forward. The electromagnets immediately next to the train are the same polarity as that of the superconducting magnets in the train; the repulsive force between these magnets helps push the train in the direction of its forward momentum.

5. The polarity of the electromagnets in the guideway continually changes, creating a magnetic wave that carries the train forward.

The realization that the earth is but a tiny speck in the vastness of the universe has served also as a stimulus for learning more about this infinity surrounding us. Many of the riddles of the universe are being unraveled, but what remains to be learned has dimensions with an immensity of the universe itself.

16th Century

Until the mid-1500s, it was the belief of even the most learned that the earth was the center of the universe. All other bodies in the heavens were lesser, some of them stationary and others moving about the earth. Then Copernicus described the solar system much as we know it today, with the sun as its center and the earth and other planets orbiting around it. In his system, however, the orbits were circles rather than ellipses, an error corrected soon by other scientists.

17th Century

Galileo turned his telescope to the sky and reported for the first time that our moon had a mountainous rather than a smooth surface. He noted also that the planet Venus shines by reflected light, that Jupiter had four moons, and that the Milky Way is made up of countless stars. His observations were amazingly accurate considering the primitiveness of his telescope. His observations were also revolutionary and resulted in his being put on trial for heretical opinions.

Chapter 25 Exploring the Universe
Chapter 26 The Large and the Small

19th Century

Telescopes were made larger and more powerful in the 1800s, enabling astronomers to see the planets, stars, and other objects in the skies as they had never before been seen. At Yerkes Observatory at Williams Bay, Wisconsin not far from Chicago, a refractor telescope with a 40-inch (1 m) aperture was turned skyward in the late 1800s. It is still the world's largest telescope of that type.

20th Century

Quasars are not new in the universe, but astronomers first detected them in 1963 by using both optical and radio telescopes. Most astronomers believe they represent stages in the development of galaxies. Quasars are examples that there are still new things to be discovered in the sky. The exploring has just begun. Most spectacular of the advancements in astronomy in this century has been the invasion of space with space vehicles and equipment. Discoveries from space and from telescopes on earth have revealed a universe much larger and more complex than previously imagined.

CHAPTER 25
Exploring the Universe

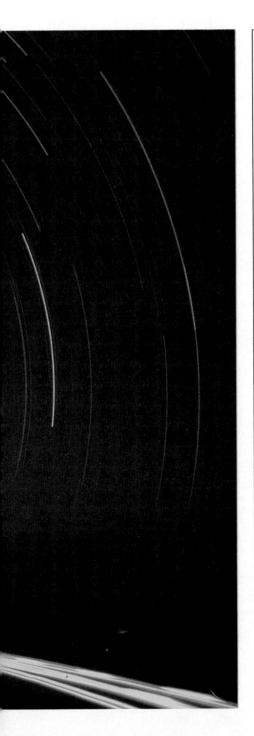

The time-exposure photograph shows "star tracks." The circular lines mark the stars' paths as they moved through the night sky for two hours. The picture was taken at an observatory on Mauna Kea, Hawaii.

Organizing Your Study Skills The outline below will help you see how the chapter is organized and what you should learn as you read.

I. Section 25-1: The Development of Stars
   A. What is the role of gravity in the birth of a star?
   B. What makes stars shine?
   C. How do astronomers study light from the stars?
   D. How do astronomers study other radiation from the stars?

II. Section 25-2: Aging Stars
   A. When does a star become a red giant?
   B. How do white dwarfs and supernovas compare?
   C. What are neutron stars and pulsars?
   D. How do black holes form?
   E. How might astronomers detect a black hole?

III. Section 25-3: The Milky Way Galaxy
   A. Where is the sun's position in the Milky Way Galaxy?
   B. Why do astronomers think there might be a black hole in the center of the Milky Way Galaxy?

IV. Section 25-4: A Universe of Galaxies
   A. How are galaxies classified by shape?
   B. What is an example of a cluster of galaxies?

After completing this section you will be able to

A. Describe the role of gravity in the birth of a star.
B. Describe the process that makes stars shine.
C. Explain how astronomers study light from the stars.
D. Explain how astronomers study other radiation from the stars.

Figure 25-1 The Eagle Nebula shows young stars at upper left and dark clouds of gas and dust in which new stars are forming.

25-1 The Development of Stars

How Stars Form

Many people think the space between stars is empty. Actually, space contains much gas and dust. In some places, large amounts of gas and dust collect and form new stars. *Figure 25-1* shows a huge cloud of gas and dust called a **nebula**. The small dark spots within it are clumps of gas and dust that have started collapsing to form stars.

Stars form in nebulas. Gravity draws the gas and dust together. As matter in the clump concentrates, gravity between the particles increases.

The gas becomes more and more compressed as this process continues. The material in the center of the clump becomes very hot as a result of the compression. Atoms in the gas break down into nuclei and electrons.

The final event in the birth of a star happens as the pressure and density at its center become very great. As the temperature rises above 1 000 000° C, some of the nuclei pass so close together that they combine through nuclear fusion. When this happens, a star is born. In *Figure 25-2*, the dust surrounding the new born star has begun to glow. The new star is buried in the dust, but it produces infrared rays which we can detect.

Energy from nuclear fusion causes a high pressure in the center of the star. Soon pressure pushing outward balances gravity, which is pulling the gas inward. The star then enters its long middle age.

Nuclear Fusion Makes Stars Shine

Stars get their energy from nuclear fusion. Scientists are now experimenting with ways to hold hot gas in place on the earth to allow fusion to take place. Using magnetic fields, they have succeeded in reaching a temperature on the earth of 200 000 000° C, but only for a fraction of a second.

In the center of stars, however, gravity holds hot gas in place long enough for fusion to take place. In most stars, four hydrogen nuclei fuse with each other to form a helium nucleus. The helium nucleus contains slightly less matter than the four hydrogen nuclei that formed it. Some of the extra matter changes into energy that flows outward to the star's surface. Stars shine because they give off some of this energy as light.

Figure 25-2 The red dot at the lower center is an image of a star being born, seen from the infrared waves it sent out.

The diagram on page 181 shows how hydrogen nuclei react to make one helium nucleus. This process takes place in stars like the sun. The process starts when two hydrogen nuclei ($_1^1H$) fuse to make a nucleus of deuterium ($_1^2H$), a form of heavy hydrogen. In the next step, two of these deuterium nuclei fuse to become helium-3 ($_2^3He$), an unusual form of helium. Finally, two of these helium-3 nuclei fuse to make one helium-4 ($_2^4He$) nucleus, with two hydrogen nuclei ($_1^1H$) left over. Thus four of the hydrogen-1 nuclei went to make the helium-4 nucleus. This process is called the proton-proton chain, because a hydrogen-1 nucleus ($_1^1H$) is just a proton.

Figure 25-3 Fusion energy will keep the sun shining for another five billion years.

In stars hotter than the sun, a different process helps groups of four hydrogen nuclei undergo fusion to become one helium nucleus. In these stars, a hydrogen nucleus attaches itself to a carbon nucleus. A nitrogen nucleus results. Gradually, hydrogen nuclei are added one by one, forming new and different nuclei each time. Once a total of four hydrogen nuclei have been added, though, the nucleus breaks apart. It turns into the original form of carbon again as well as a helium nucleus. The process is called the carbon-nitrogen cycle.

Most stars are now fusing hydrogen into helium in one of these two ways. These stars are called **dwarfs**. Our sun, shown in the picture, is a dwarf. It "burns" 540 000 000 metric tons of hydrogen per second, turning almost all of it into helium. The sun has been shining from this type of fusion energy for the last five billion years. Astronomers think it will keep shining for another five billion years.

The greater a star's mass, the more rapidly fusion goes on inside it and the more quickly it uses up its hydrogen. Some stars have fifty times the mass of the sun. They use up their hydrogen much more quickly than the sun and have much shorter lifetimes. Other stars have only about one-tenth the sun's mass. These stars shine more faintly but much longer than the sun.

We think of the sun as an average star, since some stars are much hotter, while others are much cooler, and some stars are much brighter, while others are much fainter. The sun's center, where the fusion takes place, is at 15 000 000° C. Its surface temperature is 6000° C.

Have You Heard?

Almost everything in the universe is hydrogen and helium. The heavy elements that make up our body and so much of our world amount to less than 1% of the matter in the universe.

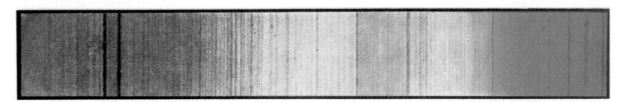

Studying Light from the Stars

Some of the energy that forms deep in stars comes to us as light—the form of energy we can see with our eyes. Astronomers collect starlight with optical telescopes that use large lenses or mirrors to gather much more light than your eyes alone can collect. Recall that the larger the lens or mirror in a telescope, the more light it can collect.

Astronomers can study a star by breaking up its light into a spectrum of colors. Each element in a star gives off or takes up its own set of colors, and those sets of colors are different for stars at different temperatures. Astronomers use photographs of a spectrum to determine the elements in a star and the star's temperature.

The sun's spectrum is shown in *Figure 25-4*. Studies of more detailed photographs show that it is mainly hydrogen. The sun also contains helium and small amounts of many other elements. The spectrum shows over seventy elements.

All stars have gases above their visible surfaces, but only the sun is close enough for us to observe these gases directly. About once a year, the moon passes directly between the earth and the sun. This event, called a total solar eclipse, allows us to see the outermost layers of the sun. The sky becomes dark during an eclipse, even though it is day. As you see in the picture, a halo of sunlight becomes visible around the dark, back side of the moon. The halo is the outermost layer of the sun. This layer, called the **corona**, is normally fainter than the daylight sky. For this reason, the corona can be seen clearly only when an eclipse darkens the sky. During an eclipse, astronomers study the corona to determine its shape and how the gas in it moves. Astronomers also want to find out why it is so hot—2 000 000° C.

Studying Other Radiation from the Stars

All stars give off radiation of all types, but each star gives off most of its radiation in one part of the spectrum. The sun gives off most of its radiation in the visible part.

Figure 25-4 This drawing was made by the first scientist to spread out the sun's spectrum in a way that showed the dark lines caused by the elements in the sun's atmosphere.

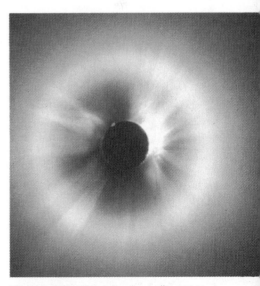

Figure 25-5 A total solar eclipse, showing the solar corona

Figure 25-6 The control room of a spacecraft that is used to make ultraviolet observations of stars. An ultraviolet spectrum of a star is on the screen.

Slightly hotter stars give off most of their radiation in the ultraviolet part. The hottest stars give off more X rays and gamma rays. Especially hot parts of the sun, like the corona, also give off X rays and gamma rays.

X rays and gamma rays do not pass through the earth's atmosphere. Therefore, they can be studied only from spacecraft. Most ultraviolet rays from objects in outer space can also be studied only from above the atmosphere. Look at the photograph showing the control room of a satellite that makes ultraviolet observations. The image on the large television screen is made by ultraviolet radiation from the outer part of a star. These studies tell us new facts about the outer parts of stars that cannot be learned with ordinary light.

Stars cooler than the sun give off more infrared than visible radiation. Still cooler objects, like dust in space, also give off mostly infrared radiation. Since some of these cooler objects are stars that are just forming, studies of the infrared part of the spectrum tell us about the birth of stars. *Figure 25-7* shows an infrared view of the constellation in Orion. It shows mainly glowing dust. If we want to study the dust between the stars, we are better off observing infrared radiation.

Radio waves have longer wavelengths than infrared. On the earth, radio waves bring us television pictures and sound. But hot gases in space make radio waves naturally. Radio telescopes collect and focus these waves. Astronomers use the data to find out about some of the hottest regions in space.

Soon astronomers hope to study radiation from the universe with the first large telescope in space—the *Hubble Space Telescope*. This telescope should "see" seven times more clearly than any telescope on the earth. It will send back images in the ultraviolet and the visible parts of the spectrum.

Section Review

1. What is the role of gravity in forming a star?
2. Where does the energy of a star come from?
3. What can we learn from a star's spectrum?
4. Why do astronomers study other types of radiation besides visible light?

Challenge: In some very hot stars, three helium-4 nuclei combine one at a time to make carbon-12. Draw a diagram to show how this might happen.

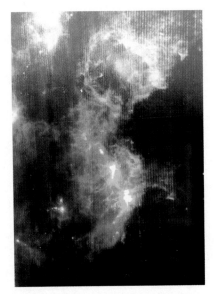

Figure 25-7 The constellation Orion, observed with the *Infrared Astronomical Satellite*

Using a Spectroscope

Purpose

To make a device for viewing a spectrum

Materials

- 2-cm square of clear diffraction grating
- paper towel tube
- black construction paper
- clear tape
- sharp blade or knife
- ruler
- scissors
- fluorescent lamp
- ordinary lamp
- colored pencils

Procedure and Observations

1. Trace the open end of the tube on construction paper. Repeat the procedure.
2. Draw a circle 2 cm larger in diameter around each of the tracings. Cut out the two larger circles.
3. Make several cuts between the bigger circles and the smaller ones, as in **a**.

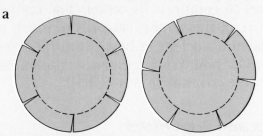

a

4. Use the knife to cut a slit about 2 cm x 1 mm in the center of one disk.
5. Place the disk over one end of the tube and tape the flaps to the tube, as shown in **b**.

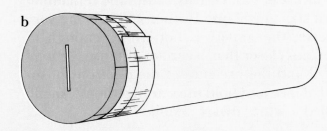

b

6. Cut a 1-cm square window in the other disk. Tape the diffraction grating over the opening, as in **c**.
7. Darken the room.

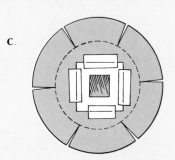

c

8. Hold the disk with the diffraction grating over the open end of the tube. Look through the grating and line up the slit with a light source so that the light will strike the grating. *CAUTION: Do not look directly toward the sun through your spectroscope. You could seriously damage your eyes.*
9. Rotate the disk until you see a clear spectrum. Tape the disk in this position. You have made a spectroscope.
10. Look through your spectroscope with the slit pointed toward an ordinary light bulb. You should see at least one spectrum.
11. Sketch what you see with colored pencils.
12. Look through your spectroscope at a fluorescent lamp and sketch what you see.

Analysis and Conclusions

1. Contrast the spectrum of one bulb with that of the other.
2. How do you think a spectrum's colors help determine the elements that make up a star?

After completing this section you
will be able to

A. Explain how a star becomes a
red giant.
B. Compare white dwarfs and supernovas.
C. Describe neutron stars and pulsars.
D. Describe how black holes form.
E. Explain how astronomers might
detect a black hole.

25-2 Aging Stars

Red Giants

Stars go through different stages of "life." A star's life is a constant battle between gravity pulling inward and pressure pushing outward. For most of its life, neither gravity nor pressure wins.

A star gradually turns most of the hydrogen in its center into helium. When not enough hydrogen is left for fusion to continue, the pressure at the star's center decreases. Gravity becomes overpowering. As a result, the star begins to collapse.

As the star collapses, its matter is compressed. As a result, the hydrogen in the star's middle layers heats up. Fusion of this heated hydrogen begins. The energy produced causes the outer layers to expand. The star brightens as it gets bigger. However, the outer layers of gas cool as they expand, just as any gas would. As the temperature drops, the star gives off redder light. The star is a **red giant.** The star Betelgeuse in the constellation Orion, shown in *Figure 25-8* is a red giant. Even with your naked eye, you can see that Betelgeuse looks slightly redder than the other stars.

While the outer layers of a red giant expand and cool, gravity continues to compress its center. The temperature and pressure in the center increases so much that the fusion of helium nuclei can begin to form heavier elements, such as carbon. What happens to the star next depends mainly on how much mass it has.

Figure 25-8 The constellation Orion is one of the easiest to pick out in the sky because three bright stars in a row mark its belt. The star Betelgeuse in Orion's shoulder is a red giant.

White Dwarfs and Supernovas

A star's life story depends on how much mass it has. Stars with about as much mass as the sun, or with less mass, lose their outer layers after becoming red giants. *Figure 25-9* shows the Ring Nebula in the constellation Lyra. This nebula is one in which the central star has lost its outer layers of gas. Gravity causes the remaining part of such a star to collapse further and become very dense. However, the gravity is not strong enough to pack the electrons closer than a certain distance. Gravity pulling inward and the pressure of the electrons pushing outward balance and hold the star together. A small, faint star called a **white dwarf** results.

A white dwarf is a dead star. Fusion no longer occurs inside it. But it still has so much energy that cooling takes billions of years. In fact, the time a white dwarf needs to cool completely is thought to be longer than the estimated age of the universe! Therefore, astronomers believe all white dwarfs that formed in the universe are still shining.

Most stars are not alone in space. They have companions, and are called **double stars.** When a white dwarf has a red giant companion, some of the mass from the companion can fall onto the white dwarf. If enough extra mass piles up, the white dwarf's gravity becomes strong enough to overwhelm the pressure of electrons pushing outward. The white dwarf collapses, and it grows so hot that it completely burns up. When we see a place in the sky where a star grows millions of times brighter than it had been before, we are seeing a **supernova.** A supernova can grow bright in a few days and then take months to fade.

Stars that have more mass than the sun keep swelling after they become red giants. These stars are called **supergiants**. Fusion inside a supergiant produces the heavier elements up to iron. The star then explodes violently, as does the other type of supernova.

Figure 25-10a shows a supernova whose light reached us in 1987. It was the nearest supernova we have seen since the year 1604. This star became bright enough to see with the unaided eye. Elements heavier than iron are formed only in supernovas. The violent explosion spreads these heavy elements through space. The heavy elements that make up your body were formed in supernovas long ago.

Explore!

Find out why scientists are so excited about the supernova in the Large Magellanic Cloud in 1987. Where do you have to be to see the Large Magellanic Cloud?

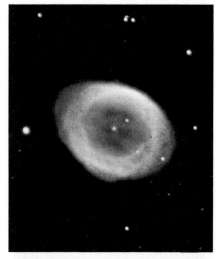

Figure 25-9 The Ring Nebula in the constellation Lyra shows gas lost by the bluish star in the center. This star is on its way to becoming a white dwarf. The sun will end in this way in perhaps 5 billion years.

Figure 25-10 a Light from this supernova reached us in 1987. **b** The arrow shows the star before it became a supernova.

Figure 25-11 The boxed region in the Crab Nebula (above) is shown in the series of photographs below.

Neutron Stars

Some supernovas leave behind part of the star. The push of the explosion and gravity cause this remainder to collapse. First consider what happens to the remainder of a supernova that contains less than three times the mass of the sun. Its strong gravity presses the electrons into the protons in the nuclei. Now the remainder consists only of neutrons. When neutrons are tightly packed, they push away from one another, just as electrons do in a white dwarf. Eventually, the outward pressure of the neutrons balances the inward pull of gravity, and a **neutron star** results.

Scientists had predicted that neutron stars should exist, but they did not know how to discover them. In 1968, Jocelyn Bell was studying the observations she had taken with a special type of radio telescope. She noticed that sometimes a signal appeared for a short time. Careful study showed that the signal was a series of pulses appearing regularly, about one per second. She soon found four of these **pulsars,** each giving off regular pulses of radio waves.

Scientists soon figured out that the pulsars are really neutron stars. Some neutron stars give off radio waves in a narrow beam. As the star turns, the beam may sweep past the earth. On the earth, we detect a pulse of radio waves each time the beam sweeps by, like flashes of light from a lighthouse.

A few neutron stars also give off pulses of visible light. The Crab Nebula contains such a star. The series of photographs in *Figure 25-11* takes place within 1/30 second, the duration of one pulse of the pulsar. You can see the pulsar turn on, fade a little, turn on again, and then turn off, all within 1/30 second. This star also gives off pulses of X rays.

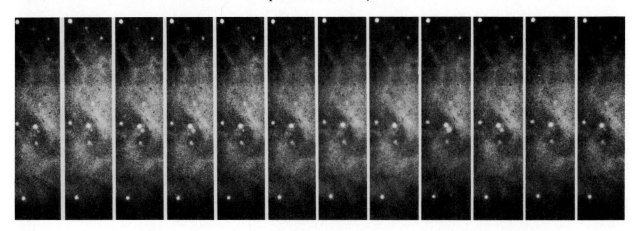

Now scientists can study neutron stars in other ways as well. Some neutron stars are parts of double stars. They are companions to other stars. When some of the gas from the other star falls on the neutron star, it gives off X rays that scientists can detect.

Black Holes

After the most massive stars explode as supernovas, sometimes a lot of mass is left. If three or more times the mass of the sun remains, even neutrons pressing on each other cannot resist gravity. The star continues to shrink and nothing can stop it.

Astronomers have calculated that the pull of gravity from such an object would be strong enough to keep everything, even light, from escaping the dying star. Because no light could escape, we could not see the object. It is called a **black hole.** A black hole is too small to be seen, even if it passes in front of glowing gas. A black hole that contains three times as much mass as the sun is only 18 kilometers across, the size of a city. If the earth were to be compressed enough to be a black hole, the whole earth would be only 1.7 centimeters across!

To understand black holes, astronomers study what happens when gravity is very strong. An object with a huge mass has strong gravity, and the space around the object is strongly curved. The curved space bends any light that passes by. In a similar way, a warped golf green makes the paths of golf balls bend, even though the golf balls have been putted straight.

Notice in *Figure 25-12* how starlight passing by the sun demonstrates this effect. The space around the sun is curved, and it bends the light from a star behind the sun. But when we look out from the earth, we usually assume that light is approaching in a straight line. The dotted line shows where the star appears to be. Black holes have much more mass than the sun. Astronomers think the space around black holes is so curved that it keeps light in the black hole.

Only one of the kinds of black holes forms as stars die. Other black holes can form from much larger masses of gas. Some black holes may contain millions of times as much mass as the sun. Black holes less massive than three times the mass of the sun will not form by their own gravity. But some may have formed if small amounts of matter were compressed enough.

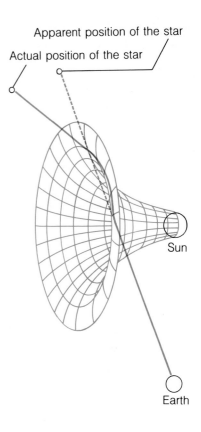

Apparent position of the star
Actual position of the star

Sun

Earth

Figure 25-12 If light's path toward us is changed by warped space, we think we see the object at a place different from its actual position.

Applying Science

The pulsar with the shortest known period spins 642 times each second. If you play its radio signals over a loudspeaker, it sounds like a note between E and E flat above high C on a piano. This pulsar is spinning so regularly, without slowing down, that scientists may use it as a clock. It seems to be more accurate than any other type of clock we have. It can keep time to billionths of billionths of a second over a few years.

Figure 25-13 The black hole is invisibly small in the middle of the disk that forms around it. The disk contains matter the black hole's gravity draws off from the companion star.

Detecting a Black Hole

A black hole may be invisible, but it does affect space around it. Astronomers try to detect black holes from these effects. Astronomers calculate that a black hole's gravity should make gas form a disk around it. This disk should heat up and give off X rays. But many types of objects give off X rays, so astronomers need a better way to detect black holes.

Thus, astronomers look for signs of a black hole's gravity. Imagine two dancers swinging each other. If one dancer were invisible, you could still see the other one moving back and forth. Similarly, astronomers look for stars that move back and forth as if they were being pulled by an invisible "dancer." If the dancer is fainter than a normal star but still has over three times the mass of the sun, it must be a black hole.

In the constellation Cygnus, astronomers have found a star that seems to be pulled by something invisible. Bursts of X rays come from this spot in the sky. Astronomers think the gravitational force of a black hole holds the star close and pulls off gas from the star's outer layers. As *Figure 25-13* shows, the gas forms a disk around the black hole, heats up, and gives off X rays before falling into the black hole. Astronomers know of two other objects that also seem to be black holes.

Section Review

1. When will the sun become a red giant?
2. What determines what happens to a star after it becomes a red giant?
3. How do scientists detect pulsars?
4. Explain the name "black hole."
5. How do astronomers look for black holes?

Challenge: What would happen to a spaceship if it approached a black hole?

25-3 The Milky Way Galaxy

Characteristics of the Milky Way Galaxy

Almost everything our eyes can see in the sky is a part of a group of stars, gas, and dust called the **Milky Way Galaxy.** Like other galaxies, this **galaxy** is a group of hundreds of billions of stars, plus gas and dust. The galaxy is so large that it takes light 100 000 years to travel from one side to the other.

From the earth, if we look in certain directions, we can see right out of the galaxy. We do not see many stars in these directions, and only a few clouds of gas and dust block our view. We see black sky with a few stars. But if we look toward or away from the center of our galaxy, we see many stars and much gas and dust. The stars, gas, and dust appear to us as the **Milky Way,** the hazy band of light shown in the photograph. The Milky Way is part of the Milky Way Galaxy. The shape of the galaxy and our position in it cause the view from one side of the galaxy to the other to look like a band, filled with stars, gas, and dust.

The sun and all its planets are part of the Milky Way Galaxy, too. In *Figure 25-15* you see two views of the Milky Way Galaxy. We cannot photograph our galaxy from this view because we are inside it. As the drawing shows, our sun is located in one of the spiral arms that unwind from the center of the Milky Way Galaxy.

Objectives

After completing this section you will be able to

A. Describe the sun's position in the Milky Way Galaxy.

B. Explain why astronomers think there might be a black hole in the center of the Milky Way Galaxy.

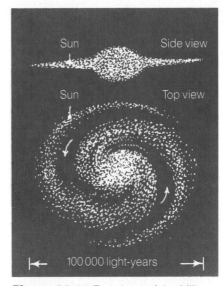

Figure 25-15 Two views of the Milky Way Galaxy, showing the sun's approximate location

Figure 25-14 From Earth, we see one part of the disk of our own Milky Way Galaxy stretch across the sky.

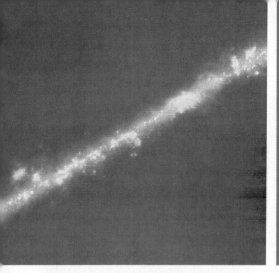

Figure 25-17 An infrared view of our galaxy from the *Infrared Astronomical Satellite* shows the dust.

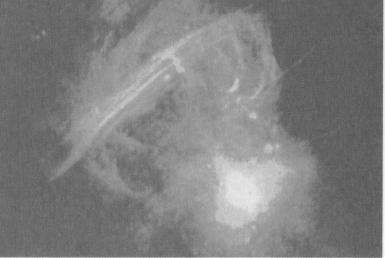

Figure 25-16 A detailed view of the innermost part of our galaxy in radio radiation

New Views of the Milky Way Galaxy

The Milky Way has so much gas and dust that we cannot see through them all the way to the center of our galaxy. But radio waves, infrared light, and X rays reach us from the center of our galaxy.

Radio waves penetrate the gas and dust. *Figure 25-16* reveals the complex structure of gas in the innermost part of our galaxy that radio observations found. So much energy comes from such a small region in the center of our galaxy that a giant black hole may be present there. Scientists know of no other way that so much energy can come from such a small region.

X rays also show the small central source in our galaxy that may be a black hole. Both X rays and radio waves show many other regions of hot gas in our galaxy. For example, they both show many remainders of supernova explosions.

The infrared view of our galaxy shows the dust best. In *Figure 25-17*, each of the colors represents a different infrared wavelength. The warmest material is shown as blue and the coldest material as red. Find the blobs of yellow and green that are giant clouds in which stars may be forming.

Section Review

1. Why does the Milky Way appear as a band of light?
2. Why do astronomers think a black hole may be in the center of our galaxy?

Challenge: Imagine that you were 1 mm tall and were in the middle of a dinner plate. What would you see in different directions? What if you were halfway out toward the edge?

Activity 25-2

Infrared Observations of the Milky Way Galaxy

Purpose

To detect radiation other than visible light

Materials

- prism
- thermometer
- slide projector
- variable voltage controller
- 5-cm × 5-cm piece of cardboard
- sharp knife for cutting cardboard
- two blocks of wood about 10 cm high
- masking tape
- white paper

Procedure and Observations

PART A
1. In the middle of the cardboard, cut a slit about 5 mm wide and 15 mm long.
2. Use the cardboard in place of a slide in the projector to make the projector project a horizontal slit of light.
3. Darken the room.
4. Let the light fall on a prism that is laid across the two blocks of wood to hold it off the table. Let the spectrum that results fall on the white paper taped up on a wall.
5. Notice the temperature reading of the thermometer before inserting it in the

beam of light. Record the temperature. Throughout the activity, hold the thermometer from its top so that your body heat does not register.
6. Insert the bulb of the thermometer into the blue part of the spectrum for 2 minutes. Record the temperature.
7. Take the thermometer out of the beam to let it cool down.
8. Insert the bulb of the thermometer into the red part of the spectrum for 2 minutes. Record the temperature.
9. Take the thermometer out of the beam to let it cool down.
10. Place the bulb of the thermometer slightly beyond the red end of the spectrum for 2 minutes. Record the temperature.
11. Repeat Step 10 slightly farther beyond the red.

PART B
1. Connect the projector to the variable voltage device.
2. As in part A, allow a slit of light to fall on the prism, making a spectrum on the screen.
3. Reduce the voltage slightly and notice the effect on the distribution of light in the colors of the spectrum.
4. Repeat Step 3 four times.

Analysis and Conclusions

1. How do you know that energy is present beyond the red in a spectrum?
2. How does the change in red light show what may be happening with infrared light as you vary the voltage?
3. Why is infrared light more useful than ultraviolet light for studying dust in the Milky Way Galaxy?

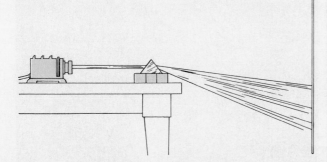

25-4 A Universe of Galaxies

Shapes of Galaxies

The stars we can see in the sky with just our eyes are part of the Milky Way Galaxy. But powerful telescopes have shown astronomers that all the stars in the universe are grouped into galaxies. Galaxies are the basic building blocks of the universe.

Galaxies differ in shape. The hardest galaxy of all to study is our own, because we cannot see it from outside. Studying our galaxy is like solving a maze while standing inside it. It is much easier to solve a maze if you can look down at it. Still, astronomers think that our galaxy has a central region with arms coming out from it like a pinwheel. They think our galaxy looks like the one in *Figure 25-18a*. Galaxies like this are **spiral galaxies.**

Galaxies are too far away for us to move around them. We can see each galaxy at only one angle. But we can see millions of galaxies, so we have many different examples at different angles. *Figure 25-18b* shows a spiral galaxy seen edge-on. You can see a bulge at its center and a flat disk. Notice the dark disk of dust across the middle of its bright disk of stars.

Figure 25-18a Spiral galaxy, seen face-on **b** Spiral galaxy, seen edge-on

Some galaxies look like ellipses, and they show no spiral structure. They are called **elliptical galaxies**. Elliptical galaxies, like the one in *Figure 25-19*, contain only old stars. Spiral galaxies, on the other hand, contain stars of all ages.

The elliptical galaxy shown is not quite regular. You can see a jet of matter going off to one side. A galaxy that is not quite regular is a **peculiar galaxy**. Therefore, the galaxy pictured in *Figure 25-19* is classified as a peculiar elliptical galaxy.

Another peculiar galaxy appears in *Figure 25-20a*. This galaxy looks more like a spiral galaxy in which an explosion has taken place. It is thus a peculiar spiral galaxy. Each galaxy in the sky has its own individual appearance. Just as you can tell individual people apart, astronomers can tell individual galaxies apart.

Some galaxies show no regular shape at all. The Small Magellanic Cloud is an example of such an **irregular galaxy**. The Small Magellanic Cloud, shown in *Figure 25-20b*, is a satellite galaxy of our own Milky Way Galaxy. It is much smaller than our galaxy. The Small Magellanic Cloud is never visible in the sky in the United States. Instead, you have to go to the southern hemisphere in order to see it.

Figure 25-19 The peculiar elliptical galaxy M87

Figure 25-20a The peculiar spiral galaxy M82 **b** An irregular galaxy

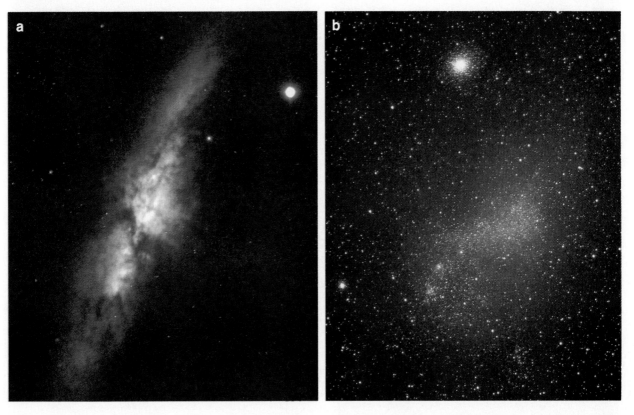

Explore!

In a star atlas or field guide, find a chart showing the Virgo Cluster of galaxies. How large a region of the sky in degrees does it cover from side to side?

Clusters of Galaxies

Just as stars have companions, most galaxies have companions, too. Our own Milky Way Galaxy has the Large Magellanic Cloud and the Small Magellanic Cloud as close companions. They are so close to us that people in the southern hemisphere can see them with unaided eyes. The crew of Magellan's around-the-world voyage discovered them hundreds of years ago when they got far enough south. *Figure 25-21* shows how these galaxies appear in the sky.

Our Milky Way Galaxy is also accompanied by two other spiral galaxies and about two dozen elliptical galaxies. These galaxies together are known as the **Local Group.** The Local Group is an outlying part of a larger cluster of galaxies. The cluster we belong to is known as the Virgo Cluster because most of the galaxies appear to us in the constellation Virgo. Even though most of the galaxies in the Virgo Cluster are very distant, the Virgo Cluster is so large and is close enough that its members are found in a large part of the sky. In fact, they cover too wide a range of sky to photograph on one piece of film.

Figure 25-21 The Magellanic Clouds can be seen from the southern hemisphere of the earth. They are neighbors of our Milky Way Galaxy and are part of the Local Group.

In *Figure 25-22* you see a photograph of a more distant cluster of galaxies. Like most clusters, this cluster shows a variety of types of galaxies. Some are spiral and some are elliptical. As astronomers develop better ways of finding the distances to galaxies quickly, they are better able to study clusters of galaxies.

Figure 25-22 A cluster of galaxies in the constellation Fornax

Section Review

1. How do galaxies differ in shape?
2. To what cluster of galaxies do we belong?

Challenge: Elliptical galaxies contain older, cooler stars than do spiral galaxies. Which type of galaxy appears redder?

Have You Heard?

Clusters of galaxies may together act as even greater clusters. Such a cluster of clusters is beyond the Virgo Cluster, pulling it and us by its strong gravity.

People and Science

Cecilia Payne-Gaposchkin, Astronomer

We know today that the sun and other stars consist largely of hydrogen and that the intense heat of fusion converts some of the hydrogen into helium. But we have not always known this fact. Our knowledge came as a result of research by Cecilia Payne-Gaposchkin when she was a graduate student at Harvard University in 1925.

Until then it was believed that the sun and all bodies in the heavens consisted of the same elements as the earth and that they occurred in roughly the same proportions as on earth. This was based on studies of their spectra. It was assumed also that the earth was formed from the sun.

Using the quantum theory and statistical mechanics, Cecilia arrived at the surprising result that stellar atmospheres appeared to consist primarily of hydrogen and helium. A prominent astronomer reviewed her report and told her that the results she had arrived at were "clearly impossible." Cecilia was using the information in a dissertation for her Ph.D. degree, and so to avoid jeopardizing getting the degree, she modified the result in her writing. She was convinced, however, that her results were accurate and after her degree was granted, she pursued her findings.

Within five years, astronomers everywhere were agreeing, and it was this basic work that became the core for today's understanding that hydrogen and helium are the elements from which heavier elements are synthesized in the stars. The other elements occur, but they are in small and mainly fractional percentages.

Plotting Points to Make a Model of the Milky Way

The Milky Way contains so much dust that we see about equally well in all directions in the disk of our galaxy, either toward or away from the center of our galaxy. Until the 1920s, scientists thought we were in the center of our galaxy. Then the American astronomer Harlow Shapley figured out how to measure the distances to a certain type of cluster of stars. He plotted their distances and directions, and discovered that they formed a circle about some distant point. He concluded that the center of our galaxy must be that point. The following data points were derived from Shapley's measurements.

(5,1) (6,2) (−1,9) (14,2) (14,4) (18,3)
(14,−4) (6,−5) (−2,−6) (6,12) (10,10)
(6,7) (7,5) (4,4) (15,5) (14,7) (12,7)

Plot the points, then use your graph to answer the questions that follow. Make the x-axis and y-axis of your graph intersect near the center of your paper. Label the point of intersection as 0,0. Label both positive and negative numbers on each axis. (Remember that the first number in each pair of coordinates is measured along the x-axis and the second number is measured along the y-axis.)

1. Look at the points on your graph. Use a blue pencil to mark where you *think* the center of the galaxy would be.

2. Find the actual center of the points you graphed by finding the average value of the x, y-coordinates. Round each number to the nearest whole number. Plot this point in red.

3. On this graph, the sun would be at (0,0). Use your graph to determine the relative position of the sun in the galaxy.

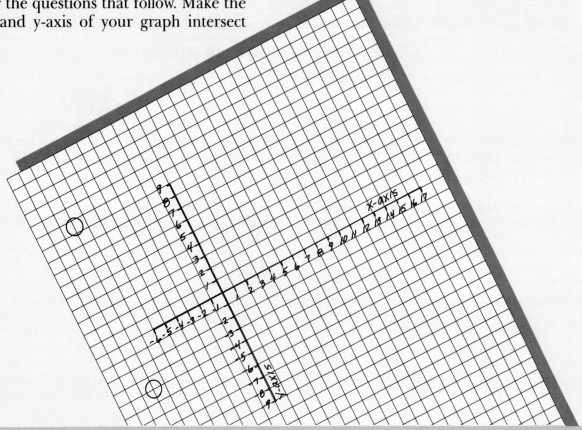

✓ Summary

25-1 The Development of Stars

A. Stars form as gravity draws gas and dust together, and they become hotter as they are compressed further by gravity.

B. Energy that stars give off as light is produced by nuclear fusion.

C. One important way in which astronomers study a star is to break up its light into a spectrum of colors.

D. Astronomers also analyze radiation in the form of infrared, ultraviolet, and X rays.

25-2 Aging Stars

A. A red giant is formed after a star's center runs out of hydrogen for fusion, the star is compressed as a result of gravity, and the hydrogen in the star's middle layers heats up enough to undergo fusion.

B. A white dwarf is a small, faint, dead star, but it can become one kind of supernova if it gains enough mass from a companion star.

C. A neutron star consists of tightly packed neutrons, and as the star rotates it gives off energy in beams that may be detected on the earth as periodic pulses.

D. A black hole forms when a supernova retains three or more times the mass of the sun.

E. Scientists may be able to detect a black hole by its effect on a nearby star.

25-3 The Milky Way Galaxy

A. Our sun is located in one of the spiral arms of the Milky Way Galaxy.

B. Scientists think that there might be a black hole at the center of the Milky Way Galaxy, because they do not know how so much energy can come from such a small region otherwise.

25-4 A Universe of Galaxies

A. Most galaxies are classified by their shapes.

B. The Milky Way Galaxy is part of a large cluster of galaxies known as the Virgo Cluster.

Vocabulary

For each of the following terms, write a sentence that uses the term correctly.

black hole	galaxy	nebula	spiral galaxy
corona	irregular galaxy	neutron star	supergiant
double star	Local Group	peculiar galaxy	supernova
dwarf	Milky Way	pulsar	white dwarf
elliptical galaxy	Milky Way Galaxy	red giant	

Check Your Knowledge

Part I: Matching Match the definition in Column I with the correct term in Column II.

Column I
1. a huge cloud of gas and dust
2. our sun is this type of star
3. the outermost layer of the sun
4. a small, faint, dead star
5. two companion stars
6. no light can escape from this object
7. a type of galaxy that contains only old stars
8. a hazy band of light that is seen in the sky at night
9. the Milky Way Galaxy is of this type
10. a type of galaxy with no regular shape

Column II
a. black hole
b. corona
c. double star
d. dwarf
e. elliptical galaxy
f. irregular galaxy
g. Milky Way
h. nebula
i. red giant
j. spiral galaxy
k. white dwarf

Part II: Multiple Choice Choose the letter of the best answer.
11. When stars form in nebulas, the gas and dust are drawn together by (a) nuclear fusion. (b) a black hole. (c) electrical attraction. (d) gravity.
12. The element present in greatest amount in the sun is (a) helium. (b) carbon. (c) hydrogen. (d) nitrogen.
13. The sun gives off most of its radiation in what part of the spectrum? (a) visible (b) ultraviolet (c) infrared (d) X-ray
14. Objects in space that are cooler than the sun give off most of their radiation in what part of the spectrum? (a) visible (b) ultraviolet (c) infrared (d) X-ray
15. Our sun will probably wind up as a (a) white dwarf. (b) black hole. (c) supergiant. (d) supernova.
16. Pulsars are (a) neutron stars. (b) white dwarfs. (c) red giants. (d) supergiants.
17. An object from which light cannot escape is a (a) black hole. (b) supernova. (c) neutron star. (d) white dwarf.
18. A group of hundreds of billions of stars, plus gas and dust, is called a (a) nebula. (b) corona. (c) galaxy. (d) supergiant.
19. Scientists believe that the energy source at the center of our galaxy may be a (a) supernova. (b) supergiant. (a) white dwarf. (d) black hole.
20. The view of our galaxy that shows the dust best is in what part of the spectrum? (a) ultraviolet (b) infrared (c) visible (d) X-ray

Part III: Completion Write the word or words that complete the sentence correctly.
21. Stars get the energy to shine from _____.
22. Astronomers can study a star by breaking up its light into a _____ of colors.
23. A star gradually turns most of the hydrogen in its center into _____.
24. Elements heavier than iron are formed only in _____.
25. An outlying part of a large cluster of galaxies includes our Milky Way Galaxy and is known as the _____.

Check Your Understanding

1. Explain how conditions of gravity and pressure change during a star's lifetime.
2. How would studying the sun help us learn about other stars?
3. How does mass affect the length of a star's lifetime?
4. Compare a neutron star and a black hole.
5. Can we see farther in our galaxy when we look up out of the Milky Way or when we try to look through the Milky Way? Explain.
6. Why are there no photographs of the Milky Way Galaxy showing the sun in one of its spiral arms?

 Apply Your Knowledge

1. Individual stars can live for billions of years, so astronomers cannot observe any star from its birth to its death. How, then, can astronomers learn about the life history of stars?
2. Why will the sun not become a pulsar?
3. Does the mass of a black hole that results from a collapsed star tend to increase or decrease? Why?
4. One type of supernova comes only from massive stars, which have short lifetimes. Why do we not find this type of supernova in elliptical galaxies?

 Extend Your Knowledge

Research/Projects

1. Visit a planetarium in your area and attend its sky show. Report on what you learn.
2. On a clear night, observe the stars with a pair of binoculars for at least half an hour. Note the differences in color and brightness among the stars and how they move across the sky. If Orion is visible, report on the appearance of Betelgeuse and of the nebula below the left star in Orion's belt.
3. Obtain a map of the night sky for the current time of the year and find as many constellations and planets as you can. By observing the night sky once a week, you can see the movement of some planets among the stars.

Readings

Berger, Melvin. *Bright Stars, Red Giants and White Dwarfs*. Putnam, 1983. Describes stages in the life cycle of stars and discusses theories about the future of the universe.

Gallant, Roy A. *101 Questions and Answers About the Universe*. Macmillan, 1984. Answers to questions asked by students visiting a planetarium. An ideal resource for astronomy study.

Pasachoff, Jay M. *First Guide to Astronomy*. Houghton, 1988. A field guide that both students and adults who are just beginning to learn astronomy will find very useful and informative.

CHAPTER 26
The Large and the Small

The giant clouds of gas in this photograph make up the spiral arms of the Andromeda galaxy. The two smaller oval objects just above and below Andromeda are two companion galaxies. Many new methods of looking at the universe are giving us a more complete view of what it is like.

Organizing Your Study Skills The outline below will help you see how the chapter is organized and what you should learn as you read.

I. **Section 26-1: Galaxies and Our Understanding of the Universe**
   A. What do we learn from the motion of galaxies?
   B. What is a Doppler redshift?
   C. How is the universe like a sponge?

II. **Section 26-2: Quasars and Other Active Galaxies**
   A. What is a quasar?
   B. What is a possible source for quasars' energy?
   C. What is a radio galaxy?
   D. What is an X-ray galaxy?
   E. What is special about an infrared galaxy?

III. **Section 26-3: Theories About the Universe**
   A. What is the big bang theory?
   B. What is the inflationary universe?
   C. Why do astronomers think the universe has a large amount of invisible mass?
   D. What are three possibilities for the future of the universe?

IV. **Section 26-4: Whisper from Space**
   A. What is the background radiation and how does it support the big bang theory?
   B. What does the background radiation tell us about the universe?

Objectives

After completing this section you will be able to

A. Describe what the motion of galaxies teaches us about the universe.

B. Explain how astronomers use the Doppler effect to study the universe.

C. Describe how matter is spread through the universe.

Explore!

A nearby galaxy is moving away from us at a velocity of 1000 km/s. If you could travel at the same rate, how long would it take you to reach California from New York?

Figure 26-1 The universe expands, carrying galaxies outward at an increasing rate, just as raisin bread dough expands, carrying raisins away from each other.

26-1 Galaxies and Our Understanding of the Universe

The Motion of Galaxies

What does the picture of raisin-bread dough have to do with physical science? Astronomers have developed a model of the universe that compares galaxies to the raisins in bread dough that is rising.

Imagine that you are on a raisin in some bread dough that is bigger than your city. As the dough rises, it carries the raisins with it in all directions. The raisins stay the same size, but the dough expands. From your raisin, you can see this expansion in all directions.

You also can see that all the other raisins are moving away from you. The farther away a raisin is from you, the more dough there is to expand. Therefore, the farther the raisin, the faster it moves away.

In the universe, the galaxies are like the raisins and the space is like dough. The galaxies are moving away from us, but they are moving away from all the other galaxies as well. The farther a galaxy is from us, the faster it is moving away. The galaxies move away from us as they do because space is expanding in all directions. Thus, the motion of the galaxies shows us that the universe is expanding.

Figure 26-2 An astronomer at work

However, there are important differences between the universe and the raisin bread model. For example, even a large batch of dough has an edge. The universe, on the other hand, goes on forever without an edge.

Doppler Redshifts

How do scientists know that galaxies are moving away from us? They use the Doppler effect to observe galaxies' motions. Because of the Doppler effect you hear the pitch of a motorcycle's engine change as the motorcycle passes you. Just as sound waves show the Doppler effect, so do all other waves, including light. Light waves show the Doppler effect by changing wavelength. Light from an object moving away from us shifts to longer wavelengths. Scientists call this change a **redshift.** The term "redshift" means a shift to longer wavelengths because red is at the longest optical wavelength. Even for infrared and radio waves, which have longer wavelengths than red, the term "redshift" means a shift to longer wavelengths. The greater the redshift, the faster the source is moving.

In 1929, the American astronomer Edwin Hubble reported that all the distant galaxies show redshifts. He proposed that these galaxies must all be moving away from us. Hubble also found that the farther away a galaxy is, the greater its redshift, and the faster it is moving away from us. Astronomers now are able to study galaxies much farther away than Hubble could. They find that Hubble's conclusions are still true.

In the photograph, the astronomer is holding a special picture of the light from a distant galaxy. The smear of light is the galaxy's spectrum.

Applying Science

Optical fibers are used to measure the spectra of several galaxies at the same time. Usually the light from only one galaxy can have its spectrum taken at a time. In some cases, astronomers make special metal plates that hold the ends of two dozen optical fibers at the places where the images of two galaxies fall. The optical fibers can be bent to bring the light to the spectrograph so that the spectra of all the galaxies can be measured at the same time. Because the fibers are "optical," one of the devices is called a "fiber optopus."

Closeups of the spectra of three galaxies are shown below. Astronomers can easily "read" the spectra from left to right. If you look closely, you can see two dark breaks in the spectra. The arrows below the lines across show how much they are shifted from where they would appear if the galaxies were not moving. The farthest galaxy has the greatest redshift.

At the left of the spectra, you can see pictures of the galaxies at the same scale. The farthest one appears smallest because it is at such a great distance from the earth. Studies of the Doppler effect in the light of distant galaxies provide evidence that the universe is expanding.

The Universe Is Like a Sponge

How do astronomers make a map of the universe? They cannot go outside the universe to get a top view. Actually, they look in many directions. For each direction, they find the distances to all the objects they can. When they plot the distances and directions on a graph, they have a three-dimensional view of the universe.

Maps of the universe are very hard to make. To find the distance to each distant galaxy, astronomers must study its spectrum. Until a few years ago, the spectrum had to be photographed. Making a single photograph of a faint galaxy often took all night.

Figure 26-3 Spectra for a member of a cluster of galaxies in Virgo, Ursa Major, and Hydra, respectively.

Member galaxy
of cluster in

Virgo

Ursa Major

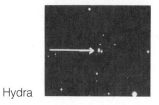

Hydra

Red shifts in
kilometers
per second

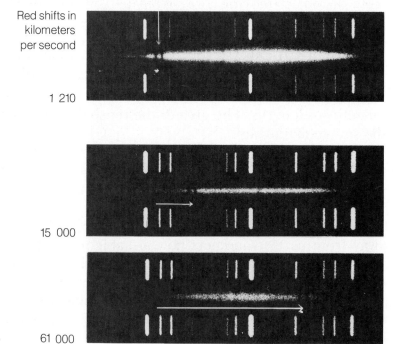

1 210

15 000

61 000

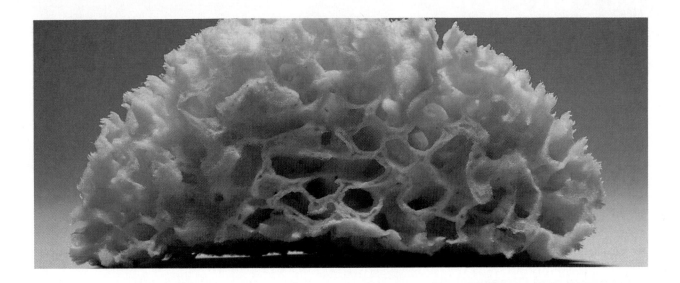

Figure 26-4 The most recent map of the universe resembles a giant sponge.

Recently, though, CCD's (charge-coupled devices) and other electronic devices have allowed astronomers like those in the photograph to make a spectrum of a faint galaxy in a few minutes. So astronomers can measure the redshifts of many more galaxies, and can plot many more points on a map of the universe.

The new maps of the universe show many features that astronomers had not expected to find. The clusters of galaxies seem to connect with each other. They make giant threads that stretch through the universe. In between the threads, giant empty spaces seem to contain no galaxies. We cannot be certain, though, that invisible matter does not exist there.

As a result of the new mapping, astronomers have a new picture of the universe. The universe seems to be like a giant sponge, such as the one shown, in which regions crowded with matter and regions with little matter are mixed together. The regions of matter are connected to each other. The regions of little matter are connected to each other as well. If we could switch the regions of sponge and holes, both the sponge and the holes would look about the same.

Section Review

1. Why do astronomers think the universe is expanding?
2. What is a redshift?
3. Describe the most recent model of the universe.

Challenge: What would a blueshift in a galaxy's light show?

Activity 26-1

The Expanding Universe

Purpose

To demonstrate how the universe expands

Materials

- balloon (not red or black)
- red marker pen
- black marker pen
- metric tape measure

Procedure and Observations

1. Copy the table shown in **a**.
2. Ask your partner to blow up a balloon just enough to make it taut, and to hold it closed. Measure the balloon's diameter.
3. To represent the galaxies, draw red dots about 2 cm apart all over the balloon.
4. Circle one dot with the black marker.
5. Choose 6 other dots, some close and some far away from the circled dot. Number the dots 1 through 6, as shown in **b**.

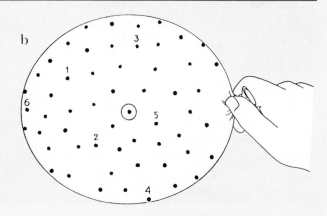

b

a

6. Measure the distance from the circled dot to the 6 numbered dots. Record the distances in Column 2 of the table.
7. Ask your partner to blow into the balloon until the diameter is doubled and hold the balloon's end closed.
8. Measure the distances from the circled dot to the 6 numbered dots again. Record these distances in Column 3 of the table.
9. Subtract the numbers in Column 2 from those in Column 3. Record your answers in Column 4.
10. Divide the numbers in Column 3 by the numbers in Column 2. Record your answers in Column 5.

Analysis and Conclusions

1. Blowing up the balloon represents the expansion of the universe. Explain how the changes in distances between galaxies depend on how far apart the galaxies were originally. (Compare the numbers in Columns 2 and 4 of your table.)
2. Does the factor by which the distances between galaxies changed also depend on how far apart the galaxies were originally? (Compare the numbers in Columns 2 and 5 of your table.) Explain your answer.

Data Table

Dot No.	Original Distances	Distances After Expansion	Change in Distances	Factor by which the Distances Changed
1				
2				
3				
4				
5				
6				

26-2 Quasars and Other Active Galaxies

The Most Distant Objects in the Universe

Our galaxy is not expanding, so the stars in our galaxy have no large redshifts. Thus, astronomers were surprised in 1963 to discover objects that had huge redshifts, yet looked like stars in our galaxy. These objects gave off large amounts of radio waves. The photograph shows the first of these sources to be discovered. In addition to the round part of its image, it has a jet of matter going off it.

On careful inspection, such objects do not look completely stellar—or like stars—because their images seem fuzzy. Thus, astronomers described them as quasistellar objects, because "quasi-" means "almost like" or "partly like." These bright objects with huge redshifts are called **quasars,** which stands for quasistellar radio sources. Later, other quasars were discovered with similarly large redshifts, but they did not all give off radio signals.

Some of the quasars have the largest redshifts known. For this reason, they are probably the most distant objects in the universe. Some quasars are so far away that their light takes 15 billion years to reach us. This means that the light we are seeing now left the quasars 15 billion years ago. The universe has changed a lot since then. The quasars help us look back in time to those early days of the universe.

New ways of observing are sensitive enough to show that quasars are in the midst of galaxies whose arms are too faint to be seen easily. Perhaps quasars are early stages of galaxies.

Objectives

After completing this section you will be able to

A. Explain what quasars are.
B. Describe a possible source for quasars' energy.
C. Explain what radio galaxies are.
D. Explain what X-ray galaxies are.
E. Explain what is special about infrared galaxies.

Explore!

Light travels 9.6×10^{12} kilometers per year. Multiply this number by 15 billion (15×10^9) years to find out the distance to a quasar such as the one mentioned on this page. If you could go a billion kilometers per hour, how long would you take to go this distance?

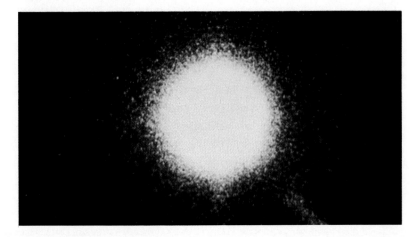

Figure 26-5 One of the nearest quasars, with its jet

Figure 26-6 A long X-ray exposure from a satellite showed not only the nearby quasar 3C 273 but also a more distant quasar.

Where Quasars Get Their Energy

Astronomers study quasars by measuring the light, radio waves, and X rays they give off. *Figure 26-6* shows an X-ray view of the same quasar whose visible-light image you saw on page 609. On the image, a new quasar was discovered! Astronomers had to take its spectrum to prove that it was a quasar. Only when they saw that it had a huge redshift did they know it was a quasar.

Even though quasars are far away, astronomers can easily detect many with telescopes. Therefore, quasars must give off amazing amounts of energy. No one knows for certain where all the energy comes from. Most astronomers think the energy comes from a giant black hole in the middle of each quasar. According to this theory, as the black hole draws surrounding matter toward it, the matter heats up. What we observe is the energy the matter gives off before the black hole swallows it.

A few quasars in the sky appear as a pair or trio. Astronomers are excited to think that the two or three images may actually be of the same quasar. A huge mass between the quasar and us could be bending the quasar's light around it. The light reaches us from slightly different angles in the sky, so it appears to come from slightly different directions, as *Figure 26-7 a* and *b* show.

In *a*, you see the two images of the quasar as they appear in the sky. In *b*, the right image has been subtracted from the left image. The image remaining, shown at the lower left, must be from the mass that is bending the light. In this way, astronomers are finding these masses, known as gravitational lenses.

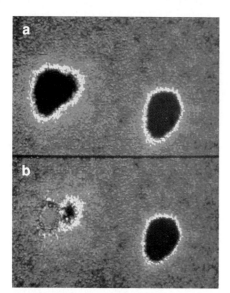

Figure 26-7 a You see what looks like two nearby quasars but what is probably two images of a single quasar. **b** The result of subtracting the right image from the left image is shown at the lower left, where you see the object that forms the gravitational lens that is bending the quasar's light. The image of the top right galaxy is repeated at bottom right.

Radio Studies Show New Views of Galaxies

When scientists began using radio waves to map the sky, they discovered that the brightest radio objects were usually in different places than the brightest optical objects. Some of these radio objects are quasars and other active galaxies. For many years, they could only measure the strengths of radio sources but could not see their shapes. Because radio waves are so much longer than light waves, astronomers need bigger radio telescopes than optical telescopes to see the same amount of detail.

In the last decade, astronomers have been able to use groups of telescopes linked together. Used in this way, each group operates as one large radio telescope. Scientists can use such a group to measure the shapes of radio sources. *Figure 26-8* shows the biggest group of radio telescopes—the Very Large Array. This set of 27 radio telescopes is in New Mexico.

In our visible sky, no galaxy is as bright as a star. By contrast, some galaxies are among the brightest radio sources in the sky. Also, the galaxies, when seen in radio waves, are much bigger than the same galaxies when seen in light. *Figure 26-9a* shows how a galaxy gives off most of its radio waves from two regions on opposite sides of its center. The visible galaxy falls within the red spot at its center. The colors were added by a computer at the Very Large Array to show the brightness of the radio waves. The long, straight regions are made of gas that has been thrown off the central part of the galaxy.

Other observations show that, in some galaxies, the long, straight regions are swept back, as in *Figure 26-9b*. Scientists think that the gas was swept back when it ran into other gas as the galaxy moved through a cluster of galaxies.

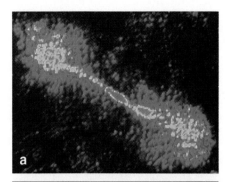
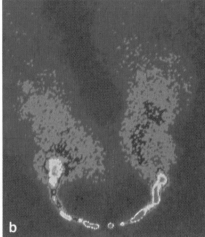

Figure 26-9 a Radio waves from this galaxy come from two regions on opposite sides of the image of the galaxy in visible light. **b** In this galaxy, the regions of gas are swept back.

Figure 26-8 The Very Large Array in New Mexico contains 27 telescopes that can be spread out in a Y-shape 27 kilometers across.

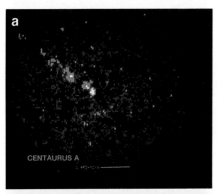

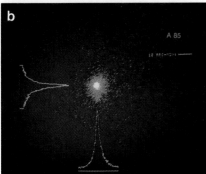

Figure 26-11 a Centaurus X-1 is the nearest of the active galaxies. It has a jet that emits X rays. **b** In younger clusters of galaxies, the X rays come from the central region of the cluster.

X-Ray Studies of Galaxies

X rays do not pass through the earth's atmosphere. However, telescopes in satellites above our atmosphere can study the X rays from space. X rays come from regions that are very hot or in which motions are very violent. A European X-ray satellite sent back the picture in *Figure 26-10*. It shows X rays coming from hot regions along our Milky Way. In some nearby galaxies, the American X-ray satellite known as the *Einstein Observatory* showed that all the X rays come from stars, rather than from hot gas spread out between the stars. Normal galaxies do not give off much energy in the form of X rays.

On the other hand, active galaxies are hundreds of times as strong in radio waves and X rays as normal galaxies. *Figure 26-11a* shows an X-ray image of the nearest of the active galaxies. It shows X rays coming from a jet of gas that is being ejected from the galaxy's center. Radio astronomy studies also show the jet.

X-ray studies are especially good for showing the very hot gas that is between the galaxies in a cluster of galaxies. The temperature of this gas is 100 million degrees Celsius. In some clusters of galaxies, as *Figure 26-11b* shows, the X rays are centered in the middle of the cluster. In other clusters of galaxies, the X rays are more spread out. Astronomers think that in younger clusters, the gas giving off X rays is still near the galaxies that gave it off. In time, the gas spreads out to be more uniform through a cluster.

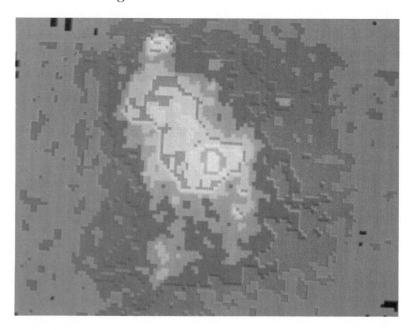

Figure 26-10 A ridge of gas emitting X rays lies along the Milky Way

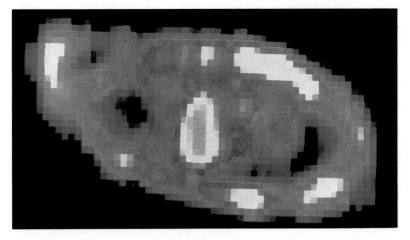

Figure 26-12 The bright yellow regions show the strongest infrared radiation in this view of the Andromeda Galaxy, a nearby spiral galaxy like our own Milky Way Galaxy.

Infrared Galaxies Show Stars in Formation

Scientists have long known that infrared shows dust that surrounds stars that are being born. When the international *Infrared Astronomical Satellite* (IRAS) was able to send back infrared images in 1983, the pictures showed where in galaxies star formation was going on. In the picture of the nearby Andromeda Galaxy, the strongest infrared radiation is coming from the areas colored yellow. You can see that most stars are forming in a ring around the center.

Astronomers were surprised to find that very bright infrared radiation came from some regions of the sky in which they could not see any object in visible light. Some of these regions contain galaxies that are hundreds of times more powerful in the infrared than normal galaxies. Astronomers think that stars are forming in bursts in these "starburst galaxies."

Section Review

1. Why do astronomers think quasars are the most distant objects in the universe?
2. What is a likely source of a quasar's energy?
3. Compare the sizes and shapes of optical and radio galaxies.
4. How do X rays tell us the ages of clusters of galaxies?
5. In the Andromeda Galaxy, where are the regions where stars are forming?

Challenge: Sources of radiation grow fainter with the square of their distance from us. Suppose a quasar appears to be the same brightness as a star in our own galaxy. The star is 1000 light-years away, and the quasar is 10 billion light-years away. How much brighter is the quasar than the star?

Have You Heard?

The European Space Agency is planning Infrared Space Observatory (ISO) and NASA is planning Space Infrared Telescope Facility (SIRTF) for launch in the 1990s. They will carry more sensitive infrared telescopes than IRAS. (IRAS was a joint project of the United States, the United Kingdom, and the Netherlands.)

After completing this section you will be able to

A. Describe the big bang theory.
B. Describe the inflationary universe.
C. Explain why astronomers think the universe has a large amount of invisible mass.
D. Contrast three possibilities for the future of the universe.

26-3 Theories About the Universe

The Big Bang Theory

Throughout the ages, people have wondered how the universe formed, how old the universe is, and how the universe might end. We know that stars go through stages of life. Does the universe go through stages, too?

A galaxy's redshift helps astronomers figure out its speed. Because galaxies are moving away from each other, all the matter in the universe was close together at one time. Knowing how fast galaxies are now moving away, scientists can calculate how long the universe has been expanding. They have concluded that all the matter in the galaxy was once packed together in a hot, dense mass. Ten to twenty billion years ago, the matter exploded in a big bang. This explosion had no center. It took place everywhere at the same time, because the hot, dense matter filled the universe, as shown in *Figure 26-13a.*

The details of the **big bang theory** are worked out with the mathematics of Einstein's theories. The results show that this giant explosion sent matter and strong radiation in all directions. About one minute after the big bang, most of the radiation changed into matter. The nuclei of the lightest elements, such as hydrogen and helium, probably were formed at this time.

Millions of years later, galaxies formed from this matter, as *b* indicates. As the galaxies developed over the past billions of years, they continued to speed through space in all directions, as in *c.*

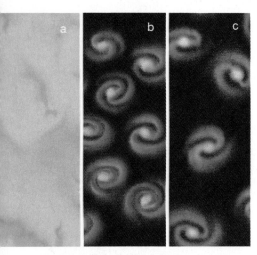

Figure 26-13 a The universe was originally very hot and dense. **b** Galaxies eventually formed. **c** The galaxies continue to move away from each other even now.

The Universe Inflated

Matter in our universe today appears to be in clumps, which are connected together and are separated by regions of similar size in which there is little or no matter. Why is the universe so uniform? Why do we see alternating regions of matter and no matter in every direction? Scientists are searching for answers to questions such as these.

The **inflationary universe theory** improves on older versions of the big bang theory. According to this theory, the universe grew very much bigger in a tiny fraction of a second during the first second of time.

The steep line in the graph shows the rapid expansion. The universe grew so much larger that small, uniform regions spread out rapidly into very big regions. Though galaxies and clusters of galaxies have formed since, we still see about as many galaxies and clusters of galaxies in all directions. In other words, the universe looks more or less uniform.

Invisible Mass in Galaxies

The photograph shows a cluster of galaxies. All the objects that are not round are galaxies.

Astronomers determine how much mass a cluster of galaxies has by studying the motion of each galaxy in the cluster. If each galaxy moved rapidly enough, it would escape from the cluster. Since the cluster has not broken apart, it must have strong gravity to hold its galaxies together. Because strong gravity results from a large mass, the cluster must have a large mass.

Astronomers are surprised by the amount of mass in clusters of galaxies, because only a small part of this mass is visible. Astronomers do not know why the rest of the mass is invisible. They think some of it may be hidden in black holes. Some may be hidden in the form of particles that are very hard to detect. On earth, physicists are trying to create some of those particles to study. As scientists continue to experiment and to propose new theories, they are finding more and more links between the study of the universe as a whole and the study of the tiniest particles of matter.

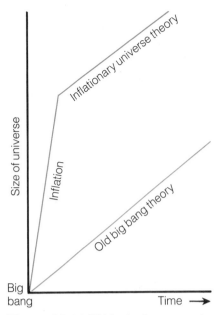

Figure 26-14 Within the first second after the big bang, the universe grew 10^{100} times bigger.

Figure 26-15 A cluster of galaxies. Studying the motions of the galaxies in such a cluster has shown that most of the matter in the universe is invisible.

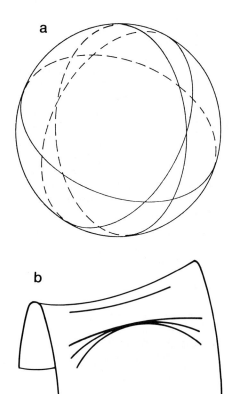

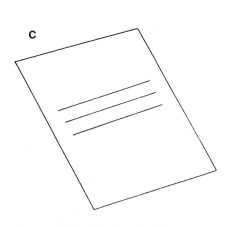

Figure 26-16 Three possible shapes for the universe are spherical (**a**), saddle-shaped (**b**), and flat (**c**).

The Future of the Universe

What will happen to the universe and its galaxies in the distant future? We know that for the present the universe is expanding. But will the expansion continue, or will the universe eventually contract?

Astronomers think that the answer to this question lies in how much mass the universe contains. If matter is densely enough packed in every region, gravity would add up enough to stop the expansion. The galaxies would fall back together as the universe contracted. Scientists call a universe that will eventually contract a **closed universe.** In any case, we can tell from the rate at which the universe is expanding that the universe would not contract for at least another 50 billion years.

If the universe is closed, perhaps another big bang will occur after all the matter in it is densely packed together. Perhaps our universe is the result of only the most recent in a series of big bangs. On the other hand, perhaps we are in the only cycle of expansion and contraction it will ever undergo.

Another possibility is that the universe is an **open universe.** An open universe does not have enough mass to cause it to contract. Instead, it will continue to expand forever, becoming less and less dense.

The inflationary universe leads to a third possibility—that the universe is neither open nor closed. An inflationary universe will keep expanding, but the rate of expansion will grow less and less. Still, the expansion will never quite stop. If the inflationary universe theory is correct, the universe is on the dividing line between open and closed.

Theories of the universe link the three dimensions of space and the one dimension called time into a four-dimensional **spacetime.** We cannot picture four dimensions, so let us think of only two of them at a time. If the universe is closed, its spacetime is a little like the surface of a ball, such as *a* in *Figure 26-16.* If you go far enough on a ball, for example, as the picture shows, you come back to where you started. Straight lines that go around the ball meet at two points, never at only one point.

If the universe is open, its spacetime is a little like a saddle, as in *b* of *Figure 26-16.* Through a point on a saddle-shaped figure, you can draw many different lines parallel to a first line.

If the inflationary universe is correct, however, the universe is almost flat, as *c* shows. In a flat universe, parallel lines always stay the same distance apart.

Astronomers have used large optical and radio telescopes like the ones shown to count the numbers of galaxies at different distances. Their counts might help determine which picture of the universe is the case. Unfortunately, some of the galaxies are so far away that they have changed between the time they gave off their light and now. These changes make it difficult to be certain about the shape and future of the universe.

We might still find out if the universe will continue to expand or will eventually contract by studying its density. Density refers to the amount of mass in a given region. Furthermore, scientists study how much of some forms of hydrogen and helium is left in the universe now from the time when matter first formed. They have discovered that the answer is linked to the density of the universe. This method does not show enough matter for the universe to be closed. But new kinds of matter that are not measured by this method could still be present in the universe.

Scientists wish they knew the answer to the future of the universe. They wish that the matter we can see would make up most of the universe instead of only a tiny part. But, at present, we must accept what we have found and continue to try to understand the universe's past and future.

Never have more large telescopes been under construction at the same time. Several telescopes, each eight meters across or more, are now being built. One of their most important tasks will be to study distant, faint galaxies to try to uncover the future of the universe.

Section Review

1. According to the big bang theory, how did the universe begin?
2. How does the inflationary universe theory differ from the older big bang theory?
3. Why do astronomers think there is invisible mass in the universe?
4. How is a closed universe different from an open universe?

Challenge: Why are astronomers unable to find the total mass of the universe with ordinary telescopes?

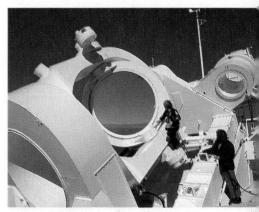

Figure 26-17 This telescope, used to study the sun, is just one of many types of telescopes astronomers use to study the universe.

Curving Space

Purpose

To show how knowing how the universe curves can tell us its future

Materials

- clay
- pointed objects to draw lines in clay
- straightedge or ruler
- protractor
- three sheets of paper
- scissors
- clear tape
- marking pen

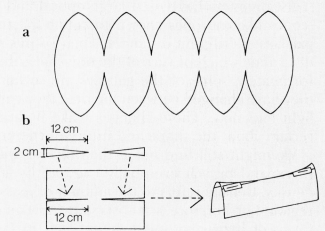

Procedure and Observations

PART A

1. Out of clay, make a sphere, a saddle, and a flat sheet, each about 10 cm across.
2. On the flat sheet, use the pointed object and straightedge to draw a large triangle.
3. On the sphere, describe the poles and the equator. Draw a triangle that extends from pole to equator, 1/4 of the way around the equator, and back to the pole.
4. On the saddle, describe a triangle of similar size.
5. Use the protractor to measure each of the angles of each triangle.
6. Make a table giving, for each shape figure, the sum of the angles for the triangle.
7. Draw different-sized triangles on each.
8. Repeat steps 5 and 6.

PART B

1. Draw, cut out, and tape the shapes shown in **a** and **b**, forming a spherical and a saddle-shaped figure. To get the curved surface for **b**, widen the two slits cut in a piece of paper by taping a thin triangle in each slit. Do not tape either figure heavily, since you will be taking each apart again.
2. Using the marking pen, draw dots about every 3 mm apart all over each of the figures.
3. Take off the tape and spread out each figure.

Analysis and Conclusions

1. How might you distinguish among different types of curving by measuring triangles?
2. For each type of curving, if the dots are galaxies, would the galaxies look normally spread out, bunched close in, or bunched far away if we flattened out the universe?
3. In a flat universe, the area of a thin ring increases with the square of the ring's distance from the center. From the number of galaxies in a small ring, we can predict the number of galaxies in a larger ring using this idea. If galaxies were evenly spread through the universe, would we count more, the same number, or fewer in a larger ring for each of the kinds of curving?

26-4 Whisper from Space

Background Radiation

In 1965, the two American scientists shown here, A.A. Penzias and R.W. Wilson, were using the big telescope behind them to study radio waves from space. Among other aims, they were trying to improve the quality of telephone calls that bounced off satellites. Week after week, they adjusted their aparatus. Always, though, they found a faint hiss in the background.

At the same time, other scientists were thinking about the early years of the universe. They were figuring out whether any signals were left over. Before about 100 000 years after the big bang, the electrons in the universe prevented radiation from traveling around. This was a short time for the universe, less than 1/1000 of one percent of its current age. During that period, the universe was like a giant fog. Then the universe cooled off a bit. For the first time, the electrons and protons in the universe could combine with each other. Once they made atoms, radiation could travel freely through the universe.

The radiation that became free to travel then was made up of gamma rays. But in the 10 or 20 billion years since then, the universe has continued to expand. The wavelengths of the radiation have been stretched until most of the radiation is now in the radio part of the spectrum. The scientists calculated that there should be a faint radio hiss to be heard.

The predicted hiss was the same as the one discovered in 1965. It comes evenly from all directions in space. Because it forms a uniform background of radiation, it is called the **background radiation.** It is a whisper from space, the faint signal that is left over from the period when the atoms formed.

Background Radiation in the Universe

Since its discovery, scientists have been able to measure the background radiation at many wavelengths. The hotter a gas is, the shorter most of its wavelengths are. The hot gas soon after the big bang gave off gamma rays, which have very short wavelengths. The background radiation is now strongest at the infrared end of the radio spectrum.

Objectives

After completing this section you will be able to

A. Describe what background radiation is and how it supports the big bang theory.

B. Describe what the background radiation tells us about the universe.

Applying Science

The background radiation was discovered accidentally when scientists working for a telephone company were exploring static that might affect long-distance calls. The present goal of telephone companies is to send half the calls by satellite and half by wire or optical fibers. Then if there is trouble with either method, the other method will remain useful. Other investigations of ways to improve telephone calls have led to the discovery of the transistor. Maybe more research will lead to other basic discoveries.

Figure 26-18 These scientists used the giant antenna behind them to discover the whisper from space.

Although these wavelengths are the shortest possible radio wavelengths, they are much longer than those of visible light. These wavelengths are the same as those from a gas at a temperature of $-270°$ C, only 3° above the coldest possible temperature. Thus the faint signal is sometimes called the 3° background radiation.

Scientists have studied the background radiation carefully in many different directions. They find no variation from point to point, so it certainly is not from individual objects like stars or galaxies. Their observations confirm the idea that the background radiation is from the early years of the universe.

The only variation the scientists find is that the temperature of the radiation seems to be slightly higher on one side of the sky than on the opposite side. They can explain the difference as a Doppler effect. If the earth and sun are moving in space in some direction, the wavelengths would be slightly shorter and the temperature would be slightly higher in that direction. Studies of the background radiation have apparently shown us that we are moving in space. Scientists can even tell the direction and speed that we are moving with respect to the overall universe.

Figure 26-19 shows a model of the *Cosmic Background Explorer,* a satellite that will soon be launched to study the background radiation. It should give us better measurements of the temperature in different directions.

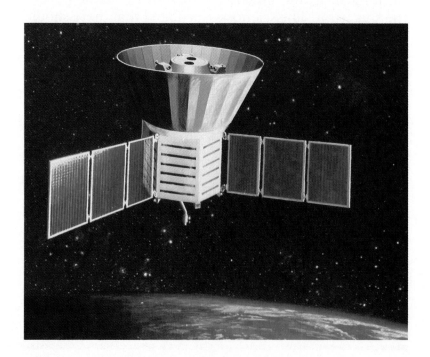

Figure 26-19 This spacecraft, the *Cosmic Background Explorer,* will soon be launched to make precise measurements of the background radiation.

The background radiation formed as far back in time as we can now look. Physical science explores questions about the universe as it has changed since then. In your lifetime, many of today's questions of physical science will be answered. Also, many new questions will be asked. As long as people are curious about the universe, they will search for answers to these questions. Perhaps you will become one of the many people who contribute to our knowledge of how our world and universe work.

Section Review

1. In what part of the spectrum is the background radiation?
2. How can the background radiation tell us about our motion?

Challenge: If the faint radio waves discovered in 1965 were found to come from only a few directions, how would the importance of their discovery be affected?

People and Science

Jocelyn Bell Burnell, Astronomer

In 1968 an English astronomer, Jocelyn Burnell, discovered pulsars by accident. Dr. Burnell was a graduate student at England's University of Cambridge. She was making radio surveys of the sky to locate quasars by their radio emissions. By chance, she noted that radio waves came from certain places in the skies and at regular intervals. The pulses lasted only about 1/100th of a second with about 1 second intervals between one pulse and the next. They were extremely regular, as precise as the most accurate clock on earth.

Dr. Burnell asked other researchers to examine her observations. At first, they believed the pulses came from some source on earth, because no known radio transmissions from space

were as regular. Finally, they decided the pulses were from space, possibly from extraterrestrial life! For a short time, the source of these pulses was designated by the initials LGM, standing for Little Green Men. In time, they called the sources pulsars, from the word "pulsating."

Soon other pulsars were detected, and now several hundred are known. Scientists have proposed that pulsars are neutron stars—the leftovers of collapsed giant stars. They consist of a mass packed so tightly that one neutron star with a diameter of 10 kilometers may have a density of 100 billion tons per cubic centimeter. A pulsar can spin as rapidly as 642 times per second. This type of star gives off strong radio waves in a specific direction, like the beam of a powerful searchlight. They are detected by radio telescopes on each sweep.

Jocelyn Burnell's discovery of pulsars gave astronomy a whole new dimension.

Using Flow Charts to Understand Processes in Astronomy

Processes in astronomy, such as the evolution of the universe, can be difficult to understand when they are described in words alone. A flow chart, which is a diagram that incorporates words and symbols, can help you understand such complex processes.

In a flow chart, circles indicate the beginning and end points of the process; arrows show the order in which the flow chart should be read; rectangles give the steps in the process; diamonds pose yes-or-no questions that indicate two possible outcomes of the process at that point.

PART A

On a separate sheet of paper, copy and enlarge the empty flow chart below. Start by writing, "Big bang occurs." in the circle on the left. Then complete the flow chart using the six statements listed at the right. Refer to pages 614–617 if necessary. (Clue: Two of the statements in the table need to be changed to question form.)

PART B

Answer the following questions.

1. Whose mathematical theories did scientists use to help them explain the big bang?
2. The closed universe theory states that the universe will eventually contract. If the universe were to contract, when would this start to happen?

Statements For Flow Chart

- The universe will always expand.

- The universe will explode again.

- Matter is densely packed in every region.

- The universe will contract to be infinitesimally small.

- The universe expands.

- The universe will eventually contract because of gravity.

- Big bang occurs.

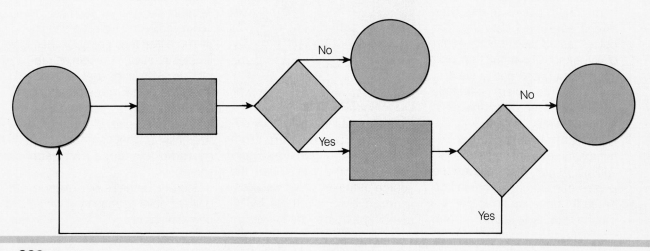

✔ Summary

26-1 Galaxies and Our Understanding of the Universe

A. The galaxies' movements indicate that the universe is expanding.

B. By finding out the amount of redshift of a galaxy's spectrum, due to the Doppler effect, astronomers can find out how fast the galaxy is moving away from us.

C. The universe appears to be like a huge sponge that contains connected regions of matter and connected regions of no matter.

26-2 Quasars and Other Active Galaxies

A. Quasars are objects that have large redshifts, and may give off large amounts of radio waves.

B. Most astronomers think that a quasar gets its energy from a giant black hole at its center.

C. Radio galaxies are the brightest sources of radio waves in the sky.

D. Galaxies that give off X rays are known as X-ray galaxies.

E. Infrared radiation shows where stars are being formed in a galaxy.

26-3 Theories About the Universe

A. According to the big bang theory, all the matter in the universe exploded 10 to 20 billion years ago.

B. The inflationary universe theory, the universe grew much bigger in the first tiny fraction of a second following the big bang.

C. Since clusters of galaxies are held together by gravity more strongly than the amount of visible mass in the cluster can account for, scientists think that the universe contains a lot of invisible mass.

D. The universe may contract or continue to expand.

26-4 Whisper from Space

A. The faint signal that is left over from the period in the history of the universe when atoms were formed is called the background radiation.

B. The presence of background radiation confirms the big bang theory.

Vocabulary

For each of the following terms, write a sentence that uses the term correctly.

background radiation	**open universe**
big bang theory	**quasar**
closed universe	**redshift**
inflationary universe theory	**spacetime**

✓ Check Your Knowledge

Part I: Matching Match the definition in Column I with the correct term in Column II.

Column I
1. among the most distant known objects
2. universe grew much bigger in a very short time
3. change in its spectrum due to the moving away of an object
4. radiation that shows where stars are forming in galaxies
5. among brightest sources of radio waves
6. four-dimensional system
7. model in which universe expands forever
8. model in which universe contracts
9. needed to account for gravity in galaxy clusters
10. faint signal confirming big bang theory

Column II
a. background radiation
b. closed universe
c. inflationary universe theory
d. infrared
e. invisible mass
f. open universe
g. quasars
h. radio galaxies
i. redshift
j. spacetime
k. X-ray galaxies

Part II: Multiple Choice Choose the letter of the best answer.

11. Which of the following may look somewhat starlike? (a) black holes (b) quasars (c) X rays (d) radio waves
12. Quasars probably get their energy from (a) their very great speeds. (b) their huge redshifts. (c) their companion stars. (d) very large black holes at their centers.
13. Which of the following can astronomers *not* detect? (a) X rays (b) infrared rays (c) radio waves (d) invisible mass
14. Which galaxy would show the largest redshift? (a) nearby, moving toward the earth (b) nearby, moving away from the earth (c) far away, moving toward the earth (d) far away, moving away from the earth
15. Star formation in a galaxy is shown by (a) X rays. (b) radio waves. (c) infrared rays. (d) gamma rays.

16. If the universe expands forever, it is (a) open. (b) closed. (c) inflationary. (d) indeterminate.
17. If the universe contracts, it is (a) open. (b) closed. (c) inflationary. (d) indeterminate.
18. The background radiation now consists of (a) gamma rays. (b) X rays. (c) radio waves. (d) visible light.

Part III: Completion Write the word or words that complete the sentence correctly.
19. Three dimensions of space and one dimension of time make up _____.
20. The redshifts of most galaxies we can see indicate that the universe is _____.
21. Astronomers can find the shapes of radio sources by using groups, or arrays, of _____.
22. Today's map of the universe is said to resemble a _____.
23. All matter in the universe exploded 10 to 20 billion years ago, according to the _____ theory.

☑ Check Your Understanding

1. Why do astronomers think the universe is expanding?
2. How do quasars help us look back in time?
3. Why do some radio galaxies look straight while others look curved?
4. Draw two 5-cm × 5-cm squares. In the left cone, draw where X rays would come from in an old cluster. In the right one, draw where X rays would come from in a young cluster.
5. Is our galaxy a starburst galaxy? Explain.
6. Why do astronomers want to know the average mass density of the universe?
7. What discovery confirmed the big bang theory?

☑ Apply Your Knowledge

1. If astronomers found a distant galaxy with a blueshift, how would the discovery affect our understanding of the universe?
2. Name one way in which a quasar resembles a star and one way in which it resembles a galaxy.
3. How does the Doppler effect help astronomers discover the mass of clusters of galaxies?
4. What effect does the number of black holes in the universe have on the future of the universe?
5. The universe is 10 or 20 billion years old. In 10 billion years from now, will the background radiation be hotter or cooler? Explain.
6. A quasar can give off 10^{36} joules of energy each second. At 10^8 joules available from burning a liter of gasoline in your car, how many liters of gasoline would it take to keep a quasar lighted for one second?

☑ Extend Your Knowledge

Research/Projects

1. Look up "cosmology" in a reference book. Find out what Olbers's Paradox is. Indicate how the expansion of the universe explains this paradox.
2. Look in recent astronomy books or magazines to find out how far away the farthest quasar is.
3. Find out how the Doppler shift differs for velocities close to the velocity of light.

Readings

Asimov, Isaac. *How Did We Find Out About the Universe?* Walker, 1983. Explains how our understanding of the universe has gradually been changed by the evidence of astronomers.

Stwertka, Albert and Eve. *Physics: From Newton to the Big Bang.* Watts, 1986. The dual nature of light and the relationship of energy and matter are discussed and applied to a possible explanation of the formation and future of the universe.

Are We Alone in the Universe?

For more than twenty years scientists have been searching for signs of life on other planets. Most of these searches have been done over the radio, a scanning of the electromagnetic waves that come to us from outer space. The hope is that someone out there may be trying to contact us. Scientists also have sent radio and television messages, as well as messages on spacecraft traveling through space, on the chance that someone may be receptive to such messages.

The most extensive search for intelligence planned so far involves using powerful radio-telescopes to listen to signals from about 1000 stars, all within 100 light years of Earth. In addition, astronomers will scan the entire sky to "listen" for radio messages from more distant stars. Using a computer, astronomers will be able to monitor more than 8 million channels at one time. Scientists are looking for any signal that stands out from the background noise, such as a long, loud pulse or a strong tone that could have traveled great distances.

What are the chances that other intelligent life exists in our galaxy? Of the 200 billion stars in the Milky Way galaxy, scientists estimate that five percent—10 billion stars—are like our sun. They are medium size stars, probably with planets. Of these solar systems, perhaps half of them— 5 billion—have a planet like Earth. Such a planet would be a reasonable distance from the star for temperatures to be right for the evolution of life. Based on the estimate of 5 billion inhabitable planets in our galaxy, most scientists agree that chances are likely that one or more of these planets supports some life.

However, many scientists wonder whether intelligent life—organisms who can communicate with us—exists on other planets. Some be-lieve that twenty years of searching with no hint of an intelligible message indicates that no one is out there. They say that the evolution of intelligence comparable to ours is unlikely, and perhaps not even advantagous for most creatures in most environments. Insects, perhaps the most evolutionarily successful of all organisms on Earth, for instance, could not communicate over radio waves.

Other scientists believe that our search has been neither long enough nor extensive enough to rule out the possibility that intelligent life exists in our galaxy. Although our solar system is only about 5 billion years old, our galaxy is about 20 billion years old. In that time some scientists think it is likely that civilizations much more advanced than ours have developed. Perhaps these civilizations are sending us no signals; perhaps we have not recognized the signals they have sent us. If we hope to find intelligent life, these scientists believe that we have to keep looking.

For Discussion

1. How are scientists looking for signs of intelligent life in the Milky Way?

2. Which group of scientists do you side with—those who think there is no intelligent life elsewhere in the galaxy or those who think there is intelligent life in the galaxy? Give reasons for your opinion.

Space Telescope

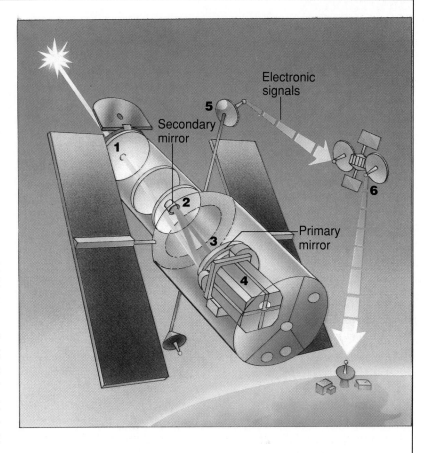

Since Galileo's time, astronomers have probed the sky with telescopes. The most powerful of the earthbound telescopes can detect the light from galaxies over 10 billion light years away. Using a telescope in orbit above the surface of the earth, astronomers will be able to study objects at greater distances. This space telescope intercepts light and radio waves before they can be distorted by the atmosphere, making it the most powerful instrument yet built for examining the heavens.

Astronomers plan to use the space telescope to look for evidence of planets in other solar systems, gather more information about planets in our own solar system, and search for black holes. They also hope to be able to determine the age of the universe by measuring how fast it is expanding.

Launched by the space shuttle and powered by solar cells on its surface, the space telescope will be serviced every three to five years by astronauts that rendezvous with it from the shuttle. Follow the steps in the diagram to learn how the space telescope works.

1. Light enters the space telescope through a small aperture and strikes the primary mirror, which is 240 cm in diameter. Before launch, the mirror had to be kept free of even minute amounts of dust and moisture.

2. The light reflects off the primary mirror and strikes the smaller secondary mirror, which concentrates the light.

3. The light is reflected through a hole in the primary mirror and forms an image behind the mirror.

4. The image is analyzed by several different instruments. The wide field planetary camera analyzes dense clouds of dust that may contain clues about the formation of new planets and stars. The faint object camera captures light from extremely distant objects. The faint object spectograph analyzes light from distant stars and galaxies. The high resolution spectograph gives detailed analyses of light from many different sources in the universe. The high speed photometer measures the variation in brightness of different objects.

5. The information generated by the scientific instruments is encoded as electronic signals, which are transmitted to a relay satellite.

6. The satellite transmits the information to earth.

APPENDIX 1
Biographies

Archimedes
(287-212 B.C.)

Archimedes was a Greek mathematician and scientist who made discoveries about the behavior of solids and liquids. He explained the principles behind simple machines such as the lever. Referring to the power of a lever to help people move heavy loads, he proclaimed, "Give me a place to stand on, and I will move the earth." He also formulated mathematical ideas that are the basis of scientific notation. Archimedes is sometimes called the father of experimental science because, unlike other Greek philosophers, he actually tested his ideas.

Archimedes was born in Syracuse, a city on the island of Sicily. Archimedes wrote about many of his discoveries; however, his manuscripts were lost for several hundred years during the Middle Ages. They were rediscovered in the 1500s. After reading Archimedes' newly rediscovered works, the Italian scientist Galileo was inspired to devise experiments for testing his own ideas. This led to a rebirth of experimental science in the Renaissance.

One of Archimedes' most famous discoveries was the method of measuring the volume of an object by measuring the volume of water the object displaces. Legend has it that he developed this method of measurement when asked to find a way to detect if the crown of the King of Sicily was made of pure gold. Archimedes also discovered that an object in water is held up by a buoyant force equal to the weight of the water the object displaces.

Daniel Bernoulli
(1700-1782)

Daniel Bernoulli was one of several distinguished scientists from the same Swiss family. The Bernoullis, including Daniel, his father, Johann, and his uncle, Jakob, made contributions to physics, to astronomy, to oceanography, to engineering sciences, and to the newly formed branch of mathematics called calculus. Daniel is best known for his research into the movement of fluids.

Although Daniel Bernoulli was born in Holland, his family moved to Basil, Switzerland when he was five years old. There, his father, Johann Bernoulli, took over the position of mathematics professor left vacant by the death of Jakob Bernoulli, Daniel's uncle.

Like the rest of his family, Daniel was talented in mathematics and science. He began his career in 1725 as a mathematics professor in St. Petersburg, Russia (now Leningrad, USSR). Later, he returned to the university in Basil where he held successive posts as professor of anatomy, botony, philosophy, and physics.

Daniel's most important contribution to science was Bernoulli's principle, which states that as the velocity of a fluid increases, its pressure decreases. Bernoulli's principle explains the lift of an airplane wing. The wing is shaped so that the speed of air flowing over the top is greater than that flowing beneath the wing. Therefore, the pressure beneath the wing is greater than on top, and the air exerts an upward force.

Niels Bohr
(1885-1962)

In 1913, Niels Bohr, a Danish physicist, published a revolutionary theory concerning the structure of the atom. Based on a previous theory proposed by another physicist, Ernest Rutherford, Bohr's theory made a break from certain accepted ideas about physics. Bohr's theory led the way to the development of the field called quantum mechanics. This field of physics explains the structure of the atoms and the movements of atomic particles. It also explains how atoms give off light and other matters related to atomic events.

Niels Bohr was born and grew up in Denmark. After Bohr received his doctorate in physics from the University of Copenhagen, he moved to England, where he worked under the physicist, Ernest Rutherford.

In time, Bohr became dissatisfied with certain parts of Rutherford's theory about the structure of the atom. Bohr agreed with the basic principles of Rutherford's model, in which the atom was compared to the solar system with the nucleus being the "sun" and the electrons revolving around it like "planets." But according to this model, the electrons would eventually lose energy and collapse into the nucleus. Instead, Bohr proposed that electrons are confined to certain orbits and the electrons lose energy only when they move from one orbit to another. Rutherford supported Bohr's observations and conclusions. In 1922, Bohr was awarded the Nobel Prize for Physics for his atomic theory.

Marie Sklodowska Curie
(1867-1934)

While working in a simple, basement laboratory, the Polish-born chemist and physicist, Marie Curie discovered two new elements. This scientist was born and educated in Warsaw, Poland. Marie Sklodowska was a bright child. She graduated from high school with honors. After high school, Marie attended classes in the homes of teachers.

In 1891, Marie was accepted at the Sorbonne, a university in Paris. She was a physics major and ranked first in her class when she graduated in 1893. In 1894, Marie met the physicist, Pierre Curie. One year later, the two were married.

In 1896, Marie began her studies of radiation in a laboratory in the basement of the School of Physics and Chemistry, where Pierre Curie worked as a professor. She was interested in Antoine Henri Becquerel's discovery that uranium gives off radiation. Marie wondered where this radiation was coming from.

In 1898, Marie, with her husband Pierre, discovered two new radioactive elements. She named the one *polonium* for her native country, Poland. They named the second element *radium*.

For the next four years, Marie and Pierre worked to separate a measurable amount of radium from pitchblende, a uranium ore.

In 1903, the Curies and Becquerel were awarded the Nobel Prize in physics for their work in isolating radium. Marie received another Nobel Prize in 1911. Madame Curie was the first person to win two Nobel Prizes.

Michael Faraday
(1791-1867)

Michael Faraday, a British physicist and chemist, was one of the greatest experimental scientists in history. He is best known for his discovery that moving a magnet through a wire coil causes, or induces, an electric current to flow. This phenomenon is called electromagnetic induction and made the practical use of electricity possible.

Faraday was born on September 22, 1791 in Newington, England, an area which is now part of London. At the age of 14, Faraday became the apprentice to a bookseller and a bookbinder. There in the book shop, he eagerly read the books on science. Seven years later, at the age of 21, Faraday became the assistant to the scientist Humphry Davy.

In 1831, Faraday performed a famous experiment in which he demonstrated electromagnetic induction. In doing so, Faraday actually produced the first generator. Also, Faraday showed that a wire carrying an electric current produces an electric field. Faraday's explanations for his discoveries were the foundation for the theory of electromagnetism developed by the Scottish physicist James Clerk Maxwell.

In the 1840s, Faraday made another major contribution to science. Through his study of the relationship between light and magnetism, he made a discovery that led to the understanding that light is electromagnetic.

Faraday also made significant discoveries in the field of chemistry. He was the first person to liquefy chlorine gas.

Galileo Galilei
(1564-1642)

Galileo Galilei was one of the first European scientists to promote the scientific method, relying on observation and experimentation to make new discoveries. His experiments on motion were known by English scientist Isaac Newton. Newton wrote of his own discoveries, "If I have seen further, it is by standing on the shoulders of giants." Galileo was one of those "giants" to whom Newton referred.

Galileo, was born on February 15, 1564 in Pisa, Italy. He entered the University of Pisa when he was 17. There he studied science and mathematics. In Galileo's time scientists did not do experiments but rather read the works of Aristotle and other ancient Greeks, simply assuming that what these philosophers said was true. Galileo, however, questioned Aristotle's assumptions. This attitude earned him the nickname the "wrangler."

Galileo left school for financial reasons. However, he continued studying on his own. In 1689, he became a professor of mathematics, teaching first in Pisa and then in Padua.

Galileo did many famous experiments. His experiment on motion demonstrated that objects of different masses fall at the same rate.

Galileo's most controversial work was his support of Copernicus's view that the earth circles the sun. He devised a telescope and observed the moons of Jupiter and the phases of Venus. He cited these and other observations as proof of Copernicus's views in a book he published in 1632.

Irene Joliot-Curie, daughter of Marie and Pierre Curie, was also a physicist who made major contributions to the study of radioactivity and nuclear science. She and her husband, Frederic Joliot-Curie, discovered artificial radioactivity.

While Irene's parents, Marie and Pierre Curie worked in their laboratory, Irene's grandfather, Dr. Eugene Curie cared for her. Her early education was unique. Marie Curie arranged for Irene and several other children to study chemistry in the laboratory at the Sorbonne, to study mathematics under a noted French mathematician, to learn design from a sculptor, English and German from one of Marie's friends, and physics from Marie Curie herself.

Later, Irene studied physics at the Sorbonne. She also took courses in nursing and radiology.

Irene began her career as a laboratory assistant for her mother at the Radium Institute. There, Irene met Frederic Joliot, also Marie Curie's assistant. Irene and Frederic were married in 1926, and like Irene's famous parents, the couple continued to study the effects of radioactivity.

At the Radium Institute, Irene studied the alpha particles emitted from polonium. Alpha particles are one kind of radiation. Irene and Frederic's research in alpha particles led the way to the discovery of the neutron.

Continuing their work, Irene and her husband produced the first example of artificial radioactivity.

Lise Meitner
(1878-1968)

Lise Meitner was an Austrian physicist whose research in nuclear physics paved the way for the development of nuclear energy. She first became interested in atomic physics after reading newspaper accounts of Marie and Pierre Curie's discovery of radium.

In 1908, Meitner moved to Berlin and began her experimental work in radioactivity with Dr. Otto Hahn. In 1918, Meitner, together with Hahn, discovered the radioactive element protactinium.

As part of a team of physicists at the Kaiser Wilhelm Institute in Berlin, Meitner performed experiments in which she bombarded uranium with neutrons. Some of the results of these experiments were unexpected. Barium, an element not used in the experiment was produced, and the scientists could not understand why this happened.

In 1938, Meitner moved to Sweden and began to work at the Nobel Institute in Stockholm, Sweden. She determined mathematically the cause for the mysterious appearance of barium. She published a report describing her conclusions. Her report explained that the unexpected appearance of barium meant that the uranium atoms had split into smaller atoms of barium and krypton. Meitner observed that the mass of the two new parts together was less than that of the original uranium atom. After discussions with physicist Otto Frisch and other scientists, Meitner decided that the missing mass had changed into energy.

Dimitri Mendeleev
(1834-1907)

Dimitri Ivanovich Mendeleev was a Russian chemist who developed the periodic table of elements. He was born in Tobolsk, Siberia on February 7, 1834. Since his father was blind, his mother worked to support the family. After a series of disasters struck the family, Mendeleev's mother left Siberia with Dimitri and his sister, the only two remaining dependents in the family. They moved to Moscow with the hope of getting Dimitri into the university.

In 1856, Mendeleev received a degree in chemistry, and for the next ten years, taught, studied chemistry, and did scientific writing.

He became a professor at the university in St. Petersburg in 1867, and began to write *The Principles of Chemistry,* a classic textbook.

While writing his book, Mendeleev attempted to organize a system of classification for the elements. He studied the relationship between the properties of the elements. Mendeleev arranged all the known elements in order of increasing atomic weights, and showed that those elements with similar properties occur at regular intervals—that is, periodically.

Mendeleev's table had empty spaces. He predicted that these spaces would be filled by new, undiscovered elements. Within the next twenty years, three new elements were discovered, which had properties predicted by Mendeleev.

Sir Isaac Newton
(1642-1737)

Sir Isaac Newton is considered one of the greatest scientists of all times. He formulated a set of concise laws that unified the isolated descriptions that were known as science. Newton's contributions include his laws of motion and the law of gravity, his analysis of light and color, including the discovery that sunlight is a mixture of light of all colors, his invention of the reflecting telescope, and the invention of a branch of mathematics called calculus.

Newton was born in a small town in eastern England on December 25, 1642. As a boy, he was interested in making small mechanical inventions, such as a clock that worked by the force of dropping water. He entered Cambridge University at age 18, graduated, did research, and then became a professor of mathematics.

Newton made his most important scientific discoveries when he was in his early twenties. However, he did not publish his findings for many years. In 1864 the English astronomer Edmund Halley came to Newton with a question about the motion of planets. Newton showed him his work from twenty years back that contained the answer. In 1687, at Halley's urging, Newton published this work in a book commonly called the *Principia*.

In 1699 Newton was put in charge of England's mint. He became president of the Royal Society in 1703 and was reelected annually until his death.

Chien Shiung Wu
(1912-)

Chien Shiung Wu, an American experimental physicist, became known for her contributions to the research of nuclear forces and structure. In 1956, she earned world-wide attention for the results of her experiments involving subatomic particles.

Chien Shiung Wu was born in Liu Ho, China on May 29, 1912. China and Japan were engaged in war during Wu's university years. Despite the troubles, however, she received her degree from the university in Nanking in 1936. That same year, Wu came to the United States. She earned her doctorate from the University of California in 1940.

The focus of much of Dr. Wu's career was the study of nuclear forces and structure, especially beta disintegration. Beta particles are produced when many radioactive substances decay.

In 1956, Dr. Wu was invited by Dr. Tsung Dao Lee and Dr. Chen Ning Yang at Princeton to conduct experiments involving subatomic particles.

In her work, she conducted experiments showing that an established law of physics, known as the law of conservation of parity, does not apply to subatomic particles. As a result of these experiments, Dr. Lee and Dr. Yang shared the Nobel Prize for Physics in 1957. For her contributions, Dr. Wu was awarded the Research Corporation Award— the first woman to receive that award.

Hideki Yukawa
(1907-1981)

Hideki Yukawa, a theoretical physicist, developed a theory in which he forecast the existence and the properties of a subatomic particle called a meson. In 1947, 12 years after formulating his theory, Yukawa's subatomic particle was discovered.

Yukawa was born in Tokyo, Japan on January 23, 1907. He was reading the Chinese classics by the age of five. While in high school, he read the German edition of Max Planck's *An Introduction to Theoretical Physics,* which inspired him to study physics.

Yukawa enrolled in Kyoto University in 1926. The exciting discoveries being made in quantum mechanics at this time led him to the study of theoretical physics. After getting his master's degree in 1929, Yukawa began his study of the atomic nucleus and cosmic rays.

One sleepless night in 1934, Yukawa was struck by inspiration, launching a major breakthrough in his research. Using mathematical reasoning, he developed a theory of the existence of a subatomic particle that would be larger than an electron and smaller than a proton.

In 1947, two kinds of mesons were discovered. One kind fit Yukawa's theoretical description. These mesons could be found in cosmic radiation only at high altitudes.

Yukawa was awarded the Nobel Prize for physics in 1949 for his theoretical work.

APPENDIX 2
The 109 Elements Listed Alphabetically

Element	Symbol	Atomic Number	Element	Symbol	Atomic Number	Element	Symbol	Atomic Number
Actinium	Ac	89	Hahnium	Ha	105	Radium	Ra	88
Aluminum	Al	13	Helium	He	2	Radon	Rn	86
Americium	Am	95	Holmium	Ho	67	Rhenium	Re	75
Antimony	Sb	51	Hydrogen	H	1	Rhodium	Rh	45
Argon	Ar	18	Indium	In	49	Rubidium	Rb	37
Arsenic	As	33	Iodine	I	53	Ruthenium	Ru	44
Astatine	At	85	Iridium	Ir	77	Rutherfordium	Rf	104
Barium	Ba	56	Iron	Fe	26	Samarium	Sm	62
Berkelium	Bk	97	Krypton	Kr	36	Scandium	Sc	21
Beryllium	Be	4	Lanthanum	La	57	Selenium	Se	34
Bismuth	Bi	83	Lawrencium	Lr	103	Silicon	Si	14
Boron	B	5	Lead	Pb	82	Silver	Ag	47
Bromine	Br	35	Lithium	Li	3	Sodium	Na	11
Cadmium	Cd	48	Lutetium	Lu	71	Strontium	Sr	38
Calcium	Ca	20	Magnesium	Mg	12	Sulfur	S	16
Californium	Cf	98	Manganese	Mn	25	Tantalum	Ta	73
Carbon	C	6	Mendelevium	Md	101	Technetium	Tc	43
Cerium	Ce	58	Mercury	Hg	80	Tellurium	Te	52
Cesium	Cs	55	Molybdenum	Mo	42	Terbium	Tb	65
Chlorine	Cl	17	Neodymium	Nd	60	Thallium	Tl	81
Chromium	Cr	24	Neon	Ne	10	Thorium	Th	90
Cobalt	Co	27	Neptunium	Np	93	Thulium	Tm	69
Copper	Cu	29	Nickel	Ni	28	Tin	Sn	50
Curium	Cm	96	Niobium	Nb	41	Titanium	Ti	22
Dysprosium	Dy	66	Nitrogen	N	7	Tungsten	W	74
Einsteinium	Es	99	Nobelium	No	102	Unnilennium	Une	109
Erbium	Er	68	Osmium	Os	76	Unnilhexium	Unh	106
Europium	Eu	63	Oxygen	O	8	Unniloctium	Uno	108
Fermium	Fm	100	Palladium	Pd	46	Unnilpentium	Unp	105
Fluorine	F	9	Phosphorus	P	15	Unnilquadium	Unq	104
Francium	Fr	87	Platinum	Pt	78	Unnilseptium	Uns	107
Gadolinium	Gd	64	Plutonium	Pu	94	Uranium	U	92
Gallium	Ga	31	Polonium	Po	84	Vanadium	V	23
Germanium	Ge	32	Potassium	K	19	Wolfram	W	74
Gold	Au	79	Praseodymium	Pr	59	Xenon	Xe	54
Hafnium	Hf	72	Promethium	Pm	61	Ytterbium	Yb	70
			Protactinium	Pa	91	Yttrium	Y	39
						Zinc	Zn	30
						Zirconium	Zr	40

Blimps are inflated with helium gas.

APPENDIX 3
SI Units

At an international meeting in 1960, scientists set up the International System of Units (SI). They established certain metric units as the preferred units for scientific measurements of seven quantities: time, mass, amount of substance, length, luminous intensity, electric current and temperature. These units, which are called the seven basic units, are listed below. You will be using all but the candela, Kelvin scale, and the mole in this text.

Seven Basic SI Units	Measured Quantity
Mole (mol)	Amount of Substance
Ampere (A)	Electric Current
Meter (m)	Length
Candela (cd)	Luminous Intensity
Kilogram (kg)	Mass
Kelvin (K)	Temperature
Second (s)	Time

In addition, to the basic units, the SI system includes many "derived" units. A derived unit is one that mathematically combines two or more basic units. Some derived units you will see in this text are shown here.

Derived SI Unit	Derived Quantity
Joule, J $(J = N\text{-}m)$	Energy
Newton, N $(N = m\text{-}kg/sec^2)$	Force
Pascal, Pa $(Pa = N/m^2)$	Pressure
Cubic Meter, m^3 $(m \times m \times m)$	Volume
Kilogram per cubic meter, kg/m^3	Density (mass/volume)

The prefixes below make the SI units more flexible, and, thus, more useful.

Prefix	Symbol	Multiply SI Unit Times:
exa	E	$= 10^{18}$
peta	P	$= 10^{15}$
tera	T	$= 10^{12}$
giga	G	$= 10^{9}$
mega	M	$= 10^{6}$
kilo	k	$= 10^{3}$
hecto	h	$= 10^{2}$
deka	da	$= 10$
deci	d	$= 10^{-1}$
centi	c	$= 10^{-2}$
milli	m	$= 10^{-3}$
micro	μ	$= 10^{-6}$
nano	n	$= 10^{-9}$
pico	p	$= 10^{-12}$
femto	f	$= 10^{-15}$
atto	a	$= 10^{-18}$

APPENDIX 4
Scientific Notation

In science you will be dealing with very small values, such as the wavelength of light, and very large values, such as distances to stars. You can use scientific notation to express such numbers. Scientific notation is based on the powers of ten. Some examples of the powers of ten are shown in the tables.

Note that 10^0 equals one. Therefore, 10^1 equals 10, 10^2 equals 100, and so on. The value of the exponent indicates where the decimal point is located in the number written in "standard form."

Values of less than 1 are shown by negative exponents. Again, the exponent tells where the decimal point is located in the number written in standard form.

In scientific notation, a value is written as the product of a number (between 1 and 10) multiplied times a power of ten in exponential form. For example, 322 (standard form) is written 3.22×10^2 because the decimal point is moved two places to the left. On the other hand, 0.25 is written 2.5×10^{-1}, because the decimal point is moved one place to the right. If the number in scientific notation shows only the power of ten, the missing number from 1 to 10 is understood to be 1. For instance, $10^3 = 1 \times 10^3$.

You can multiply, divide, add, and subtract numbers written in scientific notation.

1. To multiply, multiply the numbers from 1 to 10, and *add* the exponents.

   a. $10^5 \times 10^3 = 10^8$

   b. $(2.0 \times 10^{-2})(4.0 \times 10^{-3}) = 8.0 \times 10^{-5}$

2. To divide, divide the numbers from 1 to 10, and *subtract* the exponents.

   $(5.0 \times 10^5) \div (5 \times 10^3) = 1 \times 10^2$

3. To add (or subtract), first write both values to the same power of ten, then add (or subtract) the numbers from 1 to 10.

   $(1.22 \times 10^8 \, g) + (6.0 \times 10^6 \, g)$

   $= (1.22 \times 10^8 \, g) + (0.06 \times 10^8 \, g)$
   $= 1.28 \times 10^8 \, g$

Powers of Ten for Numbers Equal to or Greater Than 1
$10^6 = 1\,000\,000$
$10^5 = 100\,000$
$10^4 = 10\,000$
$10^3 = 1000$
$10^2 = 100$
$10^1 = 10$
$10^0 = 1$

Powers of Ten for Numbers Less Than 1
$10^{-1} = 0.1$
$10^{-2} = 0.01$
$10^{-3} = 0.001$
$10^{-4} = 0.0001$
$10^{-5} = 0.00001$

This coliseum holds about 4.8×10^4 people (48 000)

APPENDIX 5
Using Powers of Ten

The table below will give you an idea of how some dimensions are described in the powers of ten.

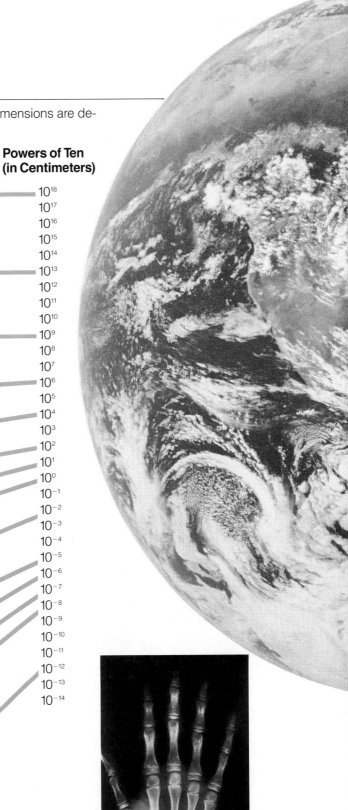

Size or Distance	Powers of Ten (in Centimeters)
Distance light travels in one year (1 light year)	10^{18}
	10^{17}
	10^{16}
	10^{15}
	10^{14}
An average earth/sun distance (about 1.5×10^{13} cm)	10^{13}
	10^{12}
	10^{11}
	10^{10}
Earth's diameter at the equator (about 1.3×10^{9} cm)	10^{9}
	10^{8}
	10^{7}
Distance you might be able to see from the top of a hill	10^{6}
	10^{5}
	10^{4}
Lengths of some radio waves	10^{3}
	10^{2}
	10^{1}
	10^{0}
Meter stick	10^{-1}
Width of an adult male's hand (an average)	10^{-2}
	10^{-3}
	10^{-4}
Pencil's width	10^{-5}
Thickness of a piece of paper	10^{-6}
	10^{-7}
	10^{-8}
	10^{-9}
	10^{-10}
Wavelength of visible light	10^{-11}
	10^{-12}
	10^{-13}
Diameter of a molecule	10^{-14}
Wavelength of an X ray	
Diameter of an atom (1 angstrom = 10^{-8} cm)	
Diameter of an atomic nucleus	

APPENDIX 6
Metric/English Conversion Tables

Length

Unit	Multiplied By:	Gives
inches	2.54	centimeters
centimeters	0.3937	inches
feet	0.3048	meters
meters	3.281	feet
miles	1.6093	kilometers
kilometers	0.6214	miles
kilometers	3281	feet
feet	0.0003048	kilometers

Weight and Mass

Unit	Multiplied By:	Gives
ounces	28.350	grams
grams	0.0353	ounces
pounds	0.4536	kilograms
kilograms	2.205	pounds
tons	0.9072	metric tons
metric tons	1.102	tons

	Unit	Multiplied By:	Gives
Temperature	degrees Fahrenheit minus 32	0.5555	degrees Celsius
	degrees Celsius	1.80	degrees Fahrenheit plus 32
Liquid Measure	fluid ounces	0.0296	liters
	gallons	3.7854	liters
	liters	0.2642	gallons
	liters	33.8140	fluid ounces
Pressure (Force)	pounds	4.448	newtons
	newtons	0.225	pounds
	millimeters of mercury	133.32	pascals (newtons per square meter)
	pounds per square inch	6.895	kilopascals (1000 pascals)
	pascals	0.0075	millimeters mercury at 0° C
	kilopascals	0.1450	pounds per square inch

GLOSSARY

The pronunciation of each word is shown just after the word, in this way: **ab bre vi ate** (ə brē′vē āt). The letters and signs used are pronounced as in the words below. The mark ′ is placed after a syllable with primary or heavy accent, as in the example above. The mark ′ after a syllable shows a secondary or lighter accent, as in **ab bre vi a tion** (ə brē′vē ā′shən).

a	hat, cap	f	fat, if
ā	age, face	g	go, bag
ä	father, far	h	he, how
b	bad, rob	it	it, pin
ch	child, much	ī	ice, five
d	did, red		
		j	jam, enjoy
e	let, best	k	kind, seek
ē	equal, be	l	land, coal
ėr	term, learn	m	me, am

n	no, in	u	cup, butter
ng	long, bring	ù	full, put
		ü	rule, move
o	hot, rock		
ō	open, go	v	very, save
ô	order, all	w	will, woman
oi	oil, voice	y	young, yet
ou	house, out	z	zero, breeze
		zh	measure, seizure
p	paper, cup		
r	run, try	ə	represents:
s	say, yes		a in about
sh	she, rush		e in taken
t	tell, it		i in pencil
th	thin, both		o in lemon
ŦH	then, smooth		u in circus

A

acceleration (ak sel′ə rā′shən), rate of change of velocity, usually expressed in meters/second/second.

acceleration due to gravity, rate at which the velocity of a freely falling object changes as it falls under the influence of gravity alone; about 10 meters/second/second.

acid, substance that produces hydronium ions in water.

action force, any force applied to an object; a term used to distinguish this applied force from the reaction force of Newton's third law.

adhesion, the force that attracts particles of one substance to particles of another substance.

air resistance (ri zis′təns), frictional force from air molecules hitting an object as it moves through the air.

alternating current (a.c.), electric current that reverses its direction many times each second.

amorphous, when the particles of a solid are not arranged in an orderly pattern.

ampere (am′pir), unit used to measure an amount of current.

amplifier (am′plə fī′ər), electronic device that increases the strength of changes in electrical signals it receives.

amplitude (am′plə tüd), height of a wave from its mid position to its crest or trough.

Archimedes' principle, states that the buoyant force on an object is equal to the weight of the liquid it displaces.

artificial intelligence, ways of making the computer more closely mimic human thinking.

atom, smallest bit of an element that has all the characteristics of that element.

atomic mass, mass of an average atom of an element, taking into account the percentages of its isotopes that exist naturally.

atomic number, number of protons in an atom's nucleus.

axis (ak′sis), imaginary straight line around which an object rotates.

B

background radiation, natural environmental radiation that constantly bombards the earth.

balance, instrument used to measure the amount of mass of a substance by comparing its mass with that of a known mass.

balanced forces, forces that cancel each other out because they are equal in strength and opposite in direction.

base, substance that produces hydroxide ions in water.

BASIC, short for, "**B**eginners's **A**ll-Purpose **S**ymbol **I**nstruction **C**ode", a computer language.

Bernoulli's principal, as the velocity of a gas increases, the pressure it exerts decreases; as the velocity decreases, the pressure increases.

Big bang theory, theory that the universe started expanding from a very hot, dense condition about 15 billion years ago.

biomass, possible fuel that comes from living organisms.

black hole, region of space in which so much mass is concentrated that nothing, not even light, can escape; the result of the death of massive stars.

boiling point, temperature at which a substance changes from a liquid to a gas under normal atmospheric pressure.

breeder reactors, a reactor that produces at least as much fissionable material as it uses.

buoyant force, states that the lightness of an object is due to the upward force that water exerts on it.

C

calorimeter (kal′ə rim′ə tər), closed container that is used to measure the amount of heat given off or taken in by a material.

carbohydrates, substance made from carbon dioxide and water by green plants in sunlight.

catalyst (kat′əl ist), substance that changes the rate at which a reaction takes place without itself undergoing a net change.

cathode-ray tube, a type of vacuum tube in which an electron beam moves from side to side.

central process unit (cpu), the part of a computer that actually does the computing.

center of gravity, place on an object around which torques are balanced and from which the object could be suspended and remain motionless; the single point in an object at which gravity can be assumed to be acting.

centripetal (sen tri′pə təl) s**force,** force pulling an object inward toward the center of a curving path.

chain reaction, reaction that, once started, keeps itself going as one individual reaction causes adjacent ones to take place.

chemical bond, attractive force that binds atoms together.

chemical change, change in a substance or substances that produces a new substance with different chemical properties.

chemical energy, form of potential energy that depends on the arrangement of atoms, molecules, or ions in a substance.

chemical equation, set of symbols identifying the substances involved before and after a chemical reaction.

chemical property, characteristic of a substance that describes how the substance reacts with other substances.

chemical reaction, one step in or part of a chemical change between substances.

chemical symbol, the shorthand form of an element's name.

chemically stable, condition of an atom when its outer electron level is filled.

chip, tiny piece of silicon containing layers of impurities to make the equivalent of thousands of circuits.

circuit (ser′kit), closed path around which a current flows.

circuit breaker, safety device that switches off when too much current flows in a circuit.

circular motion, movement around a central position.

closed universe, universe that is dense enough to stop expanding and begin to contract.

cohesion, the force that keeps particles of the same substance together.

coinage metals, copper, silver, and gold; they have been used for centuries to make coins because they are durable and do not undergo chemical changes easily.

colloid (kol′oid), suspension in which the particles of one substance remain mixed in another.

compass, object used to tell direction; a magnetic compass is a free-swinging magnet allowed to align itself with the earth's magnetic poles.

compound (kom′pound), substance that results when two or more elements join together chemically in definite amounts.

compound machine, combination of two or more simple machines.

compression (kəm presh′ən), place in a compressional wave where the density of the material's particles is relatively high.

compressional wave, way of transmitting energy through slight motions of matter back and forth along the direction the energy is traveling.

concave lens, lens whose middle part is thinner than its edges so that it spreads out light rays.

concave mirror, mirror whose middle part curves away from an object so that it reflects light rays together from that object.

concentrated (kon′sən trā′tid), *concentrated solution:* solution with a relatively large amount of solute dissolved in it.

condensation (kon′den sā′shən), process by which a gas changes to a liquid even though the gas has not reached its boiling point.

condense, when water vapor changes into a liquid.

conduction, transfer of energy by direct contact between particles of a substance.

conductor (kən duk′tər) *of heat,* material through which heat passes easily; *of electricity,* material through which electric current passes easily.

conservation, saving energy, using less energy, or using energy wisely.

contraction, decrease in the size of an object or material.

controlled experiment, experiment involving two setups, one control and one variable.

convection, transfer of energy by the movement of rather large masses of a liquid or gas.

convection current, liquid or gas moving during the process of convection.

convex lens, lens whose middle part is thicker than its edges so that it bends light rays together.

convex mirror, mirror whose center curves toward an object so that it spreads out light rays from the object.

cornea (kor′nē ə), the eye's transparent covering that helps focus light rays.

corona, outermost layer of the sun which becomes visible during a total solar eclipse.

covalent (kō vā′lənt) **bond,** chemical bond that results when two atoms share a pair of electrons.

cracking, process of breaking down large, single-bonded hydrocarbons into smaller, double-bonded ones.

crest, top of a transverse wave.

crystal (kris′tl), structural unit in most solids that has an orderly, repeating arrangement.

D

data, recorded observations or facts about a substance or an event.

decibel (des′ə bel), one-tenth of a bel, a unit used to express the intensity of sound; an increase in intensity of ten decibels means that the intensity of the sound is multiplied by 10.

decomposition (dē′kom pə zish′ən) **reaction,** chemical reaction in which one substance breaks down into simpler substances.

degree Celsius, SI unit of measure for temperature.

density, amount of mass in a standard volume; found by dividing mass by volume and usually expressed in grams/centimeter³ or grams/milliliter.

deuterium, a form of hydrogen with one proton and one neutron.

diatomic (dī′ə tom′ik) **molecule,** molecule made up of two atoms that are covalently bonded.

dilute (də lüt′), *dilute solution,* solution with only a small amount of solute dissolved in it.

direct current, (d.c.), electric current that flows in a single direction.

displacement, measure of the distance and direction that an object moves.

distance, length of a path over which an object travels, usually expressed in meters or kilometers.

DNA, deoxyribonucleic acid, found in the nuclei of all living cells.

domain, small region in a magnet in which the magnetism of most of the atoms lines up.

Doppler (dop′lər) **effect,** apparent change in the frequency or wavelenth of a wave caused by motion of the observer or the source of the waves relative to each other.

double-replacement reaction, a chemical reaction in which the elements in two compounds switch places.

double star, a star which has a companion in space.

dry cell, electrical cell in which current is contained in a gelatin or paste so as not to spill.

ductile (duk′təl), able to be drawn into a wire, as some metals are.

dwarf, a star which fuses hydrogen into helium.

E

efficiency, percentage found by comparing the amount of useful work obtained from a machine to the amount of work put into the machine.

effort arm, distance on a lever from the point at which a force is exerted to the fulcrum.

electric current (ker′ənt), flow of electric charge, expressed in amperes.

electric force, provides the attraction or repulsion between charged particles.

electrical energy, kind of energy carried by moving charges.

electromagnet, temporary magnet formed by passing electric current through a coiled wire.

electromagnetic (i lek′trō mag net′ik) **induction,** process by which a changing magnetic field causes an electric current to flow in a wire loop.

electromagnetic spectrum, entire range of electromagnetic waves arranged in order of their frequencies or wavelengths.

electromagnetic wave, energy traveling through space as a result of changing electricity and magnetism.

electromagnetism, theory that shows how electricity and magnetism result from a single force.

electron (i lek′tron), negatively charged particle, often found in an atom, that usually moves around the nucleus.

electronic device, any device which operates using electric current in the form of signals.

electronics, study of moving electrons and their use in devices such as radios, television, and computers.

element, any of the simplest substances of matter that cannot be decomposed by chemical means.

ellipse (i lips′), kind of curve resembling a squashed circle; planets travel in ellipses.

elliptical galaxy, a galaxy which looks like an ellipse and contains only old stars.

emulsifier (i mul′sə fī′er), substance that keeps the particles of one liquid mixed in another liquid.

emulsion (i mul′shən), colloid in which one liquid is mixed in another.

endoscope, a device which allows doctors to see inside a patient's body.

endothermic (en′dō ther′mik) **reaction,** chemical reaction that takes in energy.

end point, point at which an acid and a base have reacted completely.

energy, ability to do work, usually expressed in joules.

energy level, path of an electron around an atom's nucleus that corresponds to a certain amount of energy.

equilibrium (ē kwə lib′rē əm), condition of an object when no net force acts on it.

escape velocity, the speed at which an object may escape the earth's gravitational pull.

evaporate, when water changes from a liquid to a gas.

evaporation (i vap′ə rā′shən), process by which fast-moving molecules escape from a liquid, changing the liquid into a gas, even though the liquid has not reached its boiling point.

excited state, condition of an atom when at least one of its electrons is in an energy level above its usual, lowest possible energy level.

exothermic (ek′sō ther′mik) **reaction,** chemical reaction that gives off energy.

expansion, increase in the size of an object or material.

F

farsighted, condition in which the eye does not properly focus objects that are relatively nearby.

flow chart, shows the steps in the order the computer should follow.

focal length, distance from the optical center of a lens or mirror to the principal point of focus.

focal point, single location to which parallel rays of light are brought together.

foci, the two fixed points of an ellipse.

force, any action that accelerates an object, expressed in newtons.

forced vibration, vibration of an object not at its natural frequency but at the frequency of another object that is causing the vibration.

formula (for′myə lə), arrangement of symbols that indicates the kind of atoms and their numbers in a compound.

fossil (fos′əl) **fuel,** substance formed over millions of years from the remains of dead organisms that can be burned to release energy; coal, oil, and natural gas.

fractional distillation (dis′tl ā′shən), process of separating components of a mixture that have different boiling points by vaporizing each one at its boiling point.

frame of reference (ref′ər əns), set of points of view that are not moving in relation to an object or observer.

free electron laser, a type of laser which uses free electrons, which are not bound to atoms, to produce laser light.

freezing, the change of phase from liquid to solid.

freezing point, temperature at which a substance changes from a liquid to a solid.

frequency (frē′kwen sē), number of waves passing a specific point within a unit period of time, expressed in hertz.

friction, force between surfaces that resists the motion of one object or surface past another.

fulcrum (ful′krəm), point at which a lever is supported.

fuse, safety device in which a metal strip melts to open a circuit when too much current flows through it.

G

galaxy (gal′ek sē), large, distinct group of stars, gas, and dust held together by gravity.

gas, physical state of matter that does not have a definite shape or volume.

gas laser, a laser used to give off a steady beam of light in a very narrow range of colors.

Geiger counter, an instrument used to detect radiation from radioactive material, developed by Hans Geiger in 1908.

generator (jen′ə rā′tər), device that uses electromagnetic induction to change mechanical energy into electricity.

geothermal (jē′ō ther′məl) **energy,** energy obtained from the earth's interior heat.

graduated cylinder, cylinder marked with regular divisions (graduations) that is used to measure the volume of a liquid.

gram, g, metric unit of mass.

group, elements located in a column of the periodic table and having similar chemical properties.

H

half-life, time it takes for half the nuclei in a quantity of a radioactive substance to decay.

hardware, the parts of a computer, other than the data and instructions.

heat, transfer of energy from one substance to another so that the energy appears as kinetic energy of the atoms in the substance; expressed in joules.

heat source, anything that can give off heat because its temperature is higher than that of its surroundings.

hertz (herts), one cycle per second, a unit used to measure a wave's frequency.

hologram (hol′ə gram), image made by using the interference properties of radiation, often made with a laser; holograms show more information than a photograph does.

hydrocarbon (hī′drō kär′bən), any of a group of compounds that contain only carbon and hydrogen.

hydroelectric (hī′drō i lek′trik) **power,** power from moving water turning a turbine that turns a generator to produce electricity.

hydrogen ion, a hydrogen atom which has lost its electron, also refered to as a proton.

hydronium (hī drō′nē əm) **ion,** H_3O^+, an ion containing the equivalent of an ordinary water molecule and an extra proton; forms when an acid is added to water.

hydroxide ion, OH^-, an ion containing oxygen and hydrogen; forms when a base is added to water.

hypothesis (hī poth′ə sis; plural, hī poth′ə sēz′), reasonable guess about how or why an event happens; hypotheses form the basis for further testing.

I

inclined plane, simple machine consisting of a slanting, flat surface.

indicator, dye that changes color at a certain pH value.

inertia (in er′shə), tendency of an object to maintain its motion or its condition of rest unless something disturbs it.

inflationary universe theory, theory which states that the universe grew very much bigger in a tiny fraction of a second during the first second of time.

infrasonic, sound waves with frequencies too low for people to hear.

input, the information going into a computer.

insulator (in′sə lā′tər) *of heat,* material through which heat does not pass easily; *of electricity,* material through which electric current does not pass easily.

integrated (in′tə grāt′id) **circuit,** electronic chip that contains the equivalent of thousands of electronic components and circuits.

intensity (in ten′sə tē), strength of light falling on a certain area.

interference (in′tər fir′əns), situation resulting from overlapping waves in which the waves subtract and cancel each other or add and reinforce each other.

internal energy, total energy of all the particles that make up an object.

ion (ī′on), atom or molecule that has lost or gained one or more electrons and so has a positive or negative charge.

ionic (ī on′ik) **bond,** chemical bond that results when one or more electrons is transferred from one atom to another.

irregular galaxy, a galaxy which shows no regular shape.

isotopes (ī′sə tōps), forms of an element with the same number of protons but different numbers of neutrons.

J

joule (joul or jül), *J,* one newton-meter; a unit of measurement used to express an amount of energy or work.

K

Kepler's first law, statement that each planet orbits the sun in an ellipse, with the sun at one focus.

Kepler's second law, statement that the speed of a planet in its orbit varies so that the line joining the planet and the sun sweeps out equal areas in equal times; the effect is that planets move fast-

est when they are closest to the sun and slowest when they are farthest away.

Kepler's third law, statement that the square of the period of revolution of a planet is proportional to the cube of its average distance from the sun; the law tells by how much a planet with a larger orbit has a longer period than a planet with a smaller orbit.

kinetic (ki net′ik) **energy,** energy of motion, which depends on an object's mass and the square of its velocity ($1/2mv^2$); expressed in joules.

kinetic theory of matter, theory that all matter is made up of small particles that are always in motion.

L

laser (lā′zər), device that amplifies light by causing atoms to give up light of a certain wavelength; it results in light of a single wavelength with all the waves lines up.

laser fusion, energy produced using lasers to fuse hydrogen atoms.

latent (lāt′nt) **heat,** energy needed to change a substance from one physical state to another.

law of conservation of energy, statement that energy cannot be created or destroyed; it can change from one form into another, but the total amount of energy stays the same; valid only in cases where matter and energy are not transformed into each other.

law of conservation of mass, statement that matter can change its form but cannot be created or destroyed; valid only in cases where matter and energy are not transformed into each other.

law of conservation of mass-energy, statement that the total amount of energy and matter remains the same, though matter and energy can change into each other.

law of conservation of momentum, statement that if no outside forces act on a system, the total momentum of all the particles in the system remains the same.

law of gravity, statement that the force of gravity between two objects increases with the masses of the objects and decreases with the square of the distance between them.

lens, a piece of glass or other transparent material shaped so that it will bend light to form an image.

lever (lev′ər), simple machine made of a rigid bar making contact with a single pivot point called a fulcrum.

liquid, physical state of matter that has a definite volume but no definite shape.

liquid laser, a laser which usually contains dyes, which are dissolved in wood alcohol or another liquid.

liter, SI unit of measure for volume.

Local Group, collective name for our galaxy plus 14 other nearby galaxies.

lubricant (lü′brə kənt), substance that reduces the friction that occurs when one surface moves past another surface.

luminous (lü′mə nəs), giving off light.

luster (lus′tər), property that describes the amount of shine of a surface.

M

machine, device which makes work easier by increasing force, changing the direction in which the force is exerted, or changing the speed at which the force acts.

magnetic field, region around a magnet in which an object feels a magnetic force.

magnetism, one of the forces of nature that exists near a magnet.

malleable (mal′ē ə bəl), able to be hammered, rolled, or shaped without breaking, as some metals are.

mass, amount of matter that an object has, usually expressed in grams or kilograms.

mass number, total number of protons and neutrons in the nucleus of an atom.

mechanical advantage (M.A.), number of times by which a machine increases the force applied to it.

mechanical energy, energy an object has because of its motion and the forces acting on it; mechanical energy occurs as both kinetic and potential energy.

melting, the change of phase from solid to liquid.

melting point, temperature at which a substance changes from a solid to a liquid.

metal, class of elements that are usually solid at room temperature, exhibit luster, and are good conductors of heat and electricity.

metalloid (met′l oid), class of elements that have some properties of metals and some properties of nonmetals.

meter, *m*, unit for measuring length in the metric system; SI basic unit of length.

metric system, system of measurement, originally set up in the 18th century, based on a few standard units and prefixes that reflect the multiplication of these units by powers of ten.

microgravity (mī′krō grav′ə tē), condition that occurs when objects are accelerating equally so that gravity seems to disappear.

microprocessor (mī′krō pros′es ər), chip that contains all a computer's problem-solving circuits.

Milky Way, the stars, gas, and dust which appear to us as a hazy band of light.

Milky Way Galaxy, the galaxy our solar system is in.

mirage, optical illusion caused by the refraction of light rays from the distant scene by air layers of different temperatures.

mixture (miks′chər), combination of two or more substances in variable amounts in such a way that they are not chemically combined.

model, an idea or set of equations that brings together bits and pieces of different information about a single concept.

molecule (mol′ə kyül), group of atoms held together by covalent bonds; the smallest example of a covalently bonded substance.

momentum (mō men′təm), measure of the strength of an object's motion, depending on both an object's mass and its velocity.

motor, a device that converts any form of energy into mechanical energy.

N

natural frequency, an object's characteristic frequency of vibration that depends on an object's size, shape, and material.

nearsighted, condition in which the eye does not properly focus objects that are relatively far away.

nebula (neb′yə lə), cloud of gas and dust in space.

net force, resulting force on an object after all the forces acting on it and their directions are added up.

neutral, *neutral solution,* having a pH of 7, because the number of hydronium ions equals the number of hydroxide ions.

neutralization (nü′trə lə zā′shən) **reaction,** chemical reaction in which an acid and a base react forming a salt and water.

neutron (nü′tron), particle having no electric charge and found either by itself or in a nucleus.

neutron star, star in which the inward force of gravity is balanced by the outward pressure of tightly packed neutrons.

newton, *N*, metric unit of measurement that tells the strength of a force; $1 \text{ N} = 1 \text{ kg·m/s/s}$.

newton-meter, *N·m*, unit of measurement of work.

Newton's first law of motion, statement that an object will stay at rest or continue to move in the same direction and at the same speed unless a force acts on it.

Newton's second law of motion, statement that an object accelerates because a force acts on it; $F = ma$.

Newton's third law of motion, statement that for every action force, there is a reaction force of equal strength but opposite in direction.

noise, unpleasant or unwanted sound.

nonmetal, class of elements whose properties are opposite to the properties of metals.

nonrenewable energy resource, any energy resource that is not being replaced in a reasonable amount of time as it is being used up.

north pole *of a magnet,* end that always points north when the magnet is allowed to turn freely.

nuclear energy, energy that is released when mass is transformed into energy as atoms split apart (undergo fission) or join together (undergo fusion).

nuclear fission (fish′ən), splitting of heavy nuclei into lighter ones.

nuclear fusion (fyü′zhən), joining of light nuclei to make a heavier nucleus.

nuclear reaction, process by which one type of nucleus changes into another.

nucleus (nü′klē əs; plural, nü′klē ī), positively charged core of an atom that contains neutrons and protons.

O

ohm (ōm), unit used to express the amount of electrical resistance.

opaque, any object which light does not pass through.

open universe, universe that would keep expanding forever.

optical fiber (op′tə kəl fī′bər), narrow, transparent tube through which light travels, even around curves, because of internal reflection.

optical pyrometer (op′tə kəl pī rom′ə tər), instrument that measures the temperature of a glowing object by the color of light the object gives off.

orbit (or′bit), periodic path of one object around another resulting from a force between them.

orbital velocity, the speed at which you would circle the earth, for your distance from the earth's center.

output, the results from a comuter.

oxidation, a reaction in which a substance loses electrons.

oxidation-reduction reaction, a chemical reaction in which one substance gains electrons given off by another substance.

P

parallel circuit, circuit connecting several objects, in which the removal of one object does not break the circuit of the other objects.

Pascal's principle, states that if the pressure of a liquid in one part of a container changes, the pressure changes throughout the container.

peculiar galaxy, a galaxy which is not quite regular.

period, row of elements in the periodic table.

period of revolution, length of time it takes to complete one orbit around a central object.

periodic (pir′ē od′ik) **table of elements,** an arrangement of the known elements according to their atomic numbers.

personal computer, a computer designed to be used by an individual at home or at work.

phase of matter, condition in which matter exists, such as solid, liquid, or gas.

pH scale, range of numbers from 0-14 that indicates the relative acidic or basic character of a solution; a pH lower than 7 indicates an acid, a pH of 7 indicates a neutral solution, and a pH greater than 7 indicates a base.

photon (fō′ton), bundle of energy given off or taken in by an atom or nucleus as it changes its energy state.

physical change, change in a substance that does not alter its identity or nature.

physical property, property of a substance that remains as long as the substance does not undergo a chemical change.

pitch *of a screw,* number of threads that are in a unit length of a screw; *of sound,* how high or low a sound seems, resulting mainly from the sound's frequency.

plane mirror, smooth, flat surface that reflects light.

plasma, a gas which is broken up into negatively and positively charged particles.

polarized (pō′lə rīzd′) **wave,** set of waves that are all vibrating in the same plane.

pole *of a magnet,* location where the magnetism is strongest; the poles of a magnet are often at its ends.

pollutant (pə lüt′nt), any substance that is harmful to the environment.

polymer (pol′ə mər), a giant molecule that contains repeating patterns of atoms linked together; a substance composed of these giant molecules.

polymerization (pol′ə mər ə zā′shən) **reaction,** chemical reaction in which chains of double-bonded hydrocarbon molecules join together to form one giant single-bonded molecule.

potential (pə ten′shəl) **energy,** energy an object has because of its position (mgh when due to gravity); expressed in joules.

power, rate at which work is done or energy is used; found by dividing work (or energy) by time; expressed in watts.

precipitation reaction, a chemical reaction in which an insoluble product forms when two solutions mix.

pressure (presh′ər), force per unit of area.

primary colors in light, the three colors which form white light; red, blue, and green.

primary colors in paint, three colors, magenta, yellow, and cyan, which when combined in various cominations, can make a wide variety of colors.

prism (priz′əm), wedge-shaped transparent object that separates light into its different wavelengths (colors).

product, newly formed substance that results from a chemical reaction.

program, step-by-step instructions that tell a computer what to do.

projectile (prə jek′təl), any freely falling object that was thrown, hurled, hit, or shot forward.

proton (prō′ton), positively charged particle found free or in a nucleus.

pulley, simple machine consisting of a rope that passes over a grooved wheel.

pulsar (pul′sär), dying or dead star from which we receive regular pulses of radio waves; pulsars are thought to be rotating neutron stars.

Q

quark (kwôrk), basic unit that makes up nuclear particles.

quasar (kwā′sär), object in the sky whose image is close to that of a star but whose spectrum reveals that it is traveling away very fast; quasars are thought to be exceptionally bright cores of distant galaxies.

R

radiant (rā′dē ənt) **energy,** energy that is carried through space in the form of electromagnetic waves.

radiation (rā′dē ā′shən), either radiant energy or sub-atomic particles given off during radioactivity or fission.

radiation (rā′dē ā′shən), transfer of energy through space in waves.

radioactivity (rā′dē ō ak tiv′ə tē), spontaneous decay of a nucleus into a lighter nucleus, very tiny particles, and radiation.

rare earth elements, the elements with atomic numbers 58–71, they are silvery metals that combine well with nonmetals.

rarefaction (rer′ə fak′shən), any of the places in a compressional wave in which the density of the material's particles is relatively low.

reactant (rē ak′tənt), substance that interacts chemically with another substance during a chemical reaction.

reaction force, force, called for by Newton's third law, that is equal in strength but opposite in direction to an action force.

real image, image formed by a lens or mirror for which the rays of light actually come together and can be focused on a screen.

red giant, first stage of a star as it begins to die; a rather large star that glows slightly reddish, since it is relatively cool.

red shift, apparent increase in the wavelength (the Doppler effect) of light, resulting from the object or the observer moving away from the other.

reducing agent, any agent which removes oxygen.

reduction, a reaction in which a substance gains electrons.

reflection (ri flek′shən), bouncing of a wave off the surface it hits.

refraction (ri frak′shən), change in direction of a wave as it moves from one material to another and the wave's speed changes.

relative motion, changing position with respect to the position of another object.

renewable resource, energy resource that is being replaced as it is used in a reasonable amount of time.

replacement reaction, chemical reaction in which

one free element replaces an element that is part of a compound.

resistance (ri zis′təns), measure of how much the flow of electric current is opposed, expressed in ohms.

resistance arm, distance between the resistance on a lever (the object to be moved) and the fulcrum.

resonance (rez′ə nəns), phenomenon that occurs when the vibrations of one object reinforce the vibrations of another object because they have the same natural frequency.

retina (ret′n a), in the eyeball, the back, inside lining that is sensitive to light.

rolling friction, weak, backwards force that arises as a round object rolls over a surface.

S

salt, substance that is formed when a positive ion from a base bonds to a negative ion from an acid as a result of neutralization.

saturated (sach′ə rā′tid), *saturated solution:* containing as much solute as can be dissolved at a specific temperature and pressure.

scalar quantity, quantity that represents only size.

scientific law, accepted explanation that should apply over and over again throughout the universe.

scientific method, logical method often used by scientists to solve problems; involves collecting data, making and testing hypotheses, and drawing conclusions.

scientific notation, a simple way of keeping track of the number of zeros in a number.

screw, inclined plane in a spiral form.

semiconductor, material that conducts electricity better than an insulator but not as well as a conductor, often made of silicon and germanium combined with other elements, and used in electronic circuits.

semiconductor laser, laser made of two layers of material with different electric charges.

series circuit, circuit connecting several objects one after the other so that the current follows in a single path.

shadow, area that is not lit or is only partially lit because an object is blocking light from reaching it.

short circuit, situation that occurs when the current in a circuit is drawn into another path so that not enough current goes into the original circuit.

SI, initials for the French words meaning International System of Measurements, the version of the metric system now internationally agreed upon.

simple machine, any tool that is made up of only one or two parts.

single-replacement reaction, a chemical reaction in which one element replaces another element in a compound.

sliding friction, backwards force that exists between the surfaces of objects that are sliding over each other.

software, the data and instructions given the computer.

solar cell, object that gives off electricity when it is hit by sunlight.

solar collector, object that traps the sun's energy and heats up a fluid.

solid, physical state of matter that has a definite shape and a definite volume.

solid laser, laser which uses a solid to produce light.

solid-state device, device which contains electronic components that are made of solid semiconductors instead of vacuum tubes.

solubility, ability of one substance to be dissolved in another substance.

soluble, capacity of one substance to dissolve in another substance.

solute (sol′yüt), substance that is dissolved by a solvent.

solution (sə lü′shən), uniform mixture of particles too small to be seen in which one or more substances is dissolved in another.

solvent (sol′vənt), substance that dissolves other substances.

south pole *of a magnet,* end that always points south when the magnet is allowed to turn freely.

spacetime, theories of the universe linking the three dimensions of space and the one dimension called time.

specific heat, measure of a material's ability to take in or give off heat; the amount of heat necessary to raise the temperature of 1 gram of a material by 1°C.

spectrum (spek′trəm; plural, spek′trə), characteristic pattern of energies, often visible, given off by an element's atoms as they release energy.

speed, rate of motion; found by dividing the distance an object moves by the time the object takes to go that distance and usually expressed in meters/second.

spiral galaxy, a galaxy with arms coming out of a central region which resembles a pinwheel.

spontaneous (spon tā′nē əs) **reaction,** chemical reaction that happens without any outside help.

starch, a naturally abundant nutrient carbohydrate.

static (stat′ik) **friction,** force in the direction that opposes any motion between the surfaces of objects that are touching but not moving past each other.

strong force, one of the basic forces of nature; the force that holds the particles in a nucleus together.

sublime, the process by which a solid changes directly into a gas,without passing through the liquid phase.

sublimation, when ice becomes a gas without going through a liquid phase.

substitution reaction, chemical reaction in which hydrogen atoms of single-bonded hydrocarbons are replaced with other elements.

supergiant, star more massive than the sun in a late stage in its life in which it becomes even larger and brighter than a red giant.

surface tension, makes the surface of a liquid act as if it were a stretched elastic sheet.

supernova (su′pər nō və), explosion of a massive, dying supergiant.

suspension (sə spen′ shən), mixture in which the particles of one substance are scattered in another but are not dissolved; the particles of one substance may separate from the other.

sympathetic vibration, vibration of an object at its natural frequency that occurs when another object vibrates at the same frequency.

synfuel, oil or gas made from coal.

synthesis (sin′the sis) **reaction,** chemical reaction in which two or more elements, compounds, or both join to make a new compound.

T

temperature, number that is a measure of the average kinetic energy of all the particles in an object or material, expressed in degrees Celsius.

terminal (ter′mən nəl) **velocity,** final velocity that a falling object reaches when air resistance balances the force of gravity.

theory (thē′ər ē), well-tested explanation of observations that can make predictions about the outcomes of other tests.

thermal pollution, form of pollution where heated water is released into rivers or lakes.

thermogram (ther′mə gram), image of an object made by measuring the infrared rays it gives off.

thermometer, an instrument that measures temperature.

thermostat, instrument that maintains a constant temperature in some object by turning a heat source on and off in response to changing temperatures in the surroundings.

thread, spiral path around a screw.

torque (tôrk), how strongly an object is turning, which depends both on the strength of a force on the object and the force's distance from the object's axis.

transformer (tran′sfôr′mər), device that raises or lowers voltage.

transistor (tran zis′tər), solid-state electronic component made of a semiconductor.

translational motion, motion in a straight line.

transmit, to let light through.

transparent, an object which allows light to pass through.

transverse (tranz vers′) **wave,** way of transmitting energy in which the crests and troughs of the wave are perpendicular to the direction in which the wave is traveling.

tritium, an isotope of hydrogen containing one proton and two neutrons.

trough (trôf), bottom of a transverse wave.

U

ultrasonic (ul′trə son′ik), sound frequency above 20,000 hertz, which the human ear cannot hear.

universal indicator, mixture of indicators that turns a different color at different pH values.

V

vacuum (vak′yü əm), space that contains no matter at all.

vacuum tube, early device used to control the flow of electrons; consisting of a glass tube emptied of air containing a positively charged plate that pulls electrons away from a negatively charged wire.

vaporization (vā′pər ə zā′shən), process by which a substance at its boiling point changes from a liquid to a gas.

variable, in a controlled experiment, the quantity that is changed or varied.

vector quantity, quantity that represents both size and direction.

velocity (və los′ə tē), quantity giving both the speed and the direction that an object is moving.

vibration (vī brā′shən), rapid back-and-forth motion, often resulting in a sound wave.

vibrational motion, movement back-and-forth from a central position.

virtual (ver′chü əl) **image,** image at which the light rays appear to meet but actually do not; therefore, a virtual image does not appear on a screen placed at the image's position.

viscosity (vi skos′ə tē), property of a liquid that causes it to resist flowing.

visible spectrum, part of the electromagnetic spectrum that people can see.

volt, unit used to express an amount of voltage.

voltage (vōl′tij), push needed to move an electron from one place to another, expressed in volts.

volume, the amount of space an object takes up.

W

watt, one joule per second, the unit of measure for power.

wavelength, distance between two similar points in a wave's cycle.

weak force, involved in the interactions that allow nuclei to undergo radioactive decay.

wedge, simple machine that consists of an inclined plane with one or two sloping sides.

weight, force that gravity exerts on a mass, expressed in newtons.

wet cell, a battery in which a series of plates are immersed in a solution of sulfuric acid.

wheel and axle, simple machine that consists of a wheel and a shaft that turns with the wheel and supports its center.

white dwarf, rather faint, dead star about the size of the earth but containing about as much mass as the sun; the end state of stars containing as much mass as the sun or less.

work, product of the force exerted on an object and the distance the force moves the object in the direction of the force, expressed in newton-meters or joules.

INDEX

A

acceleration, 65
  defined, 39, 41
  and force of gravity, 76–78
  measuring, 39–40
  and Newton's second law of
    motion, 54–56
  and velocity, 39–42
acid rain, 290, 366
acid(s)
  defined, 270
  and hydronium ions, 273–275
  and hydroxide ions, 275–276
  importance of, 272
  indicators for, 278–279
  and neutralization reactions,
    282–284
  and pH scale, 280–281
  properties of, 270
  safe handling of, 10
  weak and strong, 274–275
  See also Base
actinide elements, 164
action, and reaction, 60–61
adhesion, 108
air pressure, 113, 119
  and boiling point, 119
air resistance, 53, 65, 77
alpha particles, 177
alternating current (a.c.), 519,
    538, 550.
  See also Direct current;
    Electric current
Alvarez, Luis A., 174
ammonium hydroxide, 276
amorphous solids, 105–106
amperes, 513
amplifier, 551–552
amplitude, of waves, 391, 392,
    395
Angel, Roger, 438
Archimedes, 111, 434, 628
  and concept of density, 136
Archimedes' principle, 111,
    115, 628
Aristotle, 14
artificial intelligence, 559
astigmatism, 444
atom(s), 102, 128
  atomic number of, 153
  and chemical bonds, 220–223
  and chemical equations,
    233–236

and covalent bonds, 229–232
defined, 128, 148
and electric force, 506–508
and electrons, 148–151
in elements, 128, 157–164
energy levels of, 150, 151
excited state of, 150
and formation of stars, 580
and ionic bonds, 225–228
isotopes of, 153–154, 176
and magnetic domains, 533–535
mass number of, 154–155
and neutrons, 151, 153–155
and nuclear energy, 329
and nucleus, 149
and periodic table, 158–164
and production of light, 413
and protons, 151
and quarks, 173–175
spectrum of, 150
theories about, 148–151
  See also Atomic nucleus;
    Electron; Molecule;
    Neutron; Particles;
    Periodic table; Proton
atomic mass, 154–155
atomic nucleus
  of atom, 149
  and atomic number, 153
  and nuclear fission, 184–186
  and nuclear fusion, 188
  and protons, neutrons, 173
  and quarks, 173–175
  and radioactivity, 175–177
  and strong force, 172–173
  and weak force, 176
  See also Atom; Electron;
    Neutron; Proton
atomic number, 153
  and periodic table, 158–159
average acceleration, 41
average speed, 35
axis and rotation, 68–69

B

background radiation, 619–621
balance, in measurement, 18
balanced forces, 63–65
  and buoyancy, 110–111
Barton, Jacqueline K., 251
base(s)
  characteristics of, 271
  defined, 271

and hydroxide ions, 275–276
importance of, 272
indicators of, 278–279
and neutralization
  reactions, 282–284
and pH scale, 280–281
safe handling of, 10
weak and strong, 276
  See also Acid
**BASIC (Beginner's All–
    purpose Symbol
    Instruction Code),** 559,
    560
battery, 511, 512, 574
Becquerel, Henri, 175
Bernoulli, Daniel, 115, 628
Bernoulli's principle, 115–116
beta particles, 177
big bang theory, 614, 616–617,
    620–621
biomass, 371, 372
black holes, 589–590, 610, 615
  in Milk Way Galaxy, 592
block and tackle, 303
Bohr, Niels, 149, 628
Bohr model of atom, 149, 150
boiling point, 119, 342
  of an element, 135
  of hydrocarbons, 232
breeder reactor, 369
bromine, 132, 134, 253–254
buoyant force, 110–112, 115,
    628
Burnell, Jocelyn Bell, 588, 621

C

calcium, 226
calcium chloride, 235
calcium fluoride, 226
calorimeter, 344
cameras, 447
carbohydrates, 263
carbon, 179
  and covalent bonding, 230–
    232
carbon compounds
  of living organisms, 262–263
  reactions of, 260–261
  See also Hydrocarbons
carbon dioxide, 375
  and chemical reactions, 246
  dot diagram for, 236
  in solutions, 207
  as synthesis reaction, 250

carbon–nitrogen cycle, 582
Careers
aerospace engineer, 57
architect, 368
assayer, 133
auto mechanic, 313
automobile mechanic, 313
electrical engineer, 521
heating and A. C. installer, 355
laser technician, 459
mechanical engineer, 330
pharmacist, 282
pilot, 42
service technician, 543
studio engineer, 491
surveyor, 8
X–ray technician, 405
Carlisle, Anthony, 13
catalyst, 246
cathode–ray tube, 551–552
CAT scanner, 403
Cavendish, Henry, 13
Celsius (temperature), 18
center
of gravity, 82–83
of mass, 83
central processing unit (CPU), 557
centrifuge, 154
centripetal force, 67
defined, 67
Chadwick, James, 151
chain reaction, 185
chemical bonds
defined, 220
and electrons, 220–222
See also Ionic bonds
chemical change, 140, 244
chemical energy, 328, 329, 330
producing heat, 347
chemical equations, 233–236
balancing, 234
and chemical reactions, 246–247
of decomposition reactions, 250–251
defined, 233
for double-replacement reactions, 254
for neutralization reactions, 282
for oxygen-reduction reactions, 258–259
for single-replacement reactions, 252, 254
for synthesis, 249–250
See also Equations
chemical formulas
for acids, 270, 273
for bases, 275–276

chemical properties of matter, 139
chemical reactions, 233
and catalysts, 246
characteristics of, 244
and chemical equations, 246–247
classifying, 256–257
decomposition reactions, 250–251
and double-replacement reactions, 254
and electric current, 511–512
endothermic, 245
energy in, 245
exothermic, 245
and lasers, 472
neutralization reactions, 282–284
oxidation-reduction reactions, 257–259
and reactivities of elements, 253–254
single-replacement reactions, 252–254
speed of, 245–246
spontaneous, 244
synthesis reaction, 249–250
See also Chemical equations
chemical symbols, 130
Chernobyl, 186, 369
chip
computer, 562
integrated circuit, 556
chloride, 229
chlorine, 225
chromium, 131
circuit, electric. See Electric circuit
circuit breakers, 517
circular motion, 32, 66–69
climate, and greenhouse effect, 384
closed universe, 616–617
coal, 365, 366, 375
coefficients, in chemical equation, 247
cohesion, 108
coinage metals, 162
colloids, 212
color(s), 135
and acid, base indicators, 278–279
and chemical reactions, 244
and electromagnetic spectrum, 402
of lasers, 458–459
of light, 416–419

and light from stars, 583
and pH scale, 280–281
primary colors in light, 422–423
primary colors in paint, 423–424
and radiant energy, 343, 351
and reflected light, 420–421
and transmitted light, 421
and temperature, 343
and visible spectrum, 416–419
See also Electromagnetic spectrum; Light
comet, 119
compass, 528, 530, 536
complex machines
defined, 310
and efficiency, 312–313
See also Machines; Simple machines
compound machines
defined, 310
mechanical advantage of, 311
See also Machines; Simple machines
compound(s)
breakdown of, 201, 250–251
carbon, 231–232
and chemical bonds, 222–223
and covalent bonds, 229–232
and decomposition reactions, 250–251
dot diagrams for, 235–236
formation of, 200
formulas for, 200, 202
and ionic bonds, 226–228
and mixtures, 204, 206
and oxidation-reduction reactions, 256–259
and solutions, 207, 210
and synthesis reactions, 249–250
See also Chemical bonds; Hydrocarbons; Ionic bonds; Mixture; Solution; Suspension
compressional wave, 395–396
and sound, 482
computers, 550
and artificial intelligence, 559
in business and industry, 564
central processing unit, 557
characteristics of, 558–559
in engineering and sciences, 565–568
in government, law enforcement, 565

hardware, 557
input for, 557
languages for, 559
in medicine, 568–569
microprocessors, 562–563
output from, 557
parts of, 557
personal computers, 562
programming, 558, 560
software, 557
using, 563–568
concave mirrors, 434–437, 449
concentrated solutions, 208
condensation, 119
conduction, 348
conductor, 348, 510
Conservation of energy, law of, 324–325, 326, 376–378
conservation of mass–energy, 182–183
conservation of mass, law of, 234
conservation of momentum, law of, 61
contraction, 353–354
controlled experiment, 12
convection, 349
convection current, 349
convex lenses, 438–440, 450,
convex mirrors, 436–437
Copernicus, Nicholaus, 88
copper, 131, 140
cornea, 443, 445
corona, 583
cosmic rays, 177
covalent bonds
defined, 229
and dot diagrams, 236
double, 236
and molecules, 229, 230
crest, of wave, 391, 392
crude oil, 232
crystalline solids, 104–105, 135, 222–223
Curie, Marie, 129, 175, 629
Curie, Pierre, 129, 175, 629
current, electric, See Electric current

D
Dalton, John, 148
data collecting, 12
decay, of atomic nuclei, 176
deceleration, 41
decibels, 487
decomposition reactions, 250–251
Democritus, 148
density, 135

concept of, 136
of liquid, 109–110
measurement of, 19
as physical property, 135
deoxyribonucleic acid (DNA), 262–263
depth and pressure, 109–110
deuterium, 154, 155, 368
and nuclear fusion, 188
diamond, 105, 128, 134, 222
diatomic molecule, 229
direct current, 519, 538, 550
See also Alternating current; Electric current
displacement
defined, 33
and distance, 32–34
as vector quantity, 34
and work, 296–297
distance
defined, 32–33
and displacement, 32–34
and force of gravity, 88–89
as scaler quantity, 34
and speed, 34–36
domain, magnetic, 533–535
Doppler, Christian, 490
Doppler effect, 490
Doppler redshift, 605–606, 620
dot diagrams, 235–236
double-replacement reactions, 254
double stars, 587
dry cell battery, 511, 515
ductile metals, 131
Dwarf stars, 582

E
eclipse, 583
efficiency, 312–313
effort arm, 300–301
Einstein, Albert, 89, 91, 102, 181–183
electric charge, 506–508
electric circuit, 514
controlling, 517
parallel, 516
series, 515
short, 517
electric current, 510–514, 550–552
alternating, direct, 519
calculating, 512–514
and circuits, 514, 517
and electronic devices, 550
and magnetism, 536–538, 540–543
voltage sources of, 511–512

and watts, 520–521
electric force, 506
electricity, 328, 330
and acid solutions, 275
and bases, 276
and circuits, 514–517
and electric charge, 506–508
and electric current, 510–514, 519
and magnetism, 536–538, making, 362, 363
producing heat from, 346, 540–543
and resistance, 510, 512–513
using, 519–521
and voltage, 511–514
See also Electric circuit; Electric current; Electronic devices; Electronics; Magnetism
electromagnet, 537, 538
electromagnetic force, 172–173, 176
electromagnetic induction, 541
electromagnetic spectrum, 402–403
and redshift, 605–606
of stars, 583, 584
and visible light, 402–405
electromagnetic waves, 402–405
high-energy, 403–404
low-energy, 404–405
See also Electromagnetic spectrum
electromagnetism, 542
electron(s), 148
and atomic number, 153
and chemical bonds, 220–222
and chemical reactions, 257–259
and dot diagrams, 235–236
and electric charge, 506–508
and elements, 157–164
energy levels of, 150, 151, 157–164
and ionic bonds, 225–228
and lasers, 462–463
and light, 413
and periodic table, 158–164
valence, 221–222
See also Atom; Atomic nucleus; Element; Neutron; periodic table; Proton
electronic devices, 550–552
and computers, 557–560

how they work, 550–552
integrated circuits in, 555–556
for mapping the universe, 606–607
transistors in, 554

electronics
defined, 550
and electronic devices, 550–552

element(s)
and chemical bonds, 220–222
and chemical formulas, 200
and chemical symbols, 130
comparing reactivities of, 253–254
in compounds, 200
defined, 128
describing, 130–132
discovering, 129
formed in nuclear fusion, 189
isotopes of, 153–154
metalloids, 132
metals, 130–131
nonmetals, 132
and periodic table, 157–164
spectrum of, 150
See also Atom; Electron; Molecule; Neutron; Periodic table; Proton

ellipses, 86
emulsifier, 212
emulsion, 212
endoscope, 469
endothermic reaction, 245
end-point, of neutralization reaction, 284

energy
changing forms of, 329–330
chemical, 328–330, 347
in chemical reactions, 245
choosing among sources, 374–375
conduction, 348
conservation of, 376–378
conservation of mass–energy, 182–183
convection, 349
defined, 320
electrical, 328–330, 362–363
forms of, 328–329
from fossil fuels, 364–367
and heat, 340, 346–347
internal, 328–329
kinetic, 322–323
law of conservation of, 324–325

and light, 413
and matter, 102
measuring, 321
mechanical, 328–330, 347
nuclear, 329, 368–369
potential, 324–326
potential, 324–326
and power, 331–332
radiant, 329–330, 350–351
renewable sources of, 370–372
of the stars, 581–582
study of, 6
uses of, 362
and waves, 390
and work, 320
See also Electricity; Kinetic energy; Potential energy

energy levels, of electrons, 150

equations for:
acceleration, 40, 41, 55
efficiency, 312
force, 55
kinetic energy, 323–324
Ohm's law, 513
potential energy, 325
power, 332, 520
speed, 35–36, 392
work, 296–297, 332

equilibrium, 64, 65
escape velocity, 90
evaporation, 119
excited state, of electrons, 150
exothermic reactions, 245
expansion, 353–355

eyes
animals, 445
correcting vision, 444
human, 443
and medical use of lasers, 468
and optical illusions, 446

F

Faraday, Michael, 540, 629
farsightedness, 444
filters, 205
Fire Sprinkler System, How It Works, 97
Five-Speed Bicycle, How It Works, 385
fixed pulley, 303
fluorine, 132, 226, 254
focal length, 434–436, 440
focal point, 434–436, 439–440
foci, of ellipse, 86
food irradiation, 194

force
balanced and unbalanced, 63–65
buoyant, 110–111
and circular motion, 66–69
defined, 53
of gravity, 88–91
and machines, 298–299, 302
and Newton's second law of motion, 54–57, 68–69
and Newton's third law of motion, 60–61, 68–69
strong, 172–173, 176
weak, 176
and work, 296–297
See also Work

forced vibrations, 494
formulas, in compounds, 200, 202
fossil fuels, 364–367
disadvantages of, 365–366
synthetic, 366–367
fractional distillation, 232
frame of reference, 31
free electron lasers, 462–463
freezing point, 118, 342

frequency
natural, 493
of sound, 488, 489
of wave, 391, 392

friction, 326
and change in direction, 66
defined, 42
kinds of, 43–44
and Newton's first law of motion, 52
reducing, 44
rolling, 43
sliding, 43
static, 43

fulcrum, 300
fuse, 517
fusion, 116–117
fusion reactor, 369

G

galaxies
clusters of, 596, 596–597
defined, 591
infrared, 613
invisible mass in, 615
Milky Way Galaxy, 591–592
motion of, 604–607
and quasars, 609–610
and radio astronomy, 611
shapes of, 594
spiral, 594

X–ray studies of, 612
See also Milky Way Galaxy; Universe
Galileo, Galilei, 14–15, 52, 88, 448, 629
gamma rays, 177, 402, 403, 584, 620–621
gas(es)
  and Archimedes' principle, 115
  and Bernoulli's principle, 115–116
  and change in phase, 118–119
  changes in volume and temperature, 114
  defined, 102
  particles of, 103, 113
  in periodic table, 163
  physical changes, 136–137
  and plasma, 116–117
  pressure of, 113
  in solution, 207–208, 209–210
  in suspension, 211–212
  symbol for in chemical equation, 247
  See also Liquid; Solid
gas laser, 462
gears, and rotation, 68–69
Geiger counter, 178
Geiger, Hans, 178
generator, 542–543
geothermal energy, 371, 372
germanium, 132
GIGO (garbage in, garbage out), 559
glycogen, 263
gold, 131, 139
graduated cylinder, 18
gram, 18
graphite, 105, 128, 222
gravity, 63, 65, 69, 172
  and acceleration, 76–79
  and aging of stars, 586–590
  and black holes, 589–590
  center of, 82–83
  force of, 176
  and formation of stars, 580
  law of, 88–91
  and mass, weight, 80–83
  and microgravity, 81–82
  and motion of falling objects, 76–78
  and path of projectiles, 78
  and planetary motion, 86–87
greenhouse effect, 384

H
half-life, of nuclei, 176
Halley, Edmond, 89
Halley's Comet, 89
hardness, 134
hardware, 557
heat
  and conduction, 348
  and contraction, 353–354
  and convection, 349
  defined, 341
  and expansion, 353–355
  forms of energy producing, 346–347
  and kinetic theory of matter, 340
  measuring, 344
  and radiant energy, 329–330, 350–351
  sources, 346
  specific, 344
  and temperature, 341
Heisenberg, Werner, 151
helium, 581
Henry, Joseph, 540
Hertz, Heinrich, 542
Hertz (Hz), 391, 392
hologram, 474–475
Hubble, Edwin, 605
hydrocarbons
  chemical reactions of, 260–261
  compounds, 231–232
  fossil fuels, 232, 364–366
hydrochloric acid, 272, 273
hydroelectric power, 370, 372, 375
hydrogen, 149, 189
  and covalent bonding, 229, 230–232
  and formation of stars, 581–582
  isotopes of, 154, 155, 188
  in stars, 586
hydrogen chloride, 229
hydrogen ions, 273–275
hydrogen peroxide, 251
hydronium ions, 273–275
hydroxide, 226
hydroxide ions, 275–276
hypothesis, 11–15

I
inclined planes, 306–308
  defined, 306
indicators, 278–279
inertia, 52
  defined, 52
  law of, 53

inflationary universe theory, 614–615, 616–617
infrared galaxies, 613
infrared radiation, 404, 584
infrasonic sounds, 489
input, 557
insulator, 348, 510
integrated circuits, 555–556
intensity
  of light, 412
  of sound, 487
interference, of waves, 400
internal energy, 328
International System of Units (SI). See Metric system
iodine, 132
ionic bonds
  defined, 225
  and dot diagrams, 235
  and electricity, 228
  properties of ionic compounds, 227–228
  See also Chemical bonds
ions
  hydronium ions, 273–275
  hydroxide, 275–276
  and ionic bonding, 225–228
  and lasers, 472
  See also Ionic bonds
iron
  in compounds, 200, 201
  in mixtures, 204
  and oxygen-reduction reaction, 259
  reduction of from ore, 259
  and single-replacement reactions, 252
iron oxide, 252
isotopes, 153–154
  and atomic mass, 154–155
  half-life of, 176
  and method of dating, 179
  and nuclear fission, 184–185
  and radioactivity, 176–777

J
Jackson, Shirley Ann, 117
Joliot-Curie, Irene, 630
joule (*J*), 321
Jupiter, 531

K
Kepler, Johannes, 86, 88
  first law, 86
  second law, 86
  third law, 87
kilowatt (kW), 332
kilowatt-hour, 521

kinetic energy
    calculating, 322–323
    defined, 322
    and heat, 341
    and law of conservation of
        energy, 324–325
    See also Energy
kinetic theory of matter, 348,
    353

L

laboratory, safety in, 9–11
**lasers (light amplification by
    stimulated emission of
    radiation)**
    free electron, 462–463
    fusion, 472
    gas, 462
    and holograms, 474–475
    how they work, 459, 501
    in industry, 466–467
    light of, 458–459
    liquid, 461–462
    in medicine, 468–470
    and optical fibers, 465–466
    in scientific research, 471–
        472
    semiconductor, 461
    and separating isotopes, 154
    solid, 460–461
Lasers, How It Works, 501
latent heat, 120
law of conservation of energy,
    324–325, 326, 376–378
law of conservation of mass,
    234
**law of conservation of mass–
    energy,** 182–183, 184
law of inertia, 53
law of gravity, 88–90
lenses
    in cameras, 447
    concave, 449
    convex, 438–440, 448, 450
    correcting vision, 444
    of eyes, 443, 445
    and microscope, 450
    and refracting telescope,
        448, 449
levers, 300–301
    mechanical advantage of, 302
    pulleys, 303
    wheels and axles, 303–304
Lewis, G. N., 228
light
    and cameras, 447
    colors of, 420–424
    concave lenses, 441

and concave mirrors, 434–
    436, 437
and convex lenses, 438–440
and convex mirrors, 436–437
and eyes, 443–445
intensity of, 412
of lasers, 458–459
and microscope, 450
and optical illusions, 446
and plane mirrors, 432–433
primary colors in, 422–423
and primary colors in paint,
    423–424
production of, 413
reflected, 420–421, 432–433,
    432–437
and refracting telescope, 449
speed of, 181–183, 471
from the stars, 583, 605–606
transmitted, 421
traveling, 412
and visible spectrum, 416–
    419
waves, 390, 391–392, 394,
    397, 399, 400, 404
waves, particles, 414
See also Color;
    Electromagnetic spectrum;
    Lasers; Light waves
lightning, 508, 510
light waves
    and Doppler redshift, 605–
        606
    and electromagnetic
        spectrum, 402–404
    interference of, 400
    polarized, 399
lime, 251, 282
liquid(s)
    and Archimedes' principle,
        111, 628
    and buoyant force, 110–112,
        628
    and change in phase, 118–
        119, 120
    defined, 102
    particles in, 103, 108–109
    and Pascal's principle, 111–
        112
    physical changes in, 136–137
    pressure of, 109–110
    in solutions, 207–208
    surface tension of, 108–109
    in suspensions, 211–212
    symbol for in chemical
        equation, 247
    viscosity of, 109
    See also Gas; Solid

liquid lasers, 461–462
liter (L), 18
Local Group, 596
LOGO, 559
lubricant, 44
luster, of metals, 131

M

machine(s)
    compound, 310
    and efficiency, 312–313
    inclined planes, 306–308
    levers, 300–301
    pulleys, 303
    screw, 307
    simple, 300
    wedge, 307
    wheel and axle, 303–304
    and work, 296–299, 332
    See also Work
**Magnetic Levitation, How It
    Works,** 575
magnet
    and electricity, 536–538
    and magnetic domain, 533–
        534
    permanent, 535
magnetic fields, 528–531,
    540–542
magnetism
    changing into electricity,
        540–543
    of earth, 530
    from electricity, 536–538
    and magnetic domains, 533–
        535
    and magnetic fields, 528–531
    and magnets, 528
    as physical property, 135
    of planets, 530–531
    See also Electricity; Magnet
malleable metals, 131
Mars, 531
mass
    center of, 83
    defined, 54
    and energy, 182–183
    and force of gravity, 68–69,
        76–78, 88–90
    and isotopes, 153–154
    and law of gravity, 88–89
    measurement of, 18–19
    and Newton's second law of
        motion, 54–57, 68–69
    and speed, 181–182
    in universe, 615
    and weight, 80–83

matter
changes in phase of, 118–120
and chemical changes, 140
chemical properties of, 139
defined, 102
and electricity, 506–508
and elements, 128–132
and energy, 102
kinetic theory of, 340, 348, 353
phases of, 102–103
and physical changes, 136–137
and physical properties, 134–136
study of, 6
See also Atom; Gas; Element; Energy; Liquid; Solid
Maxwell, James Clerk, 542
measurement
of density, 19
of force, 55–57
limits of, 20–21
of mass and volume, 18–19
and metric system, 17–18
of radioactivity, 178
and scientific notation, 22
of sound, 487
temperature, 18
of time, 18
of waves, 392
mechanical advantage (M.A.), 302, 307, 308
of compound machines, 311
mechanical energy, 328, 329–330, 347
megawatt (MW), 332
Meitner, Lise, 630
melting point, 105, 106, 118, 120, 135
and chemical bonds, 223
of an element, 135
and ionic bonding, 227
Mendeleev, Dmitri, 157, 158, 630
meniscus, 18
Mercury, 132, 531
metalloids, 132
metal(s)
coinage, 162
as conductors, 348
ductile, 131
malleable, 131
in periodic table, 162–164
properties of, 130–131, 221
and rare earth elements, 163–164

reactivities of, 253
and single-replacement reactions, 252–254
meter (m), 17
methyl orange, 279
metric system, 17–18
microgravity, 81–82.
See also Gravity
microprocessor, 562, 563
microscope, 450
microwave landing systems, 500
Milk Way Galaxy, 591–592
and Local Group, 596
See also Galaxies; Universe
mirage, 446
mirror(s)
concave, 434–436, 437
convex, 436–437
curved, 434–437
plane, 432–433
and telescopes, 438
mixture(s)
defined, 204
nature of, 204–205
separating substances in, 205–206
and solutions, 207, 210
and suspensions, 210, 212
See also Compound; Solution; Suspension
model, 13
molecule(s), 102
and covalent bonding, 229–230
defined, 229
diatomic, 229
momentum
conservation of, 60–61
defined, 56
and Newton's second law of motion, 56–57
Moseley, Henry, 158
motion
balanced and unbalanced forces, 63–65
circular, 32, 66–69
defined, 30
distance and displacement, 32–34
and equilibrium, 64, 65
of falling objects, 76–78
and frames of reference, 31
and friction, 42–44
Newton's first law of, 52–53, 64, 65, 67
Newton's second law of, 54–57, 63, 64

Newton's third law of, 60–61, 65, 66
relative, 30
and speed, 34–36
translational, 31
types of, 31–32
and velocity, 36–37, 39–41
vibrational, 32
of waves, 394–396
See also Speed; Velocity
movable pulley, 303
Multiple Mirror Telescope, 438
music, 491–494

N
natural frequency, 493
natural gas, 231, 366
nearsightedness, 444
nebula, 580
Neon Signs, How It Works, 195
neutralization reaction(s)
defined, 282
end–point of, 284
products of, 282–283
See also Chemical reactions
neutron, 151, 173
neutron(s), 173
building blocks of, 173
and isotopes, 153–154, 176
and nuclear fission, 184–185
and nuclear fusion, 188–189
and quarks, 173–175
and strong force, 173
See also Atom; Atomic nucleus; Electron; Proton
neutron stars, 588
Newlands, John, 157
Newton, Isaac, 52, 448, 631
first law of motion, 52–53, 64, 65, 67
and law of gravity, 88–90
second law of motion, 54–57, 63, 64
third law of motion, 60–61, 65, 66
newton (N), 55
newton–meter (Joule), 321
Nicholson, William, 13
nitric acid, 272
nitrogen, 132
noble gases, 221
noise, 487
nonmetals, 132
nonrenewable energy resources, 365.
North pole, 528

nuclear energy, 329, 329–330, 368–369, 375
  disadvantages of, 368–369
nuclear fission, 368–369
  process of, 184–185
  uses of, 186
nuclear fusion
  forming elements, 189
  process of, 188
  and stars, 581–582
nuclear power plants, 186
nuclear reaction, 184
nuclear reactor, 368–369
nucleus. See Atomic nucleus
numbers
  in chemical equations, 247
  on pH scale, 280–281

O
odor, 134
Oersted, Christian, 536
ohm, 510, 512–513
Ohm, George, 513
Ohm's law, 513
oil shale, 367
opaque objects, 421
open universe, 616–617
optical fibers, 465–466, 468
optical illusions, 446
optical pyrometer, 342
optics
  concave lenses, 441
  convex lenses, 438–440
  concave mirrors, 434–436, 437, 449
  convex mirrors, 436–437
  and eyes, 443–444
  and optical illusions, 446
  and microscope, 450
  and photography, 447
  plane mirrors, 432–433
  and telescopes, 448
  See also Eyes; Lasers; Lenses; Mirror; Telescope
orbit, 86
orbital velocity, 90
ores, 252
output, 557
oxidation-reduction (redox) reactions, 257–259
  See also Chemical reactions
oxygen, 132, 140
  in compounds, 200, 201
  and oxygen-reduction reactions, 257–259

P
pacemakers, 574
parallel circuit, 516
particle accelerators, 173, 182
particles
  in atoms, 173–175, 506–508
  in gases, 113, 114, 116–117
  of light, 413–414
  in liquids, 108–109
  of matter, 103, 340, 348, 350–351, 353
  in nuclear fission, 184–185
  in nuclear fusion, 188–189
  in solids, 104
  in suspension, 210–212
  See also Atom; Atomic nucleus; Electron; Neutron; Proton; Quark
Pascal, Blaise, 111–112
Pascal's principle, 111–112
Patrick, Jennie R., 206
Payne-Gaposchkin, Cecelia, 597
periodic table of elements
  and atomic numbers, 158–159
  characteristics of some groups, 162–163
  comparing reactivities of elements, 253–254
  history of, 157
  rare earth, actinide elements, 163–164
  using, 159–161
  and valence electrons, 221
period of revolution, 87
permanent magnet, 538
personal computers, 562
phosphorus, 132, 137, 223
photons, 413, 414, 459
pH scale, 280–281, 284
physical changes of matter, 136–137
physical properties of matter, 134–136
physical science
  benefits of research, 8
  defined, 6
  importance of, 7
  laboratory, safety in, 9–11
  and scientific method, 11–15
pitch, of sound, 488, 491–494
Planck, Max, 419
plane mirrors, 432–433
planets
  magnetic fields of, 530–531
  orbits of, 86–87
  and period of revolution, 87
  revolutions around sun, 86–87
  See also Galaxies; Universe
plasma, as gas, 116–117
platinum, 131
plutonium, 164, 369
polarized waves, 399
poles, 538
pollutants, 365
polymerization, 261
polymers
  natural, 262–263
  synthetic, 261
potassium chloride, 258
potassium oxide, 258
potential energy
  defined, 324
  and friction, 326
  and law of conservation of energy, 324–325
  See also Energy; Kinetic energy
power
  calculating, 331–332
  calculating energy from, 332
  defined, 331
  See also Energy; Work
pressure
  of gases, 113, 115
  of liquids, 109–110, 111–112, 114, 115–116
primary colors
  in light, 422–423
  in paint, 423–424
prism, 416, 417
products, of chemical reactions, 244.
  See also Chemical reactions
programming, computers, 558–560
projectile, 78
proteins, 262–263
proton(s), 151, 173
  and atomic number, 153
  building blocks of, 173–175
  and chemical bonds, 220
  and elements, 157–158
  and nuclear fission, 184–185
  and quarks, 173–175
  See also Atom; Atomic nucleus; Electron; Neutron
pulleys, 303
pulsars, 588

Q

quarks, 173–175
quasars (quasisteller radio sources), 609–610

R

rad, 178
radar, 404
radiant energy, 329
radiation, 177, 350, 350–351
  effects, uses of, 179
  measuring radioactivity, 178
  types of, 177
radio, 550, 550, 551–552
radioactive waste, 186
radioactivity
  and breakdown of atomic nuclei, 175–177
  detecting, measuring, 178
  effects, uses of, 179
radio astronomy, 612
radio telescopes, 584, 611
radio waves, 402, 403, 404, 584, 592, 611, 620
rainbow, 417–418
rare earth elements, 163–164
rarefaction, in waves, 395
Rayleigh, Lord, 418
Rayleigh scattering, 418–419
reactants, 244
reaction, and action, 60–61
real image, 435
red giants, 586
Redshift, Doppler, 605–606, 609–610, 614
reflecting telescope, 449
reflection
  of light, 420–421
  from mirrors, 432, 434–435
  of sound, 485
  of waves, 396–397
refracting telescope, 448
refraction
  of light, 448
  of sound, 484
  of waves, 397–398
relative motion, 30
rem (rad equivalent in man), 178
renewable energy resources, 370–372
  choosing among, 374–375
  disadvantages of, 272
resistance, 510, 512–513
resistance arm, 300–301
resonance, 494
retina, 443, 445
revolution, period of, 87

rockets, 90
rolling friction, 43
rotation, 68–69
Runyon, Noel, 569
rust, 140, 200–201, 244
Rutherford, Ernest, 148–149, 628

S

safety
  in laboratory, 9–11
  and radioactive materials, 178
salt, 200, 202, 227
saturated solutions, 208
Saturn, 531
scalar quantity, 34
Schroedinger, Erwin, 151
scientific law, 15
scientific method, 11–15
  revising scientific information, 13–15
scientific notation, 22
scintillator, 178
screw, 308, 311
semiconductor lasers, 461
series circuit, 515
shadow, 412
shaft mines, 366
short circuit, 517
significant digits, 21
silicon, 132, 555–556
silver, 131, 135
simple machines, 300
  inclined planes, 306–308
  levers, 300–304
  pulleys, 303
  screw, 308
  wedge, 307
  wheel and axle, 303–304
  See also Compound machines; Machines
single-replacement reactions, 252–254.
  See also Chemical reactions, comparing reactivities of elements, 253–254
sliding friction, 43
Smigel, Marjorie, 206
sodium, 225
sodium chloride, 225, 227
  and chemical equation, 233
  dot diagram for, 235
sodium hydroxide, 276
software, 557
solar cells, 370
solar collectors, 370
solar energy, 370, 372, 375

solid(s)
  amorphous, 105–106
  and change in phase, 118–120
  crystalline, 104–105, 136
  defined, 102
  particles in, 103, 104
  physical changes in, 136–137
  in solution, 207–208
  in suspension, 211–212
  symbol for in chemical equation, 247
  See also Gas; Liquid
solid lasers, 460–461
solid-state device, 550
solubility, 209–210
solute, 208, 209
solution(s)
  acids in, 273–275
  bases in, 275–276
  concentrated, 208
  defined, 207
  determining solubility, 209–210
  how substances dissolve, 207–208
  and neutralization reactions, 283
  saturated, 208
  See also Compound; Mixture; Suspension
solvent, 208
sound
  decibels, 487
  and Doppler effect, 490
  frequency, 488–489, 493
  infrasonic, 489
  intensity, loudness, 487
  musical, 491–494
  and noise, 487
  pitch, 488–490, 493
  speed of, 483
  ultrasonic, 488
  and vibrations, 482
  waves, 390, 391, 392, 395, 482, 484–485
South pole, 528
Space Telescope, How It Works, 627
spacetime, 616–617
sparks, 508
special theory of relativity, 181–183
specific heat, 344
spectrum, of element, 150
  See also Color; Electromagnetic spectrum; Visible spectrum

speed
and acceleration, 39–41
of chemical reaction, 245–246
defined, 34
of light, 181–183, 471
measuring, 34–36
of sound, 483
and velocity, 36–37
of waves, 391, 392
See also Motion; Velocity
spiral galaxies, 594
spontaneous reactions, 244
star(s)
and black holes, 589–590
double, 587
dwarfs, 582
formation of, 580
light from, 583
neutron, 588
and nuclear fusion, 188–189, 581–582
plasma of, 116
radiation from, 584
red giants, 586
supergiants, 587
supernova, 587
white dwarfs, 587
See also Galaxies; Planets; Sun; Universe
static friction, 43
strip mines, 366
strong force, 172–173, 176
sublimation, 119
sugar, 202, 263
and chemical bonds, 223
in solutions, 207–208
sulfur, 132
in mixtures, 204
sulfuric acid, 272
sun
energy of, 582
nuclear fusion in, 188–189
plasma of, 116
as source of radiant energy, 351
See also Stars
supercomputers, 564
supergiants, 587
supernova, 587
surface tension, 108–109
suspension(s)
colloids, 212
defined, 210
emulsifier, 212
emulsions, 212
kinds of, 211–212
particles in, 210–211

Swimming Pool Chemistry, How It Works, 291
sympathetic vibrations, 494
synfuels, 366–367
synthesis, 249–250
synthesis reactions, 249–250

T
taste, 134
telescope, 438
with camera, 627
refracting, 448, 449
space, How It Works, 627
television, 550, 550–552
temperature
and changes in phase of matter, 118–120
and chemical reactions, 245–246
defined, 341
degrees Celsius, 18
and expansion, contraction, 353–355
of gases, 114, 118–120
and heat, 341
and kinetic theory of matter, 340
measuring, 342–343
and nuclear fusion, 188–189
and physical properties, 135
and solubility, 209–210
terminal velocity, 77
Tesla, Nicola, 529
tesla (T), 529
theory, in scientific method, 12
thermal pollution, 369
thermogram, 343
thermometer, 342, 354
thermostat, 355
Thomson, J.J., 148
thread, of screw, 308
time
and power, 331–332
and speed, 34–36
torque, 68, 68–69, 82
transformer, 363, 519
transistors, 554
translational motion, 31
transmitted light, 421
transparent objects, 421
transverse wave, 394–395
electromagnetic, 402–405
polarized, 399
tritium, 154, 155
trough, of wave, 391–392

U
ultrasonic sound, 488
ultraviolet rays, 404, 584
ultraviolet waves, 402
unbalanced forces, 63–65
Universal Product Code, 466
universe
and background radiation, 619–621
big bang theory of, 614
future of, 616–617
and inflationary universe theory, 614–615
invisible mass in, 615
looking for life in, 626
mapping of, 606–607
See also Galaxies; Milky Way Galaxy; Planets; Stars; Sun
uranium, 164, 235, 185, 368–369, 472
and nuclear reaction, 184
and radioactivity, 176
Uranus, 531

V
vacuum, 390
vacuum tube, 550–552
valence electrons, 221
vaporization, 119
variable, 12
vector quantity, 34.
See also Displacement
velocity
and acceleration, 39–41, 76–77
defined, 36
escape, 90
and force of gravity, 76–78
and momentum, 56–57
orbital, 90
representing, 37
and speed, 36–37
terminal, 77
of waves, 391, 392
See also Motion; Speed
Venus, 531
vibrational motion, 32
vibration, 482, 491–494
forced, 494
and musical sounds, 491–494
and resonance, 494
sympathetic, 494
See also Sound
virtual image, 432
viscosity, 109
visible spectrum, 416–419
colors in, 416

See also Color;
   Electromagnetic spectrum;
   Light
vision, 444.
   See also Eye; Optics
volt (V), 511–514
voltage, 511–514, 515–517
   and watts, 520–521
volume
   of gas, 114
   of liquid, 109
   of liquid, solid, gas, 102–103
   measurement of, 18–19
   Voyager, 53, 90, 96, 186
   Voyager 2, 89, 531

W
water
   boiling point of, 119
   chemical equation for, 234
   condensation of, 119
   as covalent compound, 230
   and decomposition reaction,
      251
   dot diagram for, 236
   as energy source, 371, 372
   evaporation of, 119
   freezing point of, 118
   melting point of, 118
   as product of neutralization
      reaction, 282
   in solutions, 207–208
   and sublimation, 119
   symbol for in chemical
      equation, 247
   as synthesis reaction, 250
watt (W), 332, 520–521
watt-hour, 521
watt-second, 332
wavelength, 391, 392
wave(s)
   amplitude of, 391
   compressional, 395–396
   crest of, 391
   electromagnetic, 402–405
   as energy carriers, 390
   frequency of, 391, 392
   interference of, 400
   of light, 414
   polarized, 399
   properties of, 391–392
   radio, 402, 403, 404, 584,
      592, 611, 620
   reflection of, 396–397
   refraction of, 397–398
      andspeed of, 341, 392
   sound, 390, 391, 482
   transverse, 394–395, 399

   trough of, 391
   wavelength, 391, 392
   See also Electromagnetic
      waves; Lasers; Light
      waves; Sound
weak force, 176
weather satellites, 405
wedge, 307
weight
   defined, 80
   and gravity, 80–83
   and mass, 80–83
wet cell battery, 512
white dwarfs, 587
wind power, 371, 372, 375
work
   calculating amount of, 296–
      297, 332
   defined, 296
   and energy, 320
   and machines, 298–299
   and power, 331–332
   See also Energy; Force;
      Machines; Power
Wu, Chien Shiung, 631

X
X rays, 175, 177, 402, 403,
   584, 588, 590, 592, 610,
   612

Y
Yalow, Rosalyn, 165
Yeager, Chuck, 482
Yukawa, Hideki, 631

Acknowledgments

Unless otherwise acknowledged, all photos are the property of Scott, Foresman and Company. The abbreviations indicate position of pictures (t)top, (b)bottom, (l)left, (r)right, (c)center.

Page & Position:
iii Thomas Ives
iv(t) Mark Antman/The Image Works
v Will McIntyre/Photo Researchers
vi Barry L. Runk from Grant Heilman
vii(t) Howard Sochurek
vii(b) Gerhard Gscheidle/Peter Arnold, Inc.
viii(t) James H. Karates/Peter Arnold, Inc.
viii(b) Dr. Edward S. Ross
ix(b) Michael Philip Manheim/The Stock Market
x(b) California Institute of Technology
2(l) Historical Pictures Service, Chicago
2(r) Courtesy Bausch & Lomb Optical Co.
3(l) From THE EARTH TO THE MOON by Jules Verne, The Research Libraries, New York Public Library, Astor, Lenox and Tilden Foundations
3(r) From the IMAX^R/OMNIMAX^R film THE DREAM IS ALIVE © 1985 Smithsonian Institution & Lockheed Corporation
4-5 Sandia Laboratories
5(b) Bob Hahn/Taurus Photos, Inc.
6(t) Permission granted by COLORIZATION™ Inc.
6(b) Permission granted by COLORIZATION™ Inc.
7 David R. Frazier Photolibrary
8 Keith Gunnar/Bruce Coleman Inc.
14(t) SCRIPTA MATHEMATICA, Yeshiva Univ.
14(b) Wards SCI/Science Source from Photo Researchers
15 Scala/Art Resource, NY
28-29 Coco McCoy/Rainbow
35 Peter Fronk/Click/Chicago Ltd.
40 Craig Aurness/Woodfin Camp & Associates
42 D.P. Hershkowitz/Bruce Coleman Inc.
50-51 Focus On Sports
51 Hank Morgan/Photo Researchers
52 Focus On Sports
53 NASA
57(t) Marilyn Gartman Agency
57(b) NASA
74-75 Rafael Beer
75 Tim Heneghan/West Stock
76 Harold E. Edgerton, M.I.T., Cambridge, Massachusetts
77(l) Andy Burridge/Bruce Coleman Inc.
77(r) Sygma
78(t) Harold E. Edgerton, M.I.T., Cambridge, Massachusetts
82 NASA
83(b) Harold E. Edgerton, M.I.T., Cambridge, Massachusetts
91 Courtesy California Institute of Technology Archives
96 Doug Shane/Visions
98 The Bettmann Archive
99 Hank Morgan/Rainbow
100-101 Brad Bower/Picture Group
101 British Aircraft Corporation
102 Bill Bachman/Photo Researchers
105(l) Barry L. Runk from Grant Heilman Photography
105(r) David Overcash/Bruce Coleman Inc.
106(b) Breck P. Kent
108 William H. Amos/Bruce Coleman Inc.
109 Phil Degginger/Bruce Coleman Inc.
110 Chuck Nicklin/Ocean Images
116(b) Don and Pat Valenti
117 Courtesy AT&T Archives
118 H. Armstrong Roberts
119 Howard Sochurek/Woodfin Camp & Associates
126-127 Manfred Kage/Peter Arnold, Inc.
127 Jay M. Pasachoff
128(all) Dr. E.R. Degginger
129(l) Dr. E.R. Degginger
129(c) Dr. E.R. Degginger
129(r) Martin M. Rotker/Taurus Photos, Inc.
130 Lawrence Hudetz
132(tl) Dr. E.R. Degginger
132(bl) Dr. E.R. Degginger
132(r) Bill Pierce/Rainbow
133(t) Dr. E.R. Degginger
133(b) William E. Ferguson Photography

134 Dr. E.R. Degginger
135(t) Dr. E.R. Degginger
135(b) Chip Clark
139(l) Dr. E.R. Degginger
139(r) Doug Wechsler
146-147 Hank Morgan/Rainbow
147 Fritz Goro
150 Courtesy Sargent-Welch Scientific Company
162 Dr. E.R. Degginger
163(all) From LIFE SCIENCE LIBRARY: MATTER, Photographs by Albert Fenn, © 1963 Time-Life Books, Inc.
163(br) From LIFE SCIENCE LIBRARY: MATTER, Photograph by Phil Brodatz, © 1963 Time-Life Books, Inc.
164(b) Mike Newman
164(t) David Bishop
165 AP/Wide World
170-171 Dan McCoy/Rainbow
173 Dan McCoy/Rainbow
174 Courtesy Luis Alvarez
175 AP/Wide World
178(t) Leo Touchet/Woodfin Camp & Associates
178(b) Dan McCoy/Rainbow
179 Milt & Joan Mann/Cameramann International, Ltd.
182 AP/Wide World
186 NASA
189 California Institute of Technology
194 Agricultural Research Survey/U. S. Dept. of Agriculture
196(l) The Bettmann Archive
196(r) Historical Pictures Service, Chicago
197(l) Michael Holford
197(r) Brad Hess/Black Star
206(b) John Nuhn
218-219 Courtesy of International Business Machines Corporation
227 Dr. E.R. Degginger
228 University of California at Berkeley
234 Milt & Joan Mann/Cameramann International, Ltd.
242-243 Manfred Kage/Peter Arnold, Inc.
246 Courtesy Harshaw Filtrol Partnership, Cleveland, Ohio
250 Lee Boltin
251(b) Werner Wolff/Black Star
252 Roland & Sabrina Michaud/Woodfin Camp & Associates
254 Dr. E.R. Degginger
258 Dr. E.R. Degginger
259 Milt & Joan Mann/Cameramann International, Ltd.
268-269 David R. Frazier Photolibrary
269 Micro Essential Laboratory Inc.
272 Dr. E.R. Degginger
290 Bill Eppridge/Dot Picture Agency
292(l) Courtesy of the Trustees of the British Museum
292(r) Atlas Photo/Doumie/Photo Researchers
293(l) The Bettmann Archive
293(r) David Falconer/Black Star
294-295 Clay Kelton/Peter Arnold, Inc.
311 Milt & Joan Mann/Cameramann International, Ltd.
313(t) Steve Elmore/The Stock Market
318-319 COMSTOCK
321 Dan McCoy/Rainbow
322(l) Kevin Syms/David R. Frazier Photolibrary
322(c) Keith Gunnar/Bruce Coleman Inc.
322(r) Dan McCoy/Rainbow
323(l) Kirkendall/Spring, Edmonds, Wa.
323(c) Chesher/Photo Researchers
323(r) Bob Straus/Woodfin Camp & Associates
324 Kevin Syms/David R. Frazier Photolibrary
328 Jerry Wachter/Photo Researchers
329 Milt & Joan Mann/Cameramann International, Ltd.
330 Michael Ventura/Bruce Coleman Inc.
338-339 Howard Sochurek
342 Milt & Joan Mann/Cameramann International, Ltd.
343 VANSCAN^R Thermogram by Daedalus Enterprises, Inc.
348 Albert Allen Bartlett, University of Colorado, Boulder
351 Milt & Joan Mann/Cameramann International, Ltd.
354 David R. Frazier Photolibrary
360-361 C.C. Lockwood/Bruce Coleman Inc.
361 Peter Menzel
362 Bob Gomel/Life Magazine © Time Inc.
364 Field Museum of Natural History, Chicago
365 Tom McHugh/Photo Researchers

366 Nicholas deVore III/Bruce Coleman Inc.
367 Jonathan Blair/Woodfin Camp & Associates
368 David Madison/Bruce Coleman Inc.
370(all) Earth Observation Satellite Company
371 Lowell Georgia, Science Source from Photo Researchers
372 Mark Sherman/Bruce Coleman Inc.
373 Pat & Tom Leeson/Aperture Photobank
376(t) Sipa
376(b) Sipa
384 Fiona Sunquist/Tom Stack & Associates
386(l) Giraudon/Art Resource, NY
386(r) Instituto E Museo Di Storia Della Scienza
387(l) The Bettmann Archive
387(r) Fred Ward/Black Star
388-389 Darrell Ray Jones/The Stock Market
389 Runk/Schoenberger from Grant Heilman Photography
391 Vince Cavation, Allsport from Woodfin Camp & Associates
399(all) Milt & Joan Mann/Cameramann International, Ltd.
400 Runk/Schoenberger from Grant Heilman Photography
403 Dan McCoy/Rainbow
404 Milt & Joan Mann/Cameramann International, Ltd.
405(t) NOAA
405(b) Stan Levy/Photo Researchers
410-411 Manfred P. Kage/Peter Arnold, Inc.
416 Runk/Schoenberger from Grant Heilman Photography
419 The Bettmann Archive
430-431 Manfred Kage/Peter Arnold, Inc.
431 David Wells/The Image Works
437 Dan McCoy/Rainbow
438 George Kew, University of Arizona, Tucson
445 Dr. Edward S. Ross
448 Milt & Joan Mann/Cameramann International, Ltd.
449 Jay M. Pasachoff
450 Runk/Schoenberger from Grant Heilman Photography
456-457 Chuck O'Rear/West Light
457 Chuck O'Rear/West Light
459 Hank Morgan/Photo Researchers
462 Orville Andrews/Science Source from Photo Researchers
465 Stuart L. Craig, Jr./Bruce Coleman Inc.
466(b) William James Warren/West Light
467 Michael Pettypool/Uniphoto
468 Chuck O'Rear/Woodfin Camp & Associates
469 James Prince/Photo Researchers
471 NASA
474 Chuck O'Rear/Woodfin Camp & Associates
475(t) Dan McCoy/Rainbow
475(b) Philippe Plailly/Science Source from Photo Researchers
480-481 Bruce Aiken/Bruce Coleman Inc.
481 George Hall/Woodfin Camp & Associates
482(r) NASA
488 Howard Sochurek
492 Courtesy Steinway & Sons
496(all) Robert Frerck/Odyssey Productions, Chicago
500 Courtesy Hazeltine Corporation
502 Historical Pictures Service, Chicago
503(l) Thomas Alva Edison Foundation/The Edison Institute
503(r) Yerkes Observatory, University of Chicago/Milt & Joan Mann/
    Cameramann International, Ltd.
504-505 Frank Lane/Bruce Coleman Inc.
508 Jay M. Pasachoff
510 Milt & Joan Mann/Cameramann International, Ltd.
519 Timothy Eagan/Woodfin Camp & Associates
520 Milt & Joan Mann/Cameramann International, Ltd.
521 Christopher Springmann/The Stock Market
526-527 Dr. E.R. Degginger
529(b) Dan McCoy/Rainbow
534(t) Malcolm D. McConnell/General Electric Research and
    Development Center
537(t) David R. Frazier Photolibrary
537(b) Milt & Joan Mann/Cameramann International, Ltd.

548-549 © 1987 D. Kingsbury/Siggraph
552 University of Pennsylvania
554 Dan McCoy/Rainbow
555 Ken Biggs/The Stock Market
555(insl) T.J. Florian/Rainbow
555(insr) North American Philips Corp.
562 Courtesy A.T.& T., Bell Labs
564 Photri, Inc.
565–566 Milt & Joan Mann/Cameramann International, Ltd.
567 Jet Propulsion Laboratories
568 Milt & Joan Mann/Cameramann International, Ltd.
569 Tom Van Dyke/San Jose Mercury News
574 Peter Arnold, Inc.
576(l) The Bettmann Archive
576(r) Art Resource, NY
577(l) Milt & Joan Mann/Cameramann International, Ltd.
577(r) Steve Northup/Black Star
578-579 Roger Ressmeyer
579 California Institute of Technology and Carnegie Institute of
    Washington, Science Source from Photo Researchers
580 National Optical Astronomy Observatories
581 NASA/Science Source from Photo Researchers
582 Willard Clay
583(b) William H. Regan and Brook Sandford, Los Alamos Scientific
    Laboratory
583(t) Deutsches Museum from Jay M. Pasachoff
584(t) Jay M. Pasachoff
584(b) NASA, Science Source from Photo Researchers
587(t) California Institute of Technology
587(b) Anglo-Australian Telescope Board
588(t) California Institute of Technology
588(b) National Optical Astronomy Observatories
591 National Optical Astronomy Observatories
592(l) Jet Propulsion Laboratories
592(r) Science Source from Photo Researchers
594(all) California Institute of Technology
595(bl) Dennis diCicco
595(br) Dr. Jean Lorre, Science Photo Library from Photo Researchers
595(t) National Optical Astronomy Observatories
596 Dennis diCicco
597(b) Katherine Haramundanis
597(t) National Optical Astronomy Observatories
602-603 California Institute of Technology
603 Robert P. Carr/Bruce Coleman Inc.
605 Dennis diCicco
606(all) Mount Wilson and Palomar Observatories
609 California Institute of Technology
610(t) Harvard-Smithsonian Center for Astrophysics
610(c&b) Alan Stockton/Institute for Astronomy
611(t) Associated Universities, Inc./National Radio Astronomy
    Observatory
611(c) Associated Universities, Inc./National Radio Astronomy
    Observatory
611(b) Jay M. Pasachoff
612(tl) Harvard-Smithsonian Center for Astrophysics
612(bl) Harvard-Smithsonian Center for Astrophysics
612(r) X-ray Astronomy Group, University of Leicester, Science Photo
    Library from Photo Researchers
613 NASA from Grant Heilman Photography
615 California Institute of Technology
617 Dan McCoy/Rainbow
619 Courtesy A.T.& T., Bell Labs
620 Goddard Space Flight Center/NASA
621 B.W. Hadley, F.B.I.P., Royal Observatory, Edinburgh
626 Kevin Fitzsimons, Ohio State Univ.
632 The Granger Collection
634 Peter Menzel/Stock Boston
635(t) NASA
636 Billy E. Barnes, Click/Chicago
637(both) Milt & Joan Mann/Cameramann Intl.